Study and Review

When preparing for homework or exams, features like these will help you study and practice effectively.

Numerous, carefully written examples illustrate the concepts and skills as they are introduced, providing step-by-step directions for solving similar problems.

EXAMPLE 12 Solving Problems about Percent Increase or Decrease

(a) An electronics store marked up a laptop computer from their cost of $1200 to a selling price of $1464. What was the percent markup?

(b) The enrollment in a community college declined from 12,750 during one school year to 11,350 the following year. Find the percent decrease to the nearest tenth.

SOLUTION

(a) "Markup" is a name for an increase. Let x = the percent increase (as a decimal).

> *Subtract to find the amount of increase.*

$$x = \frac{1464 - 1200}{1200}$$ Substitute the given values.   *Use the original cost.*

$$x = \frac{264}{1200}$$

$$x = 0.22$$ Use a calculator.

The computer was marked up 22%.

(b) Let x = the percent decrease (as a decimal).

$$\text{percent decrease} = \frac{\text{amount of decrease}}{\text{original amount}}$$

> *Subtract to find the amount of decrease.*

$$x = \frac{12,750 - 11,350}{12,750}$$ Substitute the given values.   *Use the original enrollment.*

$$x = \frac{1400}{12,750}$$

$$x \approx 0.11$$ Use a calculator.

The college enrollment decreased by about 11%.

Annotations clarify these examples and help you prepare for the exercises that follow.

NEW! Pointers are annotations in the examples that provide on-the-spot reminders and warnings to help you avoid common pitfalls.

page 270

Varied exercise sets include drill, conceptual, and applied problems. Many exercises have been updated with new applications and real-life data.

6.5 EXERCISES

Decide whether each statement is true or false.

1. 300% of 12 is 36.

2. 25% of a quantity is the same as $\frac{1}{4}$ of that quantity.

3. When 759.367 is rounded to the nearest hundredth, the result is 759.40.

4. When 759.367 is rounded to the nearest hundred, the result is 759.37.

5. To find 50% of a quantity, we may simply divide the quantity by 2.

6. A soccer team that has won 12 games and lost 8 games has a winning percentage of 60%.

7. If 70% is the lowest passing grade on a quiz that has 50 items of equal value, then answering at least 35 items correctly will assure you of a passing grade.

8. 30 is more than 40% of 120.

9. .99¢ = 99 cents

10. If an item usually costs $70.00 and it is discounted 10%, then the discount price is $7.00.

Calculate each of the following using either a calculator or paper-and-pencil methods, as directed by your instructor.

11. 8.53 + 2.785

12. 9.358 + 7.2137

13. 8.74 − 12.955

14. 2.41 − 3.997

21. About how much was spent on Social Security?

22. About how much did the U.S. government spend on education and social services in 2005?

Postage Stamp Pricing Refer to For Further Thought on decimal point abuse. At one time, the United States Postal Service sold rolls of 33-cent stamps that featured fruit berries. One such stamp is shown on the left. On the right is a photo of the pricing information found on the cellophane wrapper of such a roll.

100 STAMPS PSA
.33¢ ea. TOTAL $33.00
FRUIT BERRIES
ITEM 7757
BCA

0 775700 0

23. Look at the second line of the pricing information. According to the price listed *per stamp*, how many stamps should you be able to purchase for one cent?

24. The total price listed is the amount the Postal Service actually charges. If you were to multiply the listed price *per stamp* by the number of stamps, what should the total price be?

page 272

---

81. **Population of Alabama** The 2000 U.S. census showed that the population of Alabama was 4,447,000, with 26.0% represented by African Americans. What is the best estimate of the African American population in Alabama? (*Source:* U.S. Census Bureau.)

   A. 500,000   B. 1,500,000
   C. 1,100,000   D. 750,000

82. **Population of Hawaii** The 2000 U.S. census showed that the population of Hawaii was 1,212,000, with 21.4% of the population being of two or more races. What is the best estimate of this population of Hawaii? (*Source:* U.S. Census Bureau.)

   A. 240,000   B. 300,000
   C. 21,400   D. 24,000

Gasoline Prices The line graph shows the average price, adjusted for inflation, that Americans have paid for a gallon of gasoline for selected years between 1958 and 2008. Use this information in Exercises 83 and 84.

Source: www.inflationdata.com

(c) Researchers recommend that a person reach approximately 85% of their MET when exercising. Calculate 85% of the ideal MET from part (b). Then refer to the following table. What activity can the woman do that is approximately this value?

Activity	METs	Activity	METs
Golf (with cart)	2.5	Skiing (water or downhill)	6.8
Walking (3 mph)	3.3	Swimming	7.0
Mowing lawn (power mower)	4.5	Walking (5 mph)	8.0
Ballroom or square dancing	5.5	Jogging	10.2
Cycling	5.7	Rope skipping	12.0

Source: Harvard School of Public Health.

86. Repeat parts (a)–(c) of **Exercise 85** for a 55-year-old man.

page 275

Collaborative Investigations at the end of each chapter provide an opportunity for cooperative learning through exercises that can be done in small groups or with the whole class.

COLLABORATIVE INVESTIGATION

Budgeting to Buy a Car

You are shopping for a sports car and have put aside a certain amount of money each month for a car payment. Your instructor will assign this amount to you. After looking through a variety of resources, you have narrowed your choices to the cars listed in the table.

Year/Make/Model	Retail Price	Fuel Tank Size (in gallons)	Miles per Gallon (city)	Miles per Gallon (highway)
2010 Ford Mustang	$31,395	16.0	16	24
2010 Ford Taurus SEL	$29,220	19.0	17	25
2010 Toyota Camry Hybrid	$26,150	17.2	33	34
2010 Mazda MX-5 Miata	$26,250	12.7	21	28
2010 Honda CR-V EX-L	$26,495	15.3	21	28
2010 Chevrolet Malibu Hybrid	$25,555	16.0	26	34

Source: www.edmunds.com

As a group, work through the following steps to determine which car you can afford to buy.

A. Decide which cars you think are within your budget.

B. Select one of the cars you identified in part A. Have each member of the group calculate the monthly payment for this car using a different financing option. Use the formula given below, where P is principal, r is interest rate, and m is the number of monthly payments, along with the financing options table.

Financing Options

Time (in years)	Interest Rate
4	2.0%
5	3.5%
6	5.0%

$$\text{Monthly Payment} = \frac{\dfrac{Pr}{12}}{1 - \left(\dfrac{12}{12 + r}\right)^m}$$

C. Have each group member determine the amount of money paid in interest over the duration of the loan for his or her financing option.

D. Consider fuel expenses.

  1. Assume you will travel an average of 75 miles in the city and 400 miles on the highway each week. How many gallons of gas will you need to buy each month?

  2. Using typical prices for gas in your area at this time, how much money will you need to have available for buying gas?

E. Repeat parts B–D as necessary until your group can reach a consensus on the car you will buy and the financing option you will use. Write a paragraph to explain your choices.

page 279

Charles D. Miller • Vern E. Heeren • John Hornsby

Mathematical Ideas

Custom Edition for Luzerne County Community College

Taken from:
Mathematical Ideas, Twelfth Edition
by Charles D. Miller, Vern E. Heeren, and John Hornsby

Cover Art: *Seashell 03*, by Micheal Lary.

Taken from:

Mathematical Ideas, Twelfth Edition
by Charles D. Miller, Vern E. Heeren, and John Hornsby
Copyright © 2012, 2008, 2004 by Pearson Education, Inc.
Published by Addison-Wesley
San Francisco, California 94111

This special edition published in cooperation with Pearson Learning Solutions.

Pearson Learning Solutions, 501 Boylston Street, Suite 900, Boston, MA 02116
A Pearson Education Company
www.pearsoned.com

Printed in the United States of America

 7 8 9 10 V092 16 15 14 13

000200010271279580

SW

ISBN 10: 1-256-47247-6
ISBN 13: 978-1-256-47247-6

To my special son, Christopher Michael Hornsby—DAD

To my beloved wife, Carole, my inspiration—VERN

CONTENTS

v

PREFACE

After eleven editions and over four decades, *Mathematical Ideas* continues to be one of the most popular textbooks in liberal arts mathematics education. We are proud to present the twelfth edition of a text that offers non-physical science students a practical coverage that connects mathematics to the world around them. It is a flexible book that has evolved alongside changing trends but remains steadfast to its original objectives.

This edition continues to feature a theme that was introduced in the previous edition. Movies and television have become entrenched in our society and appeal to a broad range of interests. Every chapter opener contains reference to a popular movie, television show, or event, including discussion of a scene that deals with the mathematics covered in the chapter. The margin notes, long a popular hallmark of the book, include similar references. These references are indicated with a clapboard icon 🎬. Many of the chapter openers and margin notes have been revised for this edition. We hope that users will enjoy visiting Hollywood while learning mathematics.

Mathematical Ideas is written with a variety of students in mind. It is well suited for several courses, including those geared toward the aforementioned liberal arts audience and survey courses in mathematics, finite mathematics, and mathematics for prospective and in-service elementary and middle-school teachers. Ample topics are included for a two-term course, yet the variety of topics and flexibility of sequence makes the text suitable for shorter courses as well. Our main objectives continue to be comprehensive coverage, appropriate organization, clear exposition, an abundance of examples, and well-planned exercise sets with numerous applications.

NEW TO THIS EDITION

- Movie and television references have been updated throughout the book.

- Pointers have been added to Examples. They guide students and provide on-the-spot reminders and warnings to avoid common pitfalls.

- Every chapter now includes an Extension, a mini-section that delves deeper into a related topic.

- Enhancing the already well-respected exercise sets, over 1000 exercises are new or modified.

- Graphing calculator screens have been redesigned and now show the output in Math-Print format (available on some TI-84 calculators).

- Figure and table references within the text are set using the same typeface as the figure or table, making it easier for students to identify and connect them.

- The text has been streamlined to make it easier for students to recognize key content.

- A completely new set of videos has been developed to support student learning outside the classroom. They are useful for online or hybrid courses, as well as student self-study, and are available on DVD and in MyMathLab.

OVERVIEW OF CHAPTERS

- **Chapter 1 (The Art of Problem Solving)** introduces the student to inductive reasoning, pattern recognition, and problem-solving techniques. We continue to provide exercises based on the monthly Calendar from *Mathematics Teacher* and have added new ones throughout this edition, beginning in Section 1.4. At the request of reviewers, Section 1.2 now includes coverage of arithmetic and geometric sequences.

- **Chapter 2 (The Basic Concepts of Set Theory)** includes updated exercises on surveys and a revised discussion of the work of Georg Cantor. (*Note:* Instructors should feel free to cover Chapter 3 before Chapter 2 if they desire.)

- **Chapter 3 (Introduction to Logic)** introduces the fundamental concepts of inductive and deductive logic. There is a new chapter opener from *Shrek the Third*. We have included additional exercises from the work of Raymond Smullyan and expanded the coverage of logical fallacies. The logic problems and Sudoku puzzles from the previous edition have been replaced with new ones.

- **Chapter 4 (Numeration Systems)** covers various types of numeration systems, as well as modular number systems. At reviewer request, we have expanded the former single section on historical numeration systems into two sections. Section 4.1 now includes full coverage of Roman numerals, and Section 4.2 discusses the Hindu-Arabic, Babylonian, Mayan, and Greek systems.

- **Chapter 5 (Number Theory)** presents an introduction to topics such as prime and composite numbers and the Fibonacci sequence. A new chapter opener appears in this edition. The former Section 5.1 was split into two sections. The new Section 5.2 (*Large Prime Numbers*) includes discussion of the ever-changing search for large primes.

- **Chapter 6 (The Real Numbers and Their Representations)** introduces some of the basic concepts of real numbers, their various forms of representation, and operations of arithmetic with them. The chapter opener is new. Most of the exercises involving real-life data have been updated, and several new ones have been included.

- **Chapter 7 (The Basic Concepts of Algebra)** can be used to present the basics of algebra (linear and quadratic equations, applications, exponents, polynomials, and factoring) to students for the first time, or as a review of previous courses. There is a new chapter opener, and applications have been updated in this chapter as well.

- **Chapter 8 (Graphs, Functions, and Systems of Equations and Inequalities)** is the second of our two algebra chapters, and continues with graphs, equations, and applications of linear, quadratic, exponential, and logarithmic functions and models. Systems of equations are covered, and in this edition we have split the former Section 8.7 into two sections, the second of which covers applications of systems. Many exercises in this chapter include updated data.

- **Chapter 9 (Geometry)** covers elementary plane geometry, transformational geometry, constructions, non-Euclidean geometry, and chaos and fractals. The new chapter opener comes from *The Simpsons*, which for two decades has provided many mathematics-education moments. At reviewer request, the order of former Sections 9.3 and 9.4 has been reversed, so that *The Geometry of Triangles: Congruence, Similarity, and the Pythagorean Theorem* now precedes *Perimeter, Area, and Circumference*.

  (*Note:* The former Chapter 10, *Trigonometry*, is now included in this edition as Chapter 14.)

- **Chapter 10 (Counting Methods)** focuses on elementary counting techniques, in preparation for the chapter to follow. We have included a completely new chapter opener on the coin toss in Super Bowl XLIV, added problems from *Mathematics Teacher*, and included a discussion of "unwanted ordering." The Extension on Magic Squares, formerly in Chapter 5, is now part of this chapter.

- **Chapter 11 (Probability)** covers the basics of probability, odds, and expected value. In this edition, we include problems from *Mathematics Teacher* for the first time.

- **Chapter 12 (Statistics)** is an introduction to statistics that focuses on the measures of central tendency, dispersion, and position and discusses the normal distribution, regression, and correlation. The new chapter opener provides a real life example of Simpson's paradox, and examples and exercises include updated data.

- **Chapter 13 (Personal Financial Management)** provides the student with the basics of the mathematics of finance as applied to inflation, consumer debt, and house buying. We include a section on investing, with emphasis on stocks, bonds, and mutual funds. Examples and exercises have been updated to reflect current interest rates and investment returns. A new Extension, *Ponzi Schemes and Other Investment Frauds*, has been added to this edition.

- **Chapter 14 (Trigonometry)** was formerly Chapter 10. It provides an introduction to some basic concepts of plane trigonometry, including angles in standard position, right angle trigonometry, and the laws of sines and cosines.

- **Chapter 15 (Graph Theory)** covers the basic concepts of graph theory and its applications. We have reformatted much of the discussion for easier reading.

- **Chapter 16 (Voting and Apportionment)** deals with issues in voting methods and apportionment of votes, topics which have become increasingly popular in liberal arts mathematics courses. A new chapter opener features the 2008 movie *Swing Vote*, and we have revised and streamlined exposition (particularly in Section 16.3) for readability. A new Extension, *Two Additional Apportionment Methods*, is now included.

COURSE OUTLINE CONSIDERATIONS

Chapters in the text are, in most cases, independent and may be covered in the order chosen by the instructor. The few exceptions are as follows:

- Chapter 6 contains some material dependent on the ideas found in Chapter 5.

- Chapter 6 should be covered before Chapter 7 if student background so dictates.

- Chapters 7 and 8 form an algebraic "package" and should be covered in sequential order.

- A thorough coverage of Chapter 11 depends on knowledge of Chapter 10 material, although probability can be covered without teaching extensive counting methods by avoiding the more difficult exercises.

- The latter part of Chapter 12, on inferential statistics, depends on an understanding of probability (Chapter 11).

- Chapter 14 requires some basic equation-solving ability.

FEATURES OF THE TWELFTH EDITION

ENHANCED **Chapter Openers**   In keeping with the Hollywood theme, chapter openers address a scene or situation from a popular movie or a television series or event. Many are new to this edition. Some openers illustrate the correct use of mathematics, while others address how mathematics is misused. In the latter case, we subscribe to the premise that we can all learn from the mistakes of others. Some openers include a problem statement that the reader is asked to solve. We hope that you enjoy reading these chapter openers as much as we have enjoyed preparing them.

ENHANCED **Varied Exercise Sets** We continue to present a variety of exercises that integrate drill, conceptual, and applied problems and have included over 1000 new or modified exercises to this edition. The text contains a wealth of exercises to provide students with opportunities to practice, apply, connect, and extend the mathematical skills they are learning. We have updated the exercises that focus on real-life data and have retained their titles for easy identification. Several chapters are enriched with new applications, particularly Chapters 6, 7, 8, 11, 12, and 13. We continue to use graphs, tables, and charts when appropriate. Many of the graphs use a style similar to that seen by students in today's print and electronic media.

ENHANCED **Margin Notes** This popular feature is a hallmark of this text and has been retained and updated where appropriate. These notes are interspersed throughout the text and deal with various subjects such as lives of mathematicians, historical vignettes, philatelic and numismatic reproductions, anecdotes on mathematics textbooks of the past, newspaper and magazine articles, and current research in mathematics. Several new Hollywood-related margin notes have also been added.

ENHANCED **Extensions** These mini-sections delve deeper into related topics and include their own exercise sets. New Extensions have been written for chapters that previously did not have this feature.

Collaborative Investigations The importance of cooperative learning is addressed in this end-of-chapter feature.

Problem-Solving Hints Special paragraphs labeled "Problem-Solving Hint" relate the discussion of problem-solving strategies to techniques that have been presented earlier.

ENHANCED **Optional Graphing Technology** We continue to provide sample graphing calculator screens to show how technology can be used to support results found analytically. These screens have been re-designed and now show the output in MathPrint format. It is not essential, however, that a student have a graphing calculator to study from this text. *The technology component is optional.*

Art Program The text continues to feature a full-color design. Color is used for instructional emphasis in text discussions, examples, graphs, and figures. Many new photos have been incorporated to provide visual appeal.

For Further Thought These entries encourage students to share amongst themselves their reasoning processes to gain a deeper understanding of key mathematical concepts.

Example Titles The numerous, carefully selected examples that illustrate concepts and skills are titled so that students can see at a glance the topic under consideration.

UPDATED **Emphasis on Real Data in the Form of Graphs, Charts, and Tables** We continue to use up-to-date information from magazines, newspapers, and the Internet to create real applications that are relevant and meaningful.

Chapter Tests Each chapter concludes with a chapter test so that students can check their mastery of the material.

SUPPLEMENTS

STUDENT SUPPLEMENTS

Student's Solutions Manual
ISBN-10: 0-321-69384-1; ISBN-13: 978-0-321-69384-6

- This manual by Carrie Green provides solutions to the odd-numbered exercises in the exercise sets, the Extensions, and the Appendix exercises, as well as solutions for all the Chapter Test exercises.

Video Resources on DVD with Optional Captioning
ISBN-10: 0-321-71649-3; ISBN-13: 978-0-321-71649-1

- This completely new set of videos was developed by Sue Glascoe of Mesa Community College. Making use of newer teaching technologies, the videos clearly cover important definitions, procedures, and concepts by working through examples and exercises from the textbook. They are ideal for online and hybrid courses, as well as supplemental instruction for traditional courses. Optional subtitles are available.

INSTRUCTOR SUPPLEMENTS

Annotated Instructor's Edition
ISBN-10: 0-321-69406-6; ISBN-13: 978-0-321-69406-5

- This special edition of the text provides answers next to the text exercises for quick reference, when space is available. Longer answers, indicated by an icon ⊡ after the exercise, can be found in the back of the book.

Instructor's Solutions Manual
ISBN-10: 0-321-69405-8; ISBN-13: 978-0-321-69405-8

- This manual by Carrie Green contains solutions to all end-of-section exercises, Extension, Chapter Test, and Appendix exercises.

ENHANCED **Insider's Guide with Math Goes to Hollywood Teaching Notes**
ISBN-10: 0-321-71643-4; ISBN-13: 978-0-321-71643-9

- This updated guide now includes detailed *Math Goes to Hollywood* teaching notes to help instructors integrate the movies from the text into their courses. The new movie notes include the name of the movie, clip segment times, related mathematical topics, correlation to the text, summary of mathematical content, and discussion questions.
- The *Insider's Guide* includes resources to help faculty with course preparation and classroom management. It provides helpful teaching tips correlated to each section of the text, as well as general teaching advice.

Instructor's Testing Manual (online only)
- This manual contains four tests for each chapter of the text. Answer keys are included.

TestGen® (online only)
- TestGen enables instructors to build, edit, print, and administer tests using a computerized bank of questions developed to cover all text objectives.

PowerPoint Lecture Presentation (online only)
- These fully editable lecture slides include definitions, key concepts, and examples for use in a lecture setting and are available for each section of the text.

Online supplements can be found in MyMathLab or downloaded from www.pearsonhighered.com/irc.

MEDIA SUPPLEMENTS

MyMathLab® Online Course

MyMathLab® is a text-specific, easily customizable online course that integrates interactive multimedia instruction with textbook content. MyMathLab gives instructors the tools they need to deliver all or a portion of their course online, whether their students are in a lab setting or working from home.

- **Interactive homework exercises**, correlated to the textbook at the objective level, are algorithmically generated for unlimited practice and mastery. Most exercises are free-response and provide guided solutions, sample problems, and tutorial learning aids for extra help.

- **Personalized Study Plan,** generated when students complete a test or quiz, indicates which topics have been mastered and links to tutorial exercises for topics students have not mastered. The Study Plan can be customized so that the topics available match course contents or so that students' homework results determine mastery.

- **Multimedia learning aids**, such as video lectures and podcasts, animations, and a complete multimedia textbook, help students independently improve their understanding and performance. Instructors can assign these multimedia learning aids as homework to help students grasp the concepts.

- **Homework and Test Manager** allows instructors to assign homework, quizzes, and tests that are automatically graded. They can select just the right mix of questions from the MyMathLab exercise bank, instructor-created custom exercises, and/or Test-Gen® test items.

- **Gradebook,** designed specifically for mathematics and statistics, automatically tracks students' results, lets instructors stay on top of student performance, and gives them control over how to calculate final grades. They can also add offline (paper-and-pencil) grades to the gradebook.

- **MathXL Exercise Builder** allows instructors to create static and algorithmic exercises for their online assignments. They can use the library of sample exercises as an easy starting point, or they can edit any course-related exercise.

- **Pearson Tutor Center** (www.pearsontutorservices.com) access is automatically included with MyMathLab. The Tutor Center is staffed by qualified math instructors who provide textbook-specific tutoring for students via toll-free phone, fax, email, and interactive Web sessions.

- **Specific features for** *Mathematical Ideas* include
  - Completely new concept review videos
  - Interactive mathematics and societal timeline

Students using MyMathLab® do their assignments in the Flash®-based MathXL Player, which is compatible with almost any browser (Firefox®, Safari™, or Internet Explorer®) on almost any platform (Macintosh® or Windows®). MyMathLab is powered by CourseCompass™, Pearson Education's online teaching and learning environment, and by MathXL®, our online homework, tutorial, and assessment system. MyMathLab is available to qualified adopters. For more information, visit www.mymathlab.com or contact your Pearson representative.

MathXL® Online Course

MathXL® is an online homework, tutorial, and assessment system that accompanies Pearson's textbooks in mathematics or statistics.

- **Interactive homework exercises**, correlated to the textbook at the objective level, are algorithmically generated for unlimited practice and mastery. Most exercises are free-response and provide guided solutions, sample problems, and learning aids for extra help.

- **Personalized Study Plan,** generated when students complete a test or quiz or homework, indicates which topics have been mastered and links to tutorial exercises for topics students have not mastered. Instructors can customize the available topics in the study plan to match their course concepts.

- **Multimedia learning aids**, such as video lectures and animations, help students independently improve their understanding and performance. These are assignable as homework, to further encourage their use.

- **Gradebook,** designed specifically for mathematics and statistics, automatically tracks students' results, lets instructors stay informed of student performance, and gives them control over how to calculate final grades.

- **MathXL Exercise Builder** allows instructors to create static and algorithmic exercises for their online assignments. They can use the library of sample exercises as an easy starting point or the Exercise Builder to edit any of the course-related exercises.

- **Homework and Test Manager** lets instructors create online homework, quizzes, and tests that are automatically graded. They can select just the right mix of questions from the MathXL exercise bank, instructor-created custom exercises, and/or TestGen test items.

The new, Flash®-based MathXL Player is compatible with almost any browser (Firefox®, Safari™, or Internet Explorer®) on almost any platform (Macintosh® or Windows®). MathXL is available to qualified adopters. For more information, visit our website at www.mathxl.com, or contact your Pearson representative.

ACKNOWLEDGMENTS

We wish to thank the following reviewers for their helpful comments and suggestions for this and previous editions of the text. (Reviewers of the twelfth edition are noted with an asterisk.)

H. Achepohl, *College of DuPage*

Shahrokh Ahmadi, *Northern Virginia Community College*

Richard Andrews, *Florida A&M University*

Cindy Anfinson, *Palomar College*

*Erika Asano, *University of South Florida, St. Petersburg*

Elaine Barber, *Germanna Community College*

Anna Baumgartner, *Carthage College*

James E. Beamer, *Northeastern State University*

Elliot Benjamin, *Unity College*

Jaime Bestard, *Barry University*

Joyce Blair, *Belmont University*

Gus Brar, *Delaware County Community College*

Roger L. Brown, *Davenport College*

Douglas Burke, *Malcolm X College*

John Busovicki, *Indiana University of Pennsylvania*

Ann Cascarelle, *St. Petersburg Junior College*

Kenneth Chapman, *St. Petersburg Junior College*

Gordon M. Clarke, *University of the Incarnate Word*

M. Marsha Cupitt, *Durham Technical Community College*

James Curry, *American River College*

Rosemary Danaher, *Sacred Heart University*

Ken Davis, *Mesa State College*

Nancy Davis, *Brunswick Community College*

George DeRise, *Thomas Nelson Community College*

Catherine Dermott, *Hudson Valley Community College*

Greg Dietrich, *Florida Community College at Jacksonville*

*Vincent Dimiceli, *Oral Roberts University*

Diana C. Dwan, *Yavapai College*

Laura Dyer, *Belleville Area College*

Jan Eardley, *Barat College*

Joe Eitel, *Folsom College*

Azin Enshai, *American River College*

Gayle Farmer, *Northeastern State University*

Michael Farndale, *Waldorf College*

Gordon Feathers, *Passaic County Community College*

Thomas Flohr, *New River Community College*

Bill Fulton, *Black Hawk College—East*

Anne Gardner, *Wenatchee Valley College*

*Justin M. Gash, *Franklin College*

Donald Goral, *Northern Virginia Community College*

Glen Granzow, *Idaho State University*

Larry Green, *Lake Tahoe Community College*

Arthur D. Grissinger, *Lock Haven University*

Don Hancock, *Pepperdine University*

Denis Hanson, *University of Regina*

Marilyn Hasty, *Southern Illinois University*

Shelby L. Hawthorne, *Thomas Nelson Community College*

Jeff Heiking, *St. Petersburg Junior College*

Laura Hillerbrand, *Broward Community College*

*Corinne Irwin, *University of Texas at Austin*

Jacqueline Jensen, *Sam Houston State University*

Emanuel Jinich, *Endicott College*

Frank Juric, *Brevard Community College-Palm Bay*

Karla Karstens, *University of Vermont*

*Najam Khaja, *Centennial College*

Hilary Kight, *Wesleyan College*

Barbara J. Kniepkamp, *Southern Illinois University at Edwardsville*

Suda Kunyosying, *Shepherd College*

Yu-Ju Kuo, *Indiana University of Pennsylvania*

*Stephane Lafortune, *College of Charleston*

Pam Lamb, *J. Sargeant Reynolds Community College*

John Lattanzio, *Indiana University of Pennsylvania*

John W. Legge, *Pikeville College*

*Dawn Locklear, *Crown College*

*Bin Lu, *California State University, Sacramento*

Leo Lusk, *Gulf Coast Community College*

Sherrie Lutsch, *Northwest Indian College*

Rhonda Macleod, *Florida State University*

Andrew Markoe, *Rider University*

Darlene Marnich, *Point Park College*

Victoria Martinez, *Okaloosa Walton Community College*

Chris Mason, *Community College of Vermont*

Mark Maxwell, *Maryville University*

Carol McCarron, *Harrisburg Area Community College*

Delois McCormick, *Germanna Community College*

Daisy McCoy, *Lyndon State College*

Cynthia McGinnis, *Okaloosa Walton Community College*

Vena McGrath, *Davenport College*

Robert Moyer, *Fort Valley State University*

Shai Neumann, *Brevard Community College*

Barbara Nienstedt, *Gloucester County College*

Chaitanya Nigam, *Gateway Community-Technical College*

Vladimir Nikiforov, *University of Memphis*

*Vicky Ohlson, *Trenholm State Technical College*

Jean Okumura, *Windward Community College*

*Stan Perrine, *Charleston Southern University*

Bob Phillips, *Mesabi Range Community College*

Kathy Pinchback, *University of Memphis*

Priscilla Putman, *New Jersey City University*

Scott C. Radtke, *Davenport College*

*Doraiswamy Ramachandran, *California State University, Sacramento*

John Reily, *Montclair State University*

Beth Reynolds, *Mater Dei College*

Shirley I. Robertson, *High Point University*

Andrew M. Rockett, *CW Post Campus of Long Island University*

Kathleen Rodak, *St. Mary's College of Ave Maria University*

*Cynthia Roemer, *Union County College*

*Lisa Rombes, *Washtenaw Community College*

Abby Roscum, *Marshalltown Community College*

D. Schraeder, *McLennan Community College*

Wilfred Schulte, *Cosumnes River College*

Melinda Schulteis, *Concordia University*

Gary D. Shaffer, *Allegany College of Maryland*

Doug Shaw, *University of North Iowa*

Jane Sinibaldi, *York College of Pennsylvania*

*Nancy Skocik, *California University of Pennsylvania*

Larry Smith, *Peninsula College*

Marguerite Smith, *Merced College*

Charlene D. Snow, *Lower Columbia College*

H. Jeannette Stephens, *Whatcom Community College*

Suzanne J. Stock, *Oakton Community College*

*Dawn M. Strickland, *Winthrop University*

Dian Thom, *McKendree College*

Claude C. Thompson, *Hollins University*

Mark Tom, *College of the Sequoias*

Ida Umphers, *University of Arkansas at Little Rock*

Karen Villarreal, *University of New Orleans*

*Dr. Karen Walters, *Northern Virginia Community College*

Wayne Wanamaker, *Central Florida Community College*

David Wasilewski, *Luzerne County Community College*

William Watkins, *California State University, Northridge*

*Alice Williamson, *Sussex County Community College*

Susan Williford, *Columbia State Community College*

Tom Witten, *Southwest Virginia Community College*

Fred Worth, *Henderson State University*

Rob Wylie, *Carl Albert State College*

Henry Wyzinski, *Indiana University Northwest*

A project of this magnitude cannot be accomplished without the help of many other dedicated individuals. Marnie Greenhut served as acquisitions editor for this edition. Carol Merrigan provided excellent production supervision. Anne Kelly, Greg Tobin, Tracy Patruno, Roxanne McCarley, Elle Driska, and Christine O'Brien of Pearson Addison-Wesley gave us their unwavering support.

Beth Anderson continued to provide outstanding photo research. Terry McGinnis gave her usual excellent behind-the-scenes guidance. Thanks go to Dr. Margaret L. Morrow of Plattsburgh State University and Dr. Jill Van Newenhizen of Lake Forest College, who wrote the material on graph theory and voting/apportionment, respectively. Chris Heeren and Paul Lorczak did an outstanding job of accuracy- and answer-checking. Mike McCraith of Cuyahoga Community College joined the cast with the addition of new movie cards. And finally, we thank our loyal users over these many editions for making this book one of the most successful in its market.

Vern E. Heeren
John Hornsby

THE ART OF PROBLEM SOLVING

The 1995 movie *Die Hard: With a Vengeance* stars Bruce Willis as New York Detective John McClane. In this film, McClane is tormented by villain Simon Gruber (Jeremy Irons), who plants bombs around the city and poses riddles and puzzles for disarming them. In one situation, Simon gives McClane and store owner Zeus Carver (Samuel L. Jackson) the following riddle by telephone to solve in 5 minutes.

> *On the fountain there should be two jugs. Do you see them? A 5-gallon and a 3-gallon. Fill one of the jugs with exactly 4 gallons of water, and place it on the scale, and the timer will stop. You must be precise. One ounce more or less will result in detonation.*

McClane and Carver were able to solve the riddle and defuse the bomb. Can you solve it? The answer is on page 2.

1.1 SOLVING PROBLEMS BY INDUCTIVE REASONING

Characteristics of Inductive and Deductive Reasoning • Pitfalls of Inductive Reasoning

Solution to the Chapter Opener Problem This is one way to do it: With both jugs empty, fill the 3-gallon jug and pour its contents into the 5-gallon jug. Then fill the 3-gallon jug again, and pour it into the 5-gallon jug until the latter is filled. There is now $(3 + 3) - 5 = 1$ gallon in the 3-gallon jug. Empty the 5-gallon jug, and pour the 1 gallon of water from the 3-gallon jug into the 5-gallon jug. Finally, fill the 3-gallon jug and pour all of it into the 5-gallon jug, resulting in $1 + 3 = 4$ gallons in the 5-gallon jug.

(*Note*: There is another way to solve this problem. See if you can discover the alternative solution.)

Characteristics of Inductive and Deductive Reasoning

The development of mathematics can be traced to the Egyptian and Babylonian cultures (3000 B.C.–A.D. 260) as a necessity for problem solving. To solve a problem or perform an operation, a cookbook-like recipe was given, and it was performed repeatedly to solve similar problems.

By observing that a specific method worked for a certain type of problem, the Babylonians and the Egyptians concluded that the same method would work for any similar type of problem. Such a conclusion is called a *conjecture*. A **conjecture** is an educated guess based on repeated observations of a particular process or pattern. The method of reasoning we have just described is called *inductive reasoning*.

Inductive Reasoning

Inductive reasoning is characterized by drawing a general conclusion (making a conjecture) from repeated observations of specific examples. The conjecture may or may not be true.

In testing a conjecture obtained by inductive reasoning, it takes only one example that does not work to prove the conjecture false. Such an example is called a **counterexample.**

Inductive reasoning provides a powerful method of drawing conclusions, but there is no assurance that the observed conjecture will always be true. For this reason, mathematicians are reluctant to accept a conjecture as an absolute truth until it is formally proved using methods of *deductive reasoning*. Deductive reasoning characterized the development and approach of Greek mathematics, as seen in the works of Euclid, Pythagoras, Archimedes, and others. During the classical Greek period (600 B.C.–A.D. 450), general concepts were applied to specific problems, resulting in a structured, logical development of mathematics.

Deductive Reasoning

Deductive reasoning is characterized by applying general principles to specific examples.

We now look at examples of these two types of reasoning. In this chapter, we often refer to the **natural,** or **counting, numbers:**

The three dots (*ellipsis points*) indicate that the numbers continue indefinitely in the pattern that has been established. The most probable rule for continuing this pattern is "add 1 to the previous number," and this is indeed the rule that we follow.

Now consider the following list of natural numbers:

$$2, 9, 16, 23, 30.$$

What is the next number of this list? What is the pattern? After studying the numbers, we might see that $2 + 7 = 9$, and $9 + 7 = 16$. Do we add 16 and 7 to get 23?

June

S	M	Tu	W	Th	F	S
1	2	3	4	5	6	7
8	9	10	11	12	13	14
15	16	17	18	19	20	21
22	23	24	25	26	27	28
29	30					

July

S	M	Tu	W	Th	F	S
		1	2	3	4	5
6	7	8	9	10	11	12
13	14	15	16	17	18	19
20	21	22	23	24	25	26
27	28	29	30	31		

Figure 1

Do we add 23 and 7 to get 30? Yes. It seems that any number in the given list can be found by adding 7 to the preceding number, so the next number in the list would be $30 + 7 = 37$.

We set out to find the "next number" by reasoning from observation of the numbers in the list. We may have jumped from these observations to the general statement that any number in the list is 7 more than the preceding number. This is an example of *inductive reasoning*.

By using inductive reasoning, we concluded that 37 was the next number. Suppose the person making up the list has another answer in mind. The list of numbers

$$2, 9, 16, 23, 30$$

actually gives the dates of Mondays in June if June 1 falls on a Sunday. The next Monday after June 30 is July 7. With this pattern, the list continues as

$$2, 9, 16, 23, 30, 7, 14, 21, 28, \ldots.$$

See the calendar in **Figure 1**. The correct answer would then be 7. The process used to obtain the rule "add 7" in the preceding list reveals a main flaw of inductive reasoning. *We can never be sure that what is true in a specific case will be true in general. Inductive reasoning does not guarantee a true result, but it does provide a means of making a conjecture.*

We now review some basic notation. Throughout this book, we use *exponents* to represent repeated multiplication.

$$\text{Base} \rightarrow 4^3 = 4 \cdot 4 \cdot 4 = 64 \quad \text{4 is used as a factor 3 times.}$$
$$\uparrow$$
$$\text{Exponent}$$

Exponential Expression

If a is a number and n is a counting number $(1, 2, 3, \ldots)$, then the exponential expression a^n is defined as follows.

$$a^n = \underbrace{a \cdot a \cdot a \cdot \ldots \cdot a}_{n \text{ factors of } a}$$

The number a is the **base** and n is the **exponent**.

With deductive reasoning, we use general statements and apply them to specific situations. For example, consider the **Pythagorean theorem:**

In any right triangle, the sum of the squares of the legs (shorter sides) is equal to the square of the hypotenuse (longest side).

Thus, if we know that the lengths of the shorter sides are 3 inches and 4 inches, we can find the length of the longest side. Let h represent the length of the longest side.

$$3^2 + 4^2 = h^2 \quad \text{Pythagorean theorem}$$
$$9 + 16 = h^2 \quad 3^2 = 3 \cdot 3 = 9; 4^2 = 4 \cdot 4 = 16$$
$$25 = h^2 \quad \text{Add.}$$
$$5 = h \quad \text{The positive square root of 25 is 5.}$$

Thus, the longest side measures 5 inches. We used the general rule (the Pythagorean theorem) and applied it to the specific situation.

Reasoning through a problem usually requires certain *premises*. A **premise** can be an assumption, law, rule, widely held idea, or observation. Then reason inductively or deductively from the premises to obtain a **conclusion.** The premises and conclusion make up a **logical argument.**

▌▌ **EXAMPLE 1** Identifying Premises and Conclusions

Identify each premise and the conclusion in each of the following arguments. Then tell whether each argument is an example of inductive or deductive reasoning.

(a) Our house is made of adobe. Both of my next-door neighbors have adobe houses. Therefore, all houses in our neighborhood are made of adobe.

(b) All keyboards have the symbol @. I have a keyboard. I can type the symbol @.

(c) Today is Tuesday. Tomorrow will be Wednesday.

SOLUTION

(a) The premises are "Our house is made of adobe" and "Both of my next-door neighbors have adobe houses." The conclusion is "Therefore, all houses in our neighborhood are made of adobe." Because the reasoning goes from specific examples to a general statement, the argument is an example of inductive reasoning (although it may very well have a false conclusion).

(b) Here, the premises are "All keyboards have the symbol @" and "I have a keyboard." The conclusion is "I can type the symbol @." This reasoning goes from general to specific, so deductive reasoning was used.

(c) There is only one premise here, "Today is Tuesday." The conclusion is "Tomorrow will be Wednesday." The fact that Wednesday immediately follows Tuesday is being used, even though this fact is not explicitly stated. Because the conclusion comes from general facts that apply to this special case, deductive reasoning was used. ▌▌▌

The earlier calendar example illustrated how inductive reasoning may, at times, lead to false conclusions. However, in many cases, inductive reasoning does provide correct results if we look for the most *probable* answer.

▌▌ **EXAMPLE 2** Predicting the Next Number in a Sequence

Use inductive reasoning to determine the *probable* next number in each list below.

(a) 5, 9, 13, 17, 21, 25, 29   **(b)** 1, 1, 2, 3, 5, 8, 13, 21   **(c)** 2, 4, 8, 16, 32

SOLUTION

(a) Each number in the list is obtained by adding 4 to the previous number. The probable next number is $29 + 4 = 33$. (This is an example of an *arithmetic sequence*.)

(b) Beginning with the third number in the list, 2, each number is obtained by adding the two previous numbers in the list. That is,

$$1 + 1 = 2, \quad 1 + 2 = 3, \quad 2 + 3 = 5,$$

and so on. The probable next number in the list is $13 + 21 = 34$. (These are the first few terms of the famous *Fibonacci sequence*.)

(c) It appears here that to obtain each number after the first, we must double the previous number. Therefore, the most probable next number is $32 \times 2 = 64$. (This is an example of a *geometric sequence*.) ▌▌▌

In the 2003 movie *A Wrinkle in Time*, young Charles Wallace, played by David Dorfman, is challenged to identify a particular sequence of numbers. He correctly identifies it as the **Fibonacci sequence**.

Inductive reasoning often can be used to predict an answer in a list of similarly constructed computation exercises, as shown in the next example.

▮▮ **EXAMPLE 3** Predicting the Product of Two Numbers

Consider the list of equations. Predict the next multiplication fact in the list.

$$37 \times 3 = 111$$
$$37 \times 6 = 222$$
$$37 \times 9 = 333$$
$$37 \times 12 = 444$$

SOLUTION

The left side of each equation has two factors, the first 37 and the second a multiple of 3, beginning with 3. Each product (answer) consists of three digits, all the same, beginning with 111 for 37×3. Thus, the next multiplication fact would be

$$37 \times 15 = 555, \quad \text{which is indeed true.}$$ ▮▮▮

Pitfalls of Inductive Reasoning

There are pitfalls associated with inductive reasoning. A classic example involves the maximum number of regions formed when chords are constructed in a circle. When two points on a circle are joined with a line segment, a *chord* is formed.

Locate a single point on a circle. Because no chords are formed, a single interior region is formed. See **Figure 2(a)**. Locate two points and draw a chord. Two interior regions are formed, as shown in **Figure 2(b)**. Continue this pattern. Locate three points, and draw all possible chords. Four interior regions are formed, as shown in **Figure 2(c)**. Four points yield 8 regions and five points yield 16 regions. See **Figures 2(d) and 2(e)**.

Table 1

Number of Points	Number of Regions
1	1
2	2
3	4
4	8
5	16

(a)

(b)

(c)

(d)

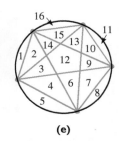
(e)

Figure 2

The results of the preceding observations are summarized in **Table 1** in the margin. The pattern formed in the column headed "Number of Regions" is the same one we saw in **Example 2(c)**, where we predicted that the next number would be 64. It seems here that for each additional point on the circle, the number of regions doubles. A reasonable inductive conjecture would be that for six points, 32 regions would be formed. But as **Figure 3** indicates, there are *only 31 regions*. The pattern of doubling ends when the sixth point is considered. Adding a seventh point would yield 57 regions. The numbers obtained here are

$$1, 2, 4, 8, 16, 31, 57.$$

For n points on the circle, the number of regions is given by the formula

$$\frac{n^4 - 6n^3 + 23n^2 - 18n + 24}{24}.^*$$

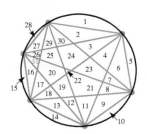
Figure 3

---

*For more information on this and other similar patterns, see "Counting Pizza Pieces and Other Combinatorial Problems," by Eugene Maier, in the January 1988 issue of *Mathematics Teacher*, pp. 22–26.

We can use a graphing calculator to construct a table of values that indicates the number of regions for various numbers of points. Using X rather than *n*, we can define Y_1 using the expression given on the previous page. (see **Figure 4(a)**). Then, creating a table of values, as in **Figure 4(b)**, we see how many regions (indicated by Y_1) there are for any number of points (X).

Figure 4

For Further Thought

Inductive Reasoning Anecdote

The following anecdote concerning inductive reasoning appears in the first volume of the *In Mathematical Circles* series by Howard Eves.

A scientist had two large jars before him on the laboratory table. The jar on his left contained 100 fleas; the jar on his right was empty. The scientist carefully lifted a flea from the jar on the left, placed the flea on the table between the two jars, stepped back, and in a loud voice said, "Jump." The flea jumped and was put in the jar on the right. A second flea was carefully lifted from the jar on the left and placed on the table

between the two jars. Again the scientist stepped back and in a loud voice said, "Jump." The flea jumped and was put in the jar on the right. In the same manner, the scientist treated each of the 100 fleas in the jar on the left, and each flea jumped as ordered.

The two jars were then interchanged and the experiment continued with a slight difference. This time the scientist carefully lifted a flea from the jar on the left, yanked off its hind legs, placed the flea on the table between the jars, stepped back, and in a loud voice said, "Jump." The flea did not jump, and was put in the jar on the right. A second flea was carefully lifted from the jar on the left, its hind legs yanked off, and then placed on the table between the two jars. Again the scientist stepped back and in a loud voice said, "Jump." The flea did not jump, and was put in the jar on the right. In this manner, the scientist treated each of the 100 fleas in the jar on the left, and in no case did a flea jump when ordered. The scientist recorded the following induction:

"A flea, if its hind legs are yanked off, cannot hear."

For Group or Individual Investigation

Discuss or research examples from advertising that lead consumers to draw incorrect conclusions.

1.1 EXERCISES

In Exercises 1–12, determine whether the reasoning is an example of deductive or inductive reasoning.

1. If the mechanic says that it will take seven days to repair your car, then it will actually take ten days. The mechanic says, "I figure it'll take a week to fix it, ma'am." Then you can expect it to be ready ten days from now.

2. If you take your vitamins, you'll feel a lot better. You take your vitamins. Therefore, you'll feel a lot better.

3. It has rained every day for the past six days, and it is raining today as well. So it will also rain tomorrow.

4. Carrie's first three children were boys. If she has another baby, it will be a boy.

5. Finley had 85 baseball cards. His mom gave him 20 more for his birthday. Therefore, he now has 105 of them.

6. If the same number is subtracted from both sides of a true equation, the new equation is also true. I know that $9 + 18 = 27$. Therefore, $(9 + 18) - 13 = 27 - 13$.

7. If you build it, they will come. You build it. Therefore, they will come.

8. All men are mortal. Socrates is a man. Therefore, Socrates is mortal.

9. It is a fact that every student who ever attended Delgado University was accepted into graduate school. Because I am attending Delgado, I can expect to be accepted to graduate school, too.

10. For the past 97 years, a rare plant has bloomed in Columbia each summer, alternating between yellow and green flowers. Last summer, it bloomed with green flowers, so this summer it will bloom with yellow flowers.

11. In the sequence $5, 10, 15, 20, 25, \ldots$, the most probable next number is 30.

12. Lady Gaga's last four single releases have reached the Top Ten in the pop charts, so her current release will also reach the Top Ten.

13. Discuss the differences between inductive and deductive reasoning. Give an example of each.

14. Give an example of faulty inductive reasoning.

Determine the most probable next term in each of the following lists of numbers.

15. $6, 9, 12, 15, 18$

16. $13, 18, 23, 28, 33$

17. $3, 12, 48, 192, 768$

18. $32, 16, 8, 4, 2$

19. $3, 6, 9, 15, 24, 39$

20. $\dfrac{1}{3}, \dfrac{3}{5}, \dfrac{5}{7}, \dfrac{7}{9}, \dfrac{9}{11}$

21. $\dfrac{1}{2}, \dfrac{3}{4}, \dfrac{5}{6}, \dfrac{7}{8}, \dfrac{9}{10}$

22. $1, 4, 9, 16, 25$

23. $1, 8, 27, 64, 125$

24. $2, 6, 12, 20, 30, 42$

25. $4, 7, 12, 19, 28, 39$

26. $-1, 2, -3, 4, -5, 6$

27. $5, 3, 5, 5, 3, 5, 5, 5, 3, 5, 5, 5, 5, 3, 5, 5, 5, 5$

28. $8, 2, 8, 2, 2, 8, 2, 2, 2, 8, 2, 2, 2, 2, 8, 2, 2, 2, 2$

29. Construct a list of numbers similar to those in **Exercise 15** such that the most probable next number in the list is 60.

30. Construct a list of numbers similar to those in **Exercise 26** such that the most probable next number in the list is 9.

Use the list of equations and inductive reasoning to predict the next equation, and then verify your conjecture.

31.
$$(9 \times 9) + 7 = 88$$
$$(98 \times 9) + 6 = 888$$
$$(987 \times 9) + 5 = 8888$$
$$(9876 \times 9) + 4 = 88{,}888$$

32.
$$(1 \times 9) + 2 = 11$$
$$(12 \times 9) + 3 = 111$$
$$(123 \times 9) + 4 = 1111$$
$$(1234 \times 9) + 5 = 11{,}111$$

33.
$$3367 \times 3 = 10{,}101$$
$$3367 \times 6 = 20{,}202$$
$$3367 \times 9 = 30{,}303$$
$$3367 \times 12 = 40{,}404$$

34.
$$15873 \times 7 = 111{,}111$$
$$15873 \times 14 = 222{,}222$$
$$15873 \times 21 = 333{,}333$$
$$15873 \times 28 = 444{,}444$$

35.
$$34 \times 34 = 1156$$
$$334 \times 334 = 111{,}556$$
$$3334 \times 3334 = 11{,}115{,}556$$

36.
$$11 \times 11 = 121$$
$$111 \times 111 = 12{,}321$$
$$1111 \times 1111 = 1{,}234{,}321$$

37.
$$3 = \frac{3(2)}{2}$$
$$3 + 6 = \frac{6(3)}{2}$$
$$3 + 6 + 9 = \frac{9(4)}{2}$$
$$3 + 6 + 9 + 12 = \frac{12(5)}{2}$$

38.
$$2 = 4 - 2$$
$$2 + 4 = 8 - 2$$
$$2 + 4 + 8 = 16 - 2$$
$$2 + 4 + 8 + 16 = 32 - 2$$

39.
$$5(6) = 6(6 - 1)$$
$$5(6) + 5(36) = 6(36 - 1)$$
$$5(6) + 5(36) + 5(216) = 6(216 - 1)$$
$$5(6) + 5(36) + 5(216) + 5(1296) = 6(1296 - 1)$$

40.
$$3 = \frac{3(3-1)}{2}$$
$$3 + 9 = \frac{3(9-1)}{2}$$
$$3 + 9 + 27 = \frac{3(27-1)}{2}$$
$$3 + 9 + 27 + 81 = \frac{3(81-1)}{2}$$

41.
$$\frac{1}{2} = 1 - \frac{1}{2}$$
$$\frac{1}{2} + \frac{1}{4} = 1 - \frac{1}{4}$$
$$\frac{1}{2} + \frac{1}{4} + \frac{1}{8} = 1 - \frac{1}{8}$$
$$\frac{1}{2} + \frac{1}{4} + \frac{1}{8} + \frac{1}{16} = 1 - \frac{1}{16}$$

42.
$$\frac{1}{1 \cdot 2} = \frac{1}{2}$$
$$\frac{1}{1 \cdot 2} + \frac{1}{2 \cdot 3} = \frac{2}{3}$$
$$\frac{1}{1 \cdot 2} + \frac{1}{2 \cdot 3} + \frac{1}{3 \cdot 4} = \frac{3}{4}$$
$$\frac{1}{1 \cdot 2} + \frac{1}{2 \cdot 3} + \frac{1}{3 \cdot 4} + \frac{1}{4 \cdot 5} = \frac{4}{5}$$

A story is often told about how the great mathematician Carl Friedrich Gauss (1777–1855) at a very young age was told by his teacher to find the sum of the first 100 counting numbers. While his classmates toiled at the problem, Carl simply wrote down a single number and handed it in to his teacher. His answer was correct. When asked how he did it, the young Carl explained that he observed that there were 50 pairs of numbers that each added up to 101. (See below.) So the sum of all the numbers must be 50 × 101 = 5050.

$$\text{50 sums of } 101 = 50 \times 101 = 5050$$

Use the method of Gauss to find each sum.

43. $1 + 2 + 3 + \cdots + 200$ **44.** $1 + 2 + 3 + \cdots + 400$

45. $1 + 2 + 3 + \cdots + 800$ **46.** $1 + 2 + 3 + \cdots + 2000$

47. Modify the procedure of Gauss to find the sum $1 + 2 + 3 + \cdots + 175$.

48. Explain in your own words how the procedure of Gauss can be modified to find the sum $1 + 2 + 3 + \cdots + n$, where *n* is an odd natural number. (When an odd natural number is divided by 2, it leaves a remainder of 1.)

49. Modify the procedure of Gauss to find the sum $2 + 4 + 6 + \cdots + 100$.

50. Use the result of **Exercise 49** to find the sum $4 + 8 + 12 + \cdots + 200$.

51. What is the most probable next number in this list?

$$12, 1, 1, 1, 2, 1, 3$$

(*Hint:* Think about a clock with chimes.)

52. What is the next term in this list?

$$O, T, T, F, F, S, S, E, N, T$$

(*Hint:* Think about words and their relationship to numbers.)

53. (a) Choose any three-digit number with all different digits. Now reverse the digits, and subtract the smaller from the larger. Record your result. Choose another three-digit number and repeat this process. Do this as many times as it takes for you to see a pattern in the different results you obtain. (*Hint:* What is the middle digit? What is the sum of the first and third digits?)

  (b) Write an explanation of this pattern.

54. Choose any number, and follow these steps.
  (a) Multiply by 2.
  (b) Add 6.
  (c) Divide by 2.
  (d) Subtract the number you started with.
  (e) Record your result.

  Repeat the process, except in Step (b), add 8. Record your final result. Repeat the process once more, except in Step (b), add 10. Record your final result.

  (f) Observe what you have done. Then use inductive reasoning to explain how to predict the final result.

55. Complete the following.
$$142,857 \times 1 = \underline{\hspace{2cm}}$$
$$142,857 \times 2 = \underline{\hspace{2cm}}$$
$$142,857 \times 3 = \underline{\hspace{2cm}}$$
$$142,857 \times 4 = \underline{\hspace{2cm}}$$
$$142,857 \times 5 = \underline{\hspace{2cm}}$$
$$142,857 \times 6 = \underline{\hspace{2cm}}$$

What pattern exists in the successive answers? Now multiply 142,857 by 7 to obtain an interesting result.

56. Refer to **Figures 2(b)–(e)** and **Figure 3**. Instead of counting interior regions of the circle, count the chords formed. Use inductive reasoning to predict the number of chords that would be formed if seven points were used.

1.2 AN APPLICATION OF INDUCTIVE REASONING: NUMBER PATTERNS

Number Sequences • Successive Differences • Number Patterns and Sum Formulas • Figurate Numbers

Number Sequences

An ordered list of numbers such as

$$3, 9, 15, 21, 27, \ldots$$

is called a *sequence.* A **number sequence** is a list of numbers having a first number, a second number, a third number, and so on, called the **terms** of the sequence.

The sequence that begins

$$5, 9, 13, 17, 21, \ldots$$

is an *arithmetic sequence,* or *arithmetic progression.* In an **arithmetic sequence,** each term after the first is obtained by adding the same number, called the **common difference.** To find the common difference, choose any term after the first and subtract from it the preceding term. If we choose $9 - 5$ (the second term minus the first term), for example, we see that the common difference is 4. To find the term following 21, we add 4 to get $21 + 4 = 25$.

Similarly, the sequence that begins

$$2, 4, 8, 16, 32, \ldots$$

is a *geometric sequence,* or *geometric progression.* In a **geometric sequence,** each term after the first is obtained by multiplying by the same number, called the **common ratio.** To find the common ratio, choose any term after the first and divide it by the preceding term. If we choose $\frac{4}{2}$ (the second term divided by the first term), for example, we see that the common ratio is 2. To find the term following 32, we multiply by 2 to get $32 \cdot 2 = 64$.

▮▮ **EXAMPLE 1** Identifying Arithmetic and Geometric Sequences

For each sequence, determine if it is an *arithmetic sequence,* a *geometric sequence,* or *neither.* If it is either arithmetic or geometric, give the next term in the sequence.

(a) $5, 10, 15, 20, 25, \ldots$ **(b)** $3, 12, 48, 192, 768, \ldots$ **(c)** $1, 4, 9, 16, 25, \ldots$

SOLUTION

(a) If we choose *any* term after the first term, and subtract the preceding term, we find that the common difference is 5.

$$10 - 5 = 5 \qquad 15 - 10 = 5 \qquad 20 - 15 = 5 \qquad 25 - 20 = 5$$

Therefore, this is an arithmetic sequence. The next term in the sequence is

$$25 + 5 = 30.$$

(b) If any term after the first is multiplied by 4, the following term is obtained.

$$\frac{12}{3} = 4 \qquad \frac{48}{12} = 4 \qquad \frac{192}{48} = 4 \qquad \frac{768}{192} = 4$$

Therefore, this is a geometric sequence. The next term in the sequence is

$$768 \cdot 4 = 3072.$$

(c) While there is a pattern here (the terms are the squares of the first five counting numbers), there is neither a common difference nor a common ratio. (Verify this) This is neither an arithmetic nor a geometric sequence.   ▮▮▮

Successive Differences

Some sequences may provide more difficulty in making a conjecture about the next term. Often the **method of successive differences** may be applied in such cases. Consider the sequence

$$2, 6, 22, 56, 114, \ldots.$$

Because the next term is not obvious, subtract the first term from the second term, the second from the third, the third from the fourth, and so on.

Now repeat the process with the sequence 4, 16, 34, 58 and continue repeating until the difference is a constant value, as shown in line (4).

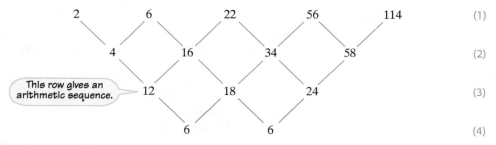

Once a line of constant values is obtained, simply work "backward" by adding until the desired term of the given sequence is obtained. Thus, for this pattern to continue, another 6 should appear in line (4), meaning that the next term in line (3) would have to be 24 + 6 = 30. The next term in line (2) would be 58 + 30 = 88. Finally, the next term in the given sequence would be 114 + 88 = **202**.

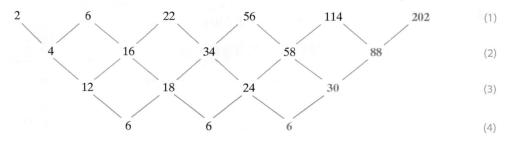

▐▐ **EXAMPLE 2** Using Successive Differences

Determine the next number in each sequence.

(a) 14, 22, 32, 44, ...   **(b)** 5, 15, 37, 77, 141, ...

SOLUTION

(a) Use the method of successive differences to obtain the following.

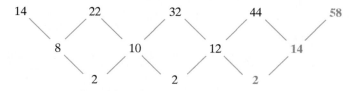

Once the row of 2s was obtained and extended, we were able to get 12 + 2 = 14, and 44 + 14 = 58, as shown above. The next number in the sequence is **58**.

(b) Proceeding as before, obtain the following diagram.

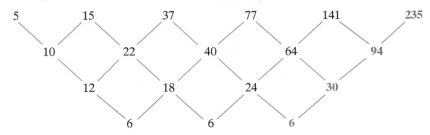

The numbers in the "diagonal" at the far right were obtained by adding: $24 + 6 = 30, 64 + 30 = 94$, and $141 + 94 = 235$. The next number in the sequence is **235**. ▇▇▇

The method of successive differences will not always work. For example, try it on the Fibonacci sequence in **Example 2(b)** of **Section 1.1** and see what happens.

Number Patterns and Sum Formulas

Mathematics features a seemingly endless variety of number patterns. Observe the following pattern.

$$1 = 1^2$$
$$1 + 3 = 2^2$$
$$1 + 3 + 5 = 3^2$$
$$1 + 3 + 5 + 7 = 4^2$$
$$1 + 3 + 5 + 7 + 9 = 5^2$$

In each case, the left side of the equation is the indicated sum of consecutive odd counting numbers beginning with 1, and the right side is the square of the number of terms on the left side. Inductive reasoning would suggest that the next line in this pattern is as follows.

$$1 + 3 + 5 + 7 + 9 + 11 = 6^2$$

Evaluating each side shows that each side simplifies to 36.

We cannot conclude that this pattern will continue indefinitely, because observation of a finite number of examples does *not* guarantee that the pattern will continue. However, mathematicians have proved that this pattern does indeed continue indefinitely, using a method of proof called **mathematical induction.** (See any standard college algebra text.)

Any even counting number may be written in the form $2k$, where k is a counting number. It follows that the kth odd counting number is written $2k - 1$. For example, the **third** odd counting number, 5, can be written

$$2(3) - 1.$$

Using these ideas, we can write the result obtained above as follows.

> **Sum of the First n Odd Counting Numbers**
>
> If n is any counting number, then the following is true.
>
> $$1 + 3 + 5 + \cdots + (2n - 1) = n^2$$

▋▋ **EXAMPLE 3** Predicting the Next Equation in a List

In each of the following, several equations are given illustrating a suspected number pattern. Determine what the next equation would be, and verify that it is indeed a true statement.

(a)
$$1^2 = 1^3$$
$$(1 + 2)^2 = 1^3 + 2^3$$
$$(1 + 2 + 3)^2 = 1^3 + 2^3 + 3^3$$
$$(1 + 2 + 3 + 4)^2 = 1^3 + 2^3 + 3^3 + 4^3$$

(b)
$$1 = 1^3$$
$$3 + 5 = 2^3$$
$$7 + 9 + 11 = 3^3$$
$$13 + 15 + 17 + 19 = 4^3$$

(c)
$$1 = \frac{1 \cdot 2}{2}$$
$$1 + 2 = \frac{2 \cdot 3}{2}$$
$$1 + 2 + 3 = \frac{3 \cdot 4}{2}$$
$$1 + 2 + 3 + 4 = \frac{4 \cdot 5}{2}$$

(d)
$$12{,}345{,}679 \times 9 = 111{,}111{,}111$$
$$12{,}345{,}679 \times 18 = 222{,}222{,}222$$
$$12{,}345{,}679 \times 27 = 333{,}333{,}333$$
$$12{,}345{,}679 \times 36 = 444{,}444{,}444$$

SOLUTION

(a) The left side of each equation is the square of the sum of the first n counting numbers, while the right side is the sum of their cubes. The next equation in the pattern would be

$$(1 + 2 + 3 + 4 + 5)^2 = 1^3 + 2^3 + 3^3 + 4^3 + 5^3.$$

Each side simplifies to 225, so the pattern is true for this equation.

(b) The left sides of the equations contain the sum of odd counting numbers, starting with the first (1) in the first equation, the second and third (3 and 5) in the second equation, the fourth, fifth, and sixth (7, 9, and 11) in the third equation, and so on. The right side contains the cube (third power) of the number of terms on the left side in each case. Following this pattern, the next equation would be

$$21 + 23 + 25 + 27 + 29 = 5^3,$$

which can be verified by computation.

(c) The left side of each equation gives the indicated sum of the first n counting numbers, and the right side is always of the form

$$\frac{n(n + 1)}{2}.$$

For the pattern to continue, the next equation would be

$$1 + 2 + 3 + 4 + 5 = \frac{5 \cdot 6}{2}.$$

Because each side simplifies to 15, the pattern is true for this equation.

(d) In each case, the first factor on the left is 12,345,679 and the second factor is a multiple of 9 (that is, 9, 18, 27, 36). The right side consists of a nine-digit number, all digits of which are the same (that is, 1, 2, 3, 4). For the pattern to continue, the next equation would be as follows.

$$12{,}345{,}679 \times 45 = 555{,}555{,}555$$

Verify that this is a true statement.

▮▮▮

The patterns established in **Examples 3(a) and 3(c)** can be written as follows.

Special Sum Formulas

For any counting number n, the following are true.

$$(1 + 2 + 3 + \cdots + n)^2 = 1^3 + 2^3 + 3^3 + \cdots + n^3$$

and

$$1 + 2 + 3 + \cdots + n = \frac{n(n + 1)}{2}$$

We can provide a general deductive argument showing how the second equation is obtained.

Let S represent the sum $1 + 2 + 3 + \cdots + n$. This sum can also be written as $S = n + (n - 1) + (n - 2) + \cdots + 1$. Write these two equations as follows.

$$
\begin{aligned}
S &= 1 && + 2 && + 3 && + \cdots + n \\
S &= n && + (n - 1) && + (n - 2) && + \cdots + 1 \\
\hline
2S &= (n + 1) && + (n + 1) && + (n + 1) && + \cdots + (n + 1) \quad \text{Add the corresponding sides.} \\
2S &= n(n + 1) && \text{There are } n \text{ terms of } n + 1. \\
S &= \frac{n(n + 1)}{2} && \text{Divide both sides by 2.}
\end{aligned}
$$

Figurate Numbers

Pythagoras and his Pythagorean brotherhood studied numbers of geometric arrangements of points, such as **triangular numbers, square numbers,** and **pentagonal numbers. Figure 5** illustrates the first few of each of these types of numbers.

The **figurate numbers** possess numerous interesting patterns. Every square number greater than 1 is the sum of two consecutive triangular numbers. (For example, $9 = 3 + 6$ and $25 = 10 + 15$.)

In the 1959 Disney animation *Donald in Mathmagic Land*, Donald Duck travels back in time to meet the Greek mathematician **Pythagoras** (c. 540 B.C.), who with his fellow mathematicians formed the Pythagorean brotherhood. The brotherhood devoted its time to the study of mathematics and music.
© Disney Enterprises, Inc.

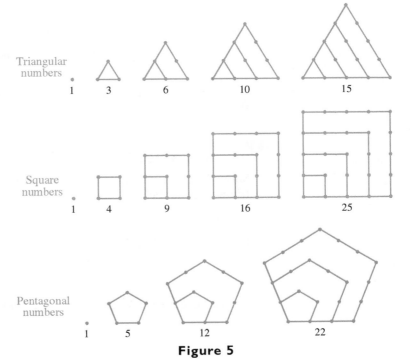

Triangular numbers   1   3   6   10   15

Square numbers   1   4   9   16   25

Pentagonal numbers   1   5   12   22

Figure 5

Every pentagonal number can be represented as the sum of a square number and a triangular number. (For example, $5 = 4 + 1$ and $12 = 9 + 3$.) Many other such relationships exist.

In the expression T_n, n is called a **subscript.** T_n is read **"T sub n,"** and it represents the triangular number in the nth position in the sequence. For example,

$$T_1 = 1, \quad T_2 = 3, \quad T_3 = 6, \quad \text{and} \quad T_4 = 10.$$

S_n and P_n represent the nth square and pentagonal numbers, respectively.

Formulas for Triangular, Square, and Pentagonal Numbers

For any natural number n, the following are true.

The nth triangular number is given by $\quad \mathbf{T}_n = \dfrac{n(n + 1)}{2}.$

The nth square number is given by $\quad \mathbf{S}_n = n^2.$

The nth pentagonal number is given by $\mathbf{P}_n = \dfrac{n(3n - 1)}{2}.$

▍▍ **EXAMPLE 4**   Using the Formulas for Figurate Numbers

Use the formulas to find each of the following.

(a) seventh triangular number

(b) twelfth square number

(c) sixth pentagonal number

SOLUTION

(a) $T_7 = \dfrac{n(n + 1)}{2} = \dfrac{7(7 + 1)}{2} = \dfrac{7(8)}{2} = \dfrac{56}{2} = 28$ Formula for a triangular number, $n = 7$

(b) $S_{12} = n^2 = 12^2 = 144$ Formula for a square number, $n = 12$

$12^2 = 12 \cdot 12$

Inside the brackets, multiply first and then subtract.

(c) $P_6 = \dfrac{n(3n - 1)}{2} = \dfrac{6[3(6) - 1]}{2} = \dfrac{6(18 - 1)}{2} = \dfrac{6(17)}{2} = 51$ ▍▍▍

▍▍ **EXAMPLE 5**   Illustrating a Figurate Number Relationship

Show that the sixth pentagonal number is equal to the sum of 6 and 3 times the fifth triangular number.

SOLUTION

From **Example 4(c)**, $P_6 = 51$. The fifth triangular number is 15. Thus,

$$51 = 6 + 3(15) = 6 + 45 = 51.$$ ▍▍▍

The general relationship examined in **Example 5** can be written as follows.

$$P_n = n + 3 \cdot T_{n-1} \quad (n \geq 2)$$

▌▌ **EXAMPLE 6** Predicting the Value of a Pentagonal Number

The first five pentagonal numbers are 1, 5, 12, 22, 35. Use the method of successive differences to predict the sixth pentagonal number.

SOLUTION

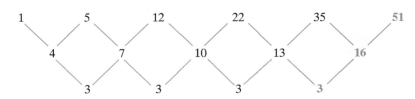

After the second line of successive differences, we work backward to find that the sixth pentagonal number is 51, which was also found in **Example 4(c).** ███

For Further Thought

Kaprekar Constants

Take any three-digit number whose digits are not all the same. Arrange the digits in decreasing order, and then arrange them in increasing order. Now subtract. Repeat the process, using a 0 if necessary in the event that the difference consists of only two digits. For example, suppose that we choose a number whose digits are 1, 4, and 8, such as 841.

$$\begin{array}{r} 841 \\ -148 \\ \hline 693 \end{array} \qquad \begin{array}{r} 963 \\ -369 \\ \hline 594 \end{array} \qquad \begin{array}{r} 954 \\ -459 \\ \hline 495 \end{array}$$

Notice that we have obtained the number 495, and the process will lead to 495 again.

The number 495 is called a **Kaprekar constant.** The number 495 will eventually always be generated if this process is applied to such a three-digit number.

For Group or Individual Investigation

1. Apply the process of Kaprekar to a two-digit number, in which the digits are not the same. (Interpret 9 as 09 if necessary.) Compare the results. What seems to be true?

2. Repeat the process for four digits, comparing results after several steps. What conjecture can be made for this situation?

1.2 EXERCISES

For each sequence, determine if it is an arithmetic *sequence, a* geometric *sequence, or* neither. *If it is either arithmetic or geometric, give the next term in the sequence.*

1. 6, 16, 26, 36, 46, . . .

2. 8, 16, 24, 32, 40, . . .

3. 5, 15, 45, 135, 405, . . .

4. 2, 12, 72, 432, 2592, . . .

5. 1, 8, 27, 81, 243, . . .

6. 2, 8, 18, 32, 50, . . .

7. 256, 128, 64, 32, 16, . . .

8. 4096, 1024, 256, 64, 16, . . .

9. 1, 3, 4, 7, 11, . . .

10. 0, 1, 1, 2, 3, . . .

11. 12, 14, 16, 18, 20, . . .

12. 10, 50, 90, 130, 170, . . .

Use the method of successive differences to determine the next number in each sequence.

13. 1, 4, 11, 22, 37, 56, . . .

14. 3, 14, 31, 54, 83, 118, . . .

15. 6, 20, 50, 102, 182, 296, . . .

16. 1, 11, 35, 79, 149, 251, . . .

17. 0, 12, 72, 240, 600, 1260, 2352, . . .

18. 2, 57, 220, 575, 1230, 2317, . . .

19. 5, 34, 243, 1022, 3121, 7770, 16799, . . .

20. 3, 19, 165, 771, 2503, 6483, 14409, . . .

21. Refer to **Figures 2 and 3** in **Section 1.1.** The method of successive differences can be applied to the sequence of interior regions,

$$1, 2, 4, 8, 16, 31,$$

to find the number of regions determined by seven points on the circle. What is the next term in this sequence? How many regions would be determined by eight points? Verify this using the formula given at the end of that section.

22. Suppose that the expression $n^2 + 3n + 1$ determines the nth term in a sequence. That is, to find the first term, let $n = 1$. To find the second term, let $n = 2$, and so on.

(a) Find the first four terms of the sequence.

(b) Use the method of successive differences to predict the fifth term of the sequence.

(c) Find the fifth term by letting $n = 5$ in the expression $n^2 + 3n + 1$. Does your result agree with the one you found in part (b)?

In Exercises 23–32, several equations are given illustrating a suspected number pattern. Determine what the next equation would be, and verify that it is indeed a true statement.

23. $(1 \times 9) - 1 = 8$
$(21 \times 9) - 1 = 188$
$(321 \times 9) - 1 = 2888$

24. $(1 \times 8) + 1 = 9$
$(12 \times 8) + 2 = 98$
$(123 \times 8) + 3 = 987$

25. $999,999 \times 2 = 1,999,998$
$999,999 \times 3 = 2,999,997$

26. $101 \times 101 = 10,201$
$10,101 \times 10,101 = 102,030,201$

27. $3^2 - 1^2 = 2^3$
$6^2 - 3^2 = 3^3$
$10^2 - 6^2 = 4^3$
$15^2 - 10^2 = 5^3$

28. $1 = 1^2$
$1 + 2 + 1 = 2^2$
$1 + 2 + 3 + 2 + 1 = 3^2$
$1 + 2 + 3 + 4 + 3 + 2 + 1 = 4^2$

29. $2^2 - 1^2 = 2 + 1$
$3^2 - 2^2 = 3 + 2$
$4^2 - 3^2 = 4 + 3$

30. $1^2 + 1 = 2^2 - 2$
$2^2 + 2 = 3^2 - 3$
$3^2 + 3 = 4^2 - 4$

31. $1 = 1 \times 1$
$1 + 5 = 2 \times 3$
$1 + 5 + 9 = 3 \times 5$

32. $1 + 2 = 3$
$4 + 5 + 6 = 7 + 8$
$9 + 10 + 11 + 12 = 13 + 14 + 15$

Use the formula $S = \dfrac{n(n + 1)}{2}$ to find each sum.

33. $1 + 2 + 3 + \cdots + 300$

34. $1 + 2 + 3 + \cdots + 500$

35. $1 + 2 + 3 + \cdots + 675$

36. $1 + 2 + 3 + \cdots + 825$

Use the formula $S = n^2$ to find each sum. (Hint: To find n, add 1 to the last term and divide by 2.)

37. $1 + 3 + 5 + \cdots + 101$

38. $1 + 3 + 5 + \cdots + 49$

39. $1 + 3 + 5 + \cdots + 999$

40. $1 + 3 + 5 + \cdots + 301$

41. Use the formula for finding the sum

$$1 + 2 + 3 + \cdots + n$$

to discover a formula for finding the sum

$$2 + 4 + 6 + \cdots + 2n.$$

42. State in your own words the following formula discussed in this section.

$$(1 + 2 + 3 + \cdots + n)^2 = 1^3 + 2^3 + 3^3 + \cdots + n^3$$

43. Explain how the following diagram geometrically illustrates the formula $1 + 3 + 5 + 7 + 9 = 5^2$.

44. Explain how the following diagram geometrically illustrates the formula $1 + 2 + 3 + 4 = \dfrac{4 \times 5}{2}$.

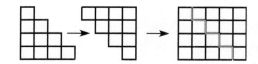

45. Use patterns to complete the table below.

Figurate Number	1st	2nd	3rd	4th	5th	6th	7th	8th
Triangular	1	3	6	10	15	21		
Square	1	4	9	16	25			
Pentagonal	1	5	12	22				
Hexagonal	1	6	15					
Heptagonal	1	7						
Octagonal	1							

46. The first five triangular, square, and pentagonal numbers may be obtained using sums of terms of sequences, as shown below.

Triangular	Square	Pentagonal
1 = 1	1 = 1	1 = 1
3 = 1 + 2	4 = 1 + 3	5 = 1 + 4
6 = 1 + 2 + 3	9 = 1 + 3 + 5	12 = 1 + 4 + 7
10 = 1 + 2 + 3 + 4	16 = 1 + 3 + 5 + 7	22 = 1 + 4 + 7 + 10
15 = 1 + 2 + 3 + 4 + 5	25 = 1 + 3 + 5 + 7 + 9	35 = 1 + 4 + 7 + 10 + 13

Notice the successive differences of the added terms on the right sides of the equations. The next type of figurate number is the **hexagonal** number. (A hexagon has six sides.) Use the patterns above to predict the first five hexagonal numbers.

47. Eight times any triangular number, plus 1, is a square number. Show that this is true for the first four triangular numbers.

48. Divide the first triangular number by 3 and record the remainder. Divide the second triangular number by 3 and record the remainder. Repeat this procedure several more times. Do you notice a pattern?

49. Repeat **Exercise 48,** but instead use square numbers and divide by 4. What pattern is determined?

50. Exercises 48 and 49 are specific cases of the following: When the numbers in the sequence of n-agonal numbers are divided by n, the sequence of remainders obtained is a repeating sequence. Verify this for $n = 5$ and $n = 6$.

51. Every square number can be written as the sum of two triangular numbers. For example, $16 = 6 + 10$. This can be represented geometrically by dividing a square array of dots with a line as shown.

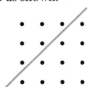

The triangular arrangement above the line represents 6, the one below the line represents 10, and the whole arrangement represents 16. Show how the square numbers 25 and 36 may likewise be geometrically represented as the sum of two triangular numbers.

52. A fraction is in **lowest terms** if the greatest common factor of its numerator and its denominator is 1. For example, $\frac{3}{8}$ is in lowest terms, but $\frac{4}{12}$ is not.

(a) For $n = 2$ to $n = 8$, form the fractions

$$\frac{n\text{th square number}}{(n + 1)\text{st square number}}.$$

(b) Repeat part (a) with triangular numbers.

(c) Use inductive reasoning to make a conjecture based on your results from parts (a) and (b), observing whether the fractions are in lowest terms.

*In addition to the formulas for T_n, S_n, and P_n, the following formulas are true for **hexagonal** numbers (H), **heptagonal** numbers (Hp), and **octagonal** numbers (O):*

$$H_n = \frac{n(4n - 2)}{2}, \quad Hp_n = \frac{n(5n - 3)}{2}, \quad O_n = \frac{n(6n - 4)}{2}.$$

Use these formulas to find each of the following.

53. the sixteenth square number

54. the eleventh triangular number

55. the ninth pentagonal number

56. the seventh hexagonal number

57. the tenth heptagonal number

58. the twelfth octagonal number

59. Observe the formulas given for H_n, Hp_n, and O_n, and use patterns and inductive reasoning to predict the formula for N_n, the nth **nonagonal** number. (A nonagon has nine sides.) Then use the fact that the sixth nonagonal number is 111 to further confirm your conjecture.

60. Use the result of **Exercise 59** to find the tenth nonagonal number.

Use inductive reasoning to answer each question.

61. If you add two consecutive triangular numbers, what kind of figurate number do you get?

62. If you add the squares of two consecutive triangular numbers, what kind of figurate number do you get?

63. Square a triangular number. Square the next triangular number. Subtract the smaller result from the larger. What kind of number do you get?

64. Choose a value of n greater than or equal to 2. Find T_{n-1}, multiply it by 3, and add n. What kind of figurate number do you get?

In an arithmetic sequence, the nth term a_n is given by the formula

$$a_n = a_1 + (n - 1)d,$$

where a_1 is the first term and d is the common difference. Similarly, in a geometric sequence, the nth term is given by

$$a_n = a_1 \cdot r^{n-1}.$$

Here r is the common ratio. Use these formulas to determine the indicated term in the given sequence.

65. The eleventh term of $2, 6, 10, 14, \ldots$

66. The sixteenth term of $5, 15, 25, 35, \ldots$

67. The 21st term of $19, 39, 59, 79, \ldots$

68. The 36th term of $8, 38, 68, 98, \ldots$

69. The 101st term of $\frac{1}{2}, 1, \frac{3}{2}, 2, \ldots$

70. The 151st term of $0.75, 1.50, 2.25, 3.00, \ldots$

71. The eleventh term of $2, 4, 8, 16, \ldots$

72. The ninth term of $1, 4, 16, 64, \ldots$

73. The 12th term of $1, \frac{1}{2}, \frac{1}{4}, \frac{1}{8}, \ldots$

74. The 10th term of $1, \frac{1}{3}, \frac{1}{9}, \frac{1}{27}, \ldots$

75. The 8th term of $40, 10, \frac{5}{2}, \frac{5}{8}, \ldots$

76. The 9th term of $10, 2, \frac{2}{5}, \frac{2}{25}, \ldots$

1.3 STRATEGIES FOR PROBLEM SOLVING

A General Problem-Solving Method • Using a Table or Chart • Working Backward • Using Trial and Error • Guessing and Checking • Considering a Similar, Simpler Problem • Drawing a Sketch • Using Common Sense

A General Problem-Solving Method

In the first two sections of this chapter we stressed the importance of pattern recognition and the use of inductive reasoning in solving problems. Probably the most famous study of problem-solving techniques was developed by George Polya (1888–1985), among whose many publications was the modern classic *How to Solve It*. In this book, Polya proposed a four-step method for problem solving.

George Polya, author of the classic *How to Solve It*, died at the age of 97 on September 7, 1985. A native of Budapest, Hungary, he was once asked why there were so many good mathematicians to come out of Hungary at the turn of the century. He theorized that it was because mathematics is the cheapest science. It does not require any expensive equipment, only pencil and paper. He authored or coauthored more than 250 papers in many languages, wrote a number of books, and was a brilliant lecturer and teacher. Yet, interestingly enough, he never learned to drive a car.

Polya's Four-Step Method for Problem Solving

Step 1 Understand the problem. You cannot solve a problem if you do not understand what you are asked to find. The problem must be read and analyzed carefully. You may need to read it several times. After you have done so, ask yourself, "What must I find?"

Step 2 Devise a plan. There are many ways to attack a problem. Decide what plan is appropriate for the particular problem you are solving.

Step 3 Carry out the plan. Once you know how to approach the problem, carry out your plan. You may run into "dead ends" and unforeseen roadblocks, but be persistent.

Step 4 Look back and check. Check your answer to see that it is reasonable. Does it satisfy the conditions of the problem? Have you answered all the questions the problem asks? Can you solve the problem a different way and come up with the same answer?

In Step 2 of Polya's problem-solving method, we are told to devise a plan. Here are some hints and strategies that may prove useful.

Fibonacci (1170–1250) discovered the sequence named after him in a problem on rabbits. Fibonacci (son of Bonaccio) is one of several names for Leonardo of Pisa. His father managed a warehouse in present-day Bougie (or Bejaia), in Algeria. Thus it was that Leonardo Pisano studied with a Moorish teacher and learned the "Indian" numbers that the Moors and other Moslems brought with them in their westward drive.

Fibonacci wrote books on algebra, geometry, and trigonometry.

PROBLEM-SOLVING HINTS

Make a table or a chart.
Look for a pattern.
Solve a similar, simpler problem.
Draw a sketch.
Use inductive reasoning.
Write an equation and solve it.

If a formula applies, use it.
Work backward.
Guess and check.
Use trial and error.
Use common sense.
Look for a "catch" if an answer seems too obvious or impossible.

Using a Table or Chart

EXAMPLE 1 Solving Fibonacci's Rabbit Problem

A man put a pair of rabbits in a cage. During the first month the rabbits produced no offspring but each month thereafter produced one new pair of rabbits. If each new pair thus produced reproduces in the same manner, how many pairs of rabbits will there be at the end of 1 year? (This problem is a famous one in the history of mathematics and first appeared in *Liber Abaci*, a book written by the Italian mathematician Leonardo Pisano (also known as Fibonacci) in the year 1202.)

SOLUTION

Step 1 **Understand the problem.** We can reword the problem as follows:

> *How many pairs of rabbits will the man have at the end of one year if he starts with one pair, and they reproduce this way: During the first month of life, each pair produces no new rabbits, but each month thereafter each pair produces one new pair?*

Step 2 **Devise a plan.** Because there is a definite pattern to how the rabbits will reproduce, we can construct **Table 2.**

Table 2 Month	Number of Pairs at Start	Number of New Pairs Produced	Number of Pairs at End of Month
1st			
2nd			
3rd			
4th			
5th			
6th			
7th			
8th			
9th			
10th			
11th			
12th			

The answer will go here.

Step 3 Carry out the plan. At the start of the first month, there is only one pair of rabbits. No new pairs are produced during the first month, so there is $1 + 0 = 1$ pair present at the end of the first month. This pattern continues. In the table, we add the number in the first column of numbers to the number in the second column to get the number in the third.

Month	Number of Pairs at Start	+	Number of New Pairs Produced	=	Number of Pairs at End of Month	
1st	1		0		1	$1 + 0 = 1$
2nd	1		1		2	$1 + 1 = 2$
3rd	2		1		3	$2 + 1 = 3$
4th	3		2		5	•
5th	5		3		8	•
6th	8		5		13	•
7th	13		8		21	•
8th	21		13		34	•
9th	34		21		55	•
10th	55		34		89	•
11th	89		55		144	•
12th	144		89		233	$144 + 89 = 233$

The answer is the final entry.

There will be 233 pairs of rabbits at the end of one year.

Step 4 Look back and check. Go back and make sure that we have interpreted the problem correctly. Double-check the arithmetic. We have answered the question posed by the problem, so the problem is solved. ▮▮▮

Working Backward

▮▮ **EXAMPLE 2** Determining a Wager at the Track

Ronnie Virgets goes to the racetrack with his buddies on a weekly basis. One week he tripled his money, but then lost $12. He took his money back the next week, doubled it, but then lost $40. The following week he tried again, taking his money back with him. He quadrupled it, and then played well enough to take that much home, a total of $224. How much did he start with the first week?

SOLUTION

This problem asks us to find Ronnie's starting amount. Since we know his final amount, the method of working backward can be applied.

Because his final amount was $224 and this represents four times the amount he started with on the third week, we *divide* $224 by 4 to find that he started the third week with $56. Before he lost $40 the second week, he had this $56 plus the $40 he lost, giving him $96. This represented double what he started with, so he started with $96 *divided by* 2, or $48, the second week. Repeating this process once more for the first week, before his $12 loss he had

$$\$48 + \$12 = \$60,$$

which represents triple what he started with. Therefore, he started with

$$\$60 \div 3 = \$20. \quad \text{Answer}$$

To check, observe the following equations that depict winnings and losses.

First week: $(3 \times \$20) - \$12 = \$60 - \$12 = \$48$

Second week: $(2 \times \$48) - \$40 = \$96 - \$40 = \$56$

Third week: $(4 \times \$56) = \$224$ His final amount ▮▮▮

Augustus De Morgan was an English mathematician and philosopher, who served as professor at the University of London. He wrote numerous books, one of which was *A Budget of Paradoxes*. His work in set theory and logic led to laws that bear his name and are covered in other chapters. He died in the same year as Charles Babbage.

Using Trial and Error

Recall that $5^2 = 5 \cdot 5 = 25$. That is, 5 squared is 25. Thus, 25 is called a **perfect square**.

$$1, \quad 4, \quad 9, \quad 16, \quad 25, \quad 36, \quad \text{and so on} \quad \text{Perfect squares}$$

▮▮ **EXAMPLE 3**   Finding Augustus De Morgan's Birth Year

The mathematician Augustus De Morgan lived in the nineteenth century. He made the following statement: "I was x years old in the year x^2." In what year was he born?

SOLUTION

We must find the year of De Morgan's birth. The problem tells us that he lived in the nineteenth century, which is another way of saying that he lived during the 1800s. One year of his life was a perfect square, so we must find a number between 1800 and 1900 that is a perfect square. Use trial and error.

$$42^2 = 42 \cdot 42 = 1764$$
$$43^2 = 43 \cdot 43 = 1849 \quad \text{← } \boxed{\text{1849 is between 1800 and 1900.}}$$
$$44^2 = 44 \cdot 44 = 1936$$

The only natural number whose square is between 1800 and 1900 is 43, since $43^2 = 1849$. Therefore, De Morgan was 43 years old in 1849. The final step in solving the problem is to subtract 43 from 1849 to find the year of his birth.

$$1849 - 43 = 1806 \quad \text{← } \boxed{\text{He was born in 1806.}}$$

Although the following check may seem unorthodox, it works: Look up De Morgan's birth date in a book dealing with mathematics history, such as *An Introduction to the History of Mathematics*, Sixth Edition, by Howard W. Eves.   ▮▮▮

Guessing and Checking

As mentioned above, $5^2 = 25$. The inverse (opposite) of squaring a number is called taking the **square root**. We indicate the positive square root using a **radical symbol** $\sqrt{}$. Thus, $\sqrt{25} = 5$. Also,

$$\sqrt{4} = 2, \quad \sqrt{9} = 3, \quad \sqrt{16} = 4, \quad \text{and so on.} \quad \text{Square roots}$$

The next problem deals with a square root and dates back to Hindu mathematics, circa 850.

▮▮ **EXAMPLE 4**   Finding the Number of Camels

One-fourth of a herd of camels was seen in the forest; twice the square root of that herd had gone to the mountain slopes; and 3 times 5 camels remained on the riverbank. What is the numerical measure of that herd of camels?

SOLUTION

The numerical measure of a herd of camels must be a counting number. Because the problem mentions "one-fourth of a herd" and "the square root of that herd," the number of camels must be both a multiple of 4 and a perfect square, so that only whole numbers are used. The least counting number that satisfies both conditions is 4. We write an equation where x represents the numerical measure of the herd, and then substitute 4 for x to see if it is a solution.

One-fourth of the herd	+	Twice the square root of that herd	+	3 times 5 camels	=	The numerical measure of the herd.

$$\frac{1}{4}x \;+\; 2\sqrt{x} \;+\; 3 \cdot 5 \;=\; x$$

$$\frac{1}{4}(4) + 2\sqrt{4} + 3 \cdot 5 = 4 \qquad \text{Let } x = 4.$$

$$1 + 4 + 15 \overset{?}{=} 4 \qquad \sqrt{4} = 2$$

$$20 \neq 4$$

Because 4 is not the solution, try **16**, the next perfect square that is a multiple of 4.

$$\frac{1}{4}(16) + 2\sqrt{16} + 3 \cdot 5 = 16 \qquad \text{Let } x = 16.$$

$$4 + 8 + 15 \overset{?}{=} 16 \qquad \sqrt{16} = 4$$

$$27 \neq 16$$

Because 16 is not a solution, try **36**.

$$\frac{1}{4}(36) + 2\sqrt{36} + 3 \cdot 5 = 36 \qquad \text{Let } x = 36.$$

$$9 + 12 + 15 \overset{?}{=} 36 \qquad \sqrt{36} = 6$$

$$36 = 36$$

Thus, 36 is the numerical measure of the herd. *Check:* "One-fourth of 36, plus twice the square root of 36, plus 3 times 5" gives 9 plus 12 plus 15, which equals 36. ▮▮▮

Considering a Similar, Simpler Problem

▮▮ **EXAMPLE 5** Finding the Units Digit of a Power

The digit farthest to the right in a counting number is called the *ones* or *units* digit, because it tells how many ones are contained in the number when grouping by tens is considered. What is the ones (or units) digit in 2^{4000}?

SOLUTION

Recall that 2^{4000} means that 2 is used as a factor 4000 times.

$$2^{4000} = \underbrace{2 \times 2 \times 2 \times \ldots \times 2}_{4000 \text{ factors}}$$

To answer the question, we examine some smaller powers of 2 and then look for a pattern. We start with the exponent 1 and look at the first twelve powers of 2.

$2^1 = 2$	$2^5 = 32$	$2^9 = 512$
$2^2 = 4$	$2^6 = 64$	$2^{10} = 1024$
$2^3 = 8$	$2^7 = 128$	$2^{11} = 2048$
$2^4 = 16$	$2^8 = 256$	$2^{12} = 4096$

Notice that in any one of the four rows above, the ones digit is the same all the way across the row. The final row, which contains the exponents 4, 8, and 12, has the ones digit 6. Each of these exponents is divisible by 4, and because 4000 is divisible by 4, we can use inductive reasoning to predict that the units digit in 2^{4000} is **6**.

(*Note:* The units digit for any other power can be found if we divide the exponent by 4 and consider the remainder. Then compare the result to the list of powers above. For example, to find the units digit of 2^{543}, divide 543 by 4 to get a quotient of 135 and a remainder of **3**. The units digit is the same as that of 2^3, which is **8**.) ▮▮▮

The 1952 film *Hans Christian Andersen* features Danny Kaye as the Danish writer of fairy tales. In a scene outside a schoolhouse, he sings a song to an inchworm: "Inchworm, inchworm, measuring the marigolds, you and your arithmetic, you'll probably go far." Following the scene, students in the schoolhouse are heard singing arithmetic facts:

Two and two are four,
Four and four are eight,
Eight and eight are sixteen,
Sixteen and sixteen are thirty-two.

Their answers are all **powers of 2.**

Drawing a Sketch

▮▮ **EXAMPLE 6** Connecting the Dots

Figure 6

An array of nine dots is arranged in a 3 × 3 square, as shown in **Figure 6**. Is it possible to join the dots with exactly four straight line segments if you are not allowed to pick up your pencil from the paper and may not trace over a segment that has already been drawn? If so, show how.

SOLUTION

Figure 7 shows three attempts. In each case, something is wrong. In the first sketch, one dot is not joined. In the second, the figure cannot be drawn without picking up your pencil from the paper or tracing over a line that has already been drawn. In the third figure, all dots have been joined, but you have used five line segments as well as retraced over the figure.

Figure 7

Figure 8

The conditions of the problem can be satisfied, as shown in **Figure 8**. We "went outside of the box," which was not prohibited by the conditions of the problem. This is an example of creative thinking—we used a strategy that often is not considered at first. ▮▮▮

Using Common Sense

PROBLEM-SOLVING HINTS Some problems involve a "catch." They seem too easy or perhaps impossible at first because we tend to overlook an obvious situation. Look carefully at the use of language in such problems. And, of course, never forget to use common sense.

🎬 In *Die Hard: With a Vengeance* (see the **Chapter Opener**), Simon taunts McClane with a riddle that has its origins in Egyptian mathematics.

*As I was going to St. Ives,
I met a man with seven wives.
Every wife had seven sacks,
Every sack had seven cats,
Every cat had seven kittens.
Kittens, cats, sacks, and wives,
How many were going to St. Ives?*

"My phone number is 555 and the answer. Call me in 30 seconds or die."

By calling 555-0001, he was able to contact Simon. Do you see why 1 is the answer to this riddle? (Use **common sense.**)

▮▮ **EXAMPLE 7** Determining Coin Denominations

Two currently minted United States coins together have a total value of $1.05. One is not a dollar. What are the two coins?

SOLUTION

Our initial reaction might be, "The only way to have two such coins with a total of $1.05 is to have a nickel and a dollar, but the problem says that one of them is not a dollar." This statement is indeed true. What we must realize here is that the one that is not a dollar is the nickel, and the *other* coin is a dollar! So the two coins are a dollar and a nickel. ▮▮▮

1.3 EXERCISES

One of the most popular features in the journal Mathematics Teacher, *published by the National Council of Teachers of Mathematics, is the monthly calendar. It provides an interesting, unusual, or challenging problem for each day of the month. Problems are contributed by the editors of the journal, teachers, and students, and the contributors are cited in each issue. Some of these exercises are problems chosen from these calendars over the past years, with the day, month, and year for the problem indicated. The authors want to thank the many contributors for permission to use these problems.*

Use the various problem-solving strategies to solve each problem. In many cases there is more than one possible approach, so be creative.

1. *Class Members* A classroom contains an equal number of boys and girls. If 8 girls leave, twice as many boys as girls remain. What was the original number of students present? (May 24, 2008)

2. *Give Me a Digit* Given a two-digit number, make a three-digit number by putting a 6 as the right-most digit. Then add 6 to the resulting three-digit number and remove the right-most digit to obtain another two digit number. If the result is 76, what is the original two-digit number? (October 18, 2009)

3. *Missing Digit* Look for a pattern and find the missing digit x.

$$
\begin{array}{cccc}
3 & 2 & 4 & 8 \\
7 & 2 & 1 & 3 \\
8 & 4 & x & 5 \\
4 & 3 & 6 & 9 \\
\end{array}
$$

(February 14, 2009)

4. *Abundancy* An integer $n > 1$ is **abundant** if the sum of its proper divisors (positive integer divisors smaller than n) is greater than n. Find the smallest abundant integer. (November 27, 2009)

5. *Cross-Country Competition* The schools in an athletic conference compete in a cross-country meet to which each school sends three participants. Erin, Katelyn, and Iliana are the three representatives from one school.

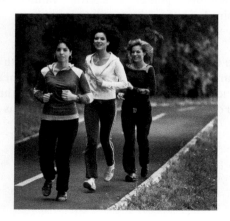

Erin finished the race in the middle position; Katelyn finished after Erin, in the 19th position; and Iliana finished 28th. How many schools took part in the race? (May 27, 2008)

6. *Gone Fishing* Four friends go fishing one day and bring home a total of 11 fish. If each person caught at least 1 fish, then which of the following *must* be true?

   A. One person caught exactly 2 fish.

   B. One person caught exactly 3 fish.

   C. One person caught fewer than 3 fish.

   D. One person caught more than 3 fish.

   E. Two people each caught more than 1 fish.

   (May 24, 2008)

7. *Cutting a Square in Half* In how many ways can a single straight line cut a square in half? (October 2, 2008)

8. *You Lie!* Max, Sam, and Brett were playing basketball. One of them broke a window, and the other two saw him break it. Max said, "I am innocent." Sam said, "Max and I are both innocent." Brett said, "Max and Sam are both innocent." If only one of them is telling the truth, who broke the window? (September 21, 2008)

9. *Bookworm Snack* A 26-volume encyclopedia (one for each letter) is placed on a bookshelf in alphabetical order from left to right. Each volume is 2 inches thick, including the front and back covers. Each cover is $\frac{1}{4}$ inch thick. A bookworm eats straight through the encyclopedia, beginning inside the front cover of volume A and ending after eating through the back cover of volume Z. How many inches of book did the bookworm eat? (November 12, 2008)

10. *Pick a Card, Any Card* Three face cards from an ordinary deck of playing cards lie facedown in a horizontal row and are arranged such that immediately to the right of a king is a queen or two queens, immediately to the left of a queen is a queen or two queens, immediately to the left of a heart is a spade or two spades, and immediately to the right of a spade is a spade or two spades. Name the three cards in order. (April 23, 2008)

11. **Catwoman's Cats** If you ask Batman's nemesis, Catwoman, how many cats she has, she answers with a riddle: "Five-sixths of my cats plus seven." How many cats does Catwoman have? (April 20, 2003)

12. **Pencil Collection** Bob gave four-fifths of his pencils to Barbara, then he gave two-thirds of the remaining pencils to Bonnie. If he ended up with ten pencils for himself, with how many did he start? (October 12, 2003)

13. **Adding Gasoline** The gasoline gauge on a van initially read $\frac{1}{8}$ full. When 15 gallons were added to the tank, the gauge read $\frac{3}{4}$ full. How many more gallons are needed to fill the tank? (November 25, 2004)

14. **Gasoline Tank Capacity** When 6 gallons of gasoline are put into a car's tank, the indicator goes from $\frac{1}{4}$ of a tank to $\frac{5}{8}$. What is the total capacity of the gasoline tank? (February 21, 2004)

15. **Number Pattern** What is the relationship between the rows of numbers?

$$18, \quad 38, \quad 24, \quad 46, \quad 42$$
$$8, \quad 24, \quad 8, \quad 24, \quad 8$$

(May 26, 2005)

16. **Unknown Number** The number in an unshaded square is obtained by adding the numbers connected with it from the row above. (The 11 is one such number.) What is the value of x? (December 22, 2008)

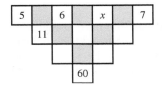

17. **Locking Boxes** You and I each have one lock and a corresponding key. I want to mail you a box with a ring in it, but any box that is not locked will be emptied before it reaches its recipient. How can I safely send you the ring? (Note that you and I each have keys to our own lock but not to the other lock.) (May 4, 2004)

18. **Woodchuck Chucking Wood** Nine woodchucks can chuck eight pieces of wood in 3 hours. How much wood can a woodchuck chuck in 1 hour? (May 24, 2004)

19. **Number in a Sequence** In the sequence 16, 80, 48, 64, A, B, C, D, each term beyond the second term is the arithmetic mean (average) of the two previous terms. What is the value of D? (April 26, 2004)

20. **Unknown Number** Cindy was asked by her teacher to subtract 3 from a certain number and then divide the result by 9. Instead, she subtracted 9 and then divided the result by 3, giving an answer of 43. What would her answer have been if she had worked the problem correctly? (September 3, 2004)

21. **Labeling Boxes** You are working in a store that has been very careless with the stock. Three boxes of socks are each incorrectly labeled. The labels say *red socks, green socks*, and *red and green socks*. How can you relabel the boxes correctly by taking only one sock out of one box, without looking inside the boxes? (October 22, 2001)

22. **Vertical Symmetry in States' Names** (If a vertical line is drawn through the center of a figure and the left and right sides are reflections of each other across this line, the figure is said to have vertical symmetry.) When spelled with all capital letters, each letter in HAWAII has vertical symmetry. Find the name of a state whose letters all have vertical and horizontal symmetry. (September 11, 2001)

23. **Sum of Hidden Dots on Dice** Three dice with faces numbered 1 through 6 are stacked as shown. Seven of the eighteen faces are visible, leaving eleven faces hidden on the back, on the bottom, and between dice. The total number of dots not visible in this view is _____.

A. 21
B. 22
C. 31
D. 41
E. 53

(September 17, 2001)

24. **Mr. Green's Age** At his birthday party, Mr. Green would not directly tell how old he was. He said, "If you add the year of my birth to this year, subtract the year of my tenth birthday and the year of my fiftieth birthday, and then add my present age, the result is eighty." How old was Mr. Green? (December 14, 1997)

25. **Unfolding and Folding a Box** An unfolded box is shown below.

Which figure shows the box folded up? (November 7, 2001)

26. **Age of the Bus Driver** Today is your first day driving a city bus. When you leave downtown, you have twenty-three passengers. At the first stop, three people exit and five people get on the bus. At the second stop, eleven people exit and eight people get on the bus. At the third stop, five people exit and ten people get on. How old is the bus driver? (April 1, 2002)

27. Matching Triangles and Squares How can you connect each square with the triangle that has the same number? Lines cannot cross, enter a square or triangle, or go outside the diagram. (October 15, 1999)

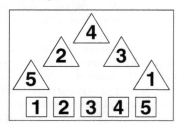

28. Squared Rectangle A **squared rectangle,** shown here, is a rectangle whose interior can be completely divided into two or more squares. The number written inside a square is the length of a side of that square. Compute the area of this squared rectangle. (September 22, 2009)

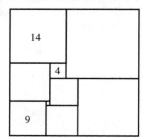

29. Forming Perfect Square Sums How must one place the integers from 1 to 15 in each of the spaces below in such a way that no number is repeated and the sum of the numbers in any two consecutive spaces is a perfect square? (November 11, 2001)

30. How Old? Pat and Chris have the same birthday. Pat is twice as old as Chris was when Pat was as old as Chris is now. If Pat is now 24 years old, how old is Chris? (December 3, 2001)

31. Difference Triangle Balls numbered 1 through 6 are arranged in a **difference triangle.** Note that in any row, the difference between the larger and the smaller of two successive balls is the number of the ball that appears below them. Arrange balls numbered 1 through 10 in a difference triangle. (May 6, 1998)

32. Clock Face By drawing two straight lines, divide the face of a clock into three regions such that the numbers in the regions have the same total. (October 28, 1998)

33. Alphametric If a, b, and c are digits for which

$$
\begin{array}{r}
7\ a\ 2 \\
-4\ 8\ b \\
\hline
c\ 7\ 3,
\end{array}
$$

then $a + b + c = $ _____.

A. 14   **B.** 15   **C.** 16   **D.** 17   **E.** 18

(September 22, 1999)

34. Perfect Square Only one of these numbers is a perfect square. Which one is it? (October 8, 1997)

329476   389372   964328
326047   724203

35. Sleeping on the Way to Grandma's House While traveling to his grandmother's for Christmas, George fell asleep halfway through the journey. When he awoke, he still had to travel half the distance that he had traveled while sleeping. For what part of the entire journey had he been asleep? (December 25, 1998)

36. Counting Puzzle (Rectangles) How many rectangles of any size are in the figure shown? (September 10, 2001)

37. Buckets of Water You have brought two unmarked buckets to a stream. The buckets hold 7 gallons and 3 gallons of water, respectively. How can you obtain exactly 5 gallons of water to take home? (October 19, 1997)

38. Multiples of 9 The first two of three consecutive multiples of 9 sum to 2511. What are the numbers? (January 4, 2010)

39. Counting Puzzle (Rectangles) How many rectangles are in the figure? (March 27, 1997)

40. Digit Puzzle Place each of the digits 1, 2, 3, 4, 5, 6, 7, and 8 in separate boxes so that boxes that share common corners do not contain successive digits. (November 29, 1997)

41. Palindromic Number (*Note:* A **palindromic number** is a number whose digits read the same left to right as right to left. For example, 383, 12321, and 9876789 are palindromic.) The odometer of the family car read 15951 when the driver noticed that the number was palindromic. "Curious," said the driver to herself. "It will be a long time before that happens again." But 2 hours later, the odometer showed a new palindromic number. (*Author's note:* Assume it was the next possible one.) How fast was the car driving in those 2 hours? (December 26, 1998)

42. How Much Is That Doggie in the Window? A man wishes to sell a puppy for $11. A customer who wants to buy it has only foreign currency. The exchange rate for the foreign currency is as follows: 11 round coins = $15, 11 square coins = $16, 11 triangular coins = $17. How many of each coin should the customer pay? (April 20, 2008)

43. Final Digits of a Power of 7 What are the final two digits of 7^{1997}? (November 29, 1997)

44. Consecutive Whole Numbers The sum of nine consecutive whole numbers is 123,456,789,987,654,321. What is the difference between the largest and smallest of these numbers? (October 4, 2008)

45. Summing the Digits When $10^{50} - 50$ is expressed as a single whole number, what is the sum of its digits? (April 7, 2008)

46. Units Digit of a Power of 3 If you raise 3 to the 324th power, what is the units digit of the result?

47. Units Digit of a Power of 7 What is the units digit in 7^{491}?

48. Frog Climbing up a Well A frog is at the bottom of a 20-foot well. Each day it crawls up 4 feet, but each night it slips back 3 feet. After how many days will the frog reach the top of the well?

49. Going Postal Joanie wants to mail a package that requires $1.53 in postage. If she has only 5-cent and 8-cent stamps, what is the smallest number of stamps she could use that would total exactly $1.53? (August 20, 2008)

50. Money Spent at a Bazaar Christine O'Brien bought a book for $10 and then spent half her remaining money on a train ticket. She then bought lunch for $4 and spent half her remaining money at a bazaar. She left the bazaar with $8. How much money did she start with?

51. Matching Socks A drawer contains 20 black socks and 20 white socks. If the light is off and you reach into the drawer to get your socks, what is the minimum number of socks you must pull out in order to be sure that you have a matching pair?

52. Counting Puzzle (Squares) How many squares are in the figure?

53. Counting Puzzle (Triangles) How many triangles are in the figure?

54. Fun with Fractions A strip of paper is $\frac{2}{3}$ meter long. Can a strip exactly $\frac{1}{2}$ meter long be made without the use of a ruler? If so, how? (September 8, 2008)

55. Perfect Number A **perfect number** is a counting number that is equal to the sum of all its counting number divisors except itself. For example, 28 is a perfect number because its divisors other than itself are 1, 2, 4, 7, and 14, and $1 + 2 + 4 + 7 + 14 = 28$. What is the least perfect number?

56. Naming Children Becky's mother has three daughters. She named her first daughter Penny and her second daughter Nichole. What did she name her third daughter?

57. Growth of a Lily Pad A lily pad grows so that each day it doubles its size. On the twentieth day of its life, it completely covers a pond. On what day was the pond half covered?

58. Interesting Property of a Sentence Comment on an interesting property of this sentence: "A man, a plan, a canal, Panama." (*Hint:* See **Exercise 41.**)

59. *High School Graduation Year of Author* One of the authors of this book graduated from high school in the year that satisfies these conditions: (1) The sum of the digits is 23; (2) The hundreds digit is 3 more than the tens digit; (3) No digit is an 8. In what year did he graduate?

60. *Analyzing Units* A day is divided into 24 hours. Each hour has 60 minutes, and each minute has 60 seconds. In another system of measurement, each day has 20 naps and each nap has 40 winks. How many seconds are in a wink? (November 10, 2008)

61. *Adam and Eve's Assets* Eve said to Adam, "If you give me one dollar, then we will have the same amount of money." Adam then replied, "Eve, if you give me one dollar, I will have double the amount of money you are left with." How much does each have?

62. *Missing Digits Puzzle* In the addition problem below, some digits are missing as indicated by the blanks. If the problem is done correctly, what is the sum of the missing digits?

$$\begin{array}{r} \_\ 3\ 5 \\ 8\ \_\ 6 \\ +\ 1\ 4\ \_ \\ \hline \_\ 4\ 0\ 8 \end{array}$$

63. *Missing Digits Puzzle* Fill in the blanks so that the multiplication problem below uses all digits 0, 1, 2, 3, …, 9 exactly once, and is correctly worked.

$$\begin{array}{r} \_\ 0\ 2 \\ \times\ \ \ \ 3\ \_ \\ \hline \_\ 5,\ \_\ \_\ \_ \end{array}$$

64. *Magic Square* A **magic square** is a square array of numbers that has the property that the sum of the numbers in any row, column, or diagonal is the same. Fill in the square below so that it becomes a magic square, and all digits 1, 2, 3, …, 9 are used exactly once.

6		8
	5	
		4

65. *Magic Square* Refer to **Exercise 64.** Complete the magic square below so that all counting numbers 1, 2, 3, . . . , 16 are used exactly once, and the sum in each row, column, or diagonal is 34.

6			9
	15		14
11		10	
16		13	

66. *Decimal Digit* What is the 100th digit in the decimal representation for $\frac{1}{7}$?

67. *Pitches in a Baseball Game* What is the minimum number of pitches that a baseball player who pitches a complete game can make in a regulation 9-inning baseball game?

68. *Weighing Coins* You have eight coins. Seven are genuine and one is a fake, which weighs a little less than the other seven. You have a balance scale, which you may use only three times. Tell how to locate the bad coin in three weighings. (Then show how to detect the bad coin in only *two* weighings.)

69. *Geometry Puzzle* When the diagram shown is folded to form a cube, what letter is opposite the face marked Z?

70. *Number Pattern* If the pattern below continues, where would the number 289 appear?

$$\begin{array}{ccccc} & & 1 & & \\ & 3 & & 5 & \\ 7 & & 9 & & 11 \end{array}$$

(November 11, 2008)

71. *Geometry Puzzle* Draw the following figure without picking up your pencil from the paper and without tracing over a line you have already drawn.

72. *Geometry Puzzle* Repeat **Exercise 71** for this figure.

73. *Paying for a Mint* Brian Altobello has an unlimited number of cents (pennies), nickels, and dimes. In how many different ways can he pay 15¢ for a chocolate mint? (For example, one way is 1 dime and 5 pennies.)

74. *Books on a Shelf* Volumes 1 and 2 of *The Complete Works of Wally Smart* are standing in numerical order from left to right on your bookshelf. Volume 1 has 450 pages and Volume 2 has 475 pages. Excluding the covers, how many pages are between page 1 of Volume 1 and page 475 of Volume 2?

75. **Area and Perimeter** Triangle *ABC* has sides 10, 24, and 26 cm long. A rectangle that has an area equal to that of the triangle is 3 cm wide. Find the perimeter of the rectangle. (November 13, 2008)

76. **Teenager's Age** A teenager's age increased by 2 gives a perfect square. Her age decreased by 10 gives the square root of that perfect square. She is 5 years older than her brother. How old is her brother?

77. **Ages** James, Dan, Jessica, and Cathy form a pair of married couples. Their ages are 36, 31, 30, and 29. Jessica is married to the oldest person in the group. James is older than Jessica but younger than Cathy. Who is married to whom, and what are their ages?

78. **Making Change** In how many different ways can you make change for a half dollar using currently minted U.S. coins, if cents (pennies) are not allowed?

79. **Days in a Month** Some months have 30 days and some have 31 days. How many months have 28 days?

80. **Dirt in a Hole** How much dirt is there in a cubical hole, 6 feet on each side?

81. **Final Digit** What is the last digit of $49{,}327^{1783}$? (April 11, 2009)

82. **Missing Digit** Find the missing digit, *x*, in the product given by

$$(172195)(572167) = 985242x6565.$$

(May 3, 2009)

83. **Geometry Puzzle** What is the maximum number of small squares in which we may place crosses (×) and not have any row, column, or diagonal completely filled with crosses? Illustrate your answer.

84. **Making Change** Webster has some pennies, dimes, and quarters in his pocket. When Josefa asks him for change for a dollar, Webster discovers that he cannot make the change exactly. What is the largest possible total value of the coins in his pocket? (October 5, 2009)

85. **Fibonacci Property** Refer to **Example 1**, and observe the sequence of numbers in color. Choose any four successive terms. Multiply the first one chosen by the fourth. Then multiply the two middle terms. Repeat this process. What do you notice when the two products are compared?

1.4 CALCULATING, ESTIMATING, AND READING GRAPHS

Calculation • Estimation • Interpretation of Graphs

The photograph shows the **Sharp EL-2139 HB,** a typical four-function calculator.

Since the introduction of hand-held calculators in the early 1970s, the methods of everyday arithmetic have been drastically altered. One of the first consumer models available was the Texas Instruments SR-10, which sold for nearly $150 in 1973. It could perform the four operations of arithmetic and take square roots, but could do very little more.

Calculation

The search for easier ways to calculate and compute has culminated in the development of hand-held calculators and computers. For the general population, a calculator that performs the operations of arithmetic and a few other functions is sufficient. These are known as **four-function calculators.** Students who take higher mathematics courses (engineers, for example) usually need the added power of **scientific calculators. Graphing calculators,** which actually plot graphs on small screens, are also available. *Always refer to your owner's manual if you need assistance in performing an operation with your calculator. If you need further help, ask your instructor or another student who is using the same model.*

Current models of calculators differ from earlier versions in that they can display both the information the user inputs and the result generated on the same screen. In this way, the user can verify that the information entered into the calculator is correct. Although it is not necessary to have a graphing calculator to study the material presented in this text, we occasionally include graphing calculator screens to support results obtained or to provide supplemental information.*

---

*Because they are the most popular models of graphing calculators, we include screens similar to those generated by TI-83 Plus and TI-84 Plus models from Texas Instruments.

The popular **TI-84 Plus** graphing calculator is shown here.

The screens that follow illustrate some common entries and operations.

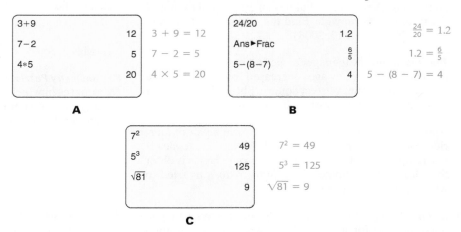

Screen A illustrates how two numbers can be added, subtracted, or multiplied. Screen B shows how two numbers can be divided, how the decimal quotient (stored in the memory cell Ans) can be converted into a fraction, and how parentheses can be used in a computation. Screen C shows how a number can be squared, how it can be cubed, and how its square root can be taken.

Screen D shows how other roots (cube root and fourth root) can be found, and how the reciprocal of a number can be found using −1 as an exponent. Screen E shows how π can be accessed with its own special key, how a **factorial** (as indicated by !) can be found and how a result might be displayed in **scientific notation**. (The "E13" following 5.627062301 means that this number is multiplied by 10^{13}. This answer is still only an approximation, because the product 6,265,804 × 8,980,591 contains more digits than the calculator can display.)

Estimation

Although calculators can make life easier when it comes to computations, many times we need only estimate an answer to a problem, and in these cases a calculator may not be necessary or appropriate.

▌▌ **EXAMPLE 1** Estimating an Appropriate Number of Birdhouses

A birdhouse for swallows can accommodate up to 8 nests. How many birdhouses would be necessary to accommodate 58 nests?

SOLUTION

If we divide 58 by 8 either by hand or with a calculator, we get 7.25. Can this possibly be the desired number? Of course not, because we cannot consider fractions of birdhouses. Do we need 7 or 8 birdhouses? To provide nesting space for the nests left over after the 7 birdhouses (as indicated by the decimal fraction), we should plan to use 8 birdhouses. In this problem, we must round our answer *up* to the next counting number.

▌▌▌

■■ EXAMPLE 2 Approximating Average Number of Yards per Carry

In 2009, Cedric Benson carried the football 301 times for 1251 yards (*Source:* www.nfl.com). Approximate his average number of yards per carry that year.

SOLUTION

Because we are are asked only to find Cedric's approximate average, we can say that he carried about 300 times for about 1200 yards, and his average was about $\frac{1200}{300} = 4$ yards per carry. (A calculator shows that his average to the nearest tenth was 4.2 yards per carry. Verify this.)   ■■■

■■ EXAMPLE 3 Comparing Proportions of Workers by Age Groups

In a recent year, there were approximately 127,000 males in the 25–29-year age bracket working on farms. This represented part of the total of 238,000 farm workers in that age bracket. Of the 331,000 farm workers in the 40–44-year age bracket, 160,000 were males. Without using a calculator, determine which age bracket had a larger proportion of males.

SOLUTION

Think in terms of thousands instead of dealing with all the zeros. First, we analyze the age bracket 25–29 years. Because there were a total of 238 thousand workers, of which 127 thousand were males, there were

$$238 - 127 = 111 \text{ thousand female workers.}$$ More than half were males.

In the 40–44-year age bracket, of the 331 thousand workers, there were 160 thousand males, giving

$$331 - 160 = 171 \text{ thousand female workers.}$$ Fewer than half were males.

The 25–29-year age bracket had the larger proportion of males.   ■■■

Interpretation of Graphs

In a **circle graph,** or **pie chart,** a circle is used to indicate the total of all the data categories represented. The circle is divided into sectors, or wedges (like pieces of a pie), whose sizes show the relative magnitudes of the categories. The sum of all the fractional parts must be 1 (for 1 whole circle).

■■ EXAMPLE 4 Interpreting Information in a Circle Graph

Use the circle graph in **Figure 9** to determine how much of the amount spent for a $3.50 gallon of gasoline in California goes to refinery margin and to crude oil cost.

Source: California Energy Commission.

Figure 9

SOLUTION

The sectors in the circle graph in **Figure 9** are sized to match how the price is divided. For example, the greatest portion of the price (32%) goes to the refinery, while the least portion (8%) goes for state sales tax. As expected, the percents total 100%. The price of gasoline is $3.50 per gallon.

$$\text{Refinery margin:} \quad \$3.50 \times \underbrace{0.32}_{\text{32\% converted to a decimal}} = \$1.12$$

$$\text{Crude oil cost:} \quad \$3.50 \times \underbrace{0.24}_{\text{24\% converted to a decimal}} = \$0.84$$

▮▮▮

A **bar graph** is used to show comparisons. It consists of a series of bars (or simulations of bars) arranged either vertically or horizontally. In a bar graph, values from two categories are paired with each other (for example, years with sales).

▮▮ **EXAMPLE 5** Interpreting Information in a Bar Graph

The bar graph in **Figure 10** shows U.S. sales of motor scooters, which have gained popularity due to their fuel efficiency. The graph compares sales in thousands.

Source: Motorcycle Industry Council.

Figure 10

(a) Estimate sales in 2000 and 2004.

(b) In what years were sales greater than 50 thousand?

(c) Describe the change in sales as the years progressed.

SOLUTION

(a) Locate the top of the bar for 2000, and move horizontally across to the vertical scale to see that it is about 40. Sales in 2000 were about 40 thousand. Follow the top of the bar for 2004 across to the vertical scale to see that it lies about halfway between 80 and 90 thousand, so sales in 2004 were about 85,000.

(b) Locate 50 on the vertical scale and follow the line across to the right. Three years—2002, 2003, and 2004—have bars that extend above the line for 50, so sales were greater than 50 thousand in those years.

(c) As the years progressed, sales increased steadily, from about 15 thousand in 1998 to about 85 thousand in 2004. ▮▮▮

A **line graph** is used to show changes or trends in data over time. To form a line graph, we connect a series of points representing data with line segments.

║║ EXAMPLE 6 Interpreting Information in a Line Graph

Current projections indicate that funding for Medicare will not cover its costs unless the program changes. The line graph in **Figure 11** shows Medicare funds in billions of dollars for the years 2004 through 2013.

Source: Centers for Medicare and Medicaid Services.
*Projected

Figure 11

(a) Estimate the funds in the years 2005 and 2006. About how much did the funding decrease from 2005 to 2006?

(b) Which is the only period in which Medicare funds increased? What is the projected trend from 2005 to 2013?

(c) In which year is it projected that funds will first show a deficit?

SOLUTION

(a) At the bottom of the graph, locate 2005, and read up to find that the point has a height of about 25 (billion dollars). Similarly, the point for 2006 has height about 10 (billion dollars). The funding *decreased* by about

$$25 - 10 = 15 \text{ billion dollars.} \quad \text{2005 amount} - \text{2006 amount}$$

(b) The graph *rises* from 2004 to 2005, so funds increased between these two years. The graph *falls* during 2005 to 2013, so funds will decrease.

(c) From 2004 to 2010, the graph is always above 0, but in 2011, it falls slightly below 0 for the first time, indicating a deficit.   ■■■

1.4 EXERCISES

Perform the indicated operations and give as many digits in your answer as shown on your calculator display. (The number of displayed digits may vary depending on the model used.)

1. $39.7 + (8.2 - 4.1)$

2. $2.8 \times (3.2 - 1.1)$

3. $\sqrt{5.56440921}$

4. $\sqrt{37.38711025}$

5. $\sqrt[3]{418.508992}$

6. $\sqrt[3]{700.227072}$

7. 2.67^2

8. 3.49^3

9. 5.76^5

10. 1.48^6

11. $\dfrac{14.32 - 8.1}{2 \times 3.11}$

12. $\dfrac{12.3 + 18.276}{3 \times 1.04}$

13. $\sqrt[5]{1.35}$

14. $\sqrt[6]{3.21}$

15. $\dfrac{\pi}{\sqrt{2}}$

16. $\dfrac{2\pi}{\sqrt{3}}$

17. $\sqrt[4]{\dfrac{2143}{22}}$

18. $\dfrac{12{,}345{,}679 \times 72}{\sqrt[3]{27}}$

19. $\dfrac{\sqrt{2}}{\sqrt[3]{6}}$

20. $\dfrac{\sqrt[3]{12}}{\sqrt{3}}$

21. Choose any number consisting of five digits. Multiply it by 9 on your calculator. Now add the digits in the answer. If the sum is more than 9, add the digits of this sum, and repeat until the sum is less than 10. Your answer will always be 9. Repeat the exercise with a number consisting of six digits. Does the same result hold?

22. Use your calculator to *square* the following two-digit numbers ending in 5: 15, 25, 35, 45, 55, 65, 75, 85. Write down your results, and examine the pattern that develops. Then use inductive reasoning to predict the value of 95^2. Write an explanation of how you can mentally square a two-digit number ending in 5.

Perform each calculation and observe the answers. Then fill in the blank with the appropriate response.

23. $\boxed{\frac{-3}{-8}}$; $\boxed{\frac{-5}{-4}}$; $\boxed{\frac{-2.1}{-4.3}}$

Dividing a negative number by another negative number gives a _____ product.
(negative/positive)

24. $\boxed{5 \cdot -4}$; $\boxed{-3 \cdot 8}$; $\boxed{2.7 \cdot -4.3}$

Multiplying a negative number by a positive number gives a _____ product.
(negative/positive)

25. $\boxed{5.6^0}$; $\boxed{\pi^0}$; $\boxed{2^0}$; $\boxed{120^0}$

Raising a nonzero number to the power 0 gives a result of _____.

26. $\boxed{1^2}$; $\boxed{1^3}$; $\boxed{1^{-3}}$; $\boxed{1^0}$

Raising 1 to any power gives a result of _____.

27. $\boxed{\frac{1}{7}}$; $\boxed{\frac{1}{-9}}$; $\boxed{\frac{1}{3}}$; $\boxed{\frac{1}{-8}}$

The sign of the reciprocal of a number is _____ the sign of the number.
(the same as/different from)

28. $\boxed{5 \div 0}$; $\boxed{9 \div 0}$; $\boxed{0 \div 0}$

Dividing a number by 0 gives a(n) _____ on a calculator.

29. $\boxed{0 \div 8}$; $\boxed{0 \div -2}$; $\boxed{0 \div \pi}$

Zero divided by a nonzero number gives a quotient of _____.

30. $\boxed{\sqrt{-3}}$; $\boxed{\sqrt{-4}}$; $\boxed{\sqrt{-10}}$

Taking the square root of a negative number gives a(n) _____ on a calculator.

31. $\boxed{-3 \cdot -4 \cdot -5}$; $\boxed{-3 \cdot -4 \cdot -5 \cdot -6 \cdot -7}$;

$\boxed{-3 \cdot -4 \cdot -5 \cdot -6 \cdot -7 \cdot -8 \cdot -9}$

Multiplying an *odd* number of negative numbers gives a _____ product.
(positive/negative)

32. $\boxed{-3 \cdot -4}$; $\boxed{-3 \cdot -4 \cdot -5 \cdot -6}$;

$\boxed{-3 \cdot -4 \cdot -5 \cdot -6 \cdot -7 \cdot -8}$

Multiplying an *even* number of negative numbers gives a _____ product.
(positive/negative)

33. Find the decimal representation of $\frac{1}{6}$ on your calculator. Following the decimal point will be a 1 and a string of 6s. The final digit will be a 7 if your calculator *rounds off* or a 6 if it *truncates*. Which kind of calculator do you have?

34. Choose any three-digit number and enter the digits into a calculator. Then enter them again to get a six-digit number. Divide this six-digit number by 7. Divide the result by 13. Divide the result by 11. What is interesting about your answer? Explain why this happens.

35. Choose any digit except 0. Multiply it by 429. Now multiply the result by 259. What is interesting about your answer? Explain why this happens.

36. Choose two natural numbers. Add 1 to the second and divide by the first to get a third. Add 1 to the third and divide by the second to get a fourth. Add 1 to the fourth and divide by the third to get a fifth. Continue this process until you discover a pattern. What is the pattern?

Give an appropriate counting number answer to each question in Exercises 37–40. (Find the least counting number that will work.)

37. Pages to Store Trading Cards A plastic page designed to hold trading cards will hold up to 9 cards. How many pages will be needed to store 563 cards?

38. Drawers for DVDs A sliding drawer designed to hold DVD cases has 20 compartments. If Chris wants to house his collection of 408 Disney DVDs, how many such drawers will he need?

39. Containers for African Violets A gardener wants to fertilize 800 African violets. Each container of fertilizer will supply up to 60 plants. How many containers will she need to do the job?

40. *Fifth-Grade Teachers Needed* False River Academy has 155 fifth-grade students. The principal, Butch LeBeau, has decided that each fifth-grade teacher should have a maximum of 24 students. How many fifth-grade teachers does he need?

In Exercises 41–46, use estimation to determine the choice closest to the correct answer.

41. *Price per Acre of Land* To build a "millennium clock" on Mount Washington in Nevada that would tick once each year, chime once each century, and last at least 10,000 years, the nonprofit Long Now Foundation purchased 80 acres of land for $140,000. Which one of the following is the closest estimate to the price per acre?

A. $1000 **B.** $2000 **C.** $4000 **D.** $11,200

42. *Time of a Round-Trip* The distance from Seattle, Washington, to Springfield, Missouri, is 2009 miles. About how many hours would a roundtrip from Seattle to Springfield and back take a bus that averages 50 miles per hour for the entire trip?

A. 60 **B.** 70 **C.** 80 **D.** 90

43. *People per Square Mile* Buffalo County in Nebraska has a population of 40,249 and covers 968 square miles. About how many people per square mile live in Buffalo County?

A. 40 **B.** 400 **C.** 4000 **D.** 40,000

44. *Revolutions of Mercury* The planet Mercury takes 88.0 Earth days to revolve around the sun once. Pluto takes 90,824.2 days to do the same. When Pluto has revolved around the sun once, about how many times will Mercury have revolved around the sun?

A. 100,000 **B.** 10,000 **C.** 1000 **D.** 100

45. *Reception Average* In 2009, Brandon Marshall of the Denver Broncos caught 101 passes for 1120 yards. His approximate number of yards gained per catch was _____.

A. $\frac{1}{11}$ **B.** 110 **C.** 1.1 **D.** 11

46. *Area of the Sistine Chapel* The Sistine Chapel in Vatican City measures 40.5 meters by 13.5 meters.

Which is the closest approximation to its area?

A. 110 meters **B.** 55 meters
C. 110 square meters **D.** 600 square meters

Immigration *The circle graph below shows the approximate percent of immigrants admitted into the United States during the 1990s. Use the graph to answer the questions in Exercises 47–50.*

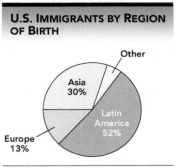

Source: U.S. Bureau of the Census.

47. What percent of the immigrants were from the "Other" group of countries?

48. What percent of the immigrants were not from Asia?

49. In a group of 2,000,000 immigrants, how many would you expect to be from Europe?

50. In a group of 4,000,000 immigrants, how many more would there be from Latin America than all the other regions combined?

Milk Production *The bar graph shows total U.S. milk production in billions of pounds for the years 2001 through 2007. Use the bar graph to work Exercises 51–54.*

Source: U.S. Department of Agriculture.

51. In what years was U.S. milk production greater than 175 billion pounds?

52. In what two years was U.S. milk production about the same?

53. Estimate U.S. milk production in 2001 and 2007.

54. Describe the change in U.S. milk production from 2001 to 2007.

Gasoline Prices The line graph shows the average price, adjusted for inflation, that Americans have paid for a gallon of gasoline for selected years since 1970. Use the line graph to work Exercises 55–58.

55. Over which 5-year period did the greatest increase in the price of a gallon of gas occur? About how much was this increase?

56. Estimate the price of a gallon of gas during 1985, 1990, 1995, and 2000.

57. Describe the trend in gas prices from 1980 to 1995.

58. During which year(s) did a gallon of gas cost approximately $1.50?

AVERAGE GASOLINE PRICES

Source: Energy Information Administration.

EXTENSION Using Writing to Learn about Mathematics

Journals • Learning Logs • Reports on Articles • Term Papers

Mathematical writing takes many forms. One of the most famous author/mathematicians was **Charles Dodgson** (1832–1898), who used the pen name **Lewis Carroll.**

Dodgson was a mathematics lecturer at Oxford University in England. Queen Victoria told Dodgson how much she enjoyed *Alice's Adventures in Wonderland* and how much she wanted to read his next book; he is said to have sent her *Symbolic Logic*, his most famous mathematical work.

The *Alice* books made Carroll famous. Late in life, however, Dodgson shunned attention and denied that he and Carroll were the same person, even though he gave away hundreds of signed copies to children and children's hospitals.

Research has indicated that the ability to express mathematical observations in writing can serve as a positive force in one's continued development as a mathematics student. The implementation of writing in the mathematics class can use several approaches.

Journals One way of using writing in mathematics is to keep a journal in which you spend a few minutes explaining what happened in class that day. The journal entries may be general or specific, depending on the topic covered, the degree to which you understand the topic, your interest level at the time, and so on. Journal entries are usually written in informal language and are often an effective means of communicating to yourself, your classmates, and your instructor what feelings, perceptions, and concerns you are having at the time.

Learning Logs Although journal entries are for the most part unstructured writings in which the student's thoughts are allowed to roam freely, entries in learning logs are typically more structured. An instructor may pose a specific question for a student to answer in a learning log. In this text, we intersperse writing exercises in each exercise set that are appropriate for answering in a learning log. For example, consider **Exercise 13** in the exercise set for the opening section in this chapter.

Discuss the differences between inductive and deductive reasoning. Give an example of each.

Here is a possible response to this exercise.

> Deductive reasoning occurs when you go from general ideas to specific ones. For example, I know that I can multiply both sides of $\frac{1}{2}x = 6$ by 2 to get $x = 12$, because I can multiply both sides of any equation by whatever I want (except 0). Inductive reasoning goes the other way. If I have a general conclusion from specific observations, that's inductive reasoning.
> Example – in the numbers 4, 8, 12, 16, and so on, I can conclude that the next number is 20, since I always add 4 to get the next number.

Reports on Articles   The motto "Publish or perish" has long been around, implying that a scholar in pursuit of an academic position must publish in a journal in his or her field. There are numerous journals that publish papers in mathematics research and/or mathematics education. In Activity 3, we suggest some articles that have appeared within the last few years. A report on such an article can help you understand what mathematicians do and what ideas mathematics teachers use to convey concepts to their students.

Term Papers   Professors in mathematics survey courses are, in increasing numbers, requiring short term papers of their students. In this way, you can become aware of the plethora of books and articles on mathematics and mathematicians, many written specifically for the layperson. In Activities 5 and 6, we provide a list of possible term paper topics.

EXTENSION ACTIVITIES

Rather than include a typical exercise set, we list some suggested activities in which writing can be used to enhance awareness and learning of mathematics.

Activity 1   Keep a journal. After each class, write for a few minutes on your perceptions about the class, the topics covered, or whatever you feel is appropriate.

Activity 2   Keep a learning log, answering at least one writing exercise from each exercise set covered in your class syllabus. Ask your teacher for suggestions of other types of specific writing assignments.

Activity 3   The National Council of Teachers of Mathematics publishes journals in mathematics education: *Teaching Children Mathematics* and *Mathematics Teacher* are two that can be found online or in the periodicals section of most college and university libraries. We have chosen several recent articles in each of these journals. Write a short report on one of these articles according to guidelines specified by your instructor.

From *Mathematics Teacher*
2004
   Devaney, Robert L. "Fractal Patterns and Chaos Games." November 2004, p. 228.
   Francis, Richard L. "New Worlds to Conquer." October 2004, p. 166.
   Hansen, Will. "War and Pieces." September 2004, p. 70.
   Mahoney, John F. "How Many Votes Are Needed to Be Elected President?" October 2004, p. 154.

2005
   Clausen, Mary C. "Did You 'Code'?" November 2005, p. 260.
   Comstock, Jocelyne M., Sean P. Madden, and James P. Downing. "Paper Moon: Simulating a Total Solar Eclipse." December 2005/January 2006, p. 312.
   Parker, Dennis. "Partitioning the Interior of a Circle with Chords." September 2005, p. 120.
   Quinn, Jennifer J., and Arthur T. Benjamin. "Revisiting Fibonacci and Related Sequences." December 2005/January 2006, p. 357.

2006
   Cline, Kelly S. "Classroom Voting in Mathematics." September 2006, p. 100.
   Gordon, Sheldon P. "Placement Tests: The Shaky Bridge Connecting School and College Mathematics." October 2006, p. 174.
   Johnson, Iris DeLoach. "Grandfather Tang Goes to High School." March 2006, p. 522.

Wong, Michael. "The Human Body's Built-In Range Finder: The Thumb Method of Indirect Distance Measurement." May 2006, p. 622.

From *Teaching Children Mathematics*

2004

Anthony, Glenda J., and Margaret A. Walshaw. "Zero: A 'None' Number?" August 2004, p. 38.

Buschman, Larry. "Teaching Problem Solving in Mathematics." February 2004, p. 302.

Joram, Elana, Christina Hartman, and Paul R. Trafton. " 'As People Get Older, They Get Taller': An Integrated Unit on Measurement, Linear Relationships, and Data Analysis." March 2004, p. 344.

Mann, Rebecca L. "Balancing Act: The Truth Behind the Equals Sign." September 2004, p. 65.

2005

Flores, Alfinio, Erin E. Turner, and Renee C. Bachman. "Posing Problems to Develop Conceptual Understanding: Two Teachers Make Sense of Division of Fractions." October 2005, p. 17.

Hansen, Laurie E. "ABCs of Early Mathematics Experiences." November 2005, p. 208.

Sherrill, Carl M. "Math Riddles: Helping Children Connect Words and Numbers." March 2005, p. 368.

Thompson, Tony, and Stephen Sproule. "Calculators for Students with Special Needs." March 2005, p. 391.

2006

Barnes, Mary Kathleen. "How Many Days 'til My Birthday? Helping Kindergarten Students Understand Calendar Connections and Concepts." February 2006, p. 290.

Cassel, Darlinda, Anne Reynolds, and Eileen Lillard. "A Mathematical Exploration of Grandpa's Quilt." March 2006, p. 340.

de Groot, Cornelis, and Timothy Whalen. "Longing for Division." April 2006, p. 410.

Nugent, Christina M. "How Many Blades of Grass Are on a Football Field?" February 2006, p. 282.

Activity 4   One of the most popular mathematical films of all time is *Donald in Mathmagic Land*, a 1959 Disney short that is available on DVD. Spend an entertaining half-hour watching this film, and write a report on it according to the guidelines of your instructor.

Activity 5   Write a report according to the guidelines of your instructor on one of the following mathematicians, philosophers, and scientists.

© Disney Enterprises, Inc.

Abel, N.	Cardano, G.	Gauss, C.	Noether, E.
Agnesi, M. G.	Copernicus, N.	Hilbert, D.	Pascal, B.
Agnesi, M. T.	De Morgan, A.	Kepler, J.	Plato
Al-Khowârizmi	Descartes, R.	Kronecker, L.	Polya, G.
Apollonius	Euler, L.	Lagrange, J.	Pythagoras
Archimedes	Fermat, P.	Leibniz, G.	Ramanujan, S.
Aristotle	Fibonacci	L'Hôspital, G.	Riemann, G.
Babbage, C.	(Leonardo	Lobachevsky, N.	Russell, B.
Bernoulli, Jakob	of Pisa)	Mandelbrot, B.	Somerville, M.
Bernoulli,	Galileo (Galileo	Napier, J.	Tartaglia, N.
Johann	Galilei)	Nash, J.	Whitehead, A.
Cantor, G.	Galois, E.	Newton, I.	Wiles, A.

Activity 6   Write a term paper on one of the following topics in mathematics according to the guidelines of your instructor.

Babylonian mathematics	Pascal's triangle
Egyptian mathematics	The origins of probability theory
The origin of zero	Women in mathematics
Plimpton 322	Mathematical paradoxes
The Rhind papyrus	Unsolved problems in
Origins of the Pythagorean	mathematics
theorem	The four-color theorem
The regular (Platonic) solids	The proof of Fermat's Last
The Pythagorean brotherhood	Theorem
The Golden Ratio (Golden	The search for large primes
Section)	Fractal geometry
The three famous construction	The co-inventors of calculus
problems of the Greeks	The role of the computer in the
The history of the approximations	study of mathematics
of π	Mathematics and music
Euclid and his "Elements"	Police mathematics
Early Chinese mathematics	The origins of complex numbers
Early Hindu mathematics	Goldbach's conjecture
Origin of the word *algebra*	The use of the Internet in
Magic squares	mathematics education
Figurate numbers	The development of graphing
The Fibonacci sequence	calculators
The Cardano/Tartaglia controversy	Mathematics education reform
Historical methods of computation	movement
(logarithms, the abacus, Napier's	Multicultural mathematics
rods, the slide rule, etc.)	The Riemann Hypothesis

Activity 7   Investigate a computer program that focuses on teaching children elementary mathematics, and write a critical review of it as if you were writing for a journal that contains software reviews of educational material. Be sure to address the higher-level thinking skills in addition to drill and practice.

Activity 8   The following Web sites provide a fascinating list of mathematics-related topics. Go to one of them, choose a topic that interests you, and report on it, according to the guidelines of your instructor.

www.mathworld.wolfram.com

www.world.std.com/~reinhold/mathmovies.html

www.maths.surrey.ac.uk/hosted-sites/R.Knott/

http://dir.yahoo.com/Science/Mathematics/

www.cut-the-knot.com/

www.ics.uci.edu/~eppstein/recmath.html

Activity 9   A theme of mathematics-related scenes in movies and television is found throughout this book. Prepare a report on one or more such scenes, and determine whether the mathematics involved is correct or incorrect. If correct, show why. If incorrect, find the correct answer. See www.math.harvard.edu/~knill/mathmovies/ and www.mathclassgoestohollywood.com.

Activity 10   The longest running animated television series is *The Simpsons*, having begun in 1989. The Web site www.simpsonsmath.com explores the occurrence of mathematics in the episodes on a season-by-season basis. Watch several episodes and elaborate on the mathematics found in them.

COLLABORATIVE INVESTIGATION

Discovering Patterns in Pascal's Triangle

One fascinating array of numbers, **Pascal's triangle,** consists of rows of numbers, each of which contains one more entry than the one before. The first six rows are shown here.

```
                1
             1     1
          1     2     1
       1     3     3     1
    1     4     6     4     1
 1     5    10    10     5     1
```

To discover some of its patterns, divide the class into groups of four students each. Within each group designate one student as A, one as B, one as C, and one as D. Then perform the following activities in order.

1. Discuss among group members some of the properties of the triangle that are obvious from observing the first six rows shown.

2. It is fairly obvious that each row begins and ends with 1. Discover a method whereby the other entries in a row can be determined from the entries in the row immediately above it. (*Hint:* In the fifth row, 6 = 3 + 3.) Then, as a group, find the next three rows of the triangle, and have each member prepare his or her own copy of the entire first nine rows for later reference.

3. Now each student in the group will investigate a particular property of the triangle. In some cases, a calculator will be helpful. All students should begin working at the same time. (A discussion follows.)

Student A: Find the sum of the entries in each row. Notice the pattern that emerges. Now write the tenth row of the triangle.

Student B: Investigate the successive differences in the diagonals from upper left to lower right. For example, in the diagonal that begins 1, 2, 3, 4,..., the successive differences are all 1; in the diagonal that begins 1, 3, 6,..., the successive differences are 2, 3, 4, and so on. Do this up through the diagonal that begins 1, 6, 21,....

Student C: Find the values of the first five powers of the number 11, starting with 11^0 (recall $11^0 = 1$).

Student D: Arrange these nine rows of the triangle with all rows "flush left," and then draw lightly dashed arrows as shown:

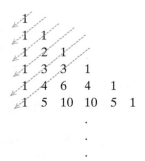

and so on. Then add along the diagonals. Write these sums in order from left to right.

4. After all students have concluded their individual investigations in Item 3, return to a group discussion.

   (a) Have student A report the result found in Item 3, and then make a prediction concerning the sum of the entries in the tenth row.

   (b) Have student B report the successive differences discovered in the diagonals. Then have all students in the group investigate the successive differences in the diagonal that begins 1, 7, 28.... (It may be necessary to write a few more rows of the triangle.)

   (c) Have student C report the relationship between the powers of 11 found, and then determine the value of 11^5. Why does the pattern not continue here?

   (d) Have student D report the sequence of numbers found. Then, as a group, predict what the next sum will be by observing the pattern in the sequence. Confirm your prediction by actual computation.

5. Choose a representative from each group to report to the entire class the observations made throughout this investigation.

6. Find a reference to Pascal's triangle on the Internet and prepare a report.

CHAPTER 1 TEST

In Exercises 1 and 2, decide whether the reasoning involved is an example of inductive or deductive reasoning.

1. Carol Britz is a sales representative for a publishing company. For the past 16 years, she has exceeded her annual sales goal, primarily by selling mathematics textbooks. Therefore, she will also exceed her annual sales goal this year.

2. For all natural numbers n, n^2 is also a natural number. 176 is a natural number. Therefore, 176^2 is a natural number.

3. *Magic Hexagon* (A **magic hexagon** has all entries in the columns and diagonals adding up to the same sum.) Find the constant sum for the magic hexagon, and fill in the numbers so that every column or diagonal has that sum. (From *Mathematics Teacher* monthly calendar, November 20, 2007.)

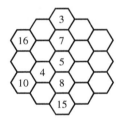

4. Use the list of equations and inductive reasoning to predict the next equation, and then verify your conjecture.

$$65,359,477,124,183 \times 17 = 1,111,111,111,111,111$$
$$65,359,477,124,183 \times 34 = 2,222,222,222,222,222$$
$$65,359,477,124,183 \times 51 = 3,333,333,333,333,333$$

5. Use the method of successive differences to find the next term in the sequence

$$3, 11, 31, 69, 131, 223, \ldots.$$

6. Find the sum $1 + 2 + 3 + \cdots + 250$.

7. Consider the following equations, where the left side of each is an octagonal number.

$$1 = 1$$
$$8 = 1 + 7$$
$$21 = 1 + 7 + 13$$
$$40 = 1 + 7 + 13 + 19$$

Use the pattern established on the right sides to predict the next octagonal number. What is the next equation in the list?

8. Use the result of **Exercise 7** and the method of successive differences to find the first eight octagonal numbers. Then divide each by 4 and record the remainder. What is the pattern obtained?

9. Describe the pattern used to obtain the terms of the Fibonacci sequence

$$1, 1, 2, 3, 5, 8, 13, 21, \ldots.$$

Use problem-solving strategies to solve each problem, taken from the date indicated in the monthly calendar of Mathematics Teacher.

10. *Building a Fraction* Each of the four digits 2, 4, 6, and 9 is placed in one of the boxes to form a fraction. The numerator and the denominator are both two-digit whole numbers. What is the smallest value of all the common fractions that can be formed? Express your answer as a common fraction. (November 17, 2004)

11. *Units Digit of a Power of 9* What is the units digit (ones digit) in the decimal representation of 9^{1997}? (January 27, 1997)

12. *Counting Puzzle (Triangles)* How many triangles are in this figure? (January 6, 2000)

13. *Make Them Equal* Consider the following:

$$1\ 2\ 3\ 4\ 5\ 6\ 7\ 8\ 9\ 0 = 100.$$

Leaving all the numerals in the order given, insert addition and subtraction signs into the expression to make the equation true. (March 23, 2008)

14. *Shrinkage* Dr. Small is 36 inches tall, and Ms. Tall is 96 inches tall. If Dr. Small shrinks 2 inches per year and Ms. Tall grows $\frac{2}{3}$ of an inch per year, how tall will Ms. Tall be when Dr. Small disappears altogether? (November 2, 2007)

15. *Units Digit of a Sum* Find the units digit (ones digit) of the decimal numeral representing the number $11^{11} + 14^{14} + 16^{16}$. (February 14, 1994)

16. Based on your knowledge of elementary arithmetic, describe the pattern that can be observed when the following operations are performed:

$$9 \times 1, \quad 9 \times 2, \quad 9 \times 3, \dots, 9 \times 9.$$

(*Hint:* Add the digits in the answers. What do you notice?)

Use your calculator to evaluate each of the following. Give as many decimal places as the calculator displays.

17. $\sqrt{98.16}$

18. 3.25^3

19. *Basketball Scoring Results* During the 2008 –09 NCAA women's basketball season, Destini Hughes of LSU made 28 of her 96 field goal attempts. This means that for every 10 attempts, she made approximately _____ of them.

A. 4   **B.** 3   **C.** 2   **D.** 1

20. *Unemployment Rate* The line graph shows the overall unemployment rate in the U.S. civilian labor force for the years 1998 through 2005.

UNEMPLOYMENT RATE

Source: U.S. Department of Labor.

(a) Between which pairs of consecutive years did the unemployment rate decrease?

(b) What was the general trend in the unemployment rate between 2000 and 2003?

(c) Estimate the overall unemployment rate in 2003 and 2004. About how much did the unemployment rate decline between 2003 and 2004?

THE BASIC CONCEPTS OF SET THEORY

2

In the movie *I.Q.*, Meg Ryan plays Catherine Boyd, Alfred Einstein's brilliant niece, who is attracted to blue-collar worker Ed Walters (Tim Robbins). Ed pretends to be a physicist.

ED: I think your uncle wants us to dance.

CATHERINE: Oh, now, don't be irrelevant, Ed. You can't get from there to here.

ED: Why not?

CATHERINE: Now don't tell me that a famous and brilliant scientist such as yourself doesn't know about Zeno's paradox.

ED: Remind me.

CATHERINE: You can't get from there to here because you always have to cover half the remaining distance, like from me to you. I have to cover half of it. Then, see, I still have half of that remaining, so I cover half that . . . and since there are infinite halves left, I can't ever get there.

ED (taking her in his arms and starting to dance): So how did that happen?

CATHERINE: I don't know.

43

Prior to the twentieth century, some ideas in *set theory* were considered *paradoxes* (wrong opinions). *Zeno's paradox,* as described by Catherine and seen in **Exercises 51 and 52** of the **Extension,** has been around in several forms for thousands of years.

2.1 SYMBOLS AND TERMINOLOGY

Designating Sets • Sets of Numbers and Cardinality • Finite and Infinite Sets • Equality of Sets

The basic ideas of set theory were developed by the German mathematician **Georg Cantor** (1845–1918) in about 1875. Cantor created a new field of theory and at the same time continued the long debate over infinity that began in ancient times. He developed counting by one-to-one correspondence to determine how many objects are contained in a set. Infinite sets differ from finite sets by not obeying the familiar law that the whole is greater than any of its parts.

Designating Sets

A **set** is a collection of objects. The objects belonging to the set are called the **elements,** or **members,** of the set. Sets are designated using the following three methods: (1) *word description,* (2) the *listing method,* and (3) *set-builder notation.*

The set of even counting numbers less than 10	Word description
$\{2, 4, 6, 8\}$	Listing method
$\{x \mid x \text{ is an even counting number less than } 10\}$	Set-builder notation

The set-builder notation above is read "the set of all x such that x is an even counting number less than 10." Set-builder notation uses the algebraic idea of a *variable.* (Any symbol would do, but just as in other algebraic applications, the letter x is a common choice.)

Variable representing
an element in general
↓
$\{x \mid x \text{ is an even counting number less than } 10\}$
↑
Criteria by which an element
qualifies for membership in the set

Sets are commonly given names (usually capital letters), such as E for the set of all letters of the English alphabet.

$$E = \{a, b, c, d, e, f, g, h, i, j, k, l, m, n, o, p, q, r, s, t, u, v, w, x, y, z\}$$

The listing notation can often be shortened by establishing the pattern of elements included and using ellipsis points to indicate a continuation of the pattern.

$$E = \{a, b, c, d, \ldots, x, y, z\}, \quad \text{or} \quad E = \{a, b, c, d, e, \ldots, z\}.$$

The set containing no elements is called the **empty set,** or **null set.** The symbol $\emptyset$ is used to denote the empty set, so $\emptyset$ and $\{\ \}$ have the same meaning. We do *not* denote the empty set with the symbol $\{\emptyset\}$ because this notation represents a set with one element (that element being the empty set).

▊▊ EXAMPLE 1 Listing Elements of Sets

Give a complete listing of all the elements of each set.

(a) the set of counting numbers between six and thirteen

(b) $\{5, 6, 7, \ldots, 13\}$

(c) $\{x \mid x \text{ is a counting number between } 6 \text{ and } 7\}$

SOLUTION

(a) This set can be denoted $\{7, 8, 9, 10, 11, 12\}$. (Notice that the word *between* excludes the endpoint values.)

(b) This set begins with the element 5, then 6, then 7, and so on, with each element obtained by adding 1 to the previous element in the list. This pattern stops at 13, so a complete listing is {5, 6, 7, 8, 9, 10, 11, 12, 13}.

(c) There are no counting numbers between 6 and 7, so this is the empty set { }, or ∅.

■■■

For a set to be useful, it must be well defined. For example, the preceding set E of the letters of the English alphabet is well defined. Given the letter q, we know that q is an element of E. Given the Greek letter θ (theta), we know that it is not an element of set E.

However, given the set C of all good singers, and a particular singer, Raeanna, it may not be possible to say whether

Raeanna is an element of C or   Raeanna is *not* an element of C.

The problem is the word "good"; how good is good? Because we cannot necessarily decide whether a given singer belongs to set C, set C is not well defined.

The letter q is an element of set E, where E is the set of all the letters of the English alphabet. To show this, the symbol ∈ is used.

$$q \in E \qquad \text{This is read "q is an element of set } E.\text{"}$$

The letter θ is not an element of E. To show this, ∈ with a slash mark is used.

$$\theta \notin E \qquad \text{This is read "} \theta \text{ is not an element of set } E.\text{"}$$

■■ EXAMPLE 2 Applying the Symbol ∈

Decide whether each statement is *true* or *false*.

(a) $3 \in \{1, 2, 5, 9, 13\}$ **(b)** $0 \in \{0, 1, 2, 3\}$ **(c)** $\frac{1}{5} \notin \left\{\frac{1}{3}, \frac{1}{4}, \frac{1}{6}\right\}$

SOLUTION

(a) Because 3 is *not* an element of the set $\{1, 2, 5, 9, 13\}$, the statement is *false*.

(b) Because 0 is indeed an element of the set $\{0, 1, 2, 3\}$, the statement is *true*.

(c) This statement says that $\frac{1}{5}$ is not an element of the set $\left\{\frac{1}{3}, \frac{1}{4}, \frac{1}{6}\right\}$, which is *true*.   ■■■

Sets of Numbers and Cardinality

Important categories of numbers are summarized below.

Sets of Numbers

Natural or Counting numbers $\{1, 2, 3, 4, \dots\}$

Whole numbers $\{0, 1, 2, 3, 4, \dots\}$

Integers $\{\dots, -3, -2, -1, 0, 1, 2, 3, \dots\}$

Rational numbers $\left\{\frac{p}{q} \mid p \text{ and } q \text{ are integers, and } q \neq 0\right\}$

(*Examples:* $\frac{3}{5}, -\frac{7}{9}, 5, 0$. Any rational number may be written as a terminating decimal number, such as 0.25, or a repeating decimal number, such as $0.666\dots$.)

Real numbers $\{x \mid x \text{ is a number that can be expressed as a decimal}\}$

Irrational numbers $\{x \mid x \text{ is a real number and } x \text{ cannot be expressed as a quotient of integers}\}$

(*Examples:* $\sqrt{2}, \sqrt[3]{4}, \pi$. Decimal representations of irrational numbers are neither terminating nor repeating.)

The number of elements in a set is called the **cardinal number,** or **cardinality,** of the set. The symbol

$$n(A), \quad \text{which is read } \textbf{"n of A,"}$$

represents the cardinal number of set A. If elements are repeated in a set listing, they should not be counted more than once when determining the cardinal number of the set.

▮▮ **EXAMPLE 3** Finding Cardinal Numbers

Find the cardinal number of each set.

(a) $K = \{2, 4, 8, 16\}$ **(b)** $M = \{0\}$ **(c)** $B = \{1, 1, 2, 2, 3\}$

(d) $R = \{4, 5, \ldots, 12, 13\}$ **(e)** $\emptyset$

SOLUTION

(a) Set K contains four elements, so the cardinal number of set K is 4, and $n(K) = 4$.

(b) Set M contains only one element, 0, so $n(M) = 1$.

(c) If elements are repeated in a set listing, they should not be counted more than once when determining the cardinal number of the set. Set B has only three *distinct* elements, so $n(B) = 3$.

(d) Although only four elements are listed, the ellipsis points indicate that there are other elements in the set. Counting them all, we find that there are ten elements, so $n(R) = 10$.

(e) The empty set, $\emptyset$, contains no elements, so $n(\emptyset) = 0$. ▮▮▮

Finite and Infinite Sets

A close-up of a camera lens shows the **infinity symbol, ∞,** defined in this case as any distance greater than 1000 times the focal length of a lens.

The sign was invented by the mathematician John Wallis in 1655. Wallis used 1/∞ to represent an infinitely small quantity.

If the cardinal number of a set is a particular whole number (0 or a counting number), as in all parts of **Example 3,** we call that set a **finite set.** Given enough time, we could finish counting all the elements of any finite set and arrive at its cardinal number.

Some sets, however, are so large that we could never finish the counting process. The counting numbers themselves are such a set. Whenever a set is so large that its cardinal number is not found among the whole numbers, we call that set an **infinite set.**

▮▮ **EXAMPLE 4** Designating an Infinite Set

Designate all odd counting numbers by the three common methods of set notation.

SOLUTION

The set of all odd counting numbers	Word description
$\{1, 3, 5, 7, 9, \ldots\}$	Listing method
$\{x \mid x \text{ is an odd counting number}\}$	Set-builder notation

▮▮▮

Equality of Sets

Set Equality

Set A is **equal** to set B provided the following two conditions are met:

1. Every element of A is an element of B, and

2. Every element of B is an element of A.

Two sets are equal if they contain exactly the same elements, regardless of order.

$$\{a, b, c, d\} = \{a, c, d, b\} \quad \text{Both sets contain exactly the same elements.}$$

Repetition of elements in a set listing does not add new elements.

$$\{1, 0, 1, 2, 3, 3\} = \{0, 1, 2, 3\} \quad \text{Both sets contain exactly the same elements.}$$

▮▮ **EXAMPLE 5** Determining Whether Two Sets Are Equal

Are $\{-4, 3, 2, 5\}$ and $\{-4, 0, 3, 2, 5\}$ equal sets?

SOLUTION

Every element of the first set is an element of the second. However, 0 is an element of the second and not of the first. The sets do not contain exactly the same elements, so they are not equal.

$$\{-4, 3, 2, 5\} \neq \{-4, 0, 3, 2, 5\} \qquad \blacksquare\blacksquare\blacksquare$$

▮▮ **EXAMPLE 6** Determining Whether Two Sets Are Equal

Decide whether each statement is *true* or *false*.

(a) $\{3\} = \{x \mid x$ is a counting number between 1 and 5$\}$

(b) $\{x \mid x$ is a negative natural number$\} = \{y \mid y$ is a number that is both rational and irrational$\}$

SOLUTION

(a) The set on the right contains *all* counting numbers between 1 and 5, namely 2, 3, and 4, while the set on the left contains *only* the number 3. Because the sets do not contain exactly the same elements, they are not equal. The statement is *false*.

(b) All natural numbers are positive, so the set on the left is ∅. By definition, if a number is rational, it cannot be irrational, so the set on the right is also ∅. Because each set is the empty set, the sets are equal. The statement is *true*.   ▮▮▮

2.1 EXERCISES

Match each set in Column I with the appropriate description in Column II.

I	II
1. $\{1, 3, 5, 7, 9\}$	**A.** the set of all even integers
2. $\{x \mid x$ is an even integer greater than 4 and less than 6$\}$	**B.** the set of the five least positive integer powers of 2
3. $\{\ldots, -4, -3, -2, -1\}$	**C.** the set of even positive integers less than 10
4. $\{\ldots, -5, -3, -1, 1, 3, 5, \ldots\}$	**D.** the set of all odd integers
5. $\{2, 4, 8, 16, 32\}$	**E.** the set of all negative integers
6. $\{\ldots, -4, -2, 0, 2, 4, \ldots\}$	**F.** the set of odd positive integers less than 10
7. $\{2, 4, 6, 8, 10\}$	**G.** ∅
8. $\{2, 4, 6, 8\}$	**H.** the set of the five least positive integer multiples of 2

List all the elements of each set. Use set notation and the listing method to describe the set.

9. the set of all counting numbers less than or equal to 6

10. the set of all whole numbers greater than 8 and less than 18

11. the set of all whole numbers not greater than 4

12. the set of all counting numbers between 4 and 14

13. $\{6, 7, 8, \ldots, 14\}$

14. $\{3, 6, 9, 12, \ldots, 30\}$

15. $\{-15, -13, -11, \ldots, -1\}$

16. $\{-4, -3, -2, \ldots, 4\}$

17. $\{2, 4, 8, \ldots, 256\}$

18. $\{90, 87, 84, \ldots, 69\}$

19. $\{x \mid x \text{ is an even whole number less than } 11\}$

20. $\{x \mid x \text{ is an odd integer between } -8 \text{ and } 7\}$

Denote each set by the listing method. There may be more than one correct answer.

21. the set of all counting numbers greater than 20

22. the set of all integers between −200 and 500

23. the set of Great Lakes

24. the set of U.S. presidents who served after Richard Nixon and before Barack Obama

25. $\{x \mid x \text{ is a positive multiple of } 5\}$

26. $\{x \mid x \text{ is a negative multiple of } 6\}$

27. $\{x \mid x \text{ is the reciprocal of a natural number}\}$

28. $\{x \mid x \text{ is a positive integer power of } 4\}$

Denote each set by set-builder notation, using x as the variable. There may be more than one correct answer.

29. the set of all rational numbers

30. the set of all even natural numbers

31. $\{1, 3, 5, \ldots, 75\}$

32. $\{35, 40, 45, \ldots, 95\}$

Give a word description for each set. There may be more than one correct answer.

33. $\{-9, -8, -7, \ldots, 7, 8, 9\}$

34. $\left\{1, \dfrac{1}{2}, \dfrac{1}{3}, \dfrac{1}{4}, \ldots\right\}$

35. {Alabama, Alaska, Arizona, ..., Wisconsin, Wyoming}

36. {Alaska, California, Hawaii, Oregon, Washington}

Identify each set as finite *or* infinite.

37. $\{2, 4, 6, \ldots, 932\}$ **38.** $\{6, 12, 18\}$

39. $\left\{\dfrac{1}{2}, \dfrac{2}{3}, \dfrac{3}{4}, \ldots\right\}$

40. $\{\ldots, -100, -80, -60, -40, \ldots\}$

41. $\{x \mid x \text{ is a natural number greater than } 50\}$

42. $\{x \mid x \text{ is a natural number less than } 50\}$

43. $\{x \mid x \text{ is a rational number}\}$

44. $\{x \mid x \text{ is a rational number between 0 and 1}\}$

Find n(A) for each set.

45. $A = \{0, 1, 2, 3, 4, 5, 6, 7\}$

46. $A = \{-3, -1, 1, 3, 5, 7, 9\}$

47. $A = \{2, 4, 6, \ldots, 1000\}$

48. $A = \{0, 1, 2, 3, \ldots, 3000\}$

49. $A = \{a, b, c, \ldots, z\}$

50. $A = \{x \mid x \text{ is a vowel in the English alphabet}\}$

51. $A = $ the set of integers between −20 and 20

52. $A = $ the set of sanctioned U.S. senate seats

53. $A = \left\{\dfrac{1}{3}, \dfrac{2}{4}, \dfrac{3}{5}, \dfrac{4}{6}, \ldots, \dfrac{27}{29}, \dfrac{28}{30}\right\}$

54. $A = \left\{\dfrac{1}{2}, -\dfrac{1}{2}, \dfrac{1}{3}, -\dfrac{1}{3}, \ldots, \dfrac{1}{10}, -\dfrac{1}{10}\right\}$

55. Although x is a consonant, why can we write "x is a vowel in the English alphabet" in **Exercise 50?**

56. Explain how **Exercise 53** can be answered without actually listing and then counting all the elements.

Identify each set as well defined *or* not well defined.

57. $\{x \mid x \text{ is a real number}\}$

58. $\{x \mid x \text{ is a good athlete}\}$

59. $\{x \mid x \text{ is a difficult course}\}$

60. $\{x \mid x \text{ is a counting number less than } 2\}$

Fill each blank with either ∈ *or* ∉ *to make each statement true.*

61. 5 _____ {2, 4, 5, 7}   **62.** −4 _____ {4, 7, 8, 12}

63. −12 _____ {3, 8, 12, 18}   **64.** 0 _____ {−2, 0, 5, 9}

65. {3} _____ {2, 3, 4, 6}   **66.** {6} _____ {5 + 1, 6 + 1}

67. 8 _____ {11 − 2, 10 − 2, 9 − 2, 8 − 2}

68. The statement 3 ∈ {9 − 6, 8 − 6, 7 − 6} is true even though the *symbol* 3 does not appear in the set. Explain.

Write true *or* false *for each statement.*

69. 3 ∈ {2, 5, 6, 8}   **70.** 6 ∈ {−2, 5, 8, 9}

71. b ∈ {h, c, d, a, b}   **72.** m ∈ {l, m, n, o, p}

73. 9 ∉ {6, 3, 4, 8}   **74.** 2 ∉ {7, 6, 5, 4}

75. {k, c, r, a} = {k, c, a, r}

76. {e, h, a, n} = {a, h, e, n}   **77.** {5, 8, 9} = {5, 8, 9, 0}

78. {3, 7, 12, 14} = {3, 7, 12, 14, 0}

79. {4} ∈ {{3}, {4}, {5}}   **80.** 4 ∈ {{3}, {4}, {5}}

81. {$x \mid x$ is a natural number less than 3} = {1, 2}

82. {$x \mid x$ is a natural number greater than 10} = {11, 12, 13, ...}

Write true *or* false *for each statement.*

Let   A = {2, 4, 6, 8, 10, 12},   B = {2, 4, 8, 10},
and C = {4, 10, 12}.

83. 4 ∈ A   **84.** 8 ∈ B

85. 4 ∉ C   **86.** 8 ∉ B

87. Every element of C is also an element of A.

88. Every element of C is also an element of B.

89. The human mind likes to create collections. Why do you suppose this is so? In your explanation, use one or more particular "collections," mathematical or otherwise.

90. Explain the difference between a well-defined set and a not well-defined set. Give examples and use terms introduced in this section.

Two sets are **equal** *if they contain identical elements. However, two sets are* **equivalent** *if they contain the same number of elements (but not necessarily the same elements). For each condition, give an example or explain why it is impossible.*

91. two sets that are neither equal nor equivalent

92. two sets that are equal but not equivalent

93. two sets that are equivalent but not equal

94. two sets that are both equal and equivalent

95. *Overpaid Actors* A *Forbes* magazine survey of a recent five-year period considered 100 featured Hollywood actors. The table shows the "worst" ten actors, in terms of how much their films returned per dollar that the actor earned.

MOST OVERPAID ACTORS

Rank	Actor	Return per Dollar to Actor
1.	Will Ferrell	$3.29
2.	Ewan McGregor	$3.75
3.	Billy Bob Thornton	$4.00
4.	Eddie Murphy	$4.43
5.	Ice Cube	$4.77
6.	Tom Cruise	$7.18
7.	Drew Barrymore	$7.43
8.	Leonardo DiCaprio	$7.52
9.	Samuel L. Jackson	$8.59
10.	Jim Carrey	$8.62

Source: Forbes.com

(a) List the set of actors with a return of at least $7.40.

(b) List the set of actors with a return of at most $3.75.

96. *Burning Calories* Candice Cotton likes cotton candy, each serving of which contains 220 calories. To burn off unwanted calories, Candice participates in her favorite activities, shown below, in increments of 1 hour and never repeats a given activity on a given day.

Activity	Symbol	Calories Burned per Hour
Volleyball	v	160
Golf	g	260
Canoeing	c	340
Swimming	s	410
Running	r	680

(a) On Monday, Candice has time for no more than two hours of activities. List all possible sets of activities that would burn off at least the number of calories obtained from three cotton candies.

(b) Assume that Candice can afford up to three hours of time for activities on Wednesday. List all sets of activities that would burn off at least the number of calories in five cotton candies.

(c) Candice can spend up to four hours in activities on Saturday. List all sets of activities that would burn off at least the number of calories in seven cotton candies.

2.2 VENN DIAGRAMS AND SUBSETS

Venn Diagrams • Complement of a Set • Subsets of a Set • Proper Subsets • Counting Subsets

Venn Diagrams

In the statement of a problem, there is either a stated or implied **universe of discourse.** The universe of discourse includes all things under discussion at a given time. For example, in studying reactions to a proposal that a certain campus raise the minimum age of individuals to whom beer may be sold, the universe of discourse might be all the students at the school, the nearby members of the public, the board of trustees of the school, or perhaps all these groups of people.

In set theory, the universe of discourse is called the **universal set,** typically designated by the letter **U.** The universal set might change from problem to problem.

Also in set theory, we commonly use **Venn diagrams,** developed by the logician John Venn (1834–1923). In these diagrams, the universal set is represented by a rectangle, and other sets of interest within the universal set are depicted by circular regions (sometimes ovals or other shapes). See **Figure 1**.

The entire region bounded by the rectangle represents the universal set U, while the portion bounded by the circle represents set A.

Figure 1

Complement of a Set

The colored region inside U and outside the circle in **Figure 1** is labeled A' (read "**A prime**"). This set, called the *complement* of A, contains all elements that are contained in U but not contained in A.

> **The Complement of a Set**
>
> For any set A within the universal set U, the **complement** of A, written A', is the set of elements of U that are not elements of A. That is,
> $$A' = \{x \mid x \in U \text{ and } x \notin A\}.$$

▮▮ **EXAMPLE 1** Finding Complements

Find each set.

Let $U = \{a, b, c, d, e, f, g, h\}$, $M = \{a, b, e, f\}$, and $N = \{b, d, e, g, h\}$.

(a) M' **(b)** N'

SOLUTION

(a) Set M' contains all the elements of set U that are *not* in set M. Because set M contains a, b, e, and f, these elements will be disqualified from belonging to set M'.
$$M' = \{c, d, g, h\}$$

(b) Set N' contains all the elements of U that are not in set N, so $N' = \{a, c, f\}$. ▮▮▮

Consider the complement of the universal set, U'. The set U' is found by selecting all the elements of U that do not belong to U. There are no such elements, so there can be no elements in set U'. This means that for any universal set U,
$$U' = \emptyset.$$

Now consider the complement of the empty set, $\emptyset'$. Because $\emptyset' = \{x \mid x \in U \text{ and } x \notin \emptyset\}$ and set $\emptyset$ contains no elements, every member of the universal set U satisfies this description. Therefore, for any universal set U,
$$\emptyset' = U.$$

Subsets of a Set

Suppose that we are given the universal set $U = \{1, 2, 3, 4, 5\}$, while $A = \{1, 2, 3\}$. Every element of set A is also an element of set U. Because of this, set A is called a *subset* of set U, written

$$A \subseteq U.$$

("A is not a subset of set U" would be written $A \nsubseteq U$.)

A Venn diagram showing that set M is a subset of set N is shown in **Figure 2**.

Figure 2

> **Subset of a Set**
>
> Set A is a **subset** of set B if every element of A is also an element of B. In symbols, this is written $A \subseteq B$.

▮▮ **EXAMPLE 2** Determining Whether One Set is a Subset of Another

Write $\subseteq$ or $\nsubseteq$ in each blank to make a true statement.

(a) $\{3, 4, 5, 6\}$ _____ $\{3, 4, 5, 6, 8\}$ **(b)** $\{1, 2, 6\}$ _____ $\{2, 4, 6, 8\}$

(c) $\{5, 6, 7, 8\}$ _____ $\{5, 6, 7, 8\}$

SOLUTION

(a) Because every element of $\{3, 4, 5, 6\}$ is also an element of $\{3, 4, 5, 6, 8\}$, the first set is a subset of the second, so $\subseteq$ goes in the blank.

$$\{3, 4, 5, 6\} \subseteq \{3, 4, 5, 6, 8\}$$

(b) $\{1, 2, 6\} \nsubseteq \{2, 4, 6, 8\}$ 1 does not belong to $\{2, 4, 6, 8\}$.

(c) $\{5, 6, 7, 8\} \subseteq \{5, 6, 7, 8\}$ ▮▮▮

As **Example 2(c)** suggests, every set is a subset of itself.

$$B \subseteq B, \quad \text{for any set } B.$$

The statement of set equality in **Section 2.1** can be formally presented.

> **Set Equality (Alternative definition)**
>
> Suppose A and B are sets. Then $A = B$ if $A \subseteq B$ and $B \subseteq A$ are both true.

Proper Subsets

Suppose that we are given the following sets.

$$B = \{5, 6, 7, 8\} \quad \text{and} \quad A = \{6, 7\}$$

A is a subset of B, but A is not all of B. There is at least one element in B that is not in A. (Actually, in this case there are two such elements, 5 and 8.) In this situation, A is called a *proper subset* of B. To indicate that A is a proper subset of B, write

$$A \subset B.$$

Notice the similarity of the subset symbols, $\subset$ and $\subseteq$, to the inequality symbols from algebra, $<$ and $\leq$.

> **Proper Subset of a Set**
>
> Set A is a **proper subset** of set B if $A \subseteq B$ and $A \neq B$. In symbols, this is written $A \subset B$.

▮▮ **EXAMPLE 3** Determining Subset and Proper Subset Relationships
___

Decide whether ⊂, ⊆, or both could be placed in each blank to make a true statement.

(a) {5, 6, 7} _____ {5, 6, 7, 8}   **(b)** {a, b, c} _____ {a, b, c}

SOLUTION

(a) Every element of {5, 6, 7} is contained in {5, 6, 7, 8}, so ⊆ could be placed in the blank. Also, the element 8 belongs to {5, 6, 7, 8} but not to {5, 6, 7}, making {5, 6, 7} a proper subset of {5, 6, 7, 8}. Place ⊂ in the blank.

(b) The set {a, b, c} is a subset of {a, b, c}. Because the two sets are equal, {a, b, c} is not a proper subset of {a, b, c}. Only ⊆ may be placed in the blank. ▮▮▮

Set *A* is a subset of set *B* if every element of set *A* is also an element of set *B*. This definition can be reworded by saying that set *A* is a subset of set *B* if there are no elements of *A* that are not also elements of *B*. This second form of the definition shows that the empty set is a subset of any set.

$$\emptyset \subseteq B, \quad \text{for any set } B.$$

This is true because it is not possible to find any elements of ∅ that are not also in *B*. (There are no elements in ∅.) The empty set ∅ is a proper subset of every set except itself.

$$\emptyset \subset B \quad \text{if } B \text{ is any set other than } \emptyset.$$

Every set (except ∅) has at least two subsets, ∅ and the set itself.

▮▮ **EXAMPLE 4** Listing All Subsets of a Set
___

Find all possible subsets of each set.

(a) {7, 8}   **(b)** {a, b, c}

SOLUTION

(a) By trial and error, the set {7, 8} has four subsets: ∅, {7}, {8}, {7, 8}.

(b) Here, trial and error leads to eight subsets for {a, b, c}:

$$\emptyset, \{a\}, \{b\}, \{c\}, \{a, b\}, \{a, c\}, \{b, c\}, \{a, b, c\}. \qquad ▮▮▮$$

Counting Subsets

In **Example 4,** the subsets of {7, 8} and the subsets of {a, b, c} were found by trial and error. An alternative method involves drawing a **tree diagram,** a systematic way of listing all the subsets of a given set. See **Figure 3**.

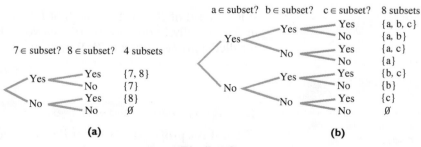

(a)   **(b)**

Figure 3

Powers of 2

$2^0 = 1$

$2^1 = 2$

$2^2 = 2 \cdot 2 = 4$

$2^3 = 2 \cdot 2 \cdot 2 = 8$

$2^4 = 2 \cdot 2 \cdot 2 \cdot 2 = 16$

$2^5 = 32$

$2^6 = 64$

$2^7 = 128$

$2^8 = 256$

$2^9 = 512$

$2^{10} = 1024$

$2^{11} = 2048$

$2^{12} = 4096$

$2^{15} = 32{,}768$

$2^{20} = 1{,}048{,}576$

$2^{25} = 33{,}554{,}432$

$2^{30} = 1{,}073{,}741{,}824$

In **Example 4,** we determined the number of subsets of a given set by making a list of all such subsets and then counting them. The tree diagram method also produced a list of all possible subsets. To obtain a formula for finding the number of subsets, we use inductive reasoning. That is, we observe particular cases to try to discover a general pattern.

Begin with the set containing the least number of elements possible—the empty set. This set, $\emptyset$, has only one subset, $\emptyset$ itself. Next, a set with one element has only two subsets, itself and $\emptyset$. These facts, together with those obtained in **Example 4** for sets with two and three elements, are summarized here.

Number of elements	0	1	2	3
Number of subsets	1	2	4	8

This chart suggests that as the number of elements of the set increases by one, the number of subsets doubles. If so, then the number of subsets in each case might be a power of 2. Since every number in the second row of the chart is indeed a power of 2, add this information to the chart.

Number of elements	0	1	2	3
Number of subsets	$1 = 2^0$	$2 = 2^1$	$4 = 2^2$	$8 = 2^3$

This chart shows that the number of elements in each case is the same as the exponent on the base 2. Inductive reasoning gives the following generalization.

Number of Subsets

The number of subsets of a set with n elements is 2^n.

Because the value 2^n includes the set itself, we must subtract 1 from this value to obtain the number of proper subsets of a set containing n elements.

Number of Proper Subsets

The number of proper subsets of a set with n elements is $2^n - 1$.

As shown in **Chapter 1,** although inductive reasoning is a good way of *discovering* principles or arriving at a *conjecture,* it does not provide a proof that the conjecture is true in general. The two formulas above are true, by observation, for $n = 0, 1, 2,$ or 3. (For a general proof, see **Exercise 69** at the end of this section.)

▮▮ **EXAMPLE 5** Finding the Numbers of Subsets and Proper Subsets

Find the number of subsets and the number of proper subsets of each set.

(a) $\{3, 4, 5, 6, 7\}$ **(b)** $\{1, 2, 3, 4, 5, 9, 12, 14\}$

SOLUTION

(a) This set has 5 elements and $2^5 = 2 \cdot 2 \cdot 2 \cdot 2 \cdot 2 = 32$ subsets. Of these, $2^5 - 1 = 32 - 1 = 31$ are proper subsets.

(b) This set has 8 elements. There are $2^8 = 256$ subsets and 255 proper subsets. ▮▮▮

2.2 EXERCISES

Match each set or sets in Column I with the appropriate description in Column II.

I

1. $\{p\}, \{q\}, \{p, q\}, \emptyset$

2. $\{p\}, \{q\}, \emptyset$

3. $\{a, b\}$

4. $\emptyset$

II

A. the proper subsets of $\{p, q\}$

B. the complement of $\{c, d\}$, if $U = \{a, b, c, d\}$

C. the complement of U

D. the subsets of $\{p, q\}$

Insert $\subseteq$ or $\nsubseteq$ in each blank so that the resulting statement is true.

5. $\{-2, 0, 2\}$ _____ $\{-2, -1, 1, 2\}$

6. $\{M, W, F\}$ _____ $\{S, M, T, W, Th\}$

7. $\{2, 5\}$ _____ $\{0, 1, 5, 3, 7, 2\}$

8. $\{a, n, d\}$ _____ $\{r, a, n, d, y\}$

9. $\emptyset$ _____ $\{a, b, c, d, e\}$

10. $\emptyset$ _____ $\emptyset$

11. $\{-5, 2, 9\}$ _____ $\{x \mid x \text{ is an odd integer}\}$

12. $\left\{1, 2, \dfrac{9}{3}\right\}$ _____ the set of rational numbers

Decide whether $\subset, \subseteq$, both, or neither can be placed in each blank to make the statement true.

13. $\{P, Q, R\}$ _____ $\{P, Q, R, S\}$

14. $\{red, blue, yellow\}$ _____ $\{yellow, blue, red\}$

15. $\{9, 1, 7, 3, 5\}$ _____ $\{1, 3, 5, 7, 9\}$

16. $\{S, M, T, W, Th\}$ _____ $\{W, E, E, K\}$

17. $\emptyset$ _____ $\{0\}$

18. $\emptyset$ _____ $\emptyset$

19. $\{0, 1, 2, 3\}$ _____ $\{1, 2, 3, 4\}$

20. $\left\{\dfrac{5}{6}, \dfrac{9}{8}\right\}$ _____ $\left\{\dfrac{6}{5}, \dfrac{8}{9}\right\}$

For Exercises 21–40, tell whether each statement is true *or* false. *U is the universal set.*

Let $U = \{a, b, c, d, e, f, g\}$, $A = \{a, e\}$,
$B = \{a, b, e, f, g\}$, $C = \{b, f, g\}$, and $D = \{d, e\}$.

21. $A \subset U$

22. $C \nsubseteq U$

23. $D \subseteq B$

24. $D \nsubseteq A$

25. $A \subset B$

26. $B \subseteq C$

27. $\emptyset \nsubseteq A$

28. $\emptyset \subseteq D$

29. $\emptyset \subseteq \emptyset$

30. $D \subset B$

31. $D \nsubseteq B$

32. $A \nsubseteq B$

33. There are exactly 6 subsets of C.

34. There are exactly 31 subsets of B.

35. There are exactly 3 proper subsets of A.

36. There are exactly 4 subsets of D.

37. There is exactly 1 subset of $\emptyset$.

38. There are exactly 128 proper subsets of U.

39. The Venn diagram below correctly represents the relationship among sets A, D, and U.

40. The Venn diagram below correctly represents the relationship among sets B, C, and U.

Find **(a)** *the number of subsets and* **(b)** *the number of proper subsets of each set.*

41. $\{a, b, c, d, e, f\}$

42. the set of days of the week

43. $\{x \mid x \text{ is an odd integer between } -4 \text{ and } 6\}$

44. $\{x \mid x \text{ is an odd whole number less than } 4\}$

Let $U = \{1, 2, 3, 4, 5, 6, 7, 8, 9, 10\}$ and find the complement of each set.

45. $\{1, 2, 3, 4, 6, 8\}$

46. $\{2, 5, 9, 10\}$

47. $\{1, 3, 4, 5, 6, 7, 8, 9, 10\}$

48. $\{1, 2, 3, 4, 5, 6, 7, 8, 9\}$

49. U

50. $\emptyset$

Vacationing in California Terry McGinnis is planning a trip with her two sons to California. In weighing her options concerning whether to fly or drive from their home in Iowa, she has listed the following characteristics.

Fly to California	Drive to California
Higher cost	Lower cost
Educational	Educational
More time to see the sights in California	Less time to see the sights in California
Cannot visit relatives along the way	Can visit relatives along the way

Refer to these characteristics in Exercises 51–56.

51. Find the smallest universal set *U* that contains all listed characteristics of both options.

Let F represent the set of characteristics of the flying option and let D represent the set of characteristics of the driving option. Use the universal set from **Exercise 51.**

52. Give the set *F'*.   **53.** Give the set *D'*.

Find the set of elements common to both sets in Exercises 54–56.

54. *F* and *D*   **55.** *F'* and *D'*

56. *F* and *D'*

Meeting in a Hospitality Suite Amie Carobrese, Bruce Collin, Corey Chapman, Dwayne Coy, and Eric Cobbe plan to meet at the hospitality suite after the CEO makes his speech at the January sales meeting of their publishing company. Denoting these five people by A, B, C, D, and E, list all the possible sets of this group in which the given number of them can gather.

57. five people   **58.** four people

59. three people   **60.** two people

61. one person   **62.** no people

63. Find the total number of ways that members of this group can gather in the suite. (*Hint:* Find the total number of sets in your answers to **Exercises 57–62.**)

64. How does your answer in **Exercise 63** compare with the number of subsets of a set of five elements? Interpret the answer to **Exercise 63** in terms of subsets.

65. The twenty-five members of the mathematics club must send a delegation to a meeting for student groups at their school. The delegation can include as many members of the club as desired, but at least one member must attend. How many different delegations are possible? (*Mathematics Teacher* calendar problem)

66. In **Exercise 65,** suppose ten of the club members say they do not want to be part of the delegation. Now how many delegations are possible?

67. *Selecting Bills* Suppose you have the bills shown here.

(a) If you must select at least one bill, and you may select up to all of the bills, how many different sums of money could you make?

(b) In part (a), remove the condition "you must select at least one bill." How many sums are possible?

68. *Selecting Coins* The photo shows a group of obsolete U.S. coins, consisting of one each of the penny, nickel, dime, quarter, and half dollar. Repeat **Exercise 65,** replacing "bill(s)" with "coin(s)."

69. In discovering the expression (2^n) for finding the number of subsets of a set with *n* elements, we observed that for the first few values of *n*, increasing the number of elements by one doubles the number of subsets. Here, you can prove the formula in general by showing that the same is true for any value of *n*. Assume set *A* has *n* elements and *s* subsets. Now add one additional element, say *e*, to the set *A*. (We now have a new set, say *B*, with *n* + 1 elements.) Divide the subsets of *B* into those that do not contain *e* and those that do.

(a) How many subsets of *B* do not contain *e*? (*Hint:* Each of these is a subset of the original set *A*.)

(b) How many subsets of *B* do contain *e*? (*Hint:* Each of these would be a subset of the original set *A*, with the element *e* inserted.)

(c) What is the total number of subsets of *B*?

(d) What do you conclude?

70. Explain why ∅ is both a subset and an element of {∅}.

2.3 SET OPERATIONS AND CARTESIAN PRODUCTS

Intersection of Sets • Union of Sets • Difference of Sets • Ordered Pairs
• Cartesian Product of Sets • Venn Diagrams • De Morgan's Laws

Intersection of Sets

Two candidates, Aimee Berger and Darien Estes, are running for a seat on the city council. A voter deciding for whom she should vote recalled the campaign promises, each given a code letter, made by the candidates.

Honest Aimee Berger	Determined Darien Estes
Spend less money, *m*	Spend less money, *m*
Emphasize traffic law enforcement, *t*	Crack down on crooked politicians, *p*
Increase service to suburban areas, *s*	Increase service to the city, *c*

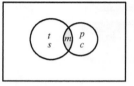

Figure 4

The only promise common to both candidates is promise *m*, to spend less money. Suppose we take each candidate's promises to be a set. The promises of Berger give the set $\{m, t, s\}$, while the promises of Estes give $\{m, p, c\}$. The common element *m* belongs to the *intersection* of the two sets, as shown in color in the Venn diagram in **Figure 4**.

$$\{m, t, s\} \cap \{m, p, c\} = \{m\} \quad \cap \text{ represents set intersection.}$$

The intersection of two sets is itself a set.

$A \cap B$

Figure 5

Intersection of Sets

The **intersection** of sets A and B, written $A \cap B$, is the set of elements common to both A and B.

$$A \cap B = \{x \mid x \in A \text{ and } x \in B\}$$

Form the intersection of sets A and B by taking all the elements included in both sets, as shown in color in **Figure 5**.

▌▌ **EXAMPLE 1** Finding Intersections

Find each intersection.

(a) $\{3, 4, 5, 6, 7\} \cap \{4, 6, 8, 10\}$ **(b)** $\{9, 14, 25, 30\} \cap \{10, 17, 19, 38, 52\}$

(c) $\{5, 9, 11\} \cap \emptyset$

SOLUTION

(a) The elements common to both sets are 4 and 6.

$$\{3, 4, 5, 6, 7\} \cap \{4, 6, 8, 10\} = \{4, 6\}$$

(b) These two sets have no elements in common.

$$\{9, 14, 25, 30\} \cap \{10, 17, 19, 38, 52\} = \emptyset$$

(c) There are no elements in $\emptyset$, so there can be no elements belonging to both $\{5, 9, 11\}$ and $\emptyset$.

$$\{5, 9, 11\} \cap \emptyset = \emptyset \qquad ▐▐▐$$

White light can be viewed as the intersection of the three primary colors.

Disjoint sets

Figure 6

Figure 7

$A \cup B$

Figure 8

Examples 1(b) and 1(c) show two sets that have no elements in common. Sets with no elements in common are called **disjoint sets.** (See **Figure 6.**) A set of dogs and a set of cats would be disjoint sets.

Sets A and B are disjoint if $A \cap B = \emptyset$.

Union of Sets

Referring again to the lists of campaign promises, suppose a pollster wants to summarize the types of promises made by the candidates. The pollster would need to study *all* the promises made by *either* candidate, or the set $\{m, t, s, p, c\}$. This set is the *union* of the sets of promises, as shown in color in the Venn diagram in **Figure 7.**

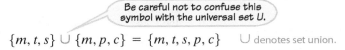

Be careful not to confuse this symbol with the universal set U.

$$\{m, t, s\} \cup \{m, p, c\} = \{m, t, s, p, c\}$$ $\cup$ denotes set union.

Again, the union of two sets is a set.

Union of Sets

The **union** of sets A and B, written $A \cup B$, is the set of all elements belonging to either A or B.

$$A \cup B = \{x \mid x \in A \text{ or } x \in B\}$$

Form the union of sets A and B by taking all the elements of set A and then including the elements of set B that are not already listed. See **Figure 8.**

▍▍   **EXAMPLE 2**   Finding Unions

Find each union.

(a) $\{2, 4, 6\} \cup \{4, 6, 8, 10, 12\}$

(b) $\{a, b, d, f, g, h\} \cup \{c, f, g, h, k\}$

(c) $\{3, 4, 5\} \cup \emptyset$

SOLUTION

(a) Start by listing all the elements from the first set, 2, 4, and 6. Then list all the elements from the second set that are not in the first set, 8, 10, and 12. The union is made up of *all* these elements.

$$\{2, 4, 6\} \cup \{4, 6, 8, 10, 12\} = \{2, 4, 6, 8, 10, 12\}$$

(b) $\{a, b, d, f, g, h\} \cup \{c, f, g, h, k\} = \{a, b, c, d, f, g, h, k\}$

(c) Because there are no elements in $\emptyset$, the union of $\{3, 4, 5\}$ and $\emptyset$ contains only the elements 3, 4, and 5.

$$\{3, 4, 5\} \cup \emptyset = \{3, 4, 5\}$$ ▍▍▍

Recall from the previous section that A' represents the *complement* of set A. *Set A' is formed by taking all the elements of the universal set U that are not in set A.*

▌▌ **EXAMPLE 3** Finding Intersections and Unions of Complements

Find each set. Let
$$U = \{1, 2, 3, 4, 5, 6, 9\}, \ A = \{1, 2, 3, 4\}, \ B = \{2, 4, 6\}, \text{ and } C = \{1, 3, 6, 9\}.$$

(a) $A' \cap B$ **(b)** $B' \cup C'$ **(c)** $A \cap (B \cup C')$ **(d)** $(A' \cup C') \cap B'$

SOLUTION

(a) First identify the elements of set A', the elements of U that are not in set A.
$$A' = \{5, 6, 9\}$$

Now, find $A' \cap B$, the set of elements belonging both to A' and to B.
$$A' \cap B = \{5, 6, 9\} \cap \{2, 4, 6\} = \{6\}$$

(b) $B' \cup C' = \{1, 3, 5, 9\} \cup \{2, 4, 5\} = \{1, 2, 3, 4, 5, 9\}$

(c) First find the set inside the parentheses.
$$B \cup C' = \{2, 4, 6\} \cup \{2, 4, 5\} = \{2, 4, 5, 6\}$$

Now, find the intersection of this set with A.
$$\begin{aligned} A \cap (B \cup C') &= A \cap \{2, 4, 5, 6\} \\ &= \{1, 2, 3, 4\} \cap \{2, 4, 5, 6\} \\ &= \{2, 4\} \end{aligned}$$

(d) $A' = \{5, 6, 9\}$ and $C' = \{2, 4, 5\}$, so
$$A' \cup C' = \{5, 6, 9\} \cup \{2, 4, 5\} = \{2, 4, 5, 6, 9\}.$$
$B' = \{1, 3, 5, 9\}$, so
$$(A' \cup C') \cap B' = \{2, 4, 5, 6, 9\} \cap \{1, 3, 5, 9\} = \{5, 9\}. \quad ▌▌▌$$

For Further Thought

Comparing Properties

The arithmetic operations of addition and multiplication, when applied to numbers, have some familiar properties. If a, b, and c are *real numbers,* then the **commutative property of addition** says that the order of the numbers being added makes no difference:
$$a + b = b + a.$$

(Is there a **commutative property of multiplication**?) The **associative property of addition** says that when three numbers are added, the grouping used makes no difference:
$$(a + b) + c = a + (b + c).$$

(Is there an **associative property of multiplication**?) The number 0 is called the **identity element for addition** since adding it to any number does not change that number:
$$a + 0 = a.$$

(What is the **identity element for multiplication**?) Finally, the **distributive property of multiplication over addition** says that
$$a(b + c) = ab + ac.$$

(Is there a distributive property of addition over multiplication?)

For Group or Individual Investigation

Now consider the operations of union and intersection, applied to sets. By recalling definitions, or by trying examples, answer the following questions.

1. Is set union commutative? Set intersection?

2. Is set union associative? Set intersection?

3. Is there an identity element for set union? If so, what is it? How about set intersection?

4. Is set intersection distributive over set union? Is set union distributive over set intersection?

■■ EXAMPLE 4   Describing Sets in Words

Describe each set in words.

(a) $A \cap (B \cup C')$ **(b)** $(A' \cup C') \cap B'$

SOLUTION

(a) This set might be described as "the set of all elements that are in A, and also are in B or not in C."

(b) One possibility is "the set of all elements that are not in A or not in C, and also are not in B."   ■■■

Difference of Sets

Suppose that $A = \{1, 2, 3, \ldots, 10\}$ and $B = \{2, 4, 6, 8, 10\}$. If the elements of B are excluded (or taken away) from A, the set $C = \{1, 3, 5, 7, 9\}$ is obtained. C is called the *difference* of sets A and B.

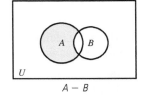

Figure 9

> ### Difference of Sets
>
> The **difference** of sets A and B, written $A - B$, is the set of all elements belonging to set A and not to set B.
>
> $$A - B = \{x \mid x \in A \text{ and } x \notin B\}$$

Because $x \notin B$ has the same meaning as $x \in B'$ the set difference $A - B$ can also be described as

$$\{x \mid x \in A \text{ and } x \in B'\}, \quad \text{or} \quad A \cap B'.$$

Figure 9 illustrates the idea of set difference. The region in color represents $A - B$.

■■ EXAMPLE 5   Finding Set Differences

Find each set.

Let $U = \{1, 2, 3, 4, 5, 6, 7\}$, $A = \{1, 2, 3, 4, 5, 6\}$,
$B = \{2, 3, 6\}$,   and $C = \{3, 5, 7\}$.

(a) $A - B$ **(b)** $B - A$ **(c)** $(A - B) \cup C'$

SOLUTION

(a) Begin with set A and exclude any elements found also in set B.

$$A - B = \{1, 2, 3, 4, 5, 6\} - \{2, 3, 6\} = \{1, 4, 5\}$$

(b) To be in $B - A$, an element must be in set B and not in set A. But all elements of B are also in A. Thus, $B - A = \emptyset$.

(c) From part (a), $A - B = \{1, 4, 5\}$. Also, $C' = \{1, 2, 4, 6\}$.

$$(A - B) \cup C' = \{1, 2, 4, 5, 6\}$$ ■■■

The results in **Examples 5(a) and 5(b)** illustrate that, in general,

$$A - B \neq B - A.$$

Ordered Pairs

When writing a set that contains several elements, the order in which the elements appear is not relevant. For example,

$$\{1, 5\} = \{5, 1\}.$$

However, there are many instances in mathematics where, when two objects are paired, the order in which the objects are written is important. This leads to the idea of the *ordered pair.* When writing ordered pairs, use parentheses rather than braces, which are reserved for writing sets.

> **Ordered Pairs**
>
> In the **ordered pair** (a, b), a is called the **first component** and b is called the **second component.** In general, $(a, b) \neq (b, a)$.

Two ordered pairs (a, b) and (c, d) are **equal** provided that their first components are equal and their second components are equal.

$$(a, b) = (c, d) \quad \textit{if and only if} \quad a = c \textit{ and } b = d.$$

▮▮ **EXAMPLE 6** Determining Equality of Sets and of Ordered Pairs

Decide whether each statement is *true* or *false.*

(a) $(3, 4) = (5 - 2, 1 + 3)$ **(b)** $\{3, 4\} \neq \{4, 3\}$ **(c)** $(7, 4) = (4, 7)$

SOLUTION

(a) Because $3 = 5 - 2$ and $4 = 1 + 3$, the first components are equal and the second components are equal. The statement is *true.*

(b) Because these are sets and not ordered pairs, the order in which the elements are listed is not important. Because these sets are equal, the statement is *false.*

(c) The ordered pairs $(7, 4)$ and $(4, 7)$ are not equal because they do not satisfy the requirements for equality of ordered pairs. The statement is *false.* ▮▮▮

Cartesian Product of Sets

A set may contain ordered pairs as elements. If A and B are sets, then each element of A can be paired with each element of B, and the results can be written as ordered pairs. The set of all such ordered pairs is called the *Cartesian product* of A and B, written $A \times B$ and read **"A cross B."** The name comes from that of the French mathematician René Descartes.

> **Cartesian Product of Sets**
>
> The **Cartesian product** of sets A and B is defined as follows.
>
> $$A \times B = \{(a, b) | a \in A \text{ and } b \in B\}$$

▮▮ **EXAMPLE 7** Finding Cartesian Products

Let $A = \{1, 5, 9\}$ and $B = \{6, 7\}$. Find each set.

(a) $A \times B$ **(b)** $B \times A$

SOLUTION

(a) Pair each element of A with each element of B. Write the results as ordered pairs, with the element of A written first and the element of B written second. Write as a set.

$$A \times B = \{(1, 6), (1, 7), (5, 6), (5, 7), (9, 6), (9, 7)\}$$

(b) Because B is listed first, this set will consist of ordered pairs that have their components interchanged when compared to those in part (a).

$$B \times A = \{(6, 1), (7, 1), (6, 5), (7, 5), (6, 9), (7, 9)\}$$ ▮▮▮

The order in which the ordered pairs themselves are listed is not important.
For example, another way to write $B \times A$ in **Example 7(b)** would be

$$\{(6, 1), (6, 5), (6, 9), (7, 1), (7, 5), (7, 9)\}.$$

▮▮ **EXAMPLE 8** Finding the Cartesian Product of a Set with Itself

Let $A = \{1, 2, 3, 4, 5, 6\}$. Find $A \times A$.

SOLUTION

Pair 1 with each element in the set, 2 with each element, and so on.

$$\begin{aligned} A \times A = \{ &(1, 1), (1, 2), (1, 3), (1, 4), (1, 5), (1, 6), \\ &(2, 1), (2, 2), (2, 3), (2, 4), (2, 5), (2, 6), \\ &(3, 1), (3, 2), (3, 3), (3, 4), (3, 5), (3, 6), \\ &(4, 1), (4, 2), (4, 3), (4, 4), (4, 5), (4, 6), \\ &(5, 1), (5, 2), (5, 3), (5, 4), (5, 5), (5, 6), \\ &(6, 1), (6, 2), (6, 3), (6, 4), (6, 5), (6, 6)\} \end{aligned}$$ ▮▮▮

The **Cartesian product** in **Example 8** represents all possible results that are obtained when two distinguishable dice are rolled. This Cartesian product is important when studying certain problems in counting techniques and probability.

From **Example 7** it can be seen that, in general,

$$A \times B \neq B \times A,$$

because they do not contain exactly the same ordered pairs. However, each set contains the same number of elements, six. Furthermore, $n(A) = 3$, $n(B) = 2$, and $n(A \times B) = n(B \times A) = 6$. Because $3 \cdot 2 = 6$, one might conclude that the cardinal number of the Cartesian product of two sets is equal to the product of the cardinal numbers of the sets. In general, this conclusion is correct.

Cardinal Number of a Cartesian Product

If $n(A) = a$ and $n(B) = b$, then the following is true.

$$n(A \times B) = n(B \times A) = n(A) \cdot n(B) = n(B) \cdot n(A) = ab = ba$$

▮▮ **EXAMPLE 9** Finding Cardinal Numbers of Cartesian Products

Find $n(A \times B)$ and $n(B \times A)$ from the given information.

(a) $A = \{a, b, c, d, e, f, g\}$ and $B = \{2, 4, 6\}$ **(b)** $n(A) = 24$ and $n(B) = 5$

SOLUTION

(a) Because $n(A) = 7$ and $n(B) = 3$, $n(A \times B)$ and $n(B \times A)$ both equal $7 \cdot 3$, or 21.

(b) $n(A \times B) = n(B \times A) = 24 \cdot 5 = 5 \cdot 24 = 120$ ▮▮▮

An **operation** is a rule or procedure by which one or more objects are used to obtain another object. The most common operations on sets are summarized in the box on the next page.

Set Operations

Let A and B be any sets, with U the universal set.

The **complement** of A, written A', is

$$A' = \{x \mid x \in U \text{ and } x \notin A\}.$$

The **intersection** of A and B is

$$A \cap B = \{x \mid x \in A \text{ and } x \in B\}.$$

The **union** of A and B is

$$A \cup B = \{x \mid x \in A \text{ or } x \in B\}.$$

The **difference** of A and B is

$$A - B = \{x \mid x \in A \text{ and } x \notin B\}.$$

The **Cartesian product** of A and B is

$$A \times B = \{(x, y) \mid x \in A \text{ and } y \in B\}.$$

Venn Diagrams

Figure 10

With a single set, we can use a Venn diagram as in **Figure 10**. The universal set U is divided into two regions, one representing set A and the other representing set A'.

Two sets A and B within the universal set suggest a Venn diagram as in **Figure 11**. Region 1 includes those elements outside of both set A and set B. Region 2 includes the elements belonging to A but not to B. Region 3 includes those elements belonging to both A and B. How would you describe the elements of region 4?

▮▮ **EXAMPLE 10** Shading Venn Diagrams to Represent Sets

Draw a Venn diagram similar to **Figure 11** and shade the region or regions representing each set.

(a) $A' \cap B$ **(b)** $A' \cup B'$

SOLUTION

Numbering is arbitrary. The numbers indicate four regions, not cardinal numbers or elements.

Figure 11

(a) Refer to **Figure 11**. Set A' contains all the elements outside of set A—in other words, the elements in regions 1 and 4. Set B is made up of the elements in regions 3 and 4. The intersection of sets A' and B is made up of the elements in the region common to (1 and 4) and (3 and 4), which is region 4. Thus, $A' \cap B$ is represented by region 4, shown in color in **Figure 12**. This region can also be described as $B - A$.

Figure 12   Figure 13

(b) Again, set A' is represented by regions 1 and 4, while B' is made up of regions 1 and 2. The union of A' and B', the set $A' \cup B'$, is made up of the elements belonging to the union of regions 1, 2, and 4, which are in color in **Figure 13**. ▮▮▮

███ **EXAMPLE 11** Locating Elements in a Venn Diagram

Place the elements of the sets in their proper locations in a Venn diagram.

Let $U = \{q, r, s, t, u, v, w, x, y, z\}$, $A = \{r, s, t, u, v\}$, and $B = \{t, v, x\}$.

SOLUTION

Because $A \cap B = \{t, v\}$, elements t and v are placed in region 3 in **Figure 14**. The remaining elements of A, that is r, s, and u, go in region 2. The figure shows the proper placement of all other elements.

Figure 14 ███

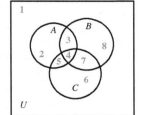

Numbering is arbitrary. The numbers indicate regions, not cardinal numbers or elements.

Figure 15

To include three sets A, B, and C within a universal set, draw a Venn diagram as in **Figure 15**, where again an arbitrary numbering of the regions is shown.

███ **EXAMPLE 12** Shading a Set in a Venn Diagram

Shade the set $(A' \cap B') \cap C$ in a Venn diagram similar to the one in **Figure 15**.

SOLUTION

Work first inside the parentheses. As shown in **Figure 16**, set A' is made up of the regions outside set A, or regions 1, 6, 7, and 8. Set B' is made up of regions 1, 2, 5, and 6. The intersection of these sets is given by the overlap of regions 1, 6, 7, 8 and 1, 2, 5, 6, or regions 1 and 6.

For the final Venn diagram, find the intersection of regions 1 and 6 with set C. As seen in **Figure 16**, set C is made up of regions 4, 5, 6, and 7. The overlap of regions 1, 6 and 4, 5, 6, 7 is region 6, the region in color in **Figure 16**. ███

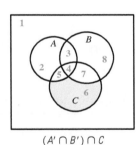

$(A' \cap B') \cap C$

Figure 16

███ **EXAMPLE 13** Verifying a Statement Using a Venn Diagram

Is the statement $(A \cap B)' = A' \cup B'$ true for every choice of sets A and B?

SOLUTION

To help decide, use the regions labeled in **Figure 11**. Set $A \cap B$ is made up of region 3, so that $(A \cap B)'$ is made up of regions 1, 2, and 4. These regions are in color in **Figure 17(a)**.

To find a Venn diagram for set $A' \cup B'$, first check that A' is made up of regions 1 and 4, while set B' includes regions 1 and 2. Finally, $A' \cup B'$ is made up of regions 1 and 4, or 1 and 2, that is, regions 1, 2, and 4. These regions are in color in **Figure 17(b)**.

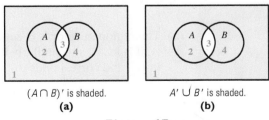

$(A \cap B)'$ is shaded. $A' \cup B'$ is shaded.
(a)   **(b)**

Figure 17

The fact that the same regions are in color in both Venn diagrams suggests that

$$(A \cap B)' = A' \cup B'.$$

███

De Morgan's Laws

The result of **Example 13** can be stated in words.

> ***The complement of the intersection of two sets is equal to the union of the complements of the two sets.***

As a result, it is natural to ask ourselves whether it is also true that the complement of the *union* of two sets is equal to the *intersection* of the complements of the two sets (where the words "intersection" and "union" are substituted for each other). This was investigated by the British logician Augustus De Morgan (1806–1871) and was found to be true. (See the margin note on **page 21.**) DeMorgan's two laws for sets follow.

De Morgan's Laws for Sets

For any sets A and B,

$$(A \cap B)' = A' \cup B' \quad \text{and} \quad (A \cup B)' = A' \cap B'.$$

The Venn diagrams in **Figure 17** strongly suggest the truth of the first of De Morgan's laws. They provide a *conjecture*. Actual proofs of De Morgan's laws would require methods used in more advanced courses on set theory.

▮▮ **EXAMPLE 14** Describing Regions in Venn Diagrams Using Symbols

---

For the Venn diagrams, write a symbolic description of the region in color, using A, B, C, $\cap$, $\cup$, $-$, and $'$ as necessary.

(a)

(b)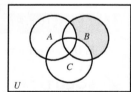

(c) Refer to the figure in part (b) and give two additional ways of describing the region in color.

SOLUTION

(a) The region in color belongs to all three sets, A and B and C. Therefore, the region corresponds to

$$A \cap B \cap C.$$

(b) The region in color is in set B and is not in A and is not in C. Because it is not in A, it is in A', and similarly it is in C'. The region is, therefore, in B and in A' and in C', and corresponds to

$$B \cap A' \cap C'.$$

(c) The region in color includes all of B, except for the regions belonging to either A or C. This suggests the idea of set difference. The region may be described as

$$B - (A \cup C), \quad \text{or equivalently,} \quad B \cap (A \cup C)'. \qquad ▮▮▮$$

2.3 EXERCISES

Match each term in Group I with the appropriate description A–F in Group II. Assume that A and B are sets.

I

1. the intersection of A and B

2. the union of A and B

3. the difference of A and B

4. the complement of A

5. the Cartesian product of A and B

6. the difference of B and A

II

A. the set of elements in A that are not in B

B. the set of elements common to both A and B

C. the set of elements in the universal set that are not in A

D. the set of elements in B that are not in A

E. the set of ordered pairs such that each first element is from A and each second element is from B, with every element of A paired with every element of B

F. the set of elements that are in A or in B or in both A and B

Perform the indicated operations, and designate each answer using the listing method.

$$Let \quad U = \{a, b, c, d, e, f, g\}, \quad X = \{a, c, e, g\},$$
$$Y = \{a, b, c\}, \quad and \quad Z = \{b, c, d, e, f\}.$$

7. $X \cap Y$ **8.** $X \cup Y$ **9.** $Y \cup Z$

10. $Y \cap Z$ **11.** $X \cup U$ **12.** $Y \cap U$

13. X' **14.** Y'

15. $X' \cap Y'$ **16.** $X' \cap Z$

17. $X \cup (Y \cap Z)$ **18.** $Y \cap (X \cup Z)$

19. $(Y \cap Z') \cup X$ **20.** $(X' \cup Y') \cup Z$

21. $(Z \cup X')' \cap Y$ **22.** $(Y \cap X')' \cup Z'$

23. $X - Y$ **24.** $Y - X$

25. $X \cap (X - Y)$ **26.** $Y \cup (Y - X)$

27. $X' - Y$ **28.** $Y' - X$

29. $(X \cap Y') \cup (Y \cap X')$ **30.** $(X \cap Y') \cap (Y \cap X')$

Describe each set in words.

31. $A \cup (B' \cap C')$ **32.** $(A \cap B') \cup (B \cap A')$

33. $(C - B) \cup A$ **34.** $B \cap (A' - C)$

35. $(A - C) \cup (B - C)$ **36.** $(A' \cap B') \cup C'$

Adverse Effects of Alcohol and Tobacco *The table lists some common adverse effects of prolonged tobacco and alcohol use.*

Tobacco	Alcohol
Emphysema, e	Liver damage, l
Heart damage, h	Brain damage, b
Cancer, c	Heart damage, h

Let T be the set of listed effects of tobacco and A be the set of listed effects of alcohol. Find each set.

37. the smallest possible universal set U that includes all the effects listed

38. A' **39.** T' **40.** $T \cap A$

41. $T \cup A$ **42.** $T \cap A'$

Describe in words each set in Exercises 43–48.

Let U = the set of all tax returns,
  A = the set of all tax returns with itemized deductions,
  B = the set of all tax returns showing business income,
  C = the set of all tax returns filed in 2009,
  D = the set of all tax returns selected for audit.

43. $B \cup C$ **44.** $A \cap D$ **45.** $C - A$

46. $D \cup A'$ **47.** $(A \cup B) - D$ **48.** $(C \cap A) \cap B'$

Assuming that A and B represent any two sets, identify each statement as either always true *or* not always true.

49. $A \subseteq (A \cup B)$

50. $A \subseteq (A \cap B)$

51. $(A \cap B) \subseteq A$

52. $(A \cup B) \subseteq A$

53. $n(A \cup B) = n(A) + n(B)$

54. $n(A \cup B) = n(A) + n(B) - n(A \cap B)$

For Exercises 55–60, use your results in parts (a) and (b) to answer part (c).

Let $U = \{1, 2, 3, 4, 5\}$, $X = \{1, 3, 5\}$, $Y = \{1, 2, 3\}$, and $Z = \{3, 4, 5\}$.

55. (a) Find $X \cup Y$.
  (b) Find $Y \cup X$.
  (c) State a conjecture.

56. (a) Find $X \cap Y$.
  (b) Find $Y \cap X$.
  (c) State a conjecture.

57. (a) Find $X \cup (Y \cup Z)$.
  (b) Find $(X \cup Y) \cup Z$.
  (c) State a conjecture.

58. (a) Find $X \cap (Y \cap Z)$.
  (b) Find $(X \cap Y) \cap Z$.
  (c) State a conjecture.

59. (a) Find $(X \cup Y)'$.
  (b) Find $X' \cap Y'$.
  (c) State a conjecture.

60. (a) Find $(X \cap Y)'$.
  (b) Find $X' \cup Y'$.
  (c) State a conjecture.

In Exercises 61 and 62, let X be the set of different letters in your last name.

61. Find $X \cup \emptyset$ and state a conjecture.

62. Find $X \cap \emptyset$ and state a conjecture.

Decide whether each statement is true or false.

63. $(3, 2) = (5 - 2, 1 + 1)$

64. $(10, 4) = (7 + 3, 5 - 1)$

65. $(6, 3) = (3, 6)$

66. $(2, 13) = (13, 2)$

67. $\{6, 3\} = \{3, 6\}$

68. $\{2, 13\} = \{13, 2\}$

69. $\{(1, 2), (3, 4)\} = \{(3, 4), (1, 2)\}$

70. $\{(5, 9), (4, 8), (4, 2)\} = \{(4, 8), (5, 9), (4, 2)\}$

Find $A \times B$ and $B \times A$, for A and B defined as follows.

71. $A = \{2, 8, 12\}$, $B = \{4, 9\}$

72. $A = \{3, 6, 9, 12\}$, $B = \{6, 8\}$

73. $A = \{d, o, g\}$, $B = \{p, i, g\}$

74. $A = \{b, l, u, e\}$, $B = \{r, e, d\}$

For the sets specified in Exercises 75–78, use the given information to find $n(A \times B)$ and $n(B \times A)$.

75. the sets in **Exercise 71**

76. the sets in **Exercise 73**

77. $n(A) = 35$ and $n(B) = 6$

78. $n(A) = 13$ and $n(B) = 5$

Find the cardinal number specified.

79. If $n(A \times B) = 72$ and $n(A) = 12$, find $n(B)$.

80. If $n(A \times B) = 300$ and $n(B) = 30$, find $n(A)$.

Place the elements of these sets in the proper locations in the given Venn diagram.

81. Let $U = \{a, b, c, d, e, f, g\}$,
  $A = \{b, d, f, g\}$,
  $B = \{a, b, d, e, g\}$.

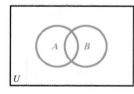

82. Let $U = \{5, 6, 7, 8, 9, 10, 11, 12, 13\}$,
  $M = \{5, 8, 10, 11\}$,
  $N = \{5, 6, 7, 9, 10\}$.

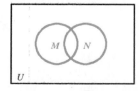

Use a Venn diagram similar to the one shown below to shade each set.

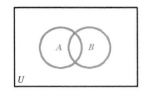

83. $B \cap A'$

84. $A \cup B$

85. $A' \cup B$

86. $A' \cap B'$

87. $B' \cup A$

88. $A' \cup A$

89. $B' \cap B$

90. $A \cap B'$

91. $B' \cup (A' \cap B')$

92. $(A \cap B) \cup B$

93. U'

94. $\emptyset'$

In Exercises 95 and 96, place the elements of the sets in the proper location in a Venn diagram similar to the one shown below.

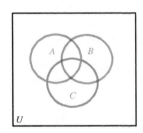

95. Let $U = \{m, n, o, p, q, r, s, t, u, v, w\}$,
    $A = \{m, n, p, q, r, t\}$,
    $B = \{m, o, p, q, s, u\}$,
    $C = \{m, o, p, r, s, t, u, v\}$.

96. Let $U = \{1, 2, 3, 4, 5, 6, 7, 8, 9\}$,
    $A = \{1, 3, 5, 7\}$,
    $B = \{1, 3, 4, 6, 8\}$,
    $C = \{1, 4, 5, 6, 7, 9\}$.

Use a Venn diagram to shade each set.

97. $(A \cap B) \cap C$

98. $(A \cap C') \cup B$

99. $(A \cap B) \cup C'$

100. $(A' \cap B) \cap C$

101. $(A' \cap B') \cap C$

102. $(A \cup B) \cup C$

103. $(A \cap B') \cup C$

104. $(A \cap C') \cap B$

105. $(A \cap B') \cap C'$

106. $(A' \cap B') \cup C$

107. $(A' \cap B') \cup C'$

108. $(A \cap B)' \cup C$

Write a symbolic description of each shaded area. Use the symbols A, B, C, $\cap$, $\cup$, $-$, and ' as necessary. More than one answer may be possible.

109.

110.

111.

112.

113.

114.

115.

116.
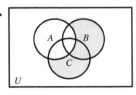

Suppose A and B are sets. Describe the conditions under which each statement would be true.

117. $A = A - B$

118. $A = B - A$

119. $A = A - \emptyset$

120. $A = \emptyset - A$

121. $A \cup \emptyset = \emptyset$

122. $A \cap \emptyset = \emptyset$

123. $A \cap \emptyset = A$

124. $A \cup \emptyset = A$

125. $A \cup A = \emptyset$

126. $A \cap A = \emptyset$

127. $A \cup B = A$

128. $A \cap B = B$

For Exercises 129–135, draw two appropriate Venn diagrams to decide whether the given statement is always true *or* not always true.

129. $A \cap A' = \emptyset$　　　**130.** $A \cup A' = U$

131. $(A \cap B) \subseteq A$　　　**132.** $(A \cup B) \subseteq A$

133. If $A \subseteq B$, then $A \cup B = A$.

134. If $A \subseteq B$, then $A \cap B = B$.

135. $(A \cup B)' = A' \cap B'$
(De Morgan's second law)

136. If A and B are sets, is it necessarily true that $n(A - B) = n(A) - n(B)$?

137. If $Q = \{x | x \text{ is a rational number}\}$ and $H = \{x | x \text{ is an irrational number}\}$, describe each set.
(a) $Q \cup H$
(b) $Q \cap H$

2.4 SURVEYS AND CARDINAL NUMBERS

Surveys • Cardinal Number Formula • Tables

Surveys

Problems involving sets of people (or objects) sometimes require analyzing known information about certain subsets to obtain cardinal numbers of other subsets. In this section, we apply three problem-solving techniques to such problems: Venn diagrams, cardinal number formulas, and tables. The "known information" is quite often (although not always) obtained by conducting a survey.

Suppose a group of students on a college campus is asked to compare some animated feature films, and the following information is produced.

34 like *Up*	12 like *Up* and *Mr. Fox*
29 like *The Princess and the Frog*	10 like *Princess* and *Mr. Fox*
26 like *Fantastic Mr. Fox*	4 like all three films
16 like *Up* and *Princess*	5 like none of these films.

To determine the total number of students surveyed, we cannot just add the eight numbers above because there is some overlap. For example, in **Figure 18**, the 34 students who like *Up* should not be positioned in region *b* but should be distributed among regions *b*, *c*, *d*, and *e*, in a way that is consistent with all of the given data. (Region *b* actually contains those students who like *Up* but do not like *The Princess and the Frog* and do not like *Fantastic Mr. Fox*.)

Because, at the start, we do not know how to distribute the 34 who like *Up*, we look first for some more manageable data. The smallest total listed, the 4 students who like all three films, can be placed in region *d* (the intersection of the three sets). The 5 who like none of the three must go into region *a*. Then, the 16 who like *Up* and *Princess* must go into regions *d* and *e*. Because region *d* already contains 4 students, we must place

$$16 - 4 = 12 \quad \text{in region } e.$$

Because 12 like *Up* and *Mr. Fox* (regions *c* and *d*), we place

$$12 - 4 = 8 \quad \text{in region } c.$$

Now that regions *c*, *d*, and *e* contain 8, 4, and 12 students, respectively, we must place

$$34 - 8 - 4 - 12 = 10 \quad \text{in region } b.$$

By similar reasoning, all regions are assigned their correct numbers. See **Figure 19** on the next page.

Figure 18

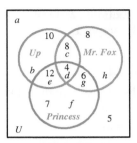

Figure 19

▮▮ **EXAMPLE 1** Analyzing a Survey

Using the survey data on student preferences for animated feature films, as summarized in **Figure 19**, answer each question.

(a) How many students like *Fantastic Mr. Fox* only?

(b) How many students like exactly two films?

(c) How many students were surveyed?

SOLUTION

(a) A student who likes *Mr. Fox* only does not like *Up* and does not like *Princess*. These students are inside the regions for *Mr. Fox* and outside the regions for *Up* and *Princess*. Region *h* is the appropriate region in **Figure 19**, and we see that eight students like *Fantastic Mr. Fox* only.

(b) The students in regions *c*, *e*, and *g* like exactly two films. The total number of such students is

$$8 + 12 + 6 = 26.$$

(c) Each student surveyed has been placed in exactly one region of **Figure 19**, so the total number surveyed is the sum of the numbers in all eight regions:

$$5 + 10 + 8 + 4 + 12 + 7 + 6 + 8 = 60. \qquad ▮▮▮$$

Cardinal Number Formula

If the numbers shown in **Figure 20** are the cardinal numbers of the individual regions, then

$$n(A) = 5 + 3 = 8, \quad n(B) = 3 + 7 = 10, \quad n(A \cap B) = 3,$$

and

$$n(A \cup B) = 5 + 3 + 7 = 15.$$

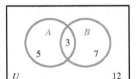

Figure 20

Notice that $n(A \cup B) = n(A) + n(B) - n(A \cap B)$ because $15 = 8 + 10 - 3$. This relationship is true for any two sets A and B.

> **Cardinal Number Formula**
>
> For any two sets A and B, the following is true.
>
> $$n(A \cup B) = n(A) + n(B) - n(A \cap B)$$

This formula can be rearranged to find any one of its four terms when the others are known.

▮▮ **EXAMPLE 2** Applying the Cardinal Number Formula

Find $n(A)$ if $n(A \cup B) = 22, n(A \cap B) = 8$, and $n(B) = 12$.

SOLUTION

We solve the cardinal number formula for $n(A)$.

$$n(A) = n(A \cup B) - n(B) + n(A \cap B)$$
$$= 22 - 12 + 8$$
$$= 18 \qquad ▮▮▮$$

Sometimes, even when information is presented as in **Example 2**, it is more convenient to fit that information into a Venn diagram as in **Example 1.**

▌▌ EXAMPLE 3 Analyzing Data in a Report

Scott Heeren, who leads a group of software engineers who investigate illegal activities on social networking sites, reported the following information.

T = the set of group members following patterns on Twitter

F = the set of group members following patterns on Facebook

L = the set of group members following patterns on LinkedIn

$$n(T) = 13 \qquad n(T \cap F) = 9 \qquad n(T \cap F \cap L) = 5$$
$$n(F) = 16 \qquad n(F \cap L) = 10 \qquad n(T' \cap F' \cap L') = 3$$
$$n(L) = 13 \qquad n(T \cap L) = 6$$

How many engineers are in Scott's group?

SOLUTION

The data supplied by Scott are reflected in **Figure 21**. The sum of the numbers in the diagram gives the total number of engineers in the group.

$$3 + 3 + 1 + 2 + 5 + 5 + 4 + 2 = 25 \qquad ▌▌▌$$

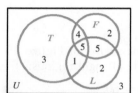

Figure 21

Tables

Sometimes information appears in a table rather than a Venn diagram, but the basic ideas of union and intersection still apply.

▌▌ EXAMPLE 4 Analyzing Data in a Table

Melanie Cutler, the officer in charge of the cafeteria on a military base, wanted to know if the beverage that enlisted men and women preferred with lunch depended on their ages. On a given day, Melanie categorized her lunch patrons according to age and preferred beverage, recording the results in a table.

		Beverage			
		Cola (C)	Iced Tea (I)	Sweet Tea (S)	Totals
Age	18–25 (Y)	45	10	35	90
	26–33 (M)	20	25	30	75
	Over 33 (O)	5	30	20	55
	Totals	70	65	85	220

Using the letters in the table, find the number of people in each set.

(a) $Y \cap C$ **(b)** $O' \cup I$

SOLUTION

(a) The set Y includes all personnel represented across the top row of the table (90 in all), while C includes the 70 down the left column. The intersection of these two sets is just the upper left entry, 45 people.

(b) The set O' excludes the bottom row, so it includes the first and second rows. The set I includes the middle column only. The union of the two sets represents

$$45 + 10 + 35 + 20 + 25 + 30 + 30 = 195 \text{ people.} \qquad ▌▌▌$$

2.4 EXERCISES

Use the numerals representing cardinalities in the Venn diagrams to give the cardinality of each set specified.

1.

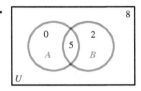

(a) $A \cap B$ (b) $A \cup B$
(c) $A \cap B'$ (d) $A' \cap B$
(e) $A' \cap B'$

2.

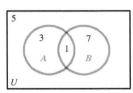

(a) $A \cap B$ (b) $A \cup B$
(c) $A \cap B'$ (d) $A' \cap B$
(e) $A' \cap B'$

3.

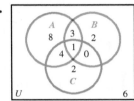

(a) $A \cap B \cap C$ (b) $A \cap B \cap C'$
(c) $A \cap B' \cap C$ (d) $A' \cap B \cap C$
(e) $A' \cap B' \cap C$ (f) $A \cap B' \cap C'$
(g) $A' \cap B \cap C'$ (h) $A' \cap B' \cap C'$

4.

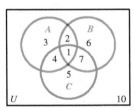

(a) $A \cap B \cap C$ (b) $A \cap B \cap C'$
(c) $A \cap B' \cap C$ (d) $A' \cap B \cap C$
(e) $A' \cap B' \cap C$ (f) $A \cap B' \cap C'$
(g) $A' \cap B \cap C'$ (h) $A' \cap B' \cap C'$

In Exercises 5–10, make use of an appropriate formula.

5. Find the value of $n(A \cup B)$ if $n(A) = 12$, $n(B) = 14$, and $n(A \cap B) = 5$.

6. Find the value of $n(A \cup B)$ if $n(A) = 16$, $n(B) = 28$, and $n(A \cap B) = 5$.

7. Find the value of $n(A \cap B)$ if $n(A) = 20$, $n(B) = 12$, and $n(A \cup B) = 25$.

8. Find the value of $n(A \cap B)$ if $n(A) = 20$, $n(B) = 24$, and $n(A \cup B) = 30$.

9. Find the value of $n(A)$ if $n(B) = 35$, $n(A \cap B) = 15$, and $n(A \cup B) = 55$.

10. Find the value of $n(B)$ if $n(A) = 20$, $n(A \cap B) = 6$, and $n(A \cup B) = 30$.

Draw an appropriate Venn diagram and use the given information to fill in the number of elements in each region.

11. $n(A) = 19$, $n(B) = 13$, $n(A \cup B) = 25$, $n(A') = 11$

12. $n(U) = 43$, $n(A) = 25$, $n(A \cap B) = 5$, $n(B') = 30$

13. $n(A') = 25$, $n(B) = 28$, $n(A' \cup B') = 40$, $n(A \cap B) = 10$

14. $n(A \cup B) = 15$, $n(A \cap B) = 8$, $n(A) = 13$, $n(A' \cup B') = 11$

15. $n(A) = 57$, $n(A \cap B) = 35$, $n(A \cup B) = 81$, $n(A \cap B \cap C) = 15$, $n(A \cap C) = 21$, $n(B \cap C) = 25$, $n(C) = 49$, $n(B') = 52$

16. $n(A) = 24$, $n(B) = 24$, $n(C) = 26$, $n(A \cap B) = 10$, $n(B \cap C) = 8$, $n(A \cap C) = 15$, $n(A \cap B \cap C) = 6$, $n(U) = 50$

17. $n(A) = 15$, $n(A \cap B \cap C) = 5$, $n(A \cap C) = 13$, $n(A \cap B') = 9$, $n(B \cap C) = 8$, $n(A' \cap B' \cap C') = 21$, $n(B \cap C') = 3$, $n(B \cup C) = 32$

18. $n(A \cap B) = 21$, $n(A \cap B \cap C) = 6$, $n(A \cap C) = 26$, $n(B \cap C) = 7$, $n(A \cap C') = 20$, $n(B \cap C') = 25$, $n(C) = 40$, $n(A' \cap B' \cap C') = 2$

Use Venn diagrams to work each problem.

19. *Writing and Producing Music* Joe Long worked on 9 music projects last year.

Joe Long, Bob Gaudio, Tommy DeVito, and Frankie Valli
The Four Seasons

He wrote and produced 3 projects.
He wrote a total of 5 projects.
He produced a total of 7 projects.

(a) How many projects did he write but not produce?

(b) How many projects did he produce but not write?

20. *Compact Disc Collection* Gitti Lindner is a fan of the music of Paul Simon and Art Garfunkel. In her collection of 25 compact discs, she has the following:

> 5 on which both Simon and Garfunkel sing
> 7 on which Simon sings
> 8 on which Garfunkel sings
> 15 on which neither Simon nor Garfunkel sings.

(a) How many of her compact discs feature only Paul Simon?

(b) How many of her compact discs feature only Art Garfunkel?

(c) How many feature at least one of these two artists?

(d) How many feature at most one of these two artists?

21. *Fan Response to Singers* Julie Davis, a pop culture analyst, wanted to evaluate the relative appeal of different singers. She interviewed 65 fans and determined the following:

> 37 like Jazmine Sullivan
> 36 like Carrie Underwood
> 31 like Brad Paisley
> 14 like Jazmine and Carrie
> 21 like Jazmine and Brad
> 14 like Carrie and Brad
> 8 like all three singers.

How many of these fans like:

(a) exactly two of these singers?

(b) exactly one of these singers?

(c) none of these singers?

(d) Jazmine, but neither Carrie nor Brad?

(e) Brad and exactly one of the other two?

22. *Financial Aid for Students* At the University of Louisiana, half of the 48 mathematics majors were receiving federal financial aid as follows:

> 5 had Pell Grants
> 14 participated in the College Work Study Program
> 4 had TOPS scholarships
> 2 had TOPS scholarships and participated in Work Study.

Those with Pell Grants had no other federal aid.

How many of the 48 math majors had:

(a) no federal aid?

(b) more than one of these three forms of aid?

(c) federal aid other than these three forms?

(d) a TOPS scholarship or Work Study?

(e) exactly one of these three forms of aid?

23. *Cooking Habits* Eric Dangerfield interviewed 140 people in a suburban shopping center to find out some of their cooking habits. He obtained the results given at the top of the next column.

> 58 use microwave ovens
> 63 use electric ranges
> 58 use gas ranges
> 19 use microwave ovens and electric ranges
> 17 use microwave ovens and gas ranges
> 4 use both gas and electric ranges
> 1 uses all three

(a) How many use exactly two of these kinds of appliances?

(b) How many use at least two of these kinds of appliances?

24. *Non-Mainline Religious Beliefs* 140 U.S. adults were surveyed.

Let $A =$ the set of respondents who believe in astrology,
$R =$ the set of respondents who believe in reincarnation,
$Y =$ the set of respondents who believe in the spirituality of yoga.

The survey revealed the following information:

$$n(A) = 35 \qquad n(R \cap Y) = 8$$
$$n(R) = 36 \qquad n(A \cap Y) = 10$$
$$n(Y) = 32 \qquad n(A \cap R \cap Y) = 6$$
$$n(A \cap R) = 19$$

How many of the respondents believe in:

(a) astrology, but not reincarnation?

(b) at least one of these three things?

(c) reincarnation but neither of the others?

(d) exactly two of these three things?

(e) none of the three?

25. *Survey on Attitudes Toward Religion* Researchers interviewed a number of people and recorded the following data. Of all the respondents:

> 240 think Hollywood is unfriendly toward religion
> 160 think the media are unfriendly toward religion
> 181 think scientists are unfriendly toward religion
> 145 think both Hollywood and the media are unfriendly toward religion
> 122 think both scientists and the media are unfriendly toward religion
> 80 think exactly two of these groups are unfriendly toward religion
> 110 think all three groups are unfriendly toward religion
> 219 think none of these three groups is unfriendly toward religion.

How many respondents:

(a) were surveyed?

(b) think exactly one of these three groups is unfriendly toward religion?

26. *Student Goals* Carol Britz, who sells college textbooks, interviewed freshmen on a community college campus to find out the main goals of today's students.

Let W = the set of those who want to be wealthy,
      F = the set of those who want to raise a family,
      E = the set of those who want to become experts in their fields.

Carol's findings are summarized here.

$$n(W) = 160 \qquad n(E \cap F) = 90$$

$$n(F) = 140 \qquad n(W \cap F \cap E) = 80$$

$$n(E) = 130 \qquad n(E') = 95$$

$$n(W \cap F) = 95 \qquad n[(W \cup F \cup E)'] = 10$$

Find the total number of students interviewed.

27. *Hospital Patient Symptoms* Jesse Fisher conducted a survey among 75 patients admitted to the cardiac unit of a Santa Fe hospital during a two-week period.

Let B = the set of patients with high blood pressure,
      C = the set of patients with high cholesterol levels,
      S = the set of patients who smoke cigarettes.

Jesse's data are as follows.

$$n(B) = 47 \qquad n(B \cap S) = 33$$

$$n(C) = 46 \qquad n(B \cap C) = 31$$

$$n(S) = 52 \qquad n(B \cap C \cap S) = 21$$

$$n[(B \cap C) \cup (B \cap S) \cup (C \cap S)] = 51$$

Find the number of these patients who:

(a) had either high blood pressure or high cholesterol levels, but not both

(b) had fewer than two of the indications listed

(c) were smokers but had neither high blood pressure nor high cholesterol levels

(d) did not have exactly two of the indications listed.

28. *Song Themes* It was once said that country-western songs emphasize three basic themes: love, prison, and trucks. A survey of the local country-western radio station produced the following data.

12 songs about a truck driver who is in love while in prison
13 about a prisoner in love
28 about a person in love
18 about a truck driver in love
 3 about a truck driver in prison who is not in love
 2 about people in prison who are not in love and do not drive trucks
 8 about people who are out of prison, are not in love, and do not drive trucks
16 about truck drivers who are not in prison

(a) How many songs were surveyed?

Find the number of songs about:

(b) truck drivers   **(c)** prisoners

(d) truck drivers in prison

(e) people not in prison

(f) people not in love.

29. Use the figure below to find the numbers of the regions belonging to each set.

(a) $A \cap B \cap C \cap D$

(b) $A \cup B \cup C \cup D$

(c) $(A \cap B) \cup (C \cap D)$

(d) $(A' \cap B') \cap (C \cup D)$

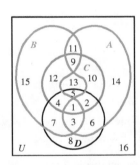

30. *Sports Viewing* A survey of 130 TV viewers was taken.

52 watch football
56 watch basketball
62 watch tennis
60 watch golf
21 watch football and basketball
19 watch football and tennis
22 watch basketball and tennis
27 watch football and golf
30 watch basketball and golf
21 watch tennis and golf
 3 watch football, basketball, and tennis
15 watch football, basketball, and golf
10 watch football, tennis, and golf
10 watch basketball, tennis, and golf
 3 watch all four of these sports
 5 don't watch any of these four sports

Use a Venn diagram to answer each question.

(a) How many of these viewers watch football, basketball, and tennis, but not golf?

(b) How many watch exactly one of these four sports?

(c) How many watch exactly two of these four sports?

Solve each problem.

31. Basketball Positions Donna DePaulis runs a basketball program in California. On the first day of the season, 60 young women showed up and were categorized by age level and by preferred basketball position, as shown in the following table.

		Guard (G)	Forward (F)	Center (N)	Totals
			Position		
	Junior High (J)	9	6	4	19
Age	Senior High (S)	12	5	9	26
	College (C)	5	8	2	15
	Totals	26	19	15	60

Using the set labels (letters) in the table, find the number of players in each of the following sets.

(a) $J \cap G$ **(b)** $S \cap N$ **(c)** $N \cup (S \cap F)$

(d) $S' \cap (G \cup N)$ **(e)** $(S \cap N') \cup (C \cap G')$

(f) $N' \cap (S' \cap C')$

32. Army Housing A study of U.S. Army housing trends categorized personnel as commissioned officers (C), warrant officers (W), or enlisted (E), and categorized their living facilities as on-base (B), rented off-base (R), or owned off-base (O). One survey yielded the following data.

		B	R	O	Totals
			Facilities		
	C	12	29	54	95
Personnel	W	4	5	6	15
	E	374	71	285	730
	Totals	390	105	345	840

Find the number of personnel in each of the following sets.

(a) $W \cap O$ **(b)** $C \cup B$

(c) $R' \cup W'$ **(d)** $(C \cup W) \cap (B \cup R)$

(e) $(C \cap B) \cup (E \cap O)$ **(f)** $B \cap (W \cup R)'$

33. Could the information of **Example 4** have been presented in a Venn diagram similar to those in **Examples 1 and 3?** If so, construct such a diagram. Otherwise, explain the essential difference of **Example 4**.

34. Explain how a cardinal number formula can be derived for the case where *three* sets occur. Specifically, give a formula relating $n(A \cup B \cup C)$ to

$$n(A), \quad n(B), \quad n(C), \quad n(A \cap B), \quad n(A \cap C),$$
$$n(B \cap C), \quad \text{and} \quad n(A \cap B \cap C).$$

Illustrate with a Venn diagram.

EXTENSION Infinite Sets and Their Cardinalities

One-to-One Correspondence and Equivalent Sets • The Cardinal Number $\aleph_0$
• Infinite Sets • Sets That Are Not Countable

One-to-One Correspondence and Equivalent Sets Georg Cantor, profiled on **page 44,** met with much resistance in the late 1800s when he first developed modern set theory because of his ideas on infinite sets. The results discussed here, however, are commonly accepted today. Recall the following from **Section 2.1.**

1. The cardinal number of a set is the number of elements it contains.

2. Two sets are *equivalent* if their cardinal numbers are equal.

3. A set is *infinite* if its cardinal number is "too large" to be found among the whole numbers.

The word **paradox** in Greek originally meant "wrong opinion" as opposed to orthodox, which meant "right opinion." Over the years, the word came to mean self-contradiction.

Before the twentieth century it was considered a paradox that any set could be placed into one-to-one correspondence with a proper subset of itself. This paradox, called **Galileo's paradox** after the sixteenth-century mathematician and scientist **Galileo** (see the picture), is now explained by saying that the ability to make such a correspondence is how we distinguish infinite sets from finite sets. What is true for finite sets is not necessarily true for infinite sets.

We can easily establish the equivalence of two finite sets by counting their elements and comparing their cardinal numbers. But the elements of an infinite set cannot be counted in the same sense. Cantor addressed this difficulty using the idea of a **one-to-one correspondence** between sets. The sets $A = \{1, 2, 3\}$ and $B = \{3, 6, 9\}$, for example, can be placed in such correspondence as follows (among other ways):

$$\{1, \quad 2, \quad 3\}$$
$$\updownarrow \quad \updownarrow \quad \updownarrow$$
$$\{3, \quad 6, \quad 9\}.$$

This correspondence is "one-to-one" because each element of each set is paired with exactly one element of the other set. The equivalence of A and B is denoted $A \sim B$.

On the other hand, the sets $C = \{1, 8, 12\}$ and $D = \{6, 11\}$ are *not* equivalent. Any correspondence between them, such as

$$\{1, \quad 8, \quad 12\}$$
$$\updownarrow \quad \searrow \nearrow$$
$$\{6, \quad 11\}$$

is not one-to-one. (Two different elements from C must be paired with a single element of D.)

Cantor extended this idea that one-to-one correspondence establishes equivalence to his study of infinite sets.

The Cardinal Number $\aleph_0$

The most basic infinite set is the set of counting numbers, $\{1, 2, 3, 4, 5, \ldots\}$. The counting numbers are said to have the infinite cardinal number $\aleph_0$ (the first Hebrew letter, aleph, with a zero subscript, read "aleph-null"). Think of $\aleph_0$ as being the "smallest" infinite cardinal number. To the question "How many counting numbers are there?", we answer "There are $\aleph_0$ of them."

Now, any set that can be placed in a one-to-one correspondence with the counting numbers will have the same cardinal number, or $\aleph_0$. There are many such sets.

■| **EXAMPLE 1**   Showing that $\{0, 1, 2, 3, \ldots\}$ Has Cardinal Number $\aleph_0$

Verify that the set of whole numbers $\{0, 1, 2, 3, \ldots\}$ has cardinal number $\aleph_0$.

SOLUTION

We know that $\aleph_0$ is the cardinal number of the set of counting numbers (by definition). To show that another set, such as the whole numbers, also has $\aleph_0$ as its cardinal number, we must show that set to be equivalent to the set of counting numbers. Equivalence is established by a one-to-one correspondence between the two sets.

$$\{1, \quad 2, \quad 3, \quad 4, \quad 5, \quad 6, \ldots, \quad n, \quad \ldots\} \text{ Counting numbers}$$
$$\updownarrow \quad \updownarrow \quad \updownarrow \quad \updownarrow \quad \updownarrow \quad \updownarrow \qquad \updownarrow \qquad \updownarrow$$
$$\{0, \quad 1, \quad 2, \quad 3, \quad 4, \quad 5, \ldots, \quad n-1, \quad \ldots\} \text{ Whole numbers}$$

The pairing of the counting number n with the whole number $n - 1$ continues indefinitely, with neither set containing any element not used up in the pairing process. Even though the set of whole numbers has an additional element (the number 0) compared to the set of counting numbers, the correspondence proves that both sets have the same cardinal number, $\aleph_0$. ■■■

The result in **Example 1** shows that intuition is a poor guide for dealing with infinite sets. Because the sets of counting numbers and whole numbers can be placed in a one-to-one correspondence, the two sets have the same cardinal number.

Aleph and other letters of the **Hebrew alphabet** are shown on a Kabbalistic diagram representing one of the ten emanations of God during Creation. Kabbalah, the ultramystical tradition within Judaism, arose in the fifth century and peaked in the sixteenth century in both Palestine and Poland.

Kabbalists believed that the Bible held mysteries that could be discovered in permutations, combinations, and anagrams of its very letters. Each letter in the aleph-bet has a numerical value (aleph = 1), and thus a numeration system exists. The letter Y stands for 10, so 15 should be YH (10 + 5). However, YH is a form of the Holy Name, so instead TW (9 + 6) is the symbol.

Infinite Sets The set $\{5, 6, 7\}$ is a proper subset of the set $\{5, 6, 7, 8\}$, and there is no way to place these two sets in a one-to-one correspondence. However, the set of counting numbers is a proper subset of the set of whole numbers, and **Example 1** showed that these two sets *can* be placed in a one-to-one correspondence. This important property is used in the formal definition of an infinite set.

> **Infinite Set**
>
> A set is **infinite** if it can be placed in a one-to-one correspondence with a proper subset of itself.

▮ **EXAMPLE 2** Showing that $\{\ldots, -3, -2, -1, 0, 1, 2, 3, \ldots\}$ Has Cardinal Number $\aleph_0$

Verify that the set of integers $\{\ldots, -3, -2, -1, 0, 1, 2, 3, \ldots\}$ has cardinal number $\aleph_0$.

SOLUTION

A one-to-one correspondence can be set up between the set of integers and the set of counting numbers.

$$\{1,\ 2,\ \ 3,\ 4,\ \ 5,\ 6,\ \ 7,\ \ldots,\ 2n,\ 2n+1,\ \ldots\}$$
$$\updownarrow\ \updownarrow\ \updownarrow\ \updownarrow\ \updownarrow\ \updownarrow\ \updownarrow\quad\ \ \updownarrow\quad\ \updownarrow$$
$$\{0,\ 1,\ -1,\ 2,\ -2,\ 3,\ -3,\ \ldots,\ n,\ \ -n,\ \ \ldots\}$$

Because of this one-to-one correspondence, the cardinal number of the set of integers is the same as the cardinal number of the set of counting numbers, $\aleph_0$. ▮▮▮

The one-to-one correspondence of **Example 2** proves that the set of integers is infinite—it was placed in one-to-one correspondence with a proper subset of itself.

As shown by **Example 2,** there are just as many integers as there are counting numbers. This result is not at all intuitive, and the next result is even less so. There is an infinite number of fractions between any two counting numbers. For example, there is an infinite set of fractions $\left\{\frac{1}{2}, \frac{3}{4}, \frac{7}{8}, \frac{15}{16}, \frac{31}{32}, \ldots\right\}$ between the counting numbers 0 and 1. This should imply that there are "more" fractions than counting numbers. However, there are just as many fractions as counting numbers.

▮ **EXAMPLE 3** Showing that the Set of Rational Numbers Has Cardinal Number $\aleph_0$

Verify that the cardinal number of the set of rational numbers is $\aleph_0$.

SOLUTION

First show that a one-to-one correspondence may be set up between the set of nonnegative rational numbers and the counting numbers. This is done by the following ingenious scheme, devised by Georg Cantor.

Look at **Figure 22** on the next page. The nonnegative rational numbers whose denominators are 1 are written in the first row. Those whose denominators are 2 are written in the second row, and so on. Every nonnegative rational number appears in this list sooner or later. For example, $\frac{327}{189}$ is in row 189 and column 327.

Figure 22

To set up a one-to-one correspondence between the set of nonnegative rationals and the set of counting numbers, follow the path drawn in **Figure 22**. Let $\frac{0}{1}$ correspond to 1, let $\frac{1}{1}$ correspond to 2, $\frac{2}{1}$ to 3, $\frac{1}{2}$ to 4 $\left(\text{skip } \frac{2}{2}, \text{ since } \frac{2}{2} = \frac{1}{1}\right)$, $\frac{1}{3}$ to 5, $\frac{1}{4}$ to 6, and so on. The numbers under the colored disks are omitted because they can be reduced to lower terms, and were thus included earlier in the listing.

This procedure sets up a one-to-one correspondence between the set of nonnegative rationals and the counting numbers, showing that both of these sets have the same cardinal number, $\aleph_0$. Now by using the method of **Example 2** (i.e., letting each negative number follow its corresponding positive number), we can extend this correspondence to include negative rational numbers as well. Thus, the set of all rational numbers has cardinal number $\aleph_0$. ■■■

A set is called **countable** if it is finite or if it has cardinal number $\aleph_0$. All the infinite sets of numbers discussed so far—the counting numbers, the whole numbers, the integers, and the rational numbers—are countable.

Sets That Are Not Countable

The Barber Paradox is a version of a paradox of set theory that Bertrand Russell proposed in the early twentieth century.

1. The men in a village are of two types: men who do not shave themselves and men who do.
2. The village barber shaves all men who do not shave themselves and he shaves only those men.

But who shaves the barber?
The barber cannot shave himself. If he did, he would fall into the category of men who shave themselves. However, (2) above states that the barber does not shave such men.

So the barber does not shave himself. But then he falls into the category of men who do not shave themselves. According to (2), the barber shaves all of these men; hence, the barber shaves himself, too.

We find that the barber cannot shave himself, yet the barber does shave himself—a paradox.

| **EXAMPLE 4** | Showing that the Set of Real Numbers Does Not Have Cardinal Number $\aleph_0$ |

Verify that the set of all real numbers does not have cardinal number $\aleph_0$.

SOLUTION

There are two possibilities:

1. The set of real numbers has cardinal number $\aleph_0$.
2. The set of real numbers does not have cardinal number $\aleph_0$.

If we assume that the first statement is true, then a one-to-one correspondence can be set up between the set of real numbers and the set of counting numbers.

In a later chapter, we show that every real number can be written as a decimal number (or simply "decimal"). Thus, in the one-to-one correspondence we are assuming, some decimal corresponds to the counting number 1, some decimal corresponds to 2, and so on. Suppose the correspondence begins as follows:

$$1 \leftrightarrow 0.68458429006\ldots$$
$$2 \leftrightarrow 0.13479201038\ldots$$
$$3 \leftrightarrow 0.37291568341\ldots$$
$$4 \leftrightarrow 0.935223671611\ldots$$
and so on.

Zeno's paradox of the Tortoise and Achilles was given in its original form by Zeno of Elea.

In the original story, the Tortoise is able to convince Achilles (the Greek hero of Homer's *The Illiad*) that in a race, given a small head start, the Tortoise is always able to defeat Achilles. (See the **Chapter Opener** and **Exercises 51 and 52** in this **Extension**.) The resolution of this paradox is discussed on the Web site www.mathacademy.com.

Assuming the existence of a one-to-one correspondence between the counting numbers and the real numbers means that every decimal is in the list above. Let's construct a new decimal K as follows. The first decimal in the above list has 6 as its first digit. Let K start as $K = 0.4. \ldots$ We picked 4 because $4 \neq 6$. (We could have used any other digit except 6.) Because the second digit of the second decimal in the list is 3, we let $K = 0.45 \ldots$ (because $5 \neq 3$). The third digit of the third decimal is 2, so let $K = 0.457 \ldots$ (because $7 \neq 2$). The fourth digit of the fourth decimal is 2, so let $K = 0.4573 \ldots$ (because $3 \neq 2$). Continue defining K in this way.

Is K in the list that we assumed to contain all decimals? The first decimal in the list differs from K in at least the first position (K starts with 4, and the first decimal in the list starts with 6). The second decimal in the list differs from K in at least the second position, and the nth decimal in the list differs from K in at least the nth position. Every decimal in the list differs from K in at least one position, so that K cannot possibly be in the list. In summary:

> We assume every decimal is in the list above.
> The decimal K is not in the list.

Because these statements cannot both be true, the original assumption has led to a contradiction. This forces the acceptance of the only possible alternative to the original assumption: It is not possible to set up a one-to-one correspondence between the set of reals and the set of counting numbers. The cardinal number of the set of reals is not equal to $\aleph_0$. ▮▮▮

The set of counting numbers is a proper subset of the set of real numbers. Because of this, it would seem reasonable to say that the cardinal number of the set of reals, commonly written c, is greater than $\aleph_0$. (The letter c here represents *continuum*.) Other, even larger, infinite cardinal numbers can be constructed. For example, the set of all subsets of the set of real numbers has a cardinal number larger than c. Continuing this process of finding cardinal numbers of sets of subsets, more and more, larger and larger infinite cardinal numbers are produced.

The six most important infinite sets of numbers were listed in **Section 2.1.** All of them have been dealt with in this **Extension,** except the irrational numbers. The irrationals have decimal representations, so they are all included among the real numbers. Because the irrationals are a subset of the reals, you might guess that the irrationals have cardinal number $\aleph_0$, just like the rationals. However, because the union of the rationals and the irrationals is all the reals, that would imply that the cardinality of the union of two disjoint countable sets is c. But **Example 2** showed that this is not the case. A better guess is that the cardinal number of the irrationals is c (the same as that of the reals). This is, in fact, true.

Cardinal Numbers of Infinite Number Sets

Infinite Set	Cardinal Number
Natural or counting numbers	$\aleph_0$
Whole numbers	$\aleph_0$
Integers	$\aleph_0$
Rational numbers	$\aleph_0$
Irrational numbers	c
Real numbers	c

EXTENSION EXERCISES

Match each set in Column I with the set in Column II that has the same cardinality. Give the cardinal number.

I	**II**
1. {6}	**A.** $\{x \mid x$ is a rational number$\}$
2. $\{-16, 14, 3\}$	**B.** {26}
3. $\{x \mid x$ is a natural number$\}$	**C.** $\{x \mid x$ is an irrational number$\}$
4. $\{x \mid x$ is a real number$\}$	**D.** {x, y, z}
5. $\{x \mid x$ is an integer between 5 and 6$\}$	**E.** $\{x \mid x$ is a real number that satisfies $x^2 = 25\}$
6. $\{x \mid x$ is an integer that satisfies $x^2 = 100\}$	**F.** $\{x \mid x$ is an integer that is both even and odd$\}$

Place each pair of sets into a one-to-one correspondence, if possible.

7. {I, II, III} and {x, y, z}

8. {a, b, c, d} and {2, 4, 6}

9. {a, d, d, i, t, i, o, n} and {a, n, s, w, e, r}

10. {Obama, Clinton, Bush} and {Michelle, Hillary, Laura}

Give the cardinal number of each set.

11. $\{a, b, c, d, \ldots, k\}$

12. $\{9, 12, 15, \ldots, 36\}$

13. $\emptyset$

14. {0}

15. $\{300, 400, 500, \ldots\}$

16. $\{-35, -28, -21, \ldots, 56\}$

17. $\left\{-\dfrac{1}{4}, -\dfrac{1}{8}, -\dfrac{1}{12}, \ldots\right\}$

18. $\{x \mid x$ is an even integer$\}$

19. $\{x \mid x$ is an odd counting number$\}$

20. {b, a, 1, 1, a, d}

21. {Jan, Feb, Mar, . . . , Dec}

22. {Alabama, Alaska, Arizona, . . . , Wisconsin, Wyoming}

23. Lew Lefton has revised the old song "100 Bottles of Beer on the Wall" to illustrate a property of infinite cardinal numbers.

Fill in the blank in the first verse of Lefton's composition:

> $\aleph_0$ bottles of beer on the wall, $\aleph_0$ bottles of beer, take one down and pass it around, _____ bottles of beer on the wall.
> (*Source:* http://people.math.gatech.edu/~llefton)

$$\aleph_0 - 1 = \, ?$$

24. Two one-to-one correspondences are considered "different" if some elements are paired differently in one than in the other.

$$\begin{array}{ccc} \{a, & b, & c\} \\ \updownarrow & \updownarrow & \updownarrow \\ \{a, & b, & c\} \end{array} \text{ and } \begin{array}{ccc} \{a, & b, & c\} \\ \updownarrow & \updownarrow & \updownarrow \\ \{c, & b, & a\} \end{array} \text{ are different,}$$

$$\text{while } \begin{array}{ccc} \{a, & b, & c\} \\ \updownarrow & \updownarrow & \updownarrow \\ \{c, & a, & b\} \end{array} \text{ and } \begin{array}{ccc} \{b, & c, & a\} \\ \updownarrow & \updownarrow & \updownarrow \\ \{a, & b, & c\} \end{array} \text{ are not.}$$

(a) How many *different* correspondences can be set up between the two sets {Jamie Foxx, Mike Myers, Madonna} and {Austin Powers, Ray Charles, Eva Peron}?

(b) Which one of these correspondences pairs each person with the appropriate famous movie role?

Determine whether each pair of sets is equal, equivalent, both, *or* neither.

25. {u, v, w}, {v, u, w}   **26.** {48, 6}, {4, 86}

27. {X, Y, Z}, {x, y, z}

28. {top}, {pot}

29. $\{x \mid x$ is a positive real number$\}$, $\{x \mid x$ is a negative real number$\}$

30. $\{x \mid x$ is a positive rational number$\}$, $\{x \mid x$ is a negative real number$\}$

Show that each set has cardinal number $\aleph_0$ by setting up a one-to-one correspondence between the given set and the set of counting numbers.

31. the set of positive even integers

32. $\{-10, -20, -30, -40, \ldots\}$

33. $\{1{,}000{,}000,\ 2{,}000{,}000,\ 3{,}000{,}000,\ \ldots\}$

34. the set of odd integers

35. $\{2, 4, 8, 16, 32, \ldots\}$
(*Hint*: $4 = 2^2$, $8 = 2^3$, $16 = 2^4$, and so on)

36. $\{-17, -22, -27, -32, \ldots\}$

In Exercises 37–40, identify the given statement as always
true *or* not always true. *If* not always true, *give a counterexample.*

37. If A and B are infinite sets, then A is equivalent to
B.

38. If set A is an infinite set and set B can be put in a one-
to-one correspondence with a proper subset of A, then
B must be infinite.

39. If A is an infinite set and A is not equivalent to the set
of counting numbers, then $n(A) = c$.

40. If A and B are both countably infinite sets, then
$n(A \cup B) = \aleph_0$.

*Exercises 41 and 42 are geometric applications of the con-
cept of infinity.*

41. The set of real numbers can be represented by an infinite line, extending indefinitely in both directions. Each
point on the line corresponds to a unique real number,
and each real number corresponds to a unique point on
the line.

(a) Use the figure below, where the line segment
between 0 and 1 has been bent into a semicircle
and positioned above the line, to prove that

> $\{x \mid x$ is a real number between 0 and 1$\}$ *is*
> *equivalent to* $\{x \mid x$ is a real number$\}$.

(b) What fact does part (a) establish about the set of
real numbers?

42. Show that the two vertical line segments shown here
both have the same number of points.

*Show that each set can be placed in a one-to-one correspon-
dence with a proper subset of itself to prove that the set is
infinite.*

43. $\{3, 6, 9, 12, \ldots\}$

44. $\{4, 7, 10, 13, 16, \ldots\}$

45. $\left\{\dfrac{3}{4}, \dfrac{3}{8}, \dfrac{3}{12}, \dfrac{3}{16}, \ldots\right\}$

46. $\left\{1, \dfrac{4}{3}, \dfrac{5}{3}, 2, \ldots\right\}$

47. $\left\{\dfrac{1}{9}, \dfrac{1}{18}, \dfrac{1}{27}, \dfrac{1}{36}, \ldots\right\}$

48. $\{-3, -5, -9, -17, \ldots\}$

49. Describe the distinction between *equal* and *equivalent*
sets.

50. Explain how the correspondence suggested in **Example 4**
shows that the set of real numbers between 0 and 1 is
not countable.

🎬 **The Paradoxes of Zeno** *The **Chapter Opener** discussed the
scene in the movie* I.Q. *that deals with Zeno's paradox.
Zeno was born about 496* B.C. *in southern Italy. Two forms of
his paradox are given below. What is your explanation for the
following two examples of Zeno's paradoxes?*

51. Achilles, if he starts out behind a tortoise, can never
overtake the tortoise even if he runs faster.

Suppose Tortoise has a head start of one meter and goes
one-tenth as fast as Achilles. When Achilles reaches the
point where Tortoise started, Tortoise is then one-tenth
meter ahead. When Achilles reaches *that* point, Tortoise
is one-hundredth meter ahead. And so on. Achilles gets
closer but can never catch up.

52. Motion itself cannot occur.

You cannot travel one meter until after you have first
gone a half meter. But you cannot go a half meter until
after you have first gone a quarter meter. And so on.
Even the tiniest motion cannot occur because a tinier
motion would have to occur first.

COLLABORATIVE INVESTIGATION

Surveying the Members of Your Class

This group activity is designed to determine the number of students present in your class without actually counting the members one by one. This will be accomplished by having each member of the class determine one particular set in which he or she belongs, and then finding the sum of the cardinal numbers of the subsets.

For this activity, we designate three sets: X, Y, and Z.

X = {students in the class registered with the Republican party}

Y = {students in the class 24 years of age or younger}

Z = {students who have never been married}

Each student in the class will belong to one of the sets X, X', one of the sets Y, Y', and one of the sets Z, Z'. (The complement of a set consists of all elements in the universe (class) that are not in the set.)

As an example, suppose that a student is a 23-year-old divorced Democrat. The student belongs to the sets X', Y, and Z'. The set to which the student belongs is

$$X' \cap Y \cap Z'.$$

In the Venn diagram that follows, the eight subsets are identified by lowercase letters (a)–(h).

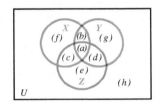

The final column in the following table will be completed when a survey is made. Each student should now determine to which set he or she belongs. (The student described earlier belongs to (g).)

Region	Description in Terms of Set Notation	Number of Class Members in the Set
(a)	$X \cap Y \cap Z$	
(b)	$X \cap Y \cap Z'$	
(c)	$X \cap Y' \cap Z$	
(d)	$X' \cap Y \cap Z$	
(e)	$X' \cap Y' \cap Z$	
(f)	$X \cap Y' \cap Z'$	
(g)	$X' \cap Y \cap Z'$	
(h)	$X' \cap Y' \cap Z'$	

The instructor will now poll the class to see how many members are in each set. *Remember that each class member will belong to one and only one set.*

After the survey is made, find the sum of the numbers in the final column. They should add up to *exactly* the number of students present. Count the class members individually to verify this.

Topics for Discussion

1. Suppose that the final column entries do not add up to the total number of class members. What might have gone wrong?

2. Why can't a class member be a member of more than one of the eight subsets listed?

CHAPTER 2 TEST

In Exercises 1–14, let

U = {a, b, c, d, e, f, g, h}, A = {a, b, c, d},

B = {b, e, a, d},   *and* C = {a, e}.

Find each set.

1. $A \cup C$

2. $B \cap A$

3. B'

4. $A - (B \cap C')$

Identify each statement as true *or* false.

5. $b \in A$

6. $C \subseteq A$

7. $B \subset (A \cup C)$

8. $c \notin C$

9. $n[(A \cup B) - C] = 4$

10. $\emptyset \subset C$

11. $A \cap B'$ is equivalent to $B \cap A'$

12. $(A \cup B)' = A' \cap B'$

Find each of the following.

13. $n(A \times C)$

14. the number of proper subsets of A

Give a word description for each set.

15. $\{-3, -1, 1, 3, 5, 7, 9\}$

16. $\{\text{January, February, March}, \ldots, \text{December}\}$

Express each set in set-builder notation.

17. $\{-1, -2, -3, -4, \ldots\}$

18. $\{24, 32, 40, 48, \ldots, 88\}$

Place $\subset$, $\subseteq$, both, or neither in each blank to make a true statement.

19. $\emptyset$ _____ $\{x \mid x \text{ is a counting number between 20 and 21}\}$

20. $\{4, 9, 16\}$ _____ $\{4, 5, 6, 7, 8, 9, 10\}$

Shade each set in an appropriate Venn diagram.

21. $X \cup Y'$ **22.** $X' \cap Y'$

23. $(X \cup Y) - Z$

24. $[(X \cap Y) \cup (Y \cap Z) \cup (X \cap Z)] - (X \cap Y \cap Z)$

Facts About Inventions *The table lists ten inventions, together with other pertinent data.*

Invention	Date	Inventor	Nation
Adding machine	1642	Pascal	France
Barometer	1643	Torricelli	Italy
Electric razor	1917	Schick	U.S.
Fiber optics	1955	Kapany	England
Geiger counter	1913	Geiger	Germany
Pendulum clock	1657	Huygens	Holland
Radar	1940	Watson-Watt	Scotland
Telegraph	1837	Morse	U.S.
Thermometer	1593	Galileo	Italy
Zipper	1891	Judson	U.S.

Let U = the set of all ten inventions,
     A = the set of items invented in the United States,
and T = the set of items invented in the twentieth century.

List the elements of each set.

25. $A \cap T$

26. $(A \cup T)'$

27. $A - T'$

28. State De Morgan's laws for sets in words rather than symbols.

29. The numerals in the Venn diagram indicate the number of elements in each particular subset.

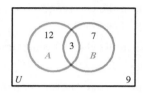

Determine the number of elements in each set.

(a) $A \cup B$ **(b)** $A \cap B'$ **(c)** $(A \cap B)'$

30. **Financial Aid to College Students**   Three major sources of financial aid are government grants, private scholarships, and the colleges themselves. Susan Brilling, Financial Aid Director of a small private Southern college, surveyed the records of 100 sophomores and found the following:

   49 receive government grants
   55 receive private scholarships
   43 receive aid from the college
   23 receive government grants and private scholarships
   18 receive government grants and aid from the college
   28 receive private scholarships and aid from the college
    8 receive help from all three sources.

How many of the students in the survey:

(a) have government grants only?

(b) have private scholarships but not government grants?

(c) receive financial aid from only one of these sources?

(d) receive aid from exactly two of these sources?

(e) receive no financial aid from any of these sources?

(f) receive no aid from the college or from the government?

INTRODUCTION TO LOGIC

In the 2007 movie *Shrek the Third*, Shrek searches for the rightful heir to the throne of the Kingdom of Far Far Away, while Prince Charming schemes to gain the throne for himself. The Prince, knowing that Pinocchio's nose grows if he lies, questions Pinocchio.

PRINCE CHARMING: So tell me puppet, where is Shrek?

PINOCCHIO: Well, I don't know where he's not.

PRINCE CHARMING: You're telling me you don't know where Shrek is?

PINOCCHIO: It wouldn't be inaccurate to assume that I couldn't exactly not say that is or isn't almost partially incorrect.

PRINCE CHARMING: So you do know where he is!

PINOCCHIO: On the contrary, I'm possibly more or less not definitely rejecting the idea that in no way, with any amount of uncertainty, that I undeniably do or do not know where he shouldn't probably be. If that indeed wasn't where he isn't. Even if he wasn't not where I knew he was, it could mean. . . .

Unable to contain his frustration with Pinocchio's roundabout answer, one of the Three Little Pigs blurts out that Shrek has gone to search for the rightful heir. The pig was unable to follow Pinocchio's logic, or lack of it. In this chapter, we examine the basics of the study of logic.

3.1 STATEMENTS AND QUANTIFIERS

Statements • Negations • Symbols • Quantifiers • Quantifiers and Number Sets

Statements

This section introduces the study of **symbolic logic,** which uses letters to represent statements, and symbols for words such as *and, or, not.* Logic is used in the study of the **truth value** (that is, the truth or falsity) of statements with multiple parts. The truth value of such statements depends on their components.

Many kinds of sentences occur in ordinary language, including factual statements, opinions, commands, and questions. Symbolic logic discusses only the type that involves facts. A **statement** is a declarative sentence that is either true or false, but not both simultaneously.

Electronic mail provides a means of communication. ⎫ Statements
$12 + 6 = 13$ ⎬ Each is either true or false.

Access the file. ⎫
Did the Saints win the Super Bowl? ⎬ Not statements
Tim Lincecum is a better baseball player than Cliff Lee. ⎪ Each cannot be identified as
This sentence is false. ⎭ being either true or false.

Of the sentences that are not statements, the first is a command, and the second is a question. The third is an opinion. "This sentence is false" is a paradox: If we assume it is true, then it is false, and if we assume it is false, then it is true.

A **compound statement** may be formed by combining two or more statements. The statements making up a compound statement are called **component statements.** Various **logical connectives,** or simply **connectives,** such as *and, or, not,* and *if . . . then,* can be used in forming compound statements. (While a statement such as "Today is not Tuesday" does not consist of two component statements, for convenience it is considered compound, because its truth value is determined by noting the truth value of a different statement, "Today is Tuesday.")

Gottfried Leibniz (1646–1716) was a wide-ranging philosopher and a universalist who tried to patch up Catholic–Protestant conflicts. He promoted cultural exchange between Europe and the East. Chinese ideograms led him to search for a universal symbolism. He was an early inventor of **symbolic logic.**

▌▌ **EXAMPLE 1** Deciding Whether a Statement Is Compound

Decide whether each statement is compound. If so, identify the connective.

(a) Lord Byron wrote sonnets, and the poem exhibits iambic pentameter.

(b) You can pay me now, or you can pay me later.

(c) If he said it, then it must be true.

(d) My pistol was made by Smith and Wesson.

SOLUTION

(a) This statement is compound, because it is made up of the component statements "Lord Byron wrote sonnets" and "the poem exhibits iambic pentameter." The connective is *and.*

(b) The connective here is *or.* The statement is compound.

(c) The connective here is *if . . . then,* discussed in more detail in **Section 3.3.** The statement is compound.

(d) While the word "and" is used in this statement, it is not used as a *logical* connective. It is part of the name of the manufacturer. The statement is not compound. ▮▮▮

Negations

The sentence "Anthony Mansella has a red truck" is a statement. The **negation** of this statement is "Anthony Mansella does not have a red truck." ***The negation of a true statement is false, and the negation of a false statement is true.***

▮▮ **EXAMPLE 2** Forming Negations

Form the negation of each statement.

(a) That city has a mayor.   **(b)** The moon is not a planet.

SOLUTION

(a) To negate this statement, we introduce *not* into the sentence: "That city does not have a mayor."

(b) The negation is "The moon is a planet." ▮▮▮

One way to detect incorrect negations is to check truth values. *A negation must have the opposite truth value from the original statement.*

The next example uses some of the inequality symbols in **Table 1**. In the case of an inequality involving a variable, the negation must have the opposite truth value for *any* replacement of the variable.

```
TEST  LOGIC
1: =
2: ≠
3: >
4: ≥
5: <
6: ≤
```

The TEST menu of the TI-83/84 Plus calculator allows the user to test the truth or falsity of statements involving =, ≠, >, ≥, <, and ≤. If a statement is true, it returns a 1. If it is false, it returns a 0.

Table 1

Symbolism	Meaning	Examples	
$a < b$	a is less than b	$4 < 9$	$\frac{1}{2} < \frac{3}{4}$
$a > b$	a is greater than b	$6 > 2$	$-5 > -11$
$a \leq b$	a is less than or equal to b	$8 \leq 10$	$3 \leq 3$
$a \geq b$	a is greater than or equal to b	$-2 \geq -3$	$-5 \geq -5$

▮▮ **EXAMPLE 3** Negating Inequalities

Give a negation of each inequality. Do *not* use a slash symbol.

(a) $x < 9$ **(b)** $7x + 11y \geq 77$

```
4<9
                    1
4>9
                    0
```

$4 < 9$ is true, as indicated by the 1.
$4 > 9$ is false, as indicated by the 0.

SOLUTION

(a) The negation of "x is less than 9" is "x is *not* less than 9." Because we cannot use "not," which would require writing $x \not< 9$, phrase the negation as "x is greater than or equal to 9," or

$$x \geq 9.$$

(b) The negation, with no slash, is

$$7x + 11y < 77.$$
▮▮▮

Symbols

The study of logic uses symbols. Statements are represented with letters, such as p, q, or r. Several symbols for connectives are shown in **Table 2**.

Table 2

Connective	Symbol	Type of Statement
and	$\wedge$	Conjunction
or	$\vee$	Disjunction
not	$\sim$	Negation

The symbol $\sim$ represents the connective *not*. If p represents the statement "Barack Obama was president in 2009" then $\sim p$ represents "Barack Obama was not president in 2009."

▌▌ **EXAMPLE 4** Translating from Symbols to Words

Let p represent "It is 70° today," and let q represent "It is Tuesday." Write each symbolic statement in words.

(a) $p \vee q$ **(b)** $\sim p \wedge q$ **(c)** $\sim(p \vee q)$ **(d)** $\sim(p \wedge q)$

SOLUTION

(a) From the table, $\vee$ symbolizes *or*. Thus, $p \vee q$ represents

It is 70° today or it is Tuesday.

(b) It is not 70° today and it is Tuesday.

(c) It is not the case that it is 70° today or it is Tuesday.

(d) It is not the case that it is 70° today and it is Tuesday. ▌▌▌

The statement in **Example 4(c)** usually is translated as **"Neither p nor q."**

Quantifiers

Quantifiers are used to indicate *how many* cases of a particular situation exist. The words **all, each, every,** and **no(ne)** are called **universal quantifiers,** while words and phrases such as **some, there exists,** and **(for) at least one** are called **existential quantifiers.** *Be careful when forming the negation of a statement involving quantifiers.*

The negation of a statement must be false if the given statement is true and must be true if the given statement is false, in all possible cases. Consider this statement.

All girls in the group are named Mary.

Many people would write the negation of this statement as "No girls in the group are named Mary" or "All girls in the group are not named Mary." But neither of these is correct. To see why, look at the three groups below.

Group I: Mary Jane Payne, Mary Meyer, Mary O'Hara
Group II: Mary Johnson, Lisa Pollak, Margaret Watson
Group III: Donna Garbarino, Paula Story, Rhonda Alessi, Kim Falgout

These groups contain all possibilities that need to be considered. In Group I, *all* girls are named Mary. In Group II, *some* girls are named Mary (and some are not). In Group III, *no* girls are named Mary. Look at the truth values in **Table 3** on the next page, and keep in mind that "some" means "at least one (and possibly all)."

Aristotle, the first to systematize the logic we use in everyday life, appears above in a detail from the painting *The School of Athens*, by Raphael. He is shown debating a point with his teacher **Plato.**

Table 3   Truth Value as Applied to:

	Group I	Group II	Group III	
(1) All girls in the group are named Mary. (Given)	T	F	F ←	
(2) No girls in the group are named Mary. (Possible negation)	F	F	T	Negation
(3) All girls in the group are not named Mary. (Possible negation)	F	F	T	
(4) Some girls in the group are not named Mary. (Possible negation)	F	T	T ←	

The negation of the given statement (1) must have opposite truth values in *all* cases. It can be seen that statements (2) and (3) do not satisfy this condition (for Group II), but statement (4) does. It may be concluded that the correct negation for "All girls in the group are named Mary" is "Some girls in the group are not named Mary." Other ways of stating the negation include the following.

> Not all girls in the group are named Mary.
>
> It is not the case that all girls in the group are named Mary.
>
> At least one girl in the group is not named Mary.

Table 4 shows how to find the negation of a statement involving quantifiers.

Table 4   Negations of Quantified Statements

Statement	Negation
All do.	Some do not. (Equivalently: Not all do.)
Some do.	None do. (Equivalently: All do not.)

The negation of the negation of a statement is simply the statement itself. For instance, the negations of the statements in the Negation column are simply the corresponding original statements in the Statement column. As an example, the negation of "Some do not" is "All do."

EXAMPLE 5   Forming Negations of Quantified Statements

Form the negation of each statement.

(a) Some cats have fleas.   **(b)** Some cats do not have fleas.

(c) No cats have fleas.

SOLUTION

(a) Because *some* means "at least one," the statement "Some cats have fleas" is really the same as "At least one cat has fleas." The negation of this is

> "No cat has fleas."

(b) The statement "Some cats do not have fleas" claims that at least one cat, somewhere, does not have fleas. The negation of this is

> "All cats have fleas."

(c) The negation is   "Some cats have fleas."   ⎯ Avoid the incorrect answer "All cats have fleas."   ■■■

Quantifiers and Number Sets

Earlier we introduced sets of numbers.

> **Sets of Numbers**
>
> **Natural or Counting numbers** $\{1, 2, 3, 4, \ldots\}$
>
> **Whole numbers** $\{0, 1, 2, 3, 4, \ldots\}$
>
> **Integers** $\{\ldots, -3, -2, -1, 0, 1, 2, 3, \ldots\}$
>
> **Rational numbers** $\left\{\frac{p}{q} \mid p \text{ and } q \text{ are integers, and } q \neq 0\right\}$
>
> (*Examples:* $\frac{3}{5}$, $-\frac{7}{9}$, 5, 0. Any rational number may be expressed as a terminating decimal number, such as 0.25, or a repeating decimal number, such as 0.666 ....)
>
> **Real numbers** $\{x \mid x \text{ is a number that can be written as a decimal}\}$
>
> **Irrational numbers** $\{x \mid x \text{ is a real number and } x \text{ cannot be written as a quotient of integers}\}$
>
> (*Examples:* $\sqrt{2}$, $\sqrt[3]{4}$, π. Decimal representations of irrational numbers are neither terminating nor repeating.)

▌▌ **EXAMPLE 6** Deciding Whether Quantified Statements Are True or False

Decide whether each statement involving a quantifier is *true* or *false*.

(a) There exists a whole number that is not a natural number.

(b) Every integer is a natural number.

(c) Every natural number is a rational number.

(d) There exists an irrational number that is not real.

SOLUTION

(a) Because there is such a whole number (it is 0), this statement is true.

(b) This statement is false, because we can find at least one integer that is not a natural number. For example, −1 is an integer but is not a natural number.

(c) Because every natural number can be written as a fraction with denominator 1, this statement is true.

(d) In order to be an irrational number, a number must first be real. Because we cannot give an irrational number that is not real, this statement is false. (Had we been able to find at least one, the statement would have then been true.) ▌▌▌

3.1 EXERCISES

Decide whether each is a statement or is not a statement.

1. February 2, 2009, was a Monday.

2. The ZIP code for Oscar, LA, is 70762.

3. Listen, my children, and you shall hear of the midnight ride of Paul Revere.

4. Yield to oncoming traffic.

5. $5 + 9 \neq 14$ and $4 - 1 = 12$

6. $5 + 9 \neq 12$ or $4 - 2 = 5$

7. Some numbers are positive.

8. Millard Fillmore was president of the United States in 1851.

9. Accidents are the main cause of deaths of children under the age of 7.

10. *The Dark Knight* was the top-grossing movie of 2008.

11. Where are you going tomorrow?

12. Behave yourself and sit down.

13. Kevin "Catfish" McCarthy once took a prolonged continuous shower for 340 hours, 40 minutes.

14. One gallon of milk weighs more than 3 pounds.

Decide whether each statement is compound.

15. I read the *Detroit Free Press*, and I read the *Sacramento Bee*.

16. My brother got married in Copenhagen.

17. Tomorrow is Saturday.

18. Mamie Zwettler is younger than 18 years of age, and so is her friend Emma Lister.

19. Jay Beckenstein's wife loves Ben and Jerry's ice cream.

20. The sign on the back of the car read "Canada or bust!"

21. If Lorri Morgan sells her quota, then Michelle Cook will be happy.

22. If Bobby is a politician, then Mitch is a crook.

Write a negation for each statement.

23. Her aunt's name is Hermione.

24. The flowers are to be watered.

25. Every dog has its day.

26. No rain fell in southern California today.

27. Some books are longer than this book.

28. All students present will get another chance.

29. No computer repairman can play blackjack.

30. Some people have all the luck.

31. Everybody loves somebody sometime.

32. Everyone loves a winner.

Give a negation of each inequality. Do not use a slash symbol.

33. $x > 12$

34. $x < -6$

35. $x \geq 5$

36. $x \leq 19$

37. Try to negate the sentence "The exact number of words in this sentence is ten" and see what happens. Explain the problem that arises.

38. Explain why the negation of "$x > 5$" is not "$x < 5$."

Let p represent the statement "She has green eyes" and let q represent the statement "He is 60 years old." Translate each symbolic compound statement into words.

39. $\sim p$

40. $\sim q$

41. $p \wedge q$

42. $p \vee q$

43. $\sim p \vee q$

44. $p \wedge \sim q$

45. $\sim p \vee \sim q$

46. $\sim p \wedge \sim q$

47. $\sim(\sim p \wedge q)$

48. $\sim(p \vee \sim q)$

Let p represent the statement "Chris collects DVDs" and let q represent the statement "Josh is an art major." Convert each compound statement into symbols.

49. Chris collects DVDs and Josh is not an art major.

50. Chris does not collect DVDs or Josh is not an art major.

51. Chris does not collect DVDs or Josh is an art major.

52. Josh is an art major and Chris does not collect DVDs.

53. Neither Chris collects DVDs nor Josh is an art major.

54. Either Josh is an art major or Chris collects DVDs, and it is not the case that both Josh is an art major and Chris collects DVDs.

55. Incorrect use of quantifiers often is heard in everyday language. Suppose you hear that a local electronics chain is having a 40% off sale, and the radio advertisement states "All items are not available in all stores." Do you think that, literally translated, the ad really means what it says? What do you think is really meant? Explain your answer.

56. Repeat **Exercise 55** for the following: "All people don't have the time to devote to maintaining their vehicles properly."

Refer to the groups of art labeled A, B, *and* C, *and identify by letter the group or groups that are satisfied by the given statements involving quantifiers.*

A

B

C

57. All pictures have frames.

58. No picture has a frame.

59. At least one picture does not have a frame.

60. Not every picture has a frame.

61. At least one picture has a frame.

62. No picture does not have a frame.

63. All pictures do not have frames.

64. Not every picture does not have a frame.

Decide whether each statement in Exercises 65–74 involving a quantifier is true *or* false.

65. Every whole number is an integer.

66. Every natural number is an integer.

67. There exists a rational number that is not an integer.

68. There exists an integer that is not a natural number.

69. All rational numbers are real numbers.

70. All irrational numbers are real numbers.

71. Some rational numbers are not integers.

72. Some whole numbers are not rational numbers.

73. Each whole number is a positive number.

74. Each rational number is a positive number.

75. Explain the difference between the following statements.

> All students did not pass the test.
> Not all students passed the test.

76. The statement "For some real number x, $x^2 \geq 0$" is true. However, your friend does not understand why, because he claims that $x^2 \geq 0$ is true for *all* real numbers x (and not *some*). How would you explain his misconception to him?

77. Write the following statement using "every": There is no one here who has not done that at one time or another.

78. Only one of these statements is true. Which one is it?
A. For some real number x, $x \not< 0$.
B. For all real numbers x, $x^3 > 0$.
C. For all real numbers x less than 0, x^2 is also less than 0.
D. For some real number x, $x^2 < 0$.

3.2 TRUTH TABLES AND EQUIVALENT STATEMENTS

Conjunctions • Disjunctions • Negations • Mathematical Statements • Truth Tables • Alternative Method for Constructing Truth Tables • Equivalent Statements and De Morgan's Laws

Conjunctions

Truth values of component statements are used to find truth values of compound statements. To begin, we must decide on truth values of the **conjunction p and q,** symbolized **$p \land q$.** Here, the connective *and* implies the idea of "both." The following statement is true, because each component statement is true.

Monday immediately follows Sunday and March immediately follows February.

True

On the other hand, the following statement is false, even though part of the statement (Monday immediately follows Sunday) is true.

Monday immediately follows Sunday and March immediately follows January.

False

For the conjunction p ∧ q to be true, both p and q must be true. This result is summarized by a table, called a **truth table,** which shows all four of the possible combinations of truth values for the conjunction *p and q.*

Truth Table for the Conjunction *p and q*		

p and q		
p	*q*	*p ∧ q*
T	T	T
T	F	F
F	T	F
F	F	F

■■ EXAMPLE 1   Finding the Truth Value of a Conjunction

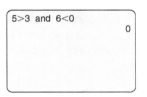

The calculator returns a "0" for 5 > 3 *and* 6 < 0, indicating that the statement is false.

Let *p* represent "5 > 3" and let *q* represent "6 < 0." Find the truth value of *p* ∧ *q.*

SOLUTION

Here *p* is true and *q* is false. Looking in the second row of the conjunction truth table shows that *p* ∧ *q* is false.   ■■■

In some cases, the logical connective *but* is used in compound statements.

He wants to go to the mountains but she wants to go to the beach.

Here, *but* is used in place of *and* to give a different emphasis to the statement. We consider this statement as we would consider the conjunction using the word *and.* The truth table for the conjunction, given above, would apply.

Disjunctions

In ordinary language, the word *or* can be ambiguous. The expression "this or that" can mean either "this or that or both," or "this or that but not both." For example, consider the following statement.

I will paint the wall or I will paint the ceiling.

This statement probably means: "I will paint the wall or I will paint the ceiling or I will paint both." On the other hand, consider the following statement.

I will drive the Lexus or the BMW to the store.

It probably means "I will drive the Lexus, or I will drive the BMW, but I will not drive both."

The symbol ∨ represents the first *or* described. That is,

p ∨ q   means   "p or q or both."   Disjunction

With this meaning of *or,* *p* ∨ *q* is called the **inclusive disjunction,** or just the **disjunction** of *p* and *q.* In everyday language, the disjunction implies the idea of "either." For example, consider the following disjunction.

I have a quarter or I have a dime.

It is true whenever I have either a quarter, a dime, or both. The only way this disjunction could be false would be if I had neither coin. **The disjunction $p \vee q$ is false only if both component statements are false.**

5>3 or 6<0   1

The calculator returns a "1" for $5 > 3$ *or* $6 < 0$, indicating that the statement is true.

Truth Table for the Disjunction p or q

p or q

p	q	$p \vee q$
T	T	T
T	F	T
F	T	T
F	F	F

▮▮ **EXAMPLE 2** Finding the Truth Value of a Disjunction

Let p represent "$5 > 3$" and let q represent "$6 < 0$." Find the truth value of $p \vee q$.

SOLUTION

Here, as in **Example 1,** p is true and q is false. The second row of the disjunction truth table shows that $p \vee q$ is true.   ▮▮▮

The symbol $\geq$ is read **"is greater than or equal to,"** while $\leq$ is read **"is less than or equal to."** If a and b are real numbers, then $a \leq b$ is true if $a < b$ or $a = b$. **Table 5** in the margin shows several statements and the reasons they are true.

Table 5

Statement	Reason That It Is True
$8 \geq 8$	$8 = 8$
$3 \geq 1$	$3 > 1$
$-5 \leq -3$	$-5 < -3$
$-4 \leq -4$	$-4 = -4$

Negations

The **negation** of a statement p, symbolized $\sim p$, must have the opposite truth value from the statement p itself. This leads to the truth table for the negation.

Truth Table for the Negation   not p

not p

p	$\sim p$
T	F
F	T

▮▮ **EXAMPLE 3** Finding the Truth Value of a Compound Statement

Suppose p is false, q is true, and r is false. What is the truth value of the compound statement $\sim p \wedge (q \vee \sim r)$?

SOLUTION

Here parentheses are used to group q and $\sim r$ together. Work first inside the parentheses. Because r is false, $\sim r$ will be true. Because $\sim r$ is true and q is true, find the truth value of $q \vee \sim r$ by looking in the first row of the *or* truth table. This row gives the result T.

Because p is false, $\sim p$ is true, and the final truth value of $\sim p \wedge (q \vee \sim r)$ is found in the top row of the *and* truth table. From the *and* truth table, when $\sim p$ is true, and $q \vee \sim r$ is true, the statement

$$\sim p \wedge (q \vee \sim r) \quad \text{is true.}$$

We can use a short-cut symbolic method that involves replacing the statements with their truth values, letting T represent a true statement and F represent a false statement.

$$\sim p \wedge (q \vee \sim r)$$
$$\sim F \wedge (T \vee \sim F)$$ — Work within parentheses first.
$$T \wedge (T \vee T)$$ ∼F gives T.
$$T \wedge T$$ T ∨ T gives T.

The compound statement is true. → T   T ∧ T gives T.   ▮▮▮

Mathematical Statements

We can use truth tables to determine the truth values of compound mathematical statements.

▮▮ **EXAMPLE 4** Deciding Whether a Compound Mathematical Statement Is True or False

Let p represent the statement $3 > 2$, q represent $5 < 4$, and r represent $3 < 8$. Decide whether each statement is *true* or *false*.

(a) $\sim p \wedge \sim q$ **(b)** $\sim(p \wedge q)$ **(c)** $(\sim p \wedge r) \vee (\sim q \wedge \sim p)$

SOLUTION

(a) Because p is true, $\sim p$ is false. By the *and* truth table, if one part of an "and" statement is false, the entire statement is false.

$$\sim p \wedge \sim q \quad \text{is false.}$$

(b) For $\sim(p \wedge q)$, first work within the parentheses. Because p is true and q is false, $p \wedge q$ is false by the *and* truth table. Next, apply the negation. The negation of a false statement is true.

$$\sim(p \wedge q) \quad \text{is true.}$$

(c) Here p is true, q is false, and r is true. This makes $\sim p$ false and $\sim q$ true. By the *and* truth table, $\sim p \wedge r$ is false, and $\sim q \wedge \sim p$ is also false. By the *or* truth table,

$$(\sim p \wedge r) \vee (\sim q \wedge \sim p) \quad \text{is false.}$$
$$\downarrow \qquad\qquad \downarrow$$
$$F \quad \vee \quad F$$

(Alternatively, see **Example 8(b)**.)   ▮▮▮

When a quantifier is used with a conjunction or a disjunction, we must be careful in determining the truth value, as shown in the following example.

▮▮ **EXAMPLE 5** Deciding Whether a Quantified Mathematical Statement Is True or False

Decide whether each statement is *true* or *false*.

(a) For some real number x, $x < 5$ and $x > 2$.

(b) For every real number x, $x > 0$ or $x < 1$.

(c) For all real numbers x, $x^2 > 0$.

SOLUTION

(a) Replacing x with 3 (as an example) gives $3 < 5$ and $3 > 2$. Because both $3 < 5$ and $3 > 2$ are true statements, the given statement is true by the *and* truth table. (Remember: *Some* means "at least one.")

not(3>2) and not (5<4)
0
not((3>2) and (5<4))
1

Example 4(a) explains why

$$\sim(3 > 2) \wedge [\sim(5 < 4)]$$

is false. The calculator returns a 0. For a true statement such as

$$\sim[(3 > 2) \wedge (5 < 4)],$$

it returns a 1.

George Boole (1815–1864) grew up in poverty. His father, a London tradesman, gave him his first mathematics lessons and taught him to make optical instruments. Boole was largely self-educated. At 16 he worked in an elementary school and by age 20 had opened his own school. He studied mathematics in his spare time. He died of lung disease at age 49.

Boole's ideas have been used in the design of computers and telephone systems.

(b) No matter which real number might be tried as a replacement for x, at least one of the two statements

$$x > 0, \quad x < 1$$

will be true. Because an "or" statement is true if one or both component statements are true, the entire statement as given is true.

(c) Because the quantifier is a universal quantifier, we need only find one case in which the inequality is false to make the entire statement false. Can we find a real number whose square is not positive (that is, not greater than 0)? Yes, we can—0 is the *only* real number whose square is not positive. This statement is false. ▮▮▮

For Further Thought

Whose Picture Am I Looking At?

Raymond Smullyan is one of today's foremost writers of logic puzzles. This professor of mathematics and philosophy is now retired from Indiana University and has written several books on recreational logic, including *What Is the Name of This Book?*, *The Lady or the Tiger?*, and *Alice in Puzzleland*. The first of these includes the following puzzle, which has been around for many years.

For Group or Individual Investigation

A man is looking at a portrait. Someone asked him, "Whose picture are you looking at?" He replied: "Brothers and sisters, I have none, but this man's father is my father's son. ("This man's father" means, of course, the father of the man in the picture.)

Whose picture was the man looking at? (The answer is on **page 96**.)

Truth Tables

p	q	Compound Statement
T	T	
T	F	
F	T	
F	F	

In the preceding examples, the truth value for a given statement was found by going back to the basic truth tables. In the long run, it is easier to first create a complete truth table for the given statement itself. Then final truth values can be read directly from this table.

In this book we use the standard format shown in the margin for listing the possible truth values in compound statements involving two component statements.

▮▮ **EXAMPLE 6** Constructing a Truth Table

Consider the statement $(\sim p \wedge q) \vee \sim q$.

(a) Construct a truth table.

(b) Suppose both p and q are true. Find the truth value of the compound statement.

SOLUTION

(a) Begin by listing all possible combinations of truth values for p and q, as above. Then list the truth values of $\sim p$, which are the opposite of those of p, as shown in the table in the margin.

p	q	$\sim p$
T	T	F
T	F	F
F	T	T
F	F	T

Use only the "~p" column and the "q" column, along with the *and* truth table, to find the truth values of ~p ∧ q. List them in a separate column.

p	q	~p	~p ∧ q
T	T	F	F
T	F	F	F
F	T	T	T
F	F	T	F

Next include a column for ~q.

p	q	~p	~p ∧ q	~q
T	T	F	F	F
T	F	F	F	T
F	T	T	T	F
F	F	T	F	T

Finally, make a column for the entire compound statement. To find the truth values, use *or* to combine ~p ∧ q with ~q.

p	q	~p	~p ∧ q	~q	(~p ∧ q) ∨ ~q
T	T	F	F	F	F
T	F	F	F	T	T
F	T	T	T	F	T
F	F	T	F	T	T

(b) Look in the first row of the final truth table above, where both *p* and *q* have truth value T. Read across the row to find that the compound statement is false.   ■■■

EXAMPLE 7 Constructing a Truth Table

Construct the truth table for $p \land (\sim p \lor \sim q)$.

SOLUTION

Proceed as shown.

p	q	~p	~q	~p ∨ ~q	p ∧ (~p ∨ ~q)
T	T	F	F	F	F
T	F	F	T	T	T
F	T	T	F	T	F
F	F	T	T	T	F

If a compound statement involves three component statements *p*, *q*, and *r*, we will use the following standard format in setting up the truth table.

p	q	r	**Compound Statement**
T	T	T	
T	T	F	
T	F	T	
T	F	F	
F	T	T	
F	T	F	
F	F	T	
F	F	F	

■■■

Emilie, Marquise du Châtelet
(1706–1749) participated in the scientific activity of the generation after Newton and Leibniz. Educated in science, music, and literature, she was studying mathematics at the time (1733) she began a long intellectual relationship with the philosopher **François Voltaire** (1694–1778). She and Voltaire competed independently in 1738 for a prize offered by the French Academy on the subject of fire. Although du Châtelet did not win, her dissertation was published by the academy in 1744.

EXAMPLE 8 Constructing a Truth Table

Consider the statement $(\sim p \wedge r) \vee (\sim q \wedge \sim p)$.

(a) Construct a truth table.

(b) Suppose p is true, q is false, and r is true. Find the truth value of this statement.

SOLUTION

(a) There are three component statements: p, q, and r. The truth table thus requires eight rows to list all possible combinations of truth values of p, q, and r. The final truth table can be found in much the same way as the ones earlier.

p	q	r	$\sim p$	$\sim p \wedge r$	$\sim q$	$\sim q \wedge \sim p$	$(\sim p \wedge r) \vee (\sim q \wedge \sim p)$
T	T	T	F	F	F	F	F
T	T	F	F	F	F	F	F
T	F	T	F	F	T	F	F
T	F	F	F	F	T	F	F
F	T	T	T	T	F	F	T
F	T	F	T	F	F	F	F
F	F	T	T	T	T	T	T
F	F	F	T	F	T	T	T

(b) By the third row of the truth table in part (a), the compound statement is false. (This is an alternative method for working part (c) of **Example 4.**) ▮▮▮

PROBLEM-SOLVING HINT One strategy for problem solving is to notice a pattern and use inductive reasoning. This strategy is applied in the next example.

EXAMPLE 9 Using Inductive Reasoning

If n is a counting number, and a logical statement is composed of n component statements, how many rows will appear in the truth table for the compound statement?

SOLUTION

To answer this question, we examine some of the earlier truth tables in this section. The truth table for the negation has one statement and two rows. The truth tables for the conjunction and the disjunction have two component statements, and each has four rows. The truth table in **Example 8(a)** has three component statements and eight rows.

Summarizing these in **Table 6** (seen in the margin) reveals a pattern encountered earlier. Inductive reasoning leads us to the conjecture that if a logical statement is composed of n component statements, it will have 2^n rows. This can be proved using more advanced concepts. ▮▮▮

Table 6

Number of Statements	Number of Rows
1	$2 = 2^1$
2	$4 = 2^2$
3	$8 = 2^3$

The result of **Example 9** is reminiscent of the formula for the number of subsets of a set having n elements.

Number of Rows in a Truth Table

A logical statement having n component statements will have 2^n rows in its truth table.

Alternative Method for Constructing Truth Tables

After making a reasonable number of truth tables, some people prefer the shortcut method shown in **Example 10,** which repeats **Examples 6 and 8.**

EXAMPLE 10 Constructing Truth Tables

Construct the truth table for each compound statement.

(a) $(\sim p \wedge q) \vee \sim q$ **(b)** $(\sim p \wedge r) \vee (\sim q \wedge \sim p)$

SOLUTION

(a) Start by inserting truth values for $\sim p$ and for q. Then, use the *and* truth table to obtain the truth values for $\sim p \wedge q$.

p	q	($\sim p$	$\wedge$	q)	$\vee$	$\sim q$
T	T	F		T		
T	F	F		F		
F	T	T		T		
F	F	T		F		

p	q	($\sim p$	$\wedge$	q)	$\vee$	$\sim q$
T	T	F	F	T		
T	F	F	F	F		
F	T	T	T	T		
F	F	T	F	F		

Now disregard the two preliminary columns of truth values for $\sim p$ and for q, and insert truth values for $\sim q$. Finally, use the *or* truth table.

p	q	($\sim p \wedge q$)	$\vee$	$\sim q$
T	T	F		F
T	F	F		T
F	T	T		F
F	F	F		T

p	q	($\sim p \wedge q$)	$\vee$	$\sim q$
T	T	F	F	F
T	F	F	T	T
F	T	T	T	F
F	F	F	T	T

These steps can be summarized as follows.

p	q	($\sim p$	$\wedge$	q)	$\vee$	$\sim q$
T	T	F	F	T	F	F
T	F	F	F	F	T	T
F	T	T	T	T	T	F
F	F	T	F	F	T	T
		①	②	①	④	③

The circled numbers indicate the order in which the various columns of the truth table were found.

(b) Work as follows.

p	q	r	($\sim p$	$\wedge$	r)	$\vee$	($\sim q$	$\wedge$	$\sim p$)
T	T	T	F	F	T	F	F	F	F
T	T	F	F	F	F	F	F	F	F
T	F	T	F	F	T	F	T	F	F
T	F	F	F	F	F	F	T	F	F
F	T	T	T	T	T	T	F	F	T
F	T	F	T	F	F	F	F	F	T
F	F	T	T	T	T	T	T	T	T
F	F	F	T	F	F	T	T	T	T
			①	②	①	⑤	③	④	③

The circled numbers indicate the order.

Equivalent Statements and De Morgan's Laws

Two statements are **equivalent** if they have the same truth value in *every* possible situation. The columns of the two truth tables that were the last to be completed will be the same for equivalent statements.

▌▌ **EXAMPLE 11** Deciding Whether Two Statements Are Equivalent

Are the following two statements equivalent?

$$\sim p \wedge \sim q \quad \text{and} \quad \sim(p \vee q)$$

SOLUTION

Construct a truth table for each statement.

p	q	$\sim p \wedge \sim q$
T	T	F
T	F	F
F	T	F
F	F	T

p	q	$\sim(p \vee q)$
T	T	F
T	F	F
F	T	F
F	F	T

Because the truth values are the same in all cases, as shown in the columns in color, the statements $\sim p \wedge \sim q$ and $\sim(p \vee q)$ are equivalent. Equivalence is written with a three-bar symbol, $\equiv$.

$$\sim p \wedge \sim q \equiv \sim(p \vee q) \qquad \blacksquare\blacksquare\blacksquare$$

In the same way, the statements $\sim p \vee \sim q$ and $\sim(p \wedge q)$ are equivalent. We call these equivalences *De Morgan's laws*.

De Morgan's Laws for Logical Statements

For any statements p and q, the following equivalences are valid.

$$\sim(p \vee q) \equiv \sim p \wedge \sim q \quad \text{and} \quad \sim(p \wedge q) \equiv \sim p \vee \sim q$$

(Compare the logic statements of De Morgan's laws with the set versions on **page 64.**) De Morgan's laws can be used to find the negations of certain compound statements.

▌▌ **EXAMPLE 12** Applying De Morgan's Laws

Find a negation of each statement by applying De Morgan's laws.

(a) I got an A or I got a B.   **(b)** She won't try and he will succeed.

(c) $\sim p \vee (q \wedge \sim p)$

SOLUTION

(a) If p represents "I got an A" and q represents "I got a B," then the compound statement is symbolized $p \vee q$. The negation of $p \vee q$ is $\sim(p \vee q)$. By one of De Morgan's laws, this is equivalent to

$$\sim p \wedge \sim q,$$

or, in words,   **I didn't get an A and I didn't get a B.**

This negation is reasonable—the original statement says that I got either an A or a B. The negation says that I didn't get *either* grade.

(b) From one of De Morgan's laws, $\sim(p \wedge q) \equiv \sim p \vee \sim q$, so the negation becomes

She will try or he won't succeed.

(c) Negate both component statements and change $\vee$ to $\wedge$.

$$\sim[\sim p \vee (q \wedge \sim p)] \equiv p \wedge \sim(q \wedge \sim p)$$

Now apply De Morgan's law again.

$$p \wedge \sim(q \wedge \sim p) \equiv p \wedge (\sim q \vee \sim(\sim p))$$
$$\equiv p \wedge (\sim q \vee p)$$

A truth table will show that the statements

$\sim p \vee (q \wedge \sim p)$ and $p \wedge (\sim q \vee p)$ are negations of each other. ■■■

3.2 EXERCISES

Use the concepts introduced in this section to answer Exercises 1–6.

1. If q is false, what must be the truth value of the statement $(p \wedge \sim q) \wedge q$?

2. If q is true, what must be the truth value of the statement $q \vee (q \wedge \sim p)$?

3. If the statement $p \wedge q$ is true, and p is true, then q must be _____.

4. If the statement $p \vee q$ is false, and p is false, then q must be _____.

5. If $\sim(p \vee q)$ is true, what must be the truth values of the component statements?

6. If $\sim(p \wedge q)$ is false, what must be the truth values of the component statements?

Let p represent a false statement and let q represent a true statement. Find the truth value of the given compound statement.

7. $\sim p$

8. $\sim q$

9. $p \vee q$

10. $p \wedge q$

11. $p \vee \sim q$

12. $\sim p \wedge q$

13. $\sim p \vee \sim q$

14. $p \wedge \sim q$

15. $\sim(p \wedge \sim q)$

16. $\sim(\sim p \vee \sim q)$

17. $\sim[\sim p \wedge (\sim q \vee p)]$

18. $\sim[(\sim p \wedge \sim q) \vee \sim q]$

19. Is the statement $6 \geq 2$ a conjunction or a disjunction? Why?

20. Why is the statement $8 \geq 3$ true? Why is $5 \geq 5$ true?

Let p represent a true statement, and q and r represent false statements. Find the truth value of the given compound statement.

21. $(p \wedge r) \vee \sim q$

22. $(q \vee \sim r) \wedge p$

23. $p \wedge (q \vee r)$

24. $(\sim p \wedge q) \vee \sim r$

25. $\sim(p \wedge q) \wedge (r \vee \sim q)$

26. $(\sim r \wedge \sim q) \vee (\sim r \wedge q)$

27. $\sim[(\sim p \wedge q) \vee r]$

28. $\sim[r \vee (\sim q \wedge \sim p)]$

29. $\sim[\sim q \vee (r \wedge \sim p)]$

30. What is the only possible case in which the statement $(p \wedge \sim q) \wedge \sim r$ is true?

Let p represent the statement $16 < 8$, let q represent the statement $5 \ngtr 4$, and let r represent the statement $17 \leq 17$. Find the truth value of the given compound statement.

31. $p \wedge r$

32. $p \vee \sim q$

33. $\sim q \vee \sim r$

34. $\sim p \wedge \sim r$

35. $(p \wedge q) \vee r$

36. $\sim p \vee (\sim r \vee \sim q)$

37. $(\sim r \wedge q) \vee \sim p$

38. $\sim(p \vee \sim q) \vee \sim r$

Give the number of rows in the truth table for each compound statement.

39. $p \vee \sim r$

40. $p \wedge (r \wedge \sim s)$

41. $(\sim p \wedge q) \vee (\sim r \vee \sim s) \wedge r$

42. $[(p \vee q) \wedge (r \wedge s)] \wedge (t \vee \sim p)$

43. $[(\sim p \wedge \sim q) \wedge (\sim r \wedge s \wedge \sim t)] \wedge (\sim u \vee \sim v)$

44. $[(\sim p \wedge \sim q) \vee (\sim r \vee \sim s)]$
    $\vee [(\sim m \wedge \sim n) \wedge (u \wedge \sim v)]$

45. If the truth table for a certain compound statement has 128 rows, how many distinct component statements does it have?

46. Is it possible for the truth table of a compound statement to have exactly 54 rows? Why or why not?

Construct a truth table for each compound statement.

47. $\sim p \wedge q$

48. $\sim p \vee \sim q$

49. $\sim(p \wedge q)$

50. $p \vee \sim q$

51. $(q \vee \sim p) \vee \sim q$

52. $(p \wedge \sim q) \wedge p$

53. $\sim q \wedge (\sim p \vee q)$ **54.** $\sim p \vee (\sim q \wedge \sim p)$

55. $(p \vee \sim q) \wedge (p \wedge q)$

56. $(\sim p \wedge \sim q) \vee (\sim p \vee q)$

57. $(\sim p \wedge q) \wedge r$

58. $r \vee (p \wedge \sim q)$

59. $(\sim p \wedge \sim q) \vee (\sim r \vee \sim p)$

60. $(\sim r \vee \sim p) \wedge (\sim p \vee \sim q)$

61. $\sim (\sim p \wedge \sim q) \vee (\sim r \vee \sim s)$

62. $(\sim r \vee s) \wedge (\sim p \wedge q)$

Use one of De Morgan's laws to write the negation of each statement.

63. You can pay me now or you can pay me later.

64. I am not going or she is going.

65. It is summer and there is no snow.

66. $\frac{1}{2}$ is a positive number and -9 is less than zero.

67. I said yes but she said no.

68. Dan La Chapelle tried to sell the software, but he was unable to do so.

69. $6 - 1 = 5$ and $9 + 13 \neq 7$

70. $8 < 10$ or $5 \neq 2$

71. Prancer or Vixen will lead Santa's reindeer sleigh next Christmas.

72. The lawyer and the client appeared in court.

Identify each statement as true *or* false.

73. For every real number x, $x < 14$ or $x > 6$.

74. For every real number x, $x > 9$ or $x < 9$.

75. There exists an integer n such that $n > 0$ and $n < 0$.

76. For some integer n, $n \geq 3$ and $n \leq 3$.

77. Complete the truth table for *exclusive disjunction*. The symbol $\underline{\vee}$ represents "one or the other is true, but not both."

p	q	$p \underline{\vee} q$
T	T	
T	F	
F	T	
F	F	

Exclusive disjunction

78. Attorneys sometimes use the phrase "and/or." This phrase corresponds to which usage of the word *or*: inclusive or exclusive disjunction?

Decide whether each compound statement is true *or* false. *Remember that* $\underline{\vee}$ *is the* exclusive disjunction *of* **Exercise 77.**

79. $3 + 1 = 4 \underline{\vee} 2 + 5 = 7$

80. $3 + 1 = 4 \underline{\vee} 2 + 5 = 10$

81. $3 + 1 = 6 \underline{\vee} 2 + 5 = 7$

82. $3 + 1 = 12 \underline{\vee} 2 + 5 = 10$

83. In his book *The Lady or the Tiger and Other Logic Puzzles,* Raymond Smullyan proposes the following problem. It is taken from the classic Frank Stockton short story, in which a prisoner must make a choice between two doors: behind one is a beautiful lady, and behind the other is a hungry tiger.

What if each door has a sign, and the man knows that only one sign is true?

The sign on Door 1 reads:

IN THIS ROOM THERE IS A LADY AND IN THE OTHER ROOM THERE IS A TIGER.

The sign on Door 2 reads:

IN ONE OF THESE ROOMS THERE IS A LADY AND IN ONE OF THESE ROOMS THERE IS A TIGER.

With this information, the man is able to choose the correct door. Can you?

84. In Raymond Smullyan's books, he writes about an island in which certain inhabitants are called knights and others are called knaves. Knights always tell the truth, and knaves always lie. Every inhabitant is either a knight or a knave.

Three inhabitants—A, B, and C—were standing together in a garden. A stranger passed by and asked A, "Are you a knight or a knave?" A answered, but rather indistinctly, so the stranger could not make out what he said. The stranger then asked B, "What did A say?" B replied "A said that he is a knave." At this point, the third inhabitant, C, said, "Don't believe B; he is lying!"

The question is, what are B and C?

3.3 THE CONDITIONAL AND CIRCUITS

Conditionals • Negation of a Conditional • Circuits

In his April 21, 1989, five-star review of *Field of Dreams*, the *Chicago Sun-Times* movie critic Roger Ebert gave an explanation of why the movie has become an American classic.

There is a speech in this movie about baseball that is so simple and true that it is heartbreaking. And the whole attitude toward the players reflects that attitude. Why do they come back from the great beyond and play in this cornfield? Not to make any kind of vast, earthshattering statement, but simply to hit a few and field a few, and remind us of a good and innocent time.

The photo above was taken in 2007 in Dyersville, Iowa, at the actual scene of the filming. The carving "Ray Loves Annie" in the bleacher seats can be seen in a quick shot during the movie. It has weathered over time.

Conditionals

"If you build it, he will come."
—The Voice in the movie *Field of Dreams*

Ray Kinsella, an Iowa farmer in the movie *Field of Dreams*, hears a voice from the sky. No one else, including his wife Annie, can hear it. Ray interprets it as a promise that if he builds a baseball field in his cornfield, then the ghost of Shoeless Joe Jackson (a baseball star in the early days of the twentieth century) would come to play on it.

This promise came in the form of a conditional statement. A **conditional** statement is a compound statement that uses the connective *if . . . then.*

$$\left.\begin{array}{l} \textit{If} \text{ I read for too long, } \textit{then} \text{ I get tired.} \\ \textit{If} \text{ looks could kill, } \textit{then} \text{ I would be dead.} \\ \textit{If} \text{ he doesn't get back soon, } \textit{then} \text{ you should go look for him.} \end{array}\right\} \begin{array}{l} \text{Conditional} \\ \text{statements} \end{array}$$

In each of these conditional statements, the component coming after the word *if* gives a condition (but not necessarily the only condition) under which the statement coming after *then* will be true. For example, "If it is over 90°, then I'll go to the mountains" tells one possible condition under which I will go to the mountains—if the temperature is over 90°.

The conditional is written with an arrow, so "if p, then q" is symbolized as follows.

$$p \rightarrow q \qquad \text{If } p, \text{then } q.$$

We read $p \rightarrow q$ as "p **implies** q" or "**if p, then q**." In the conditional $p \rightarrow q$, the statement p is the **antecedent,** while q is the **consequent.**

The conditional connective may not always be explicitly stated. That is, it may be "hidden" in an everyday expression. For example, consider the following statement.

Big girls don't cry.

It can be written in *if . . . then* form as

If you're a big girl, *then* you don't cry.

As another example, consider this statement.

It is difficult to study when you are distracted.

It can be written

If you are distracted, *then* it is difficult to study.

In the quotation "If you build it, he will come" from the movie *Field of Dreams*, the word "then" is not stated but understood from the context of the statement. "You build it" is the antecedent, and "he will come" is the consequent.

The conditional truth table is a little harder to define than the tables in the previous section. To see how to define the conditional truth table, we analyze a statement made by a politician, Senator Laura Kennedy.

If I am elected, then taxes will go down.

There are four possible combinations of truth values for the two component statements. Let p represent "I am elected," and let q represent "Taxes will go down."

The importance of **symbols** was emphasized by the American philosopher-logician **Charles Sanders Peirce** (1839–1914), who asserted the nature of humans as symbol-using or sign-using organisms. Symbolic notation is half of mathematics, Bertrand Russell once said.

As we analyze the four possibilities, it is helpful to think in terms of the following: "Did Senator Laura Kennedy lie?" If she lied, then the conditional statement is considered false. If she did not lie, then the conditional statement is considered true.

Possibility	Elected?	Taxes Go Down?	
1	Yes	Yes	p is T, q is T.
2	Yes	No	p is T, q is F.
3	No	Yes	p is F, q is T.
4	No	No	p is F, q is F.

The four possibilities are as follows.

1. In the first case assume that the senator was elected and taxes did go down (p is T, q is T). The senator told the truth, so place T in the first row of the truth table. (We do not claim that taxes went down *because* she was elected. It is possible that she had nothing to do with it at all.)

2. In the second case assume that the senator was elected and taxes did not go down (p is T, q is F). Then the senator did not tell the truth (that is, she lied). So we put F in the second row of the truth table.

3. In the third case assume that the senator was defeated, but taxes went down anyway (p is F, q is T). The senator did not lie. She only promised a tax reduction if she were elected. She said nothing about what would happen if she were not elected. In fact, her campaign promise gives no information about what would happen if she lost. Because we cannot say that the senator lied, place T in the third row of the truth table. (See the margin note.)

4. In the last case assume that the senator was defeated and taxes did not go down (p is F, q is F). We cannot blame her, because she only promised to reduce taxes if elected. Thus, T goes in the last row of the truth table.

The completed truth table for the conditional is defined as follows.

You Lie! (or Do You?) Granted, the T for Case 3 is less obvious than the F for Case 2. However, the laws of symbolic logic permit only one of two truth values. Since no lie can be established in Case 3, we give the senator the benefit of the doubt. Likewise, *any* conditional statement is declared to be true whenever its antecedent is false.

Truth Table for the Conditional   If p, then q

	If p, then q	
p	q	$p \rightarrow q$
T	T	T
T	F	F
F	T	T
F	F	T

The use of the conditional connective in no way implies a cause-and-effect relationship. Any two statements may have an arrow placed between them to create a compound statement. Consider this example.

If I pass mathematics, then the sun will rise the next day.

It is true, because the consequent is true. (See the special characteristics following **Example 1** on the next page.) There is, however, no cause-and-effect connection between my passing mathematics and the rising of the sun. The sun will rise no matter what grade I get.

EXAMPLE 1 Finding the Truth Value of a Conditional

Given that p, q, and r are all false, find the truth value of the statement.

$$(p \rightarrow \sim q) \rightarrow (\sim r \rightarrow q)$$

SOLUTION

Using the short-cut method explained in **Example 3** of the previous section, we can replace p, q, and r with F (since each is false) and proceed as before, using the negation and conditional truth tables as necessary.

$$
\begin{array}{ccll}
(p \rightarrow \sim q) & \rightarrow & (\sim r \rightarrow q) & \\
(F \rightarrow \sim F) & \rightarrow & (\sim F \rightarrow F) & \\
(F \rightarrow T) & \rightarrow & (T \rightarrow F) & \text{Use the negation truth table.} \\
T & \rightarrow & F & \text{Use the conditional truth table.} \\
& F & &
\end{array}
$$

The statement $(p \rightarrow \sim q) \rightarrow (\sim r \rightarrow q)$ is false when p, q, and r are all false. ■■■

> **Special Characteristics of Conditional Statements**
>
> 1. $p \rightarrow q$ is false only when the antecedent is *true* and the consequent is *false*.
>
> 2. If the antecedent is *false*, then $p \rightarrow q$ is automatically *true*.
>
> 3. If the consequent is *true*, then $p \rightarrow q$ is automatically *true*.

EXAMPLE 2 Determining Whether a Conditional Is True or False

Write *true* or *false* for each statement. Here T represents a true statement, and F represents a false statement.

(a) $T \rightarrow (7 = 3)$ **(b)** $(8 < 2) \rightarrow F$ **(c)** $(4 \neq 3 + 1) \rightarrow T$

SOLUTION

(a) Because the antecedent is true, while the consequent, $7 = 3$, is false, the given statement is false by the first point mentioned above.

(b) The antecedent is false, so the given statement is true by the second observation.

(c) The consequent is true, making the statement true by the third characteristic of conditional statements. ■■■

EXAMPLE 3 Constructing Truth Tables

Construct a truth table for each statement.

(a) $(\sim p \rightarrow \sim q) \rightarrow (\sim p \wedge q)$ **(b)** $(p \rightarrow q) \rightarrow (\sim p \vee q)$

SOLUTION

(a) Insert the truth values of $\sim p$ and $\sim q$. Find the truth values of $\sim p \rightarrow \sim q$.

p	q	$\sim p$	$\sim q$	$\sim p \rightarrow \sim q$
T	T	F	F	T
T	F	F	T	T
F	T	T	F	F
F	F	T	T	T

*Sidebar (left margin):*

```
PROGRAM:SIGN
: Input A
: If A>0
: Then
: Disp "POSITIVE"
:
:
```

```
PROGRAM:SIGN
:
: Else
: Disp "NOT POSITIVE"
: End
:
```

```
prgmSIGN
?3
POSITIVE
                    Done
```

```
prgmSIGN
?-5
NOT POSITIVE
                    Done
```

Conditional statements are useful in writing programs. The short program in the first two screens determines whether a number is positive. Notice the lines that begin with *If* and *Then*.

Next use $\sim p$ and q to find the truth values of $\sim p \wedge q$.

p	q	$\sim p$	$\sim q$	$\sim p \to \sim q$	$\sim p \wedge q$
T	T	F	F	T	F
T	F	F	T	T	F
F	T	T	F	F	T
F	F	T	T	T	F

Now find the truth values of $(\sim p \to \sim q) \to (\sim p \wedge q)$.

p	q	$\sim p$	$\sim q$	$\sim p \to \sim q$	$\sim p \wedge q$	$(\sim p \to \sim q) \to (\sim p \wedge q)$
T	T	F	F	T	F	F
T	F	F	T	T	F	F
F	T	T	F	F	T	T
F	F	T	T	T	F	F

(b) For $(p \to q) \to (\sim p \vee q)$, go through steps similar to the ones above.

p	q	$p \to q$	$\sim p$	$\sim p \vee q$	$(p \to q) \to (\sim p \vee q)$
T	T	T	F	T	T
T	F	F	F	F	T
F	T	T	T	T	T
F	F	T	T	T	T

▉▉▉

As the truth table in **Example 3(b)** shows, the statement

$$(p \to q) \to (\sim p \vee q)$$

is always true, no matter what the truth values of the components. Such a statement is called a **tautology.** Several other examples of tautologies (as can be checked by forming truth tables) are

$$p \vee \sim p, \quad p \to p, \quad \text{and} \quad (\sim p \vee \sim q) \to \sim (p \wedge q). \quad \text{Tautologies}$$

The truth tables in **Example 3** also could have been found by the alternative method shown in **Section 3.2.**

Negation of a Conditional

Suppose that someone makes the following conditional statement.

"If it rains, then I take my umbrella."

When will the person have lied to you? The only case in which you would have been misled is when it rains *and* the person does *not* take the umbrella. Letting p represent "it rains" and q represent "I take my umbrella," you might suspect that the symbolic statement

$$p \wedge \sim q$$

is a candidate for the negation of $p \to q$. This would imply that

$$\sim (p \to q) \equiv p \wedge \sim q.$$

This is indeed the case, as the following truth table indicates.

p	q	$p \to q$	$\sim (p \to q)$	$\sim q$	$p \wedge \sim q$
T	T	T	F	F	F
T	F	F	T	T	T
F	T	T	F	F	F
F	F	T	F	T	F

↑ = ↑

In the 1959 Disney short film *Donald in Mathmagicland,* Donald Duck, dressed as Alice from Lewis Carroll's *Through the Looking Glass,* is attacked by a "none-too-friendly group of chess pieces." Logic and **chess** have been paired for centuries. Most scholars agree that chess dates back at least 1500 years, coming from Northern India and Afghanistan following trade routes through Persia.

Good chess players rely on memory, imagination, determination, and inspiration. They are pattern thinkers that use long-established sets of consequences and probabilities.

In the end, logic does not necessarily dictate the final outcome of any chess game, for if it did, humans would not stand a chance when playing faceless, number-crunching computers.

© Disney Enterprises, Inc.

Sources: www.imdb.com, Walter A. Smart.

> **Negation of** $p \rightarrow q$
>
> The negation of $p \rightarrow q$ is $p \wedge \sim q$.

Because

$$\sim(p \rightarrow q) \equiv p \wedge \sim q,$$

by negating each expression we have

$$\sim[\sim(p \rightarrow q)] \equiv \sim(p \wedge \sim q).$$

The left side of the above equivalence is $p \rightarrow q$, and one of De Morgan's laws can be applied to the right side.

$$p \rightarrow q \equiv \sim p \vee \sim(\sim q)$$
$$p \rightarrow q \equiv \sim p \vee q$$

This final row indicates that a conditional may be written as a disjunction.

> **Writing a Conditional as a Disjunction**
>
> $p \rightarrow q$ is equivalent to $\sim p \vee q$.

■ EXAMPLE 4 Determining Negations

Determine the negation of each statement.

(a) If you build it, he will come.   **(b)** All dogs have fleas.

SOLUTION

> Do not try to negate a conditional with another conditional.

(a) If b represents "you build it" and q represents "he will come," then the given statement can be symbolized by $b \rightarrow q$. The negation of $b \rightarrow q$, as shown earlier, is $b \wedge \sim q$, so the negation of the statement is

  You build it and he will not come.

(b) First, we must restate the given statement in *if . . . then* form.

  If it is a dog, then it has fleas.

Based on our earlier discussion, the negation is

  It is a dog and it does not have fleas.   ■■■

As seen in **Example 4,** the negation of a conditional statement is written as a conjunction.

■ EXAMPLE 5 Determining Statements Equivalent to Conditionals

Write each conditional as an equivalent statement without using *if . . . then.*

(a) If the Indians win the pennant, then Johnny will go to the World Series.

(b) If it's Borden's, it's got to be good.

SOLUTION

(a) Because the conditional $p \rightarrow q$ is equivalent to $\sim p \vee q$, let p represent "The Indians win the pennant" and q represent "Johnny will go to the World Series." Restate the conditional as

  The Indians do not win the pennant or Johnny will go to the World Series.

(b) If *p* represents "it's Borden's" and if *q* represents "it's got to be good," the conditional may be restated as

It's not Borden's or it's got to be good.   ▊▊▊

Circuits

Figure 1

One of the first nonmathematical applications of symbolic logic was seen in the master's thesis of Claude Shannon in 1937. Shannon showed how logic could be used to design electrical circuits. His work was immediately used by computer designers. Then in the developmental stage, computers could be simplified and built for less money using the ideas of Shannon.

p   Series   *q*
circuit

Figure 2

To see how Shannon's ideas work, look at the electrical switch shown in **Figure 1.** We assume that current will flow through this switch when it is closed and not when it is open.

Figure 2 shows two switches connected in *series*. In such a circuit, current will flow only when both switches are closed. Note how closely a series circuit corresponds to the conjunction $p \wedge q$. We know that $p \wedge q$ is true only when both *p* and *q* are true.

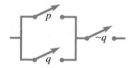

p

q

Parallel circuit

Figure 3

A circuit corresponding to the disjunction $p \vee q$ can be found by drawing a *parallel* circuit, as in **Figure 3.** Here, current flows if either *p or q* is closed or if both *p and q* are closed.

The circuit in **Figure 4** corresponds to the statement $(p \vee q) \wedge {\sim}q$, which is a compound statement involving both a conjunction and a disjunction.

p

~*q*

q

Figure 4

Simplifying an electrical circuit depends on the idea of equivalent statements from **Section 3.2.** Recall that two statements are equivalent if they have the same truth table final column. The symbol ≡ is used to indicate that the two statements are equivalent. Some equivalent statements are shown in the following box.

Equivalent Statements Used to Simplify Circuits

$$p \vee (q \wedge r) \equiv (p \vee q) \wedge (p \vee r) \qquad p \vee p \equiv p$$
$$p \wedge (q \vee r) \equiv (p \wedge q) \vee (p \wedge r) \qquad p \wedge p \equiv p$$
$$p \rightarrow q \equiv {\sim}q \rightarrow {\sim}p \qquad {\sim}(p \wedge q) \equiv {\sim}p \vee {\sim}q$$
$$p \rightarrow q \equiv {\sim}p \vee q \qquad {\sim}(p \vee q) \equiv {\sim}p \wedge {\sim}q$$

If T represents any true statement and F represents any false statement, then

$$p \vee \text{T} \equiv \text{T} \qquad p \vee {\sim}p \equiv \text{T}$$
$$p \wedge \text{F} \equiv \text{F} \qquad p \wedge {\sim}p \equiv \text{F}.$$

Circuits can be used as models of compound statements, with a closed switch corresponding to T, while an open switch corresponds to F.

▊▊ **EXAMPLE 6** Simplifying a Circuit

p   *q*

p   *r*

Figure 5

Simplify the circuit of **Figure 5.**

SOLUTION

At the top of **Figure 5,** *p* and *q* are connected in series, and at the bottom, *p* and *r* are connected in series. These are interpreted as the compound statements $p \wedge q$ and $p \wedge r$, respectively. These two conjunctions are connected in parallel, as indicated by the figure treated as a whole.

Write the disjunction of the two conjunctions.

$$(p \wedge q) \vee (p \wedge r)$$

Figure 6

(Think of the two switches labeled "p" as being controlled by the same lever.) By one of the pairs of equivalent statements in the preceding box,

$$(p \wedge q) \vee (p \wedge r) \equiv p \wedge (q \vee r),$$

which has the circuit of **Figure 6.** This circuit is logically equivalent to the one in **Figure 5,** and yet it contains only three switches instead of four—which might well lead to a large savings in manufacturing costs. ■■■

EXAMPLE 7 Drawing a Circuit for a Conditional Statement

Draw a circuit for $p \rightarrow (q \wedge \sim r)$.

SOLUTION

From the list of equivalent statements in the box, $p \rightarrow q$ is equivalent to $\sim p \vee q$. This equivalence gives $p \rightarrow (q \wedge \sim r) \equiv \sim p \vee (q \wedge \sim r)$, which has the circuit diagram in **Figure 7.** ■■■

Figure 7

3.3 EXERCISES

Rewrite each statement using the if . . . then *connective. Rearrange the wording or add words as necessary.*

1. You can believe it if you see it on the Internet.

2. It must be alive if it is breathing.

3. Every integer divisible by 10 is divisible by 5.

4. All perfect square integers have units digit 0, 1, 4, 5, 6, or 9.

5. All Marines love boot camp.

6. Every picture tells a story.

7. No pandas live in Idaho.

8. No guinea pigs are scholars.

9. An opium eater cannot have self-command.

10. Running Bear loves Little White Dove.

Decide whether each statement is true *or* false.

11. If the antecedent of a conditional statement is false, the conditional statement is true.

12. If the consequent of a conditional statement is true, the conditional statement is true.

13. If q is true, then $(p \wedge q) \rightarrow q$ is true.

14. If p is true, then $\sim p \rightarrow (q \vee r)$ is true.

15. The negation of "If pigs fly, I'll believe it" is "If pigs don't fly, I won't believe it."

16. The statements "If it flies, then it's a bird" and "It does not fly or it's a bird" are logically equivalent.

17. Given that $\sim p$ is true and q is false, the conditional $p \rightarrow q$ is true.

18. Given that $\sim p$ is false and q is false, the conditional $p \rightarrow q$ is true.

19. Explain why the statement "If $3 = 5$, then $4 = 6$" is true.

20. In a few sentences, explain how to determine the truth value of a conditional statement.

Tell whether each conditional is true (T) *or* false (F).

21. $T \rightarrow (7 < 3)$ 22. $F \rightarrow (4 \neq 8)$

23. $F \rightarrow (5 \neq 5)$ 24. $(8 \geq 8) \rightarrow F$

25. $(5^2 \neq 25) \rightarrow (8 - 8 = 16)$

26. $(5 = 12 - 7) \rightarrow (9 > 0)$

Let s represent "She has a bird for a pet," *let p represent* "he trains dogs," *and let m represent* "they raise alpacas." *Express each compound statement in words.*

27. $\sim m \rightarrow p$ **28.** $p \rightarrow \sim m$

29. $s \rightarrow (m \wedge p)$ **30.** $(s \wedge p) \rightarrow m$

31. $\sim p \rightarrow (\sim m \vee s)$ **32.** $(\sim s \vee \sim m) \rightarrow \sim p$

Let b represent "I ride my bike," *let s represent* "it snows," *and let p represent* "the play is cancelled." *Write each compound statement in symbols.*

33. If I ride my bike, then the play is cancelled.

34. If it snows, then I ride my bike.

35. If the play is cancelled, then it does not snow.

36. If I do not ride my bike, then it does not snow.

37. The play is cancelled, and if it snows then I do not ride my bike.

38. I ride my bike, or if the play is cancelled then it snows.

39. It snows if the play is cancelled.

40. I'll ride my bike if it doesn't snow.

Find the truth value of each statement. Assume that p and r are false, and q is true.

41. $\sim r \rightarrow q$ **42.** $\sim p \rightarrow \sim r$

43. $q \rightarrow p$ **44.** $\sim r \rightarrow p$

45. $p \rightarrow q$ **46.** $\sim q \rightarrow r$

47. $\sim p \rightarrow (q \wedge r)$

48. $(\sim r \vee p) \rightarrow p$

49. $\sim q \rightarrow (p \wedge r)$

50. $(\sim p \wedge \sim q) \rightarrow (p \wedge \sim r)$

51. $(p \rightarrow \sim q) \rightarrow (\sim p \wedge \sim r)$

52. $(p \rightarrow \sim q) \wedge (p \rightarrow r)$

53. Explain why, if we know that p is true, we also know that

$$[r \vee (p \vee s)] \rightarrow (p \vee q)$$

is true, even if we are not given the truth values of q, r, and s.

54. Construct a true statement involving a conditional, a conjunction, a disjunction, and a negation (not necessarily in that order), that consists of component statements p, q, and r, with all of these component statements false.

Construct a truth table for each statement. Identify any tautologies.

55. $\sim q \rightarrow p$

56. $p \rightarrow \sim q$

57. $(\sim p \rightarrow q) \rightarrow p$

58. $(\sim q \rightarrow \sim p) \rightarrow \sim q$

59. $(p \vee q) \rightarrow (q \vee p)$

60. $(p \wedge q) \rightarrow (p \vee q)$

61. $(\sim p \rightarrow \sim q) \rightarrow (p \wedge q)$

62. $r \rightarrow (p \wedge \sim q)$

63. $[(r \vee p) \wedge \sim q] \rightarrow p$

64. $[(r \wedge p) \wedge (p \wedge q)] \rightarrow p$

65. $(\sim r \rightarrow s) \vee (p \rightarrow \sim q)$

66. $(\sim p \wedge \sim q) \rightarrow (s \rightarrow r)$

67. What is the minimum number of Fs that must appear in the final column of a truth table for us to be assured that the statement is not a tautology?

68. If all truth values in the final column of a truth table are F, how can we easily transform the statement into a tautology?

Write the negation of each statement. Remember that the negation of $p \rightarrow q$ is $p \wedge \sim q$.

69. If that is an authentic Rolex watch, I'll be surprised.

70. If Minnie Ripperton reaches that note, she will shatter glass.

71. If the English measures are not converted to metric measures, then the spacecraft will crash on the surface of Saturn.

72. If you say "I do," then you'll be happy for the rest of your life.

73. "If you want to be happy for the rest of your life, never make a pretty woman your wife." *Jimmy Soul*

74. "If loving you is wrong, I don't want to be right." *Luther Ingram*

Write each statement as an equivalent statement that does not use the if . . . then *connective. Remember that*

$$p \to q \quad \text{is equivalent to} \quad \sim p \lor q.$$

75. If you give your plants tender, loving care, they flourish.

76. If the check is in the mail, I will buy you lunch.

77. If she doesn't, he will.

78. If I say "black," she says "white."

79. All residents of Pensacola are residents of Florida.

80. All women were once girls.

Use truth tables to decide which of the pairs of statements are equivalent.

81. $p \to q$; $\sim p \lor q$

82. $\sim(p \to q)$; $p \land \sim q$

83. $p \to q$; $\sim q \to \sim p$

84. $q \to p$; $\sim p \to \sim q$

85. $p \land \sim q$; $\sim q \to \sim p$

86. $p \to q$; $q \to p$

87. $p \to \sim q$; $\sim p \lor \sim q$

88. $\sim p \land q$; $\sim p \to q$

89. $q \to \sim p$; $p \to \sim q$

90. $\sim p \to q$; $p \lor q$

Write a logical statement representing each of the following circuits. Simplify each circuit when possible.

91.

92.

93.

94.

95.

96.

Draw circuits representing the following statements as they are given. Simplify if possible.

97. $p \land (q \lor \sim p)$

98. $(\sim p \land \sim q) \land \sim r$

99. $(p \lor q) \land (\sim p \land \sim q)$

100. $(\sim q \land \sim p) \lor (\sim p \lor q)$

101. $[(p \lor q) \land r] \land \sim p$

102. $[(\sim p \land \sim r) \lor \sim q] \land (\sim p \land r)$

103. $\sim q \to (\sim p \to q)$

104. $\sim p \to (\sim p \lor \sim q)$

105. Refer to **Figures 5 and 6** in **Example 6.** Suppose the cost of the use of one switch for an hour is $0.06. By using the circuit in **Figure 6** rather than the circuit in **Figure 5,** what is the savings for a year of 365 days, assuming that the circuit is in continuous use?

106. Explain why the circuit shown will always have exactly one open switch. What does this circuit simplify to?

3.4 THE CONDITIONAL AND RELATED STATEMENTS

Converse, Inverse, and Contrapositive • Alternative Forms of "If p, then q"
• Biconditionals • Summary of Truth Tables

Converse, Inverse, and Contrapositive

Alfred North Whitehead (1861–1947) and Bertrand Russell worked together on *Principia Mathematica*. During that time, Whitehead was teaching mathematics at Cambridge University and had written *Universal Algebra*. In 1910 he went to the University of London, exploring not only the philosophical basis of science but also the "aims of education" (as he called one of his books). It was as a philosopher that he was invited to Harvard University in 1924. Whitehead died at the age of 86 in Cambridge, Massachusetts.

Many mathematical properties and theorems are stated in *if . . . then* form. Any conditional statement $p \rightarrow q$ is made up of an antecedent p and a consequent q. If they are interchanged, negated, or both, a new conditional statement is formed. Suppose that we begin with a conditional statement.

If you stay, then I go.   Conditional Statement

By interchanging the antecedent ("you stay") and the consequent ("I go"), we obtain a new conditional statement.

If I go, then you stay.   Converse

This new conditional is called the **converse** of the given conditional statement.

By negating both the antecedent and the consequent, we obtain the **inverse** of the given conditional statement.

If you do not stay, then I do not go.   Inverse

If the antecedent and the consequent are both interchanged *and* negated, the **contrapositive** of the given conditional statement is formed.

If I do not go, then you do not stay.   Contrapositive

These three related statements for the conditional $p \rightarrow q$ are summarized below. (***The inverse is the contrapositive of the converse.***)

Related Conditional Statements

Conditional Statement	$p \rightarrow q$	(If p, then q.)
Converse	$q \rightarrow p$	(If q, then p.)
Inverse	$\sim p \rightarrow \sim q$	(If not p, then not q.)
Contrapositive	$\sim q \rightarrow \sim p$	(If not q, then not p.)

▌▌ **EXAMPLE 1** Determining Related Conditional Statements

Determine each of the following, given the conditional statement

If I live in Orlando, then I live in Florida.

(a) the converse   **(b)** the inverse   **(c)** the contrapositive

SOLUTION

(a) Let p represent "I live in Orlando" and q represent "I live in Florida." Then the given statement may be written $p \rightarrow q$. The converse, $q \rightarrow p$, is

If I live in Florida, then I live in Orlando.

Notice that for this statement, the converse is not necessarily true, even though the given statement is true.

(b) The inverse of $p \rightarrow q$ is $\sim p \rightarrow \sim q$. Thus, the inverse is

If I don't live in Orlando, then I don't live in Florida.

Again, this is not necessarily true.

Bertrand Russell (1872–1970) was a student of Whitehead's before they wrote the *Principia*. Like his teacher, Russell turned toward philosophy. His works include a critique of Leibniz, analyses of mind and of matter, and a history of Western thought.

Russell became a public figure because of his involvement in social issues. Deeply aware of human loneliness, he was "passionately desirous of finding ways of diminishing this tragic isolation." During World War I he was an antiwar crusader, and he was imprisoned briefly. Again in the 1960s he championed peace. He wrote many books on social issues, winning the Nobel Prize for Literature in 1950.

(c) The contrapositive, $\sim q \rightarrow \sim p$, is

If I don't live in Florida, then I don't live in Orlando.

The contrapositive, like the given conditional statement, is true.   ▮▮▮

Example 1 shows that the converse and inverse of a true statement need not be true. They *can* be true, but they need not be. The relationships between the related conditionals are shown in the truth table that follows.

		Conditional	Converse	Inverse	Contrapositive
p	q	$p \rightarrow q$	$q \rightarrow p$	$\sim p \rightarrow \sim q$	$\sim q \rightarrow \sim p$
T	T	T	T	T	T
T	F	F	T	T	F
F	T	T	F	F	T
F	F	T	T	T	T

Equivalent (Conditional ↔ Contrapositive)
Equivalent (Converse ↔ Inverse)

As this truth table shows,

1. *A conditional statement and its contrapositive always have the same truth values,* making it possible to replace any statement with its contrapositive without affecting the logical meaning.
2. *The converse and inverse always have the same truth values.*

Equivalences

A conditional statement and its contrapositive are equivalent. Also, the converse and the inverse are equivalent.

EXAMPLE 2   Determining Related Conditional Statements

For the conditional statement $\sim p \rightarrow q$, write each of the following.

(a) the converse   **(b)** the inverse   **(c)** the contrapositive

SOLUTION

(a) The converse of $\sim p \rightarrow q$ is $q \rightarrow \sim p$.

(b) The inverse is $\sim(\sim p) \rightarrow \sim q$, which simplifies to $p \rightarrow \sim q$.

(c) The contrapositive is $\sim q \rightarrow \sim(\sim p)$, which simplifies to $\sim q \rightarrow p$.   ▮▮▮

Alternative Forms of "If p, then q"

The conditional statement "if p, then q" can be stated in several other ways in English. Consider this statement.

If you go to the outlet mall, then you will find a place to park.

It can also be written as follows.

Going to the outlet mall is *sufficient* for finding a place to park.

According to this statement, going to the outlet mall is enough to guarantee finding a place to park. Going to other places, such as schools or office buildings, *might* also guarantee a place to park, but at least we *know* that going to the outlet mall does. Thus, $p \rightarrow q$ can be written "p is sufficient for q." Knowing that p has occurred is sufficient to guarantee that q will also occur.

On the other hand, consider this statement, which has a different meaning.

Having the set on is necessary for watching television. (∗)

Here, we are saying that one condition that is necessary for watching television is that the set be turned on. This may not be enough. The set might be broken, for example. The statement labeled (∗) could be written as

If you watch television, then the set was turned on.

As this example suggests, $p \rightarrow q$ is the same as "q is necessary for p." In other words, if q doesn't happen, then neither will p. Notice how this idea is closely related to the idea of equivalence between a conditional statement and its contrapositive.

Common Translations of $p \rightarrow q$

The conditional $p \rightarrow q$ can be translated in any of the following ways, none of which depends on the truth or falsity of $p \rightarrow q$.

If p, then q.	**p is sufficient for q.**
If p, q.	**q is necessary for p.**
p implies q.	**All p are q.**
p only if q.	**q if p.**

Example: If you live in Dubuque, then you live in Iowa. Statement

You live in Iowa if you live in Dubuque.
You live in Dubuque only if you live in Iowa.
Living in Iowa is necessary for living in Dubuque. } Common translations
Living in Dubuque is sufficient for living in Iowa.
All residents of Dubuque are residents of Iowa.
Being a resident of Dubuque implies residency in Iowa.

▮▮ EXAMPLE 3 Rewording Conditional Statements

Write each statement in the form "if p, then q."

(a) You'll be sorry if I go.   **(b)** Today is Tuesday only if yesterday was Monday.

(c) All nurses wear white shoes.

SOLUTION

(a) If I go, then you'll be sorry.

(b) If today is Tuesday, then yesterday was Monday.

(c) If you are a nurse, then you wear white shoes. ▮▮▮

▮▮ EXAMPLE 4 Translating from Words to Symbols

Let p represent "A triangle is equilateral," and let q represent "A triangle has three sides of equal length." Write each of the following in symbols.

(a) A triangle is equilateral if it has three sides of equal length.

(b) A triangle is equilateral only if it has three sides of equal length.

SOLUTION

(a) $q \rightarrow p$ **(b)** $p \rightarrow q$ ▮▮▮

Biconditionals

The compound statement **p if and only if q** (often abbreviated **p iff q**) is called a **biconditional.** It is symbolized $p \leftrightarrow q$, and is interpreted as the conjunction of the two conditionals $p \rightarrow q$ and $q \rightarrow p$. Using symbols, this conjunction is written $(q \rightarrow p) \wedge (p \rightarrow q)$ so that, by definition,

$$p \leftrightarrow q \equiv (q \rightarrow p) \wedge (p \rightarrow q). \quad \text{Biconditional}$$

The truth table for the biconditional $p \leftrightarrow q$ can be determined using this definition.

Truth Table for the Biconditional   p if and only if q

p if and only if *q*

p	q	$p \leftrightarrow q$
T	T	T
T	F	F
F	T	F
F	F	T

Principia Mathematica, the title chosen by Whitehead and Russell, was a deliberate reference to *Philosophiae naturalis principia mathematica,* or "mathematical principles of the philosophy of nature," Isaac Newton's epochal work of 1687. Newton's *Principia* pictured a kind of "clockwork universe" that ran via his Law of Gravitation. Newton independently invented the calculus, unaware that Leibniz had published his own formulation of it earlier.

A biconditional is true when both component statements have the same truth value. It is false when they have different truth values.

▮▮ **EXAMPLE 5** Determining Whether Biconditionals Are True or False

Determine whether each biconditional statement is *true* or *false*.

(a) $6 + 8 = 14$ if and only if $11 + 5 = 16$

(b) $6 = 5$ if and only if $12 \neq 12$

(c) $5 + 2 = 10$ if and only if $17 + 19 = 36$

SOLUTION

(a) Both $6 + 8 = 14$ and $11 + 5 = 16$ are true. By the truth table for the biconditional, this biconditional is true.

(b) Both component statements are false, so by the last line of the truth table for the biconditional, this biconditional statement is true.

(c) Because the first component $(5 + 2 = 10)$ is false, and the second is true, this biconditional statement is false.   ▮▮▮

Summary of Truth Tables

Truth tables have been derived for several important types of compound statements.

Summary of Basic Truth Tables

1. $\sim p$, the **negation** of p, has truth value opposite that of p.
2. $p \wedge q$, the **conjunction,** is true only when both p and q are true.
3. $p \vee q$, the **disjunction,** is false only when both p and q are false.
4. $p \rightarrow q$, the **conditional,** is false only when p is true and q is false.
5. $p \leftrightarrow q$, the **biconditional,** is true only when both p and q have the same truth value.

3.4 EXERCISES

*For each given conditional statement (or statement that can be written as a conditional), write (**a**) the converse, (**b**) the inverse, and (**c**) the contrapositive in* if . . . then *form. In some of the exercises, it may be helpful to first restate the given statement in* if . . . then *form.*

1. If beauty were a minute, then you would be an hour.

2. If you lead, then I will follow.

3. If it ain't broke, don't fix it.

4. If I had a nickel for each time that happened, I would be rich.

5. Walking in front of a moving car is dangerous to your health.

6. Milk contains calcium.

7. Birds of a feather flock together.

8. A rolling stone gathers no moss.

9. If you build it, he will come.

10. Where there's smoke, there's fire.

11. $p \rightarrow \sim q$

12. $\sim p \rightarrow q$

13. $\sim p \rightarrow \sim q$

14. $\sim q \rightarrow \sim p$

15. $p \rightarrow (q \vee r)$ (*Hint:* Use one of De Morgan's laws as necessary.)

16. $(r \vee \sim q) \rightarrow p$ (*Hint:* Use one of De Morgan's laws as necessary.)

17. Discuss the equivalences that exist among a given conditional statement, its converse, its inverse, and its contrapositive.

18. State the contrapositive of "If the square of a natural number is even, then the natural number is even." The two statements must have the same truth value. Use several examples and inductive reasoning to decide whether both are true or both are false.

Write each statement in the form "if p, then q."

19. If it is muddy, I'll wear my galoshes.

20. If I finish studying, I'll go to the party.

21. "19 is positive" implies that $19 + 1$ is positive.

22. "Today is Wednesday" implies that yesterday was Tuesday.

23. All integers are rational numbers.

24. All whole numbers are integers.

25. Doing logic puzzles is sufficient for driving me crazy.

26. Being in Kalamazoo is sufficient for being in Michigan.

27. A day's growth of beard is necessary for Jeff Marsalis to shave.

28. Being an environmentalist is necessary for being elected.

29. I can go from Boardwalk to Baltic Avenue only if I pass GO.

30. The principal will hire more teachers only if the school board approves.

31. No whole numbers are not integers.

32. No integers are irrational numbers.

33. The Nationals will win the pennant when their pitching improves.

34. Sarah will be a liberal when pigs fly.

35. A rectangle is a parallelogram with a right angle.

36. A parallelogram is a four-sided figure with opposite sides parallel.

37. A triangle with two perpendicular sides is a right triangle.

38. A square is a rectangle with two adjacent sides equal.

39. The square of a two-digit number whose units digit is 5 will end in 25.

40. An integer whose units digit is 0 or 5 is divisible by 5.

41. One of the following statements is not equivalent to all the others. Which one is it?
    A. r only if s.   **B.** r implies s.
    C. If r, then s.   **D.** r is necessary for s.

42. Many students have difficulty interpreting *necessary* and *sufficient.* Use the statement "Being in Vancouver is sufficient for being in North America" to explain why "p is sufficient for q" translates as "if p, then q."

43. Use the statement "To be an integer, it is necessary that a number be rational" to explain why "p is necessary for q" translates as "if q, then p."

44. Explain why the statement "A week has eight days if and only if October has forty days" is true.

Identify each statement as true *or* false.

45. $6 = 9 - 3$ if and only if $8 + 2 = 10$.

46. $3 + 1 \neq 7$ if and only if $8 \neq 8$.

47. $8 + 7 \neq 15$ if and only if $3 \times 5 \neq 8$.

48. $6 \times 2 = 18$ if and only if $9 + 7 \neq 16$.

49. George H. W. Bush was president if and only if George W. Bush was not president.

50. Burger King sells Big Macs if and only if Apple manufactures Ipods.

Two statements that can both be true about the same object are **consistent.** *For example,* "It is green" *and* "It weighs 60 pounds" *are consistent statements. Statements that cannot both be true about the same object are called* **contrary.** "It is a Nissan" *and* "It is a Mazda" *are contrary. In Exercises 51–56, label each pair of statements as either* contrary *or* consistent.

51. Michael Jackson is alive. Michael Jackson is dead.

52. Barack Obama is a Democrat. Barack Obama is a Republican.

53. That animal has four legs. That same animal is a cat.

54. That book is nonfiction. That book costs more than $150.

55. This number is a whole number. This same number is irrational.

56. This number is positive. This same number is a natural number.

57. This number is an integer. This same number is a rational number.

58. This number is a whole number. This same number is a negative number.

59. Make up two statements that are consistent.

60. Make up two statements that are contrary.

3.5　ANALYZING ARGUMENTS WITH EULER DIAGRAMS

Logical Arguments • Arguments with Universal Quantifiers • Arguments with Existential Quantifiers

Leonhard Euler (1707–1783) won the Academy prize and edged out du Châtelet and Voltaire. That was a minor achievement, as was the invention of "Euler circles" (which antedated Venn diagrams). Euler was the most prolific mathematician of his generation despite blindness that forced him to dictate from memory.

Logical Arguments

With inductive reasoning we observe patterns to solve problems. Now we study how deductive reasoning may be used to determine whether logical arguments are valid or invalid.

A logical argument is made up of **premises** (assumptions, laws, rules, widely held ideas, or observations) and a **conclusion.** Recall that *deductive* reasoning involves drawing specific conclusions from given general premises. When reasoning from the premises of an argument to obtain a conclusion, we want the argument to be valid.

> **Valid and Invalid Arguments**
>
> An argument is **valid** if the fact that all the premises are true forces the conclusion to be true. An argument that is not valid is **invalid.** It is called a **fallacy.**

"Valid" and "true" do not have the same meaning—an argument can be valid even though the conclusion is false. **(See Example 4.)**

Arguments with Universal Quantifiers

Several techniques can be used to check whether an argument is valid. One such technique is based on **Euler diagrams.**

Leonhard Euler (pronounced "Oiler") was one of the greatest mathematicians who ever lived. He is immortalized in mathematics history with the important irrational number e, named in his honor. This number appears throughout mathematics, and is discussed in **Chapters 6 and 8.**

Figure 8

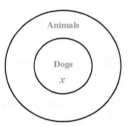

x represents Dotty.

Figure 9

▮▮ **EXAMPLE 1** Using an Euler Diagram to Determine Validity

Is the following argument valid?

> All dogs are animals.
> Dotty is a dog.
> _____
> Dotty is an animal.

SOLUTION

To begin, draw regions to represent the first premise. Because all dogs are animals, the region for "dogs" goes inside the region for "animals," as in **Figure 8.**

The second premise, "Dotty is a dog," suggests that "Dotty" would go inside the region representing "dogs." Let *x* represent "Dotty." **Figure 9** shows that "Dotty" is also inside the region for "animals." If both premises are true, the conclusion that Dotty is an animal must be true also. The argument is valid. ▮▮▮

▮▮ **EXAMPLE 2** Using an Euler Diagram to Determine Validity

Is the following argument valid?

> All rainy days are cloudy.
> Today is not cloudy.
> _____
> Today is not rainy.

SOLUTION

In **Figure 10,** the region for "rainy days" is drawn entirely inside the region for "cloudy days." Since "Today is *not* cloudy," place an *x* for "today" *outside* the region for "cloudy days." See **Figure 11.** Placing the *x* outside the region for "cloudy days" forces it also to be outside the region for "rainy days." Thus, if the two premises are true, then it is also true that today is not rainy. The argument is valid.

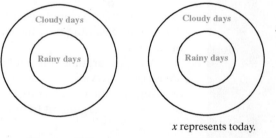

Figure 10　　　　**Figure 11**

x represents today.

▮▮▮

▮▮ **EXAMPLE 3** Using an Euler Diagram to Determine Validity

Is the following argument valid?

> All magnolia trees have green leaves.
> That plant has green leaves.
> _____
> That plant is a magnolia tree.

SOLUTION

The region for "magnolia trees" goes entirely inside the region for "things that have green leaves." See **Figure 12.** The *x* that represents "that plant" must go inside the region for "things that have green leaves," but can go either inside or outside the region for "magnolia trees." Even if the premises are true, we are not forced to accept the conclusion as true. This argument is invalid. It is a fallacy. ▮▮▮

Figure 12

▌▌ **EXAMPLE 4** Using an Euler Diagram to Determine Validity

Is the following argument valid?

All expensive things are desirable.
All desirable things make you feel good.
All things that make you feel good make you live longer.

All expensive things make you live longer.

SOLUTION

A diagram for the argument is given in **Figure 13.**

If each premise is true, then the conclusion must be true because the region for "expensive things" lies completely within the region for "things that make you live longer." Thus, the argument is valid. (This argument is an example of the fact that a *valid* argument need *not* have a true conclusion.)

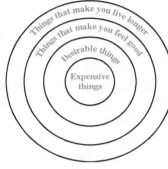

Figure 13 ▌▌▌

Arguments with Existential Quantifiers

▌▌ **EXAMPLE 5** Using an Euler Diagram to Determine Validity

Is the following argument valid?

Some students go to the beach for Spring Break.
I am a student.

I go to the beach for Spring Break.

SOLUTION

The first premise is sketched in **Figure 14,** where some (but not necessarily *all*) students go to the beach. There are two possibilities for *I*, as shown in **Figure 15.** One possibility is that *I* go to the beach. The other is that *I* don't. Since the truth of the premises does not force the conclusion to be true, the argument is invalid. ▌▌▌

Figure 14

Figure 15

For Further Thought (cont.)

3. **Loaded Question and Complex Claims** This fallacy involves one person asking a question or making a statement that is constructed in such a way as to obtain an answer in which the responder agrees to something with which he does not actually agree.

   Teenager Beth to her father: I hope you enjoyed embarrassing me in front of my friends.

   If Beth gets the expected response "No, I didn't enjoy it," the answer allows Beth to interpret that while her father didn't enjoy it, he did indeed embarrass her.

4. *Post Hoc* **Reasoning** An argument that is based on the false belief that if event A preceded event B, then A must have caused B is called *post hoc* reasoning.

   Johnny: I wore my Hawaiian shirt while watching all three playoff games, and my team won all three games. So I am going to wear that shirt every time I watch them.

   The fact that Johnny put the same shirt on before each game has nothing to do with the outcomes of the games.

5. **Red Herring** (also called *Smoke Screen,* or *Wild Goose Chase*) This fallacy involves introducing an irrelevant topic to divert attention away from the original topic, allowing the person making the argument to seemingly prevail.

   (From the movie *Field of Dreams,* in a scene where Annie and Beulah are arguing at a town meeting about the banning of books)

   Beulah: I say smut and filth like this has no place in our schools. . . . The so-called novels of Terence Mann endorse promiscuity, godlessness, the mongrelization of the races, and disrespect to high-ranking officers of the United States army. And that is why school boards across the country have been banning his books since 1969.
   Annie: Excuse me, madam. Terence Mann was a warm and gentle voice of reason in a time of great madness. He coined the phrase "Make love, not war." . . . He was talking about peace, and love, and understanding . . .
   Beulah: Oh yeah, well your husband plowed under his corn and built a baseball field . . . the weirdo. . . .
   Annie: Now there's an intelligent response.

   While most of the people in the audience agreed that Annie's husband Ray was doing strange things, those things had nothing to do with banning books.

6. **Shifting the Burden of Proof** A person making a claim usually is required to support that claim. In this fallacy, if the claim is difficult to support, that person turns the burden of proof of that claim over to someone else.

   Employee: You accuse me of embezzling money? That's ridiculous.
   Employer: Well, until you can prove otherwise, you will just have to accept it as true.

   If money has been disappearing, it is up to the employer to prove that this employee is guilty. The burden of proof is on the employer, but he is insinuating that the employee must prove that he is not the one taking the money.

7. **Straw Man** This fallacy involves creating a false image (like a scarecrow, or straw man) of someone else's position in an argument.

   Dan Quayle: I have as much experience in the Congress as Jack Kennedy did when he sought the presidency.
   Lloyd Bentsen: Senator, I served with Jack Kennedy. I knew Jack Kennedy. Jack Kennedy was a friend of mine. And Senator, you're no Jack Kennedy.
   Dan Quayle: That was really uncalled for, Senator.
   Lloyd Bentsen: You're the one that was making the comparison, Senator.

   While this was the defining moment of the 1988 vice-presidential debate, Bentsen expertly used the straw man fallacy. Quayle did not compare himself or his accomplishments to those of Kennedy, but merely stated that he had spent as much time in Congress as Kennedy had when the latter ran for president.

For Group or Individual Investigation

Use the Internet to investigate the following additional logical fallacies.

Appeal to Authority	Appeal to Common Belief	Common Practice
Two Wrongs		Wishful Thinking
Appeal to Fear	Indirect Consequences	Appeal to Pity
Appeal to Prejudice	Appeal to Loyalty	Appeal to Vanity
Guilt by Association	Appeal to Spite	Hasty Generalization
	Slippery Slope	

3.5 EXERCISES

Decide whether each argument is valid *or* invalid.

1. All amusement parks have thrill rides.
   Universal Orlando is an amusement park.

   Universal Orlando has thrill rides.

2. All disc jockeys play music.
   Phlash Phelps is a disc jockey.

   Phlash Phelps plays music.

3. All politicians lie, cheat, and steal.
   That man lies, cheats, and steals.

   That man is a politician.

4. All Southerners speak with an accent.
   Bill Leonard speaks with an accent.

   Bill Leonard is a Southerner.

5. All dogs love to bury bones.
   Puddles does not love to bury bones.

   Puddles is not a dog.

6. All vice-presidents use cell phones.
   Bob DeBiasio does not use a cell phone.

   Bob DeBiasio is not a vice-president.

7. All residents of Minnesota know how to live in freezing temperatures.
   Jessica Rockswold knows how to live in freezing temperatures.

   Jessica Rockswold lives in Minnesota.

8. All people who apply for a loan must pay for a title search.
   Kurt Massey paid for a title search.

   Kurt Massey applied for a loan.

9. Some dinosaurs were plant eaters.
   Danny was a plant eater.

   Danny was a dinosaur.

10. Some philosophers are absent minded.
    Nicole Mallon is a philosopher.

    Nicole Mallon is absent minded.

11. Some nurses wear blue uniforms.
    Dee Boyle is a nurse.

    Dee Boyle wears a blue uniform.

12. Some trucks have sound systems.
    Some trucks have gun racks.

    Some trucks with sound systems have gun racks.

13. Refer to **Example 3.** If the second premise and the conclusion were interchanged, would the argument then be valid?

14. Refer to **Example 4.** Give a different conclusion than the one given there so that the argument is still valid.

Construct a valid argument based on the Euler diagram shown.

15.
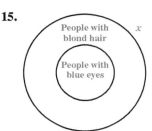

x represents Natalie Graham

16.
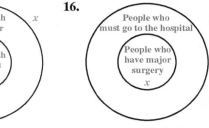

x represents Mark Robinson

As mentioned in the text, an argument can have a true conclusion yet be invalid. In these exercises, each argument has a true conclusion. Identify each argument as valid *or* invalid.

17. All birds fly.
    All planes fly.

    A bird is not a plane.

18. All cars have tires.
    All tires are rubber.

    All cars have rubber.

19. All chickens have beaks.
    All hens are chickens.

    All hens have beaks.

20. All chickens have beaks.
    All birds have beaks.

    All chickens are birds.

21. Little Rock is northeast of Texarkana.
    Little Rock is northeast of Austin.

    Texarkana is northeast of Austin.

22. Veracruz is south of Tampico.
    Tampico is south of Monterrey.

    Veracruz is south of Monterrey.

23. No whole numbers are negative.
    −3 is negative.

    −3 is not a whole number.

24. A scalene triangle has a longest side.
    A scalene triangle has a largest angle.

    The largest angle in a scalene triangle is opposite the longest side.

In Exercises 25–30, the premises marked A, B, and C are followed by several possible conclusions. Take each conclusion in turn, and check whether the resulting argument is valid or invalid.

A. *All people who drive contribute to air pollution.*

B. *All people who contribute to air pollution make life a little worse.*

C. *Some people who live in a suburb make life a little worse.*

25. Some people who live in a suburb contribute to air pollution.

26. Some people who live in a suburb drive.

27. Suburban residents never drive.

28. Some people who contribute to air pollution live in a suburb.

29. Some people who make life a little worse live in a suburb.

30. All people who drive make life a little worse.

EXTENSION Logic Problems and Sudoku

How to Solve Logic Problems • How to Solve Sudoku

Logic problems, which are based on deductive reasoning, appear in periodicals such as *Original Logic Problems, World-Class Logic Problems,* and *England's Best Logic Problems* (all PennyPress), and *Logic Puzzles* (Dell). The following explanation on solving such problems appeared in the February 2010 issue of *Original Logic Problems.*

How to Solve Logic Problems Solving logic problems is entertaining and challenging. All the information you need to solve a logic problem is given in the introduction and clues, and in illustrations, when provided. If you've never solved a logic problem before, our sample should help you get started. Fill in the Sample Solving Chart as you follow our explanation. We use a "•" to signify "Yes" and an "X" to signify "No."

Sample Logic Problem

Five couples were married last week, each on a different weekday. From the information provided, determine the woman (one is Cathy) and man (one is Paul) who make up each couple, as well as the day on which each couple was married.

1. Anne was married on Monday, but not to Wally.

2. Stan's wedding was on Wednesday. Rob was married on Friday, but not to Ida.

3. Vern (who married Fran) was married the day after Eve.

Sample Solving Chart:	PAUL	ROB	STAN	VERN	WALLY	MONDAY	TUESDAY	WEDNESDAY	THURSDAY	FRIDAY
ANNE										
CATHY										
EVE										
FRAN										
IDA										
MONDAY										
TUESDAY										
WEDNESDAY										
THURSDAY										
FRIDAY										

1	PAUL	ROB	STAN	VERN	WALLY	MONDAY	TUESDAY	WEDNESDAY	THURSDAY	FRIDAY
ANNE	×	×			×	•	×	×	×	×
CATHY						×				
EVE						×				
FRAN						×				
IDA		×				×				×
MONDAY	×	×								
TUESDAY	×	×								
WEDNESDAY	×	×	•	×	×					
THURSDAY	×	×								
FRIDAY	×	•	×	×	×					

Explanation

Anne was married Mon. (1), so put a "•" at the intersection of Anne and Mon. Put "X"s in all the other days in Anne's row and all the other names in the Mon. column. (Whenever you establish a relationship, as we did here, be sure to place "X"s at the intersections of all relationships that become impossible as a result.) Anne wasn't married to Wally (1), so put an "X" at the intersection of Anne and Wally. Stan's wedding was Wed. (2), so put a "•" at the intersection of Stan and Wed. (Don't forget the "X"s.) Stan didn't marry Anne, who was married Mon., so put an "X" at the intersection of Anne and Stan. Rob was married Fri., but not to Ida (2), so put a "•" at the intersection of Rob and Fri., and "X"s at the intersections of Rob and Ida and Ida and Fri. Rob also didn't marry Anne, who was married Mon., so put an "X" at the intersection of Anne and Rob. Now your chart should look like **chart 1.**

Vern married Fran (3), so put a "•" at the intersection of Vern and Fran. This leaves Anne's only possible husband as Paul, so put a "•" at the intersection of Anne and Paul and Paul and Mon. Vern and Fran's wedding was the day after Eve's (3), which wasn't Mon. [Anne], so Vern's wasn't Tue. It must have been Thu. [see chart], so Eve's was Wed. (3). Put "•"s at the intersections of Vern and Thu., Fran and Thu., and Eve and Wed. Now your chart should look like **chart 2.**

Chart 2

2	PAUL	ROB	STAN	VERN	WALLY	MONDAY	TUESDAY	WEDNESDAY	THURSDAY	FRIDAY
ANNE	•	×	×	×	×	•	×	×	×	×
CATHY	×			×		×		×	×	
EVE	×		×	×		×	×	•	×	×
FRAN	×	×	×	•	×	×	×	×	•	×
IDA	×	×		×		×		×	×	×
MONDAY	•	×	×	×	×					
TUESDAY	×	×	×	×						
WEDNESDAY	×	×	•	×	×					
THURSDAY	×	×	×	•	×					
FRIDAY	×	•	×	×	×					

Chart 3

3	PAUL	ROB	STAN	VERN	WALLY	MONDAY	TUESDAY	WEDNESDAY	THURSDAY	FRIDAY
ANNE	•	×	×	×	×	•	×	×	×	×
CATHY	×	•	×	×	×	×	×	×	×	•
EVE	×	×	•	×	×	×	×	•	×	×
FRAN	×	×	×	•	×	×	×	×	•	×
IDA	×	×	×	×	•	×	•	×	×	×
MONDAY	•	×	×	×	×					
TUESDAY	×	×	×	×	•					
WEDNESDAY	×	×	•	×	×					
THURSDAY	×	×	×	•	×					
FRIDAY	×	•	×	×	×					

The chart shows that Cathy was married Fri., Ida was married Tue., and Wally was married Tue. Ida married Wally, and Cathy's wedding was Fri., so she married Rob. After this information is filled in, Eve could only have married Stan. You've completed the puzzle, and your chart should now look like **chart 3.**

In summary: Anne and Paul, Mon.; Cathy and Rob, Fri.; Eve and Stan, Wed.; Fran and Vern, Thu.; Ida and Wally, Tue.

In some problems, it may be necessary to make a logical guess based on facts you've established. When you do, always look for clues or other facts that disprove it. If you find that your guess is incorrect, eliminate it as a possibility.

How to Solve Sudoku

Sudoku is a simple game that has gained great popularity in the United States during the past few years. It is believed that the game originated as Number Place in the United States over 25 years ago, but gained in popularity only after it became a sensation in Japan, where it was renamed Sudoku, meaning "single number." (*Source: Sudoku #13*, 2005, Platinum Magazine Group.)

There is only one rule in Sudoku: **"Fill in the grid so that every row, every column, and every 3 × 3 box contains the digits 1 through 9."** This involves scanning the given digits, marking up the grid, and analyzing. Here is a sample Sudoku.

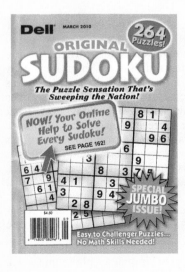

		7	3	2				
8	4		1				9	
					8	2	1
		9		8	7			5
2	8		4		1		6	3
1			5	6		9		
5	3	8						9
	9				2		1	4
				7	5	6		

Given Form

9	1	7	3	2	8	4	5	6
8	4	2	1	5	6	3	9	7
6	5	3	7	4	9	8	2	1
3	6	9	2	8	7	1	4	5
2	8	5	4	9	1	7	6	3
1	7	4	5	6	3	9	8	2
5	3	8	6	1	4	2	7	9
7	9	6	8	3	2	5	1	4
4	2	1	9	7	5	6	3	8

Solved Form

You can find Sudoku puzzles and solving strategies online at www.sudoku.org.uk and at www.pennydellsudokusolver.com.

EXTENSION EXERCISES

Follow the guidelines to solve each logic problem, which appeared in the February 2010 issue of Original Logic Problems, *published by PennyPress.*

1. Breath Taking As part of a weekly tradition, Drew and four of his friends met for lunch at Aristotle's Grill. Each person enjoyed a different lunch special, but when it came time for the post-meal conversation, the five quickly realized that they were all in need of a mint or two. Luckily, each person had a container of mints on his or her person. No two friends had the same brand of mint (one is Inti-mints), and no two friends had mints with the same flavor. A few seconds later they were all ready to talk, but they agreed that next week, they'll be a little more careful about what they order for lunch! From the information provided, can you determine the meal enjoyed by each friend, as well as the brand and flavor of mint each person used afterward?

(a) The friend who had garlic shrimp ate a couple of orange-flavored mints (which weren't Fresh Air mints). The person who ordered the spanakopita isn't the one who had wintergreen-flavored TKO mints.

(b) The friend who ate French onion soup followed it with a few Liplickers mints. Nash (who didn't have the spearmint-flavored mints) didn't order garlic shrimp.

(c) Neither Nash nor Xerxes is the one who ate a tuna-salad sandwich. The friend who had a buffalo-chicken sandwich isn't the one who freshened his or her breath with spearmint-flavored mints.

(d) One friend had a couple of cinnamon-flavored Deltoids mints. The Liplickers mints were vanilla-flavored.

(e) Ilse (who ate a buffalo-chicken sandwich) didn't have wintergreen-flavored mints. Neither Uma nor Xerxes is the friend who had a couple of Fresh Air mints.

2. Kings of Hearts Although the exact origins of the holiday are murky, the tradition of Valentine's Day probably harkens back to the Middle Ages, when it was better known as the feast of Saint Valentine. Couples exchanged gifts on this February holiday even back then, and no one gave more expensive and elaborate valentines than the royalty of that time. One Valentine's Day, each of four kings, each whom ruled a different small kingdom, gave his queen a different valuable gift. It just goes to show that love (or at least the idea of it) stands the test of time! From the information provided, can you determine the king and queen of each kingdom, as well as the gift each king gave his wife for the feast of Saint Valentine?

(a) King Jacobus didn't give his queen a platinum crown.

(b) Neither the jeweled scepter nor the platinum crown was the gift given to Queen Meyla (who was married to either King Kevrick or King Vermond).

(c) Queen Dejah (who was married to either King Fedris or King Jacobus) wasn't the ruler of Undervale.

(d) King Kevrick wasn't the ruler of the Dalelands.

(e) Neither the platinum crown nor the set of velvet robes was the gift given by King Vermond.

(f) The queen of Undervale (who was married to either King Fedris or King Jacobus) was given a golden throne by her husband.

(g) Queen Tilnara wasn't given a jeweled scepter by her husband. Queen Aasta ruled Hightop.

		QUEEN				KINGDOM				GIFT			
		AASTA	DEJAH	MEYLA	TILNARA	DALELANDS	HIGHTOP	SHADOW COAST	UNDERVALE	GOLDEN THRONE	JEWELED SCEPTER	PLATINUM CROWN	VELVET ROBES
KING	FEDRIS												
	JACOBUS												
	KEVRICK												
	VERMOND												
GIFT	GOLDEN THRONE												
	JEWELED SCEPTER												
	PLATINUM CROWN												
	VELVET ROBES												
KINGDOM	DALELANDS												
	HIGHTOP												
	SHADOW COAST												
	UNDERVALE												

3. *New Year's Revelations* Lucy and four of her friends met at the Golden Panda for dinner one evening in January. Much to their surprise, they had wandered in to the restaurant during a celebration of the Chinese New Year. Luckily for the five, this meant a discount on their meals and a free session with the mysterious medium Madame Wau Pei. The five friends had their fortunes told, one at a time. Each person told the mystic the date and year of his or her birth and learned that, according to Chinese astrology, each friend's birth year is designated by a different animal. Also, each of the five was told that he or she has a different lucky element. Before leaving the restaurant, the five friends compared their predictions, noticing that all of them had a long journey in their future—the trip back home! From the information provided, determine the order in which the five friends had their fortunes told, the year in which each person was born, and each person's lucky element.

(a) Toni was the third person to get her fortune told. The person whose lucky element is wood was the last person to see the fortune-teller.

(b) Earl (whose lucky element is fire) had his fortune told immediately before the person who was born in the Year of the Rooster. The fourth person to visit the fortune-teller was born in the Year of the Dragon.

(c) The person born in the Year of the Ox had his or her fortune told at some point before the one whose lucky element is metal. Ivana was born in the Year of the Horse.

(d) The person whose lucky element is water (who was born in the Year of the Cow) wasn't the first person to have his or her fortune told.

(e) The person whose lucky element is earth had his or her fortune told exactly two after Philip.

		FRIEND					YEAR					ELEMENT				
		EARL	IVANA	LUCY	PHILIP	TONI	COW	DRAGON	HORSE	OX	ROOSTER	EARTH	FIRE	METAL	WATER	WOOD
ORDER	FIRST															
	SECOND															
	THIRD															
	FOURTH															
	FIFTH															
ELEMENT	EARTH															
	FIRE															
	METAL															
	WATER															
	WOOD															
YEAR	COW															
	DRAGON															
	HORSE															
	OX															
	ROOSTER															

4. *Barn Again* For as long as I can remember, I've dreamed of owning my own bed-and-breakfast, and it looks like my dream is about to come true! We'd like our inn to be distinctive, so my husband and I have decided to purchase a barn and convert it into unique living quarters. We viewed five barns recently, each of which had once served a different purpose. My husband and I visited each barn with a different contractor, each of whom gave us a different estimate ($50,000, $60,000, $70,000, $80,000, or $100,000) for the conversion. Each barn has a different feature that makes it appealing (one has a functioning hoist), but we still haven't decided which one to buy—we're starting to go a little haywire! From the information provided, determine the contractor who visited each barn with us and the special feature of each structure, as well as the estimate given for the renovation of each barn.

(a) The apple barn (which has distinctive octagonal windows) will cost exactly $20,000 less to convert than the barn we visited with a Bill's Building representative. The estimate for renovating the hay barn is higher than the estimate for converting the potato barn.

(b) The barn we visited with the person from AB Contracting (which isn't the barn that has fabulous heavy beams) will cost more to renovate than the barn we viewed with the contractor from Pine Valley but exactly $10,000 less to convert than the horse barn.

(c) The estimates for converting the apple barn and the barn with lovely board-and-batten siding are the lowest and highest estimates, in some order.

(d) The barn we visited with the contractor from Dekker Ltd. will cost exactly $20,000 more to renovate than the barn with insulation worth preserving.

(e) The old dairy barn will cost more to renovate than the one we visited with the representative from Vander Estates.

		BARN					FEATURE					ESTIMATE			
		APPLE	DAIRY	HAY	HORSE	POTATO	BEAMS	HOIST	INSULATION	SIDING	WINDOWS	$50,000	$60,000	$70,000	$80,000	$100,000
CONTRACTOR	AB CONTRACTING															
	BILL'S BUILDING															
	DEKKER LTD.															
	PINE VALLEY															
	VANDER ESTATES															
ESTIMATE	$50,000															
	$60,000															
	$70,000															
	$80,000															
	$100,000															
FEATURE	BEAMS															
	HOIST															
	INSULATION															
	SIDING															
	WINDOWS															

Solve each Sudoku, which appeared in Dell Original Sudoku, *March 2010, Penny Publications. (They are categorized according to difficulty level.)*

5. Easy

	4		1	6	8			5
		9		5			2	8
	6		9					4
		4	7		9			
	3	8		4		2	9	
			2		3	8		
2				1		6		
9	7			2		5		
4			6	9	5		7	

6. Easy

2		3			8	1	4	
	7		6	2	4			
	8			3				7
8	4	7	2				6	
			8		6			
	1				9	4	8	2
7				6			2	
			9	5	7		1	
	6	9	3			5		4

7. Medium

8	3		6					1
	1			4			5	6
		6			8			
		7	1				3	8
		1		2		4		
5	4					6	1	
			5			7		
9	8			7			1	
6					1		2	3

8. Medium

			4	5		6		
4	5					3		9
	6	1			3			8
5	8			1		6		
		9		3		2		
	4		9				1	7
8			1			7	3	
1		5				9	2	
		6		7	2			

9. Hard

	1			2				4
4		9			1		7	
		8				9		
	3		6				2	
7				3				9
	9				8		5	
		2				4		
	8		2			6		5
9				8			3	

10. Hard

	2			9		6	7	
	5	6						
			6		4			5
	6	9						1
			3	6	9			
8						9	4	
1			4		7			
						4	2	
	4	8		2			3	

3.6 ANALYZING ARGUMENTS WITH TRUTH TABLES

Truth Tables (Two Premises) • Valid and Invalid Argument Forms • Truth Tables (More Than Two Premises) • Arguments of Lewis Carroll

In the 2007 Spanish film **La Habitacion de Fermat (Fermat's Room),** four mathematicians are invited to dinner, only to discover that the room in which they are meeting is designed to eventually crush them as walls creep in closer and closer. The only way for them to delay the inevitable is to answer enigmas, questions, puzzles, problems, and riddles that they are receiving on a cell phone.

One of the enigmas deals with a hermetically sealed room that contains a single light bulb. There are three switches outside the room, and only one of the switches controls the bulb. You are allowed to push any or all of the buttons as many times as you wish before you enter the room, but once you enter you cannot return to the switches outside. How can you determine which one controls the bulb? (The answer is on **page 126.**)

Truth Tables (Two Premises)

In **Section 3.5** we used Euler diagrams to test the validity of arguments. While Euler diagrams often work well for simple arguments, difficulties can develop with more complex ones, because Euler diagrams require a sketch showing every possible case. In complex arguments, it is hard to be sure that all cases have been considered.

In deciding whether to use Euler diagrams to test the validity of an argument, look for quantifiers such as "all," "some," or "no." These words often indicate arguments best tested by Euler diagrams. If these words are absent, it may be better to use truth tables to test the validity of an argument.

As an example of this method, consider the following argument:

> If the floor is dirty, then I must mop it.
> The floor is dirty.
> _____
> I must mop it.

To test the validity of this argument, we begin by identifying the *component* statements found in the argument. They are "the floor is dirty" and "I must mop it." We assign the letters p and q to represent these statements:

$$p \text{ represents "the floor is dirty";}$$
$$q \text{ represents "I must mop it."}$$

Now we write the two premises and the conclusion in symbols.

> Premise 1: $p \rightarrow q$
> Premise 2: p
> _____
> Conclusion: q

To decide if this argument is valid, we must determine whether the conjunction of both premises implies the conclusion for all possible cases of truth values for p and q. Therefore, write the conjunction of the premises as the antecedent of a conditional statement, and the conclusion as the consequent.

$$[(p \rightarrow q) \quad \wedge \quad p] \quad \rightarrow \quad q$$

premise   and   premise   implies   conclusion

Finally, construct the truth table for this conditional statement, as shown below.

p	q	$p \rightarrow q$	$(p \rightarrow q) \wedge p$	$[(p \rightarrow q) \wedge p] \rightarrow q$
T	T	T	T	T
T	F	F	F	T
F	T	T	F	T
F	F	T	F	T

Because the final column, shown in color, indicates that the conditional statement that represents the argument is true for all possible truth values of p and q, the statement is a tautology. Thus, the argument is valid.

Answer to the Light Bulb question on **page 125.**

Label the switches 1, 2, and 3. Turn switch 1 on and leave it on for several minutes. Then turn switch 1 off, turn switch 2 on, and then immediately enter the room. If the bulb is on, then you know that switch 2 controls it. If the bulb is off, touch it to see if it is still warm. If it is, then switch 1 controls it. If the bulb is not warm, then switch 3 controls it.

The pattern of the argument in the floor-mopping example

$$\begin{array}{c} p \to q \\ \underline{p} \\ q \end{array}$$

is called **modus ponens,** or the *law of detachment.*

To test the validity of an argument using a truth table, follow the steps in the box.

Testing the Validity of an Argument with a Truth Table

Step 1 Assign a letter to represent each component statement in the argument.

Step 2 Express each premise and the conclusion symbolically.

Step 3 Form the symbolic statement of the entire argument by writing the *conjunction* of *all* the premises as the antecedent of a conditional statement, and the conclusion of the argument as the consequent.

Step 4 Complete the truth table for the conditional statement formed in Step 3. If it is a tautology, then the argument is valid; otherwise, it is invalid.

■■ **EXAMPLE 1** Using a Truth Table to Determine Validity

Determine whether the argument is *valid* or *invalid*.

> If my check arrives in time, I'll register for the fall semester.
> I've registered for the fall semester.
> ―――――――――――――――――――――――――
> My check arrived in time.

SOLUTION

Let p represent "my check arrives (arrived) in time" and let q represent "I'll register (I've registered) for the fall semester." The argument can be written as follows.

$$\begin{array}{c} p \to q \\ \underline{q} \\ p \end{array}$$

To test for validity, construct a truth table for the statement $[(p \to q) \land q] \to p$.

p	q	$p \to q$	$(p \to q) \land q$	$[(p \to q) \land q] \to p$
T	T	T	T	T
T	F	F	F	T
F	T	T	T	F
F	F	T	F	T

The third row of the final column of the truth table shows F, and this is enough to conclude that the argument is invalid. ■■■

If a conditional and its converse were logically equivalent, then an argument of the type found in **Example 1** would be valid. Because a conditional and its converse are *not* equivalent, the argument is an example of what is sometimes called the **fallacy of the converse.**

■■ **EXAMPLE 2** Using a Truth Table to Determine Validity

Determine whether the argument is *valid* or *invalid*.

> If a man could be in two places at one time, I'd be with you.
> I am not with you.
> ――――――――――――――――――――――――――
> A man can't be in two places at one time.

SOLUTION

If p represents "a man could be in two places at one time" and q represents "I'd be with you," the argument is written as follows.

$$\frac{\begin{array}{l} p \to q \\ \sim q \end{array}}{\sim p}$$

The symbolic statement of the entire argument is as follows.

$$[(p \to q) \land \sim q] \to \sim p$$

The truth table for this argument indicates a tautology, and the argument is valid.

p	q	$p \to q$	$\sim q$	$(p \to q) \land \sim q$	$\sim p$	$[(p \to q) \land \sim q] \to \sim p$
T	T	T	F	F	F	T
T	F	F	T	F	F	T
F	T	T	F	F	T	T
F	F	T	T	T	T	T

The pattern of reasoning of this example is called **modus tollens,** or the *law of contraposition,* or *indirect reasoning.* ■■■

With reasoning similar to that used to name the fallacy of the converse, the fallacy

$$\frac{\begin{array}{l} p \to q \\ \sim p \end{array}}{\sim q}$$

is called the **fallacy of the inverse.** An example of such a fallacy is "If it rains, I get wet. It doesn't rain. Therefore, I don't get wet."

■ EXAMPLE 3 Using a Truth Table to Determine Validity

Determine whether the argument is *valid* or *invalid.*

> I'll buy a car or I'll take a vacation.
> I won't buy a car.
> _____
> I'll take a vacation.

SOLUTION

If p represents "I'll buy a car" and q represents "I'll take a vacation," the argument is symbolized as follows.

$$\frac{\begin{array}{l} p \lor q \\ \sim p \end{array}}{q}$$

We must set up a truth table for the statement $[(p \lor q) \land \sim p] \to q$.

p	q	$p \lor q$	$\sim p$	$(p \lor q) \land \sim p$	$[(p \lor q) \land \sim p] \to q$
T	T	T	F	F	T
T	F	T	F	F	T
F	T	T	T	T	T
F	F	F	T	F	T

The statement is a tautology and the argument is valid. Any argument of this form is valid by the law of **disjunctive syllogism.** ■■■

▌▌ **EXAMPLE 4** Using a Truth Table to Determine Validity

Determine whether the argument is *valid* or *invalid*.

> If it squeaks, then I use WD-40.
> If I use WD-40, then I must go to the hardware store.
> If it squeaks, then I must go to the hardware store.

SOLUTION

Let p represent "it squeaks," let q represent "I use WD-40," and let r represent "I must go to the hardware store." The argument takes on the following general form.

$$\frac{\begin{array}{c} p \rightarrow q \\ q \rightarrow r \end{array}}{p \rightarrow r}$$

Make a truth table for this statement, which requires eight rows.

$$[(p \rightarrow q) \wedge (q \rightarrow r)] \rightarrow (p \rightarrow r)$$

p	q	r	$p \rightarrow q$	$q \rightarrow r$	$p \rightarrow r$	$(p \rightarrow q) \wedge (q \rightarrow r)$	$[(p \rightarrow q) \wedge (q \rightarrow r)] \rightarrow (p \rightarrow r)$
T	T	T	T	T	T	T	T
T	T	F	T	F	F	F	T
T	F	T	F	T	T	F	T
T	F	F	F	T	F	F	T
F	T	T	T	T	T	T	T
F	T	F	T	F	T	F	T
F	F	T	T	T	T	T	T
F	F	F	T	T	T	T	T

This argument is valid because the final statement is a tautology. This pattern of argument is called **reasoning by transitivity,** or the *law of hypothetical syllogism.* ▌▌▌

Valid and Invalid Argument Forms

A summary of the valid and invalid forms of argument presented so far in this section follows.

Valid Argument Forms

Modus Ponens	Modus Tollens	Disjunctive Syllogism	Reasoning by Transitivity
$p \rightarrow q$ p q	$p \rightarrow q$ $\sim q$ $\sim p$	$p \vee q$ $\sim p$ q	$p \rightarrow q$ $q \rightarrow r$ $p \rightarrow r$

Invalid Argument Forms (Fallacies)

Fallacy of the Converse	Fallacy of the Inverse
$p \rightarrow q$ q p	$p \rightarrow q$ $\sim p$ $\sim q$

In a scene near the beginning of the 1974 film *Monty Python and the Holy Grail*, an amazing application of **poor logic** leads to the apparent demise of a supposed witch. Some peasants have forced a young woman to wear a nose made of wood. The convoluted argument they make is this: Witches and wood are both burned, and because witches are made of wood, and wood floats, and ducks also float, if she weighs the same as a duck, then she is made of wood and, therefore, is a witch!

Truth Tables (More Than Two Premises)

When an argument contains more than two premises, it is necessary to determine the truth values of the conjunction of *all* of them. ***If at least one premise in a conjunction of several premises is false, then the entire conjunction is false.***

▮▮ EXAMPLE 5 Using a Truth Table to Determine Validity

Determine whether the argument is *valid* or *invalid*.

If Eddie goes to town, then Mabel stays at home. If Mabel does not stay at home, then Rita will cook. Rita will not cook. Therefore, Eddie does not go to town.

SOLUTION

In an argument written in this manner, the premises are given first, and the conclusion is the statement that follows the word "Therefore." Let p represent "Eddie goes to town," let q represent "Mabel stays at home," and let r represent "Rita will cook."

$$p \rightarrow q$$
$$\sim q \rightarrow r$$
$$\underline{\sim r \qquad\qquad}$$
$$\sim p$$

To test validity, set up a truth table for this statement.

$$[(p \rightarrow q) \land (\sim q \rightarrow r) \land \sim r] \rightarrow \sim p$$

p	q	r	$p \rightarrow q$	$\sim q$	$\sim q \rightarrow r$	$\sim r$	$(p \rightarrow q) \land (\sim q \rightarrow r) \land \sim r$	$\sim p$	$[(p \rightarrow q) \land (\sim q \rightarrow r) \land \sim r] \rightarrow \sim p$
T	T	T	T	F	T	F	F	F	T
T	T	F	T	F	T	T	T	F	F
T	F	T	F	T	T	F	F	F	T
T	F	F	F	T	F	T	F	F	T
F	T	T	T	F	T	F	F	T	T
F	T	F	T	F	T	T	T	T	T
F	F	T	T	T	T	F	F	T	T
F	F	F	T	T	F	T	F	T	T

Because the final column does not contain all Ts, the statement is not a tautology. The argument is invalid. ▮▮▮

Arguments of Lewis Carroll

Consider the following verse, which has been around for many years.

For want of a nail, the shoe was lost. For want of a shoe, the horse was lost. For want of a horse, the rider was lost. For want of a rider, the battle was lost. For want of a battle, the war was lost.
Therefore, for want of a nail, the war was lost.

Each line of the verse may be written as an *if . . . then* statement. For example, the first line may be restated as "if a nail is lost, then the shoe is lost." The conclusion, "for want of a nail, the war was lost," follows from the premises, because repeated use of the law of transitivity applies. Arguments such as the one used by Lewis Carroll in the next example often take on a similar form.

▮▮ | **EXAMPLE 6** Supplying a Conclusion to Assure Validity

Supply a conclusion that yields a valid argument for the following premises.

> Babies are illogical.
> Nobody is despised who can manage a crocodile.
> Illogical persons are despised.

SOLUTION

First, write each premise in the form *if . . . then. . . .*

> If you are a baby, then you are illogical.
> If you can manage a crocodile, then you are not despised.
> If you are illogical, then you are despised.

Let *p* be "you are a baby," let *q* be "you are logical," let *r* be "you can manage a croc-odile," and let *s* be "you are despised." The statements can be written symbolically.

$$p \rightarrow \sim q$$
$$r \rightarrow \sim s$$
$$\sim q \rightarrow s$$

Begin with any letter that appears only once. Here *p* appears only once. Using the contrapositive of $r \rightarrow \sim s$, which is $s \rightarrow \sim r$, rearrange the statements as follows.

$$p \rightarrow \sim q$$
$$\sim q \rightarrow s$$
$$s \rightarrow \sim r$$

From the three statements, repeated use of reasoning by transitivity gives the conclusion

$$p \rightarrow \sim r, \quad \text{which leads to a valid argument.}$$

In words, the conclusion is "If you are a baby, then you cannot manage a crocodile," or, as Lewis Carroll would have written it, "Babies cannot manage crocodiles."

▮▮▮

Alice in the Forest of Forgetfulness
When Alice entered the Forest of Forgetfulness, she often forgot what day of the week it was. She encountered a Lion and a Unicorn, two strange creatures. The Lion lies on Mondays, Tuesdays, and Wednesdays and tells the truth on the other days of the week. The Unicorn, on the other hand, lies on Thursdays, Fridays, and Saturdays, but tells the truth on the other days of the week.

One day Alice met the Lion and the Unicorn resting under a tree. They made the following statements:

Lion: Yesterday was one of my lying days.
Unicorn: Yesterday was one of my lying days, too.

From these two statements, Alice was able to deduce the day of the week. What day was it? (The answer is on **page 133**.)

(Adapted from a problem in Raymond Smullyan's *What Is the Name of This Book?*)

3.6 EXERCISES

Each argument is either valid by one of the forms of valid arguments discussed in this section, or it is a fallacy by one of the forms of invalid arguments discussed. (See the summary boxes.) Decide whether the argument is valid *or a* fallacy, *and give the form that applies.*

1. If James Taylor comes to town, then I will go to the concert.
If I go to the concert, then I'll call in sick for work.

If James Taylor comes to town, then I'll call in sick for work.

2. If you use binoculars, then you get a glimpse of the space shuttle.
If you get a glimpse of the space shuttle, then you'll be amazed.

If you use binoculars, then you'll be amazed.

3. If Julie Nhem works hard enough, she will get a pro-motion.
Julie Nhem works hard enough.

She gets a promotion.

4. If Andrew Noble sells his quota, he'll get a bonus.
Andrew Noble sells his quota.

He gets a bonus.

5. If he doesn't have to get up at 3:00 A.M., he's ecstatic.
He's ecstatic.

He doesn't have to get up at 3:00 A.M.

6. If she buys another pair of shoes, her closet will overflow.
Her closet will overflow.

She buys another pair of shoes.

7. If Mariano Rivera pitches, the Yankees win.
The Yankees do not win.
_____
Mariano Rivera does not pitch.

8. If Nelson Dida plays, the opponent gets shut out.
The opponent does not get shut out.
_____
Nelson Dida does not play.

9. "If we evolved a race of Isaac Newtons, that would not be progress." (quote from Aldous Huxley)
We have not evolved a race of Isaac Newtons.
_____
That is progress.

10. "If I have seen farther than others, it is because I stood on the shoulders of giants." (quote from Sir Isaac Newton)
I have not seen farther than others.
_____
I have not stood on the shoulders of giants.

11. She uses e-commerce or she pays by credit card.
She does not pay by credit card.
_____
She uses e-commerce.

12. Mia kicks or Drew passes.
Drew does not pass.
_____
Mia kicks.

Use a truth table to determine whether the argument is **valid** *or* **invalid**.

13. $p \lor q$
$\underline{p }$
$\sim q$

14. $p \land \sim q$
$\underline{p }$
$\sim q$

15. $\sim p \rightarrow \sim q$
$\underline{q }$
p

16. $p \lor \sim q$
$\underline{p }$
$\sim q$

17. $p \rightarrow q$
$\underline{q \rightarrow p}$
$p \land q$

18. $\sim p \rightarrow q$
$\underline{p }$
$\sim q$

19. $p \rightarrow \sim q$
$\underline{q }$
$\sim p$

20. $p \rightarrow \sim q$
$\underline{\sim p }$
$\sim q$

21. $(p \land q) \lor (p \lor q)$
$\underline{q }$
p

22. $(p \rightarrow q) \land (q \rightarrow p)$
$\underline{p }$
$p \lor q$

23. $(\sim p \lor q) \land (\sim p \rightarrow q)$
$\underline{p }$
$\sim q$

24. $(r \land p) \rightarrow (r \lor q)$
$\underline{q \land p }$
$r \lor p$

25. $(\sim p \land r) \rightarrow (p \lor q)$
$\underline{\sim r \rightarrow p }$
$q \rightarrow r$

26. $(p \rightarrow \sim q) \lor (q \rightarrow \sim r)$
$\underline{p \lor \sim r }$
$r \rightarrow p$

27. Earlier we showed how to analyze arguments using Euler diagrams. Refer to **Example 4** in this section, restate each premise and the conclusion using a quantifier, and then draw an Euler diagram to illustrate the relationship.

28. Explain in a few sentences how to determine the statement for which a truth table will be constructed so that the arguments that follow in **Exercises 29–38** can be analyzed for validity.

Determine whether each argument is **valid** *or* **invalid**.

29. Joey loves to watch movies. If Terry likes to jog, then Joey does not love to watch movies. If Terry does not like to jog, then Carrie drives a school bus. Therefore, Carrie drives a school bus.

30. If Hurricane Gustave hit that grove of trees, then the trees are devastated. People plant trees when disasters strike and the trees are not devastated. Therefore, if people plant trees when disasters strike, then Hurricane Gustave did not hit that grove of trees.

31. If the social networking craze continues, then downloading music will remain popular. American Girl dolls are favorites or downloading music will remain popular. American Girl dolls are not favorites. Therefore, the social networking craze does not continue.

32. Carrie Underwood sings or Joe Jonas is not a teen idol. If Joe Jonas is not a teen idol, then Jennifer Hudson does not win a Grammy. Jennifer Hudson wins a Grammy. Therefore, Carrie Underwood does not sing.

33. The Dolphins will be in the playoffs if and only if Chad leads the league in passing. Tony coaches the Dolphins or Chad leads the league in passing. Tony does not coach the Dolphins. Therefore, the Dolphins will not be in the playoffs.

34. If I've got you under my skin, then you are deep in the heart of me. If you are deep in the heart of me, then you are not really a part of me. You are deep in the heart of me or you are really a part of me. Therefore, if I've got you under my skin, then you are really a part of me.

35. If Dr. Hardy is a department chairman, then he lives in Atlanta. He lives in Atlanta and his first name is Larry. Therefore, if his first name is not Larry, then he is not a department chairman.

36. If I were your woman and you were my man, then I'd never stop loving you. I've stopped loving you. Therefore, I am not your woman or you are not my man.

37. All men are created equal. All people who are created equal are women. Therefore, all men are women.

38. All men are mortal. Socrates is a man. Therefore, Socrates is mortal.

39. Suppose that you ask a stranger for the time and you get the following response:

> "If I tell you the time, then we'll start chatting. If we start chatting, then you'll want to meet me at a truck stop. If we meet at a truck stop, then we'll discuss my family. If we discuss my family, then you'll find out that my daughter is available for marriage. If you find out that she is available for marriage, then you'll want to marry her. If you want to marry her, then my life will be miserable since I don't want my daughter married to some fool who can't afford a $10 watch."

Use reasoning by transitivity to draw a valid conclusion.

40. Molly Riggs made the following observation: "If I want to determine whether an argument leading to the statement

$$[(p \rightarrow q) \wedge \sim q] \rightarrow \sim p$$

is valid, I only need to consider the lines of the truth table which lead to T for the column headed $(p \rightarrow q) \wedge \sim q$." Molly was very perceptive. Can you explain why her observation was correct?

In the arguments used by Lewis Carroll, it is helpful to restate a premise in if . . . then *form in order to more easily identify a valid conclusion. The following premises come from Lewis Carroll. Write each premise in* if . . . then *form.*

41. All my poultry are ducks.

42. None of your sons can do logic.

43. Guinea pigs are hopelessly ignorant of music.

44. No teetotalers are pawnbrokers.

45. No teachable kitten has green eyes.

46. Opium-eaters have no self-command.

47. I have not filed any of them that I can read.

48. All of them written on blue paper are filed.

Exercises 49–54 involve premises from Lewis Carroll. Write each premise in symbols, and then in the final part, give a conclusion that yields a valid argument.

49. Let *p* be "it is a duck," *q* be "it is my poultry," *r* be "one is an officer," and *s* be "one is willing to waltz."

  (a) No ducks are willing to waltz.

  (b) No officers ever decline to waltz.

  (c) All my poultry are ducks.

  (d) Give a conclusion that yields a valid argument.

50. Let *p* be "one is able to do logic," *q* be "one is fit to serve on a jury," *r* be "one is sane," and *s* be "he is your son."

  (a) Everyone who is sane can do logic.

  (b) No lunatics are fit to serve on a jury.

  (c) None of your sons can do logic.

  (d) Give a conclusion that yields a valid argument.

51. Let *p* be "one is honest," *q* be "one is a pawnbroker," *r* be "one is a promise-breaker," *s* be "one is trustworthy," *t* be "one is very communicative," and *u* be "one is a wine-drinker."

  (a) Promise-breakers are untrustworthy.

  (b) Wine-drinkers are very communicative.

  (c) A person who keeps a promise is honest.

  (d) No teetotalers are pawnbrokers. (*Hint:* Assume "teetotaler" is the opposite of "wine-drinker.")

  (e) One can always trust a very communicative person.

  (f) Give a conclusion that yields a valid argument.

52. Let *p* be "it is a guinea pig," *q* be "it is hopelessly ignorant of music," *r* be "it keeps silent while the *Moonlight Sonata* is being played," and *s* be "it appreciates Beethoven."

  (a) Nobody who really appreciates Beethoven fails to keep silent while the *Moonlight Sonata* is being played.

  (b) Guinea pigs are hopelessly ignorant of music.

  (c) No one who is hopelessly ignorant of music ever keeps silent while the *Moonlight Sonata* is being played.

  (d) Give a conclusion that yields a valid argument.

53. Let *p* be "it begins with 'Dear Sir'," *q* be "it is crossed," *r* be "it is dated," *s* be "it is filed," *t* be "it is in black ink," *u* be "it is in the third person," *v* be "I can read it," *w* be "it is on blue paper," *x* be "it is on one sheet," and *y* be "it is written by Brown."

(a) All the dated letters are written on blue paper.

(b) None of them are in black ink, except those that are written in the third person.

(c) I have not filed any of them that I can read.

(d) None of them that are written on one sheet are undated.

(e) All of them that are not crossed are in black ink.

(f) All of them written by Brown begin with "Dear Sir."

(g) All of them written on blue paper are filed.

(h) None of them written on more than one sheet are crossed.

(i) None of them that begin with "Dear Sir" are written in the third person.

(j) Give a conclusion that yields a valid argument.

54. Let *p* be "he is going to a party," *q* be "he brushes his hair," *r* be "he has self-command," *s* be "he looks fascinating," *t* be "he is an opium-eater," *u* be "he is tidy," and *v* be "he wears white kid gloves."

(a) No one who is going to a party ever fails to brush his hair.

(b) No one looks fascinating if he is untidy.

(c) Opium-eaters have no self-command.

(d) Everyone who has brushed his hair looks fascinating.

(e) No one wears white kid gloves unless he is going to a party. (*Hint:* "*a* unless *b*" ≡ ~*b* → *a*.)

(f) A man is always untidy if he has no self-command.

(g) Give a conclusion that yields a valid argument.

Answer to Alice in the Forest of Forgetfulness problem on **page 130:**

The only days the Lion can say, "I lied yesterday" are Mondays and Thursdays. The only days the Unicorn can say "I lied yesterday" are Thursdays and Sundays. Therefore the only day they can both say that is Thursday.

COLLABORATIVE INVESTIGATION

Logic Problems and Sudoku Revisited

Logic problems and Sudoku were first discussed in the **Extension** on **pages 120–124.** The problems here require more time and reasoning skills than the ones appearing in the **Extension.** They are taken from *Original Logic Problems*, February 2010, and *Dell Original Sudoku*, March 2010.

The class may wish to divide up into groups and see which group can solve these problems fastest.

EXERCISES

Note: As an exception to our usual style, answers to these Collaborative Investigation Exercises are given in the back of the book.

1. *Out to Launch* The National Space Association has scheduled five rockets for launch early next year. Each rocket (including the *Penchant*) will take off in a different month (January through May) on a different date (the 1st through the 5th). Each rocket will launch from a different site (including the San Simeon Launch Center) and engage in a different mission. For fans of the space program, next year will be a real blast! From the information provided, determine the month and date of the launch of the rocket from each launch site, as well as each rocket's mission.

(a) The date of the May launch is numbered exactly two lower than the date of the Willard Island launch. None of the rockets will launch on February 1. The mission to test a new propulsion system won't be launching in January.

(b) The *Liberty* and the rocket that will blast off in April will launch from Cape Carnival and Willard Island in some order. Neither the rocket on a mission to measure magnetic fields (which won't launch on the 1st of a month) nor the Willard Island rocket will blast off on the 3rd of a month.

(c) The *Bravura* will launch the month after the rocket that will blast off on the 4th of a month (which will launch later than the rocket that will land on the moon). The *Liberty* won't blast off on the 2nd of a month.

(d) The rocket that will launch from Cape Carnival won't be testing a new propulsion system. The *Twilight*'s mission (which isn't the mission to repair a satellite) won't begin on the 5th of a month.

(e) The rocket on a mission to investigate strange radiation will launch at some point earlier in the year than the *Liberty* (which won't be repairing a satellite) but at some point later in the year than the vessel that will blast off from the Vandyke Facility.

(f) The rocket that will blast off from Eddings Air Force Base will launch on a lower-numbered date than the one that will launch in March (which won't be testing a new propulsion system), which will blast off on a lower-numbered date than the *Falconer*.

2. *Super Challenger Puzzle* To solve the following Super Challenger puzzle, place a number into every box so that each row across, each column down, each small 16-box square (there are 16 of these), and each of the two diagonals contains each number from 1 to 16. No number may appear more than once in any one row or column, in either diagonal, or within any small 16-box square.

CHAPTER 3 TEST

Write a negation for each statement.

1. $6 - 3 = 3$

2. All men are created equal.

3. Some members of the class went on the field trip.

4. If that's the way you feel, then I will accept it.

5. She applied and got a student loan.

Let p represent "You will love me" and let q represent "I will love you." Write each statement in symbols.

6. If you won't love me, then I will love you.

7. I will love you if you will love me.

8. I won't love you if and only if you won't love me.

Using the same statements as for Exercises 6–8, write each of the following in words.

9. $\sim p \wedge q$

10. $\sim (p \vee \sim q)$

In each of the following, assume that p is true and that q and r are false. Find the truth value of each statement.

11. $\sim q \wedge \sim r$

12. $r \vee (p \wedge \sim q)$

13. $r \rightarrow (s \vee r)$ (The truth value of the statement s is unknown.)

14. $p \leftrightarrow (p \rightarrow q)$

15. Explain in your own words why, if p is a statement, the biconditional $p \leftrightarrow \sim p$ must be false.

16. State the necessary conditions for each of the following.
 (a) a conditional statement to be false
 (b) a conjunction to be true
 (c) a disjunction to be false

Construct a truth table for each of the following.

17. $p \wedge (\sim p \vee q)$

18. $\sim (p \wedge q) \rightarrow (\sim p \vee \sim q)$

Decide whether each statement is true *or* false.

19. Some negative integers are whole numbers.

20. All irrational numbers are real numbers.

Write each conditional statement in if . . . then *form.*

21. All integers are rational numbers.

22. Being a rhombus is sufficient for a polygon to be a quadrilateral.

23. Being divisible by 2 is necessary for a number to be divisible by 4.

24. She digs dinosaur bones only if she is a paleontologist.

For each statement, write (**a**) *the converse,* (**b**) *the inverse, and* (**c**) *the contrapositive.*

25. If a picture paints a thousand words, the graph will help me understand it.

26. $\sim p \rightarrow (q \wedge r)$ (Use one of De Morgan's laws as necessary.)

27. Use an Euler diagram to determine whether the argument is *valid* or *invalid*.

All members of that athletic club save money.
Don O'Neal is a member of that athletic club.
_____
Don O'Neal saves money.

28. Match each argument in parts (a)–(d) in the next column with the law that justifies its validity, or the fallacy of which it is an example, in choices A–F.

A. Modus ponens
B. Modus tollens
C. Reasoning by transitivity
D. Disjunctive syllogism
E. Fallacy of the converse
F. Fallacy of the inverse

(a) If he eats liver, then he'll eat anything.
He eats liver.
_____
He'll eat anything.

(b) If you use your seat belt, you will be safer.
You don't use your seat belt.
_____
You won't be safer.

(c) If I hear *Mr. Bojangles*, I think of her.
If I think of her, I smile.
_____
If I hear *Mr. Bojangles*, I smile.

(d) She sings or she dances.
She does not sing.
_____
She dances.

Use a truth table to determine whether each argument is valid *or* invalid.

29. If I write a check, it will bounce. If the bank guarantees it, then it does not bounce. The bank guarantees it. Therefore, I don't write a check.

30. $\sim p \rightarrow \sim q$
$q \rightarrow p$
_____
$p \vee q$

NUMBER THEORY

5

The 1997 movie *Contact*, based on the Carl Sagan novel of the same name, portrays Jodie Foster as scientist Ellie Arroway. After years of searching, Ellie makes contact with intelligent life in outer space. Her contact is verified after receiving radio signals that indicate **prime numbers:** 2, 3, 5, 7, 11, and so on. Her superiors are not convinced, asking why the aliens don't just speak English. Ellie's response:

> *Well, maybe because 70% of the planet speaks other languages. Mathematics is the only true universal language, Senator. It's no coincidence that they're using primes . . . . Prime numbers—that would be integers that are divisible only by themselves and 1.*

In this chapter, you will learn about those prime numbers, which are the building blocks of number theory, and, hence, of mathematics.

5.1 PRIME AND COMPOSITE NUMBERS

Primes, Composites, and Divisibility • The Fundamental Theorem of Arithmetic

Primes, Composites, and Divisibility

The famous German mathematician Carl Friedrich Gauss once remarked, "Mathematics is the Queen of Science, and number theory is the Queen of Mathematics." **Number theory** is the branch of mathematics devoted to the study of the properties of the **natural numbers,** also called the **counting numbers** or the **positive integers.**

$$N = \{1, 2, 3, \dots\}$$

A key concept of number theory is the idea of *divisibility*. One counting number is *divisible* by another if the operation of dividing the first by the second leaves a remainder 0.

> **Divisibility**
>
> The natural number a is **divisible** by the natural number b if there exists a natural number k such that $a = bk$. If b divides a, then we write $b \mid a$.

Notice that if b divides a, then the quotient a/b or $\frac{a}{b}$ is a natural number. For example, 4 divides 20 because there exists a natural number k such that

$$20 = 4k.$$

The value of k here is 5, because

$$20 = 4 \cdot 5.$$

The natural number 20 is not divisible by 7, since there is no natural number k satisfying $20 = 7k$. Alternatively, "20 divided by 7 gives quotient 2 with remainder 6" and since there is a nonzero remainder, divisibility does not hold. We write $7 \nmid 20$ to indicate that 7 does *not* divide 20.

If the natural number a is divisible by the natural number b, then b is a **factor** (or **divisor**) of a, and a is a **multiple** of b. For example, 5 is a factor of 30, and 30 is a multiple of 5. Also, 6 is a factor of 30, and 30 is a multiple of 6. The number 30 equals $6 \cdot 5$. This product $6 \cdot 5$ is called a **factorization** of 30. Other factorizations of 30 include

$$3 \cdot 10, \quad 2 \cdot 15, \quad 1 \cdot 30, \quad \text{and} \quad 2 \cdot 3 \cdot 5.$$

▍▍ **EXAMPLE 1** Checking Divisibility

Decide whether the first number is divisible by the second.

(a) 45; 9 **(b)** 60; 7 **(c)** 19; 19 **(d)** 26; 1

SOLUTION

(a) Is there a natural number k that satisfies $45 = 9k$? The answer is yes, because $45 = 9 \cdot 5$, and 5 is a natural number. Therefore, 9 divides 45, written $9 \mid 45$.

(b) Because the quotient $60 \div 7$ is not a natural number, 60 is not divisible by 7, written $7 \nmid 60$.

(c) The quotient $19 \div 19$ is the natural number 1, so 19 is divisible by 19. (***In fact, any natural number is divisible by itself.***)

(d) The quotient $26 \div 1$ is the natural number 26, so 26 is divisible by 1. (***In fact, any natural number is divisible by 1.***)

▍▍▍

Do not confuse $b \mid a$ with b/a. The expression $b \mid a$ denotes the *statement* "b divides a." For example, $3 \mid 12$ is a true statement, while $5 \mid 14$ is a false statement. On the other hand, b/a denotes the *operation* "b divided by a." For example, 28/4 yields the result 7.

The ideas of **even** and **odd natural numbers** are based on the concept of divisibility. A natural number is even if it is divisible by 2 and odd if it is not. Every even number can be written in the form $2k$ (for some natural number k), while every odd number can be written in the form $2k - 1$. Another way to say the same thing: 2 divides every even number but fails to divide every odd number. (If a is even, then $2 \mid a$, whereas if a is odd, then $2 \nmid a$.)

For any natural number a, it is true that $a \mid a$, and also that $1 \mid a$.

How to Use Up Lots of Chalk In 1903, the mathematician F. N. Cole presented before a meeting of the American Mathematical Society his discovery of a factorization of the number

$$2^{67} - 1.$$

He walked up to the chalkboard, raised 2 to the 67th power, and then subtracted 1. Then he moved over to another part of the board and multiplied out

193,707,721
× 761,838,257,287.

The two calculations agreed, and Cole received a standing ovation for a presentation that did not include a single word.

EXAMPLE 2 Finding Factors

Find all the natural number factors of each number.

(a) 36   **(b)** 50   **(c)** 11

SOLUTION

(a) To find the factors of 36, try to divide 36 by 1, 2, 3, 4, 5, 6, and so on. This gives the following natural number factors of 36: 1, 2, 3, 4, 6, 9, 12, 18, and 36.

(b) The factors of 50 are 1, 2, 5, 10, 25, and 50.

(c) The only natural number factors of 11 are 11 and 1.   ▪▪▪

Prime and Composite Numbers

A natural number greater than 1 that has only itself and 1 as factors is called a **prime number.** A natural number greater than 1 that is not prime is called **composite.**

Mathematicians agree that the natural number 1 is neither prime nor composite.

Alternative Definition of a Prime Number

A **prime number** is a natural number that has *exactly* two different natural number factors (which clarifies that 1 is not a prime).

There is a systematic method for identifying prime numbers in a list of numbers: 2, 3, . . . , n. The method, known as the **Sieve of Eratosthenes,** is named after the Greek geographer, poet, astronomer, and mathematician (about 276–192 B.C.).

To construct such a sieve, list all the natural numbers from 2 through some given natural number n, such as 100. The number 2 is prime, but all other multiples of 2 (4, 6, 8, 10, and so on) are composite. Circle the prime 2, and cross out all other multiples of 2. The next number not crossed out and not circled is 3, the next prime. Circle the 3, and cross out all other multiples of 3 (6, 9, 12, 15, and so on) that are not already crossed out. Circle the next prime, 5, and cross out all other multiples of 5 not already crossed out. Continue this process for all primes less than or equal to the square root of the last number in the list. For this list, we may stop with 7, because the next prime, 11, is greater than the square root of 100, which is 10. At this stage, simply circle all remaining numbers that are not crossed out.

Table 1 shows the Sieve of Eratosthenes for 2, 3, 4, . . . , 100.

Table 1 Sieve of Eratosthenes

The 25 primes between 1 and 100 are circled.

▮▮ **EXAMPLE 3** Identifying Prime and Composite Numbers

Decide whether each number is prime or composite.

(a) 97   **(b)** 59,872   **(c)** 697

SOLUTION

(a) Because 97 is circled in **Table 1**, it is prime. If 97 had a smaller prime factor, 97 would have been crossed out as a multiple of that factor.

(b) The number 59,872 is even, so it is divisible by 2. It is composite.

> *There is only one even prime, the number 2 itself.*

(c) For 697 to be composite, there must be a number other than 697 and 1 that divides into it with remainder 0. Start by trying 2, and then 3. Neither works. There is no need to try 4. (If 4 divides with remainder 0 into a number, then 2 will also.) Try 5. There is no need to try 6 or any succeeding even number. (Why?) Try 7. Try 11. (Why not try 9?) Try 13. Keep trying numbers until one works, or until a number is tried whose square exceeds the given number, 697. Try 17.

$$697 \div 17 = 41$$

The number 697 is composite, since

$$697 = 17 \cdot 41.$$ ▮▮▮

An aid in determining whether a natural number is divisible by another natural number is called a **divisibility test. Table 2** shows tests for divisibility by the natural numbers 2 through 12 (except for 7 and 11, which are covered in the exercises).

In the October 1, 1994 issue of *Science News*, Ivars Peterson gave a fascinating account of the discovery of a 75-year-old **factoring machine** ("Cranking Out Primes: Tracking Down a Long-lost Factoring Machine"). In 1989, Jeffrey Shallit of the University of Waterloo in Ontario came across an article in an obscure 1920 French journal, in which the author, Eugene Olivier Carissan, reported his invention of the factoring apparatus. Shallit and two colleagues embarked on a search for the machine. They contacted all telephone subscribers in France named Carissan and received a reply from Eugene Carissan's daughter. The machine was still in existence and in working condition, stored in a drawer at an astronomical observatory in Floirac, near Bordeaux.

Peterson explains in the article how the apparatus works. Using the machine, Carissan took just ten minutes to prove that 708,158,977 is a prime number, and he was able to factor a 13-digit number. While this cannot compare to what technology can accomplish today, it was a significant achievement for Carissan's day.

Table 2 Divisibility Tests for Natural Numbers

Divisible By	Test	Example
2	Number ends in 0, 2, 4, 6, or 8. (The last digit is even.)	9,489,994 ends in 4; it is divisible by 2.
3	Sum of the digits is divisible by 3.	897,432 is divisible by 3, since $8 + 9 + 7 + 4 + 3 + 2 = 33$ is divisible by 3.
4	Last two digits form a number divisible by 4.	7,693,432 is divisible by 4, since 32 is divisible by 4.
5	Number ends in 0 or 5.	890 and 7635 are divisible by 5.
6	Number is divisible by both 2 and 3.	27,342 is divisible by 6 since it is divisible by both 2 and 3.
8	Last three digits form a number divisible by 8.	1,437,816 is divisible by 8, since 816 is divisible by 8.
9	Sum of the digits is divisible by 9.	428,376,105 is divisible by 9 since sum of the digits is 36, which is divisible by 9.
10	The last digit is 0.	897,463,940 is divisible by 10.
12	Number is divisible by both 4 and 3.	376,984,032 is divisible by 12.

■ EXAMPLE 4   Applying Divisibility Tests

In each case, decide whether the first number is divisible by the second.

(a) 2,984,094; 4   **(b)** 4,119,806,514;   9

SOLUTION

(a) The last two digits form the number 94. Since 94 is not divisible by 4, the given number is not divisible by 4.

(b) The sum of the digits is

$$4 + 1 + 1 + 9 + 8 + 0 + 6 + 5 + 1 + 4 = 39,$$

which is not divisible by 9. The given number is, therefore, not divisible by 9.   ■■■

The Fundamental Theorem of Arithmetic

A *composite* number can be thought of as "composed" of smaller factors. For example, 42 is composite since $42 = 6 \cdot 7$. If the smaller factors are all primes, then we have a *prime factorization*. For example, $42 = 2 \cdot 3 \cdot 7$.

> **The Fundamental Theorem of Arithmetic**
>
> Every natural number can be expressed in one and only one way as a product of primes (if the order of the factors is disregarded). This unique product of primes is called the **prime factorization** of the natural number.

Because a prime natural number is not composed of smaller factors, its prime factorization is simply itself. For example, $17 = 17$.

■ EXAMPLE 5   Finding the Unique Prime Factorization of a Composite Number

Find the prime factorization of the number 1320.

SOLUTION

We use a "factor tree." The factor tree can start with $1320 = 2 \cdot 660$, as shown below on the left. Then $660 = 2 \cdot 330$, and so on, until every branch of the tree ends with a prime. All the resulting prime factors are shown circled in the diagram.

Alternatively, the same factorization is obtained by repeated division by primes, as shown on the right. (In general, you would divide by the primes 2, 3, 5, 7, 11, and so on, each as many times as possible, until the answer is no longer composite.)

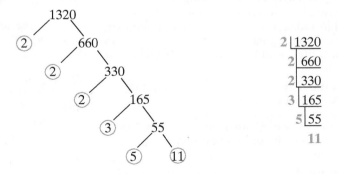

By either method, the prime factorization, in exponential form, is

$$1320 = 2^3 \cdot 3 \cdot 5 \cdot 11. \quad {\scriptstyle 2 \cdot 2 \cdot 2 \,=\, 2^3}$$

■■■

The following program, written by Charles W. Gantner and provided courtesy of Texas Instruments, can be used on the TI-83/84 Plus calculator to list all primes less than or equal to a given natural number *N*.

```
PROGRAM: PRIMES
: Disp "INPUT N ≥ 2"
: Disp "TO GET"
: Disp "PRIMES ≤ N"
: Input N
: 2 → T
: Disp T
: 1 → A
: Lbl 1
: A + 2 → A
: 3 → B
: If A > N
: Stop
: Lbl 2
: If B ≤ √(A)
: Goto 3
: Disp A
: Pause
: Goto 1
: Lbl 3
: If A/B ≤ int (A/B)
: Goto 1
: B + 2 → B
: Goto 2
```

```
prgmPRIMES

INPUT N≥2
TO GET
PRIMES ≤ N
?6
```

```
TO GET
PRIMES ≤ N
?6
                    2
                    3
                    5
                 Done
```

The display indicates that the primes less than or equal to 6 are 2, 3, and 5.

5.1 EXERCISES

Decide whether each statement is true *or* false.

1. Every natural number is divisible by 1.

2. There are no even prime numbers.

3. If n is a natural number and $9|n$, then $3|n$.

4. If n is a natural number and $5|n$, then $10|n$.

5. 1 is the least prime number.

6. Every natural number is both a factor and a multiple of itself.

7. If 16 divides a natural number, then 2, 4, and 8 must also divide that natural number.

8. The prime number 53 has exactly two natural number factors.

Find all natural number factors of each number.

9. 12

10. 20

11. 28

12. 172

Use divisibility tests to decide whether the given number is divisible by each number.

(a) 2 (b) 3 (c) 4 (d) 5 (e) 6 (f) 8
(g) 9 (h) 10 (i) 12

13. 321

14. 540

15. 36,360

16. 123,456,789

17. (a) In constructing the Sieve of Eratosthenes for 2 through 100, we said that any composite in that range had to be a multiple of some prime less than or equal to 7 (since the next prime, 11, is greater than the square root of 100). Explain.

    (b) To extend the Sieve of Eratosthenes to 200, what is the largest prime whose multiples would have to be considered?

    (c) Complete this statement: In seeking prime factors of a given number, we need only consider all primes up to and including the _____ _____ of that number, since a prime factor greater than the _____ _____ can only occur if there is at least one other prime factor less than the _____ _____.

    (d) Complete this statement: If no prime less than or equal to $\sqrt{n}$ divides n, then n is a _____ number.

18. (a) Continue the Sieve of Eratosthenes in **Table 1** from 101 to 200 and list the primes between 100 and 200. How many are there?

    (b) From your list in part (a), verify that the numbers 197 and 199 are both prime.

19. List two primes that are consecutive natural numbers. Can there be any others?

20. Can there be three primes that are consecutive natural numbers? Explain.

21. For a natural number to be divisible by both 2 and 5, what must be true about its last digit?

22. Consider the divisibility tests for 2, 4, and 8 (all powers of 2). Use inductive reasoning to predict the divisibility test for 16. Then, use the test to show that 456,882,320 is divisible by 16.

23. Redraw the factor tree of **Example 5,** assuming that you first observe that $1320 = 12 \cdot 110$, then that $12 = 3 \cdot 4$ and $110 = 10 \cdot 11$. Complete the process and give the resulting prime factorization.

24. Explain how your result in **Exercise 23** illustrates the fundamental theorem of arithmetic.

Find the prime factorization of each composite number.

25. 168

26. 300

27. 468

28. 931

Here is a divisibility test for 7.

(a) *Double the last digit of the given number, and subtract this value from the given number with the last digit omitted.*

(b) *Repeat the process of part (a) as many times as necessary until it is clear whether the number obtained is divisible by 7.*

(c) *If the final number obtained is divisible by 7, then the given number also is divisible by 7. If the final number is not divisible by 7, then neither is the given number.*

Use this divisibility test to determine whether each number is divisible by 7.

29. 214,256

30. 549,311

31. 584,854

32. 325,951

Here is a divisibility test for 11.

(a) *Starting at the left of the given number, add together every other digit.*

(b) *Add together the remaining digits.*

(c) *Subtract the smaller of the two sums from the larger. (If they are the same, the difference is 0.)*

(d) *If the final number obtained is divisible by 11, then the given number also is divisible by 11. If the final number is not divisible by 11, then neither is the given number.*

Use this divisibility test to determine whether each number is divisible by 11.

33. 6,524,846

34. 108,410,313

35. 470,933,815

36. 819,224,306

37. Consider the divisibility test for the composite number 6, and make a conjecture for the divisibility test for the composite number 15.

38. Give two factorizations of the number 75 that are not prime factorizations.

Determine all possible digit replacements for x so that the first number is divisible by the second. For example, 37, 58x is divisible by 2 if

$$x = 0, 2, 4, 6, or\ 8.$$

39. 398,87x; 2

40. 2,45x,765; 3

41. 64,537,84x; 4

42. 2,143,89x; 5

43. 985,23x; 6

44. 23, x54,470; 10

There is a method to determine the **number of divisors** *of a composite number. To do this, write the composite number in its prime factored form, using exponents. Add 1 to each exponent and multiply these numbers. Their product gives the number of divisors of the composite number. For example,*

$$24 = 2^3 \cdot 3 = 2^3 \cdot 3^1.$$

Now add 1 to each exponent:

$$3 + 1 = 4, \ 1 + 1 = 2.$$

Multiply 4 · 2 to get 8. There are 8 divisors of 24. (Because 24 is rather small, this can be verified easily. The divisors are 1, 2, 3, 4, 6, 8, 12, and 24, a total of eight as predicted.)

Find the number of divisors of each composite number.

45. 42

46. 308

47. $5^8 \cdot 29^2$

48. $2^4 \cdot 7^2 \cdot 13^3$

Leap years occur when the year number is divisible by 4. An exception to this occurs when the year number is divisible by 100 (that is, it ends in two zeros). In such a case, the number must be divisible by 400 in order for the year to be a leap year. Determine which years are leap years.

49. 1776

50. 1894

51. 2200

52. 2400

53. Why is the following *not* a valid divisibility test for 8? "A number is divisible by 8 if it is divisible by both 4 and 2." Support your answer with an example.

54. Choose any three consecutive natural numbers, multiply them together, and divide the product by 6. Repeat this several times, using different choices of three consecutive numbers. Make a conjecture concerning the result.

55. Explain why the product of three consecutive natural numbers must be divisible by 6.

56. Choose any 6-digit number consisting of three digits followed by the same three digits in the same order (for example, 467,467). Divide by 13. Divide by 11. Divide by 7. What do you notice? Why do you think this happens?

5.2 LARGE PRIME NUMBERS

The Infinitude of Primes • The Search for Large Primes

The Infinitude of Primes

One important basic result about prime numbers was proved by Euclid around 300 B.C., namely that there are infinitely many primes. This means that no matter how large a prime we identify, there are always others even larger. Euclid's proof remains today as one of the most elegant proofs in all of mathematics. (An *elegant* mathematical proof is one that demonstrates the desired result in a most direct, concise manner. Mathematicians strive for elegance in their proofs.) It is called a **proof by contradiction.**

A statement can be proved by contradiction as follows: Assume that the negation of the statement is true and use that assumption to produce some sort of contradiction, or absurdity. Logically, the fact that the negation of the original statement leads to a contradiction means that the original statement must be true.

To understand better a particular part of the proof that there are infinitely many primes, first examine the following argument.

Suppose that $M = 2 \cdot 3 \cdot 5 \cdot 7 + 1 = 211$. Now M is the product of the first four prime numbers, plus 1. If we divide 211 by each of the primes 2, 3, 5, and 7, the remainder is always 1.

The Riemann Hypothesis is an insightful conjecture stated in the mid-1800s by Georg Friedrich Bernhard Riemann (profiled on **page 508**). It concerns how the prime numbers are distributed on the number line and is undoubtedly the most important unproven claim in all of mathematics. Thousands of other "theorems" are built upon the assumption of its truth. If it were ever disproved, those results would fall apart. A proof, on the other hand, may provide sufficient understanding of the primes to demolish public key cryptography, upon which rests the security of all Internet commerce (among other things).

$$\begin{array}{cccc} 105 & 70 & 42 & 30 \\ 2\overline{)211} & 3\overline{)211} & 5\overline{)211} & 7\overline{)211} \\ 210 & 210 & 210 & 210 \\ \hline 1 & 1 & 1 & 1 \end{array}$$

All remainders are 1.

So 211 is not divisible by any of the primes 2, 3, 5, and 7.

Now we can present Euclid's proof that there are infinitely many primes. If *there is no largest prime number*, then there must be infinitely many primes.

EXAMPLE 1 Proving the Infinitude of Primes

Prove by contradiction that there are infinitely many primes.

SOLUTION

Suppose there is a largest prime number, called P. Form the number M such that

$$M = p_1 \cdot p_2 \cdot p_3 \cdots \cdot P + 1,$$

where $p_1, p_2, p_3, \ldots, P$ represent all the primes less than or equal to P. Now the number M must be either prime or composite.

1. Suppose that M is prime.
   M is obviously larger than P, so if M is prime, it is larger than the assumed largest prime P. We have reached a *contradiction*.

2. Suppose that M is composite.
   If M is composite, it must have a prime factor. But none of $p_1, p_2, p_3, \ldots, P$ are factors of M, because division by each will leave a remainder of 1. (Recall the above argument.) So if M has a prime factor, it must be greater than P. But this is a *contradiction*, because P is the assumed largest prime.

In either case 1 or 2, we reach a contradiction. The whole argument was based upon the assumption that a largest prime exists, but as this leads to contradictions, there must be no largest prime, or equivalently, ***there are infinitely many primes.*** ▮▮▮

We could never investigate all infinitely many primes directly. So, historically, people have observed properties of the smaller, familiar, ones and then tried to either "disprove" the property (usually by finding counterexamples) or prove it (usually by some deductive argument).

Here is one way to **partition** the natural numbers (divide them into subsets).

Set A: all natural numbers of the form $4k$

Set B: all natural numbers of the form $4k + 1$

Set C: all natural numbers of the form $4k + 2$

Set D: all natural numbers of the form $4k + 3$

In each case, k is some whole number, except that for set A, k cannot be 0. All natural numbers are now accounted for. Any number of the form $4k + 4$ would be in subset A, because

$$4k + 4 = 4(k + 1).$$

Any number of the form $4k + 5$ would be in subset B, because

$$4k + 5 = 4(k + 1) + 1,$$

and so on. The subset A consists of all the multiples of 4. Each of these is divisible by 4, hence, each is not a prime. Now consider C. Because

$$4k + 2 = 2(2k + 1),$$

each member is divisible by 2, hence, each is not a prime (except for 2 itself).

Under this partitioning, all primes must be in either B or D.

Marin Mersenne (1588–1648), in his *Cogitata Physico-Mathematica* (1644), claimed that M_n was prime for $n = 2, 3, 5, 7, 13, 17, 19, 31, 67, 127,$ and 257, and composite for all other prime numbers n less than 257. Other mathematicians at the time knew that Mersenne could not have actually tested all these values, but no one else could prove or disprove them either. It was more then 300 years later before all primes up to 257 were legitimately checked out, and Mersenne was finally revealed to have made five errors:

M_{61} is prime.

M_{67} is composite.

M_{89} is prime.

M_{107} is prime.

M_{257} is composite.

▌▌ **EXAMPLE 2** Partitioning the Natural Numbers

List the first eight members of each of the infinite sets $A, B, C,$ and D.

SOLUTION

$A = \{4, 8, 12, 16, 20, 24, 28, 32, \dots\}$

$B = \{1, 5, 9, 13, 17, 21, 25, 29, \dots\}$

$C = \{2, 6, 10, 14, 18, 22, 26, 30, \dots\}$

$D = \{3, 7, 11, 15, 19, 23, 27, 31, \dots\}$ ▌▌▌

As mentioned earlier, sets A and C contain no primes. All primes must lie in sets B and D. (In fact, there are infinitely many primes in each.)

▌▌ **EXAMPLE 3** Identifying Primes of the Forms $4k + 1$ and $4k + 3$

Identify all primes *specifically listed* in the following infinite sets of **Example 2.**

(a) set B **(b)** set D

SOLUTION

(a) $5, 13, 17, 29$ **(b)** $3, 7, 11, 19, 23, 31$ ▌▌▌

Pierre de Fermat (profiled on **page 200**) proved that every prime number of the form $4k + 1$ can be expressed as the sum of two squares.

▌▌ **EXAMPLE 4** Expressing Primes as Sums of Squares

Express each prime in the solution of **Example 3(a)** as a sum of two squares.

SOLUTION

$5 = 1^2 + 2^2; \qquad 13 = 2^2 + 3^2; \qquad 17 = 1^2 + 4^2; \qquad 29 = 2^2 + 5^2$ ▌▌▌

The Search for Large Primes

Identifying larger and larger prime numbers and factoring large composite numbers into their prime components is of great practical importance today, because it is the basis of modern **cryptography systems,** or secret codes. Various codes have been used for centuries in military applications. Today the security of vast amounts of industrial, business, and personal data also depends upon the theory of prime numbers. See the **Extension** following **Section 5.4.**

No reasonable formula has ever been found that will consistently generate prime numbers, much less "generate all primes." The most useful attempt, named to honor the French monk Marin Mersenne (1588–1648), is given below.

At one time, $2^{11,213} - 1$ was the largest known **Mersenne prime.** To honor its discovery, the Urbana, Illinois, post office used the cancellation picture above.

Mersenne Numbers and Mersenne Primes

For $n = 1, 2, 3, \dots,$ the **Mersenne numbers** are those generated by the formula

$$M_n = 2^n - 1.$$

(1) If n is composite, then M_n is also composite.

(2) If n is prime, then M_n may be either prime or composite.

The prime values of M_n are called the **Mersenne primes.** Large primes being verified currently are commonly Mersenne primes.

Long before Mersenne's time, there was general agreement on statement (1) in the box. (**Exercises 23–25** show how to find a factor of $2^n - 1$ whenever n is composite.) However, some early writers did not agree with statement (2), believing instead (incorrectly) that a prime n would always produce a prime M_n.

▮▮ **EXAMPLE 5** Finding Mersenne Numbers

Find each Mersenne number M_n for $n = 2, 3,$ and 5.

SOLUTION

$$M_2 = 2^2 - 1 = 3 \qquad 2^2 = 2 \cdot 2 = 4$$
$$M_3 = 2^3 - 1 = 7 \qquad 2^3 = 2 \cdot 2 \cdot 2 = 8$$
$$M_5 = 2^5 - 1 = 31 \qquad 2^5 = 2 \cdot 2 \cdot 2 \cdot 2 \cdot 2 = 32$$

Note that all three values, 3, 7, and 31, are indeed primes. ▮▮▮

It turns out that $M_7 = 2^7 - 1 = 127$ is also a prime (see **Exercise 18(a)** of **Section 5.1**), but it was discovered in 1536 that

$$M_{11} = 2^{11} - 1 = 2047 \quad \text{is not prime (since it is } 23 \cdot 89\text{).}$$

So prime values of n do* not *always produce prime M_n. Which prime values of *n do* produce prime Mersenne numbers (the so-called **Mersenne primes**)? No way was ever found to identify, in general, which prime values of n result in Mersenne primes. It is a matter of checking out each prime n value individually—not an easy task given that the Mersenne numbers rapidly become very large.

The Mersenne prime search yielded results slowly. By about 1600, M_n had been verified as prime for all prime n up to 19 (except for 11, as mentioned above). The next one was M_{31}, verified by Euler sometime between 1752 and 1772.

In 1876, French mathematician Edouard Lucas used a clever test he had developed to show that M_{127} (a 39-digit number) is prime. In the 1930s Lucas's method was further simplified by D. H. Lehmer, and the testing of Mersenne numbers for primality has been done ever since with the Lucas-Lehmer test. In 1952 an early computer verified that $M_{521}, M_{607}, M_{1279}, M_{2203},$ and M_{2281} are primes.

Over the last half century, most new record-breaking primes have been identified by computer algorithms devised and implemented by mathematicians and programmers. In 1996, the **Great Internet Mersenne Prime Search (GIMPS)** was launched and now involves about 50,000 personal computers worldwide. Of the 47 Mersenne primes presently known, the GIMPS program has discovered the thirteen largest ones. The latest one found (as of summer 2010),

$$M_{42,643,801} = 2^{42,643,801} - 1,$$

has 12,837,064 digits. Read the margin note **Prime Does Pay** to learn of a larger one, discovered earlier.

During the same general period that Mersenne was thinking about prime numbers, Pierre de Fermat (about 1601–1665) conjectured that the formula

$$2^{2^n} + 1$$

would always produce a prime, for any whole number value of n. **Table 3** on the next page shows how this formula generates the first four **Fermat numbers,** which are all primes. The fifth Fermat number (from $n = 4$) is likewise prime. Fermat had verified these first five by around 1630. But the sixth Fermat number (from $n = 5$) turns out to be 4,294,967,297, which is *not* prime. (See **Exercises 15 and 16.**) As of summer 2010, no more primes have been found among the Fermat numbers, and only F_0 to F_{11} have been completely factored.

Prime Does Pay On April 12, 2009, the 47th known Mersenne prime was identified by Odd Magnar Strindmo, from Melhus, Norway. The number,

$$2^{42,643,801} - 1, \quad \text{has} \quad 12,837,064 \text{ digits.}$$

Exceeding ten million digits, it would have qualified for a $100,000 award from The Electronic Frontier Foundation—except that it wasn't the first with that many digits. That award went to Edson Smith of the UCLA Department of Mathematics, who discovered the 45th known Mersenne prime on August 23, 2008. His number,

$$2^{43,112,609} - 1, \quad \text{has} \quad 12,978,189 \text{ digits}$$

and is still (as of summer 2010) the largest Mersenne prime known.

The Foundation now offers $150,000 to the first person or group to discover a 100-million-digit prime. But at present GIMPS participation rates, that discovery could take ten years or more.

If you would like to join the **Great Internet Mersenne Prime Search** (or just learn more about it), check out www.mersenne.org.

Distributed Computing is a way of achieving great computer power by having lots of individual machines do separate parts of the computation. One example is the **Great Internet Mersenne Prime Search (GIMPS)**, described in this section. Another example is **SETI@home (Search for Extraterrestrial Intelligence)**, which assigns the analysis of signal data from small patches of the "sky" to participants. (The movie *Contact* was fiction, but still the search goes on.)

A third example, **Folding@home,** based at Stanford University, investigates the folding of proteins in living organisms into complex shapes and how they interact with other biological molecules.

Table 3 The Generation of Fermat Numbers

n	2^n	2^{2^n}	$2^{2^n} + 1$
0	1	2	3
1	2	4	5
2	4	16	17
3	8	256	257

Of historical note are a couple of polynomial formulas that produce primes. (A *polynomial* in a given variable involves adding or subtracting integer multiples of whole number powers of the variable. Discussed in **Section 7.6,** polynomials are among the most basic mathematical functions.) In 1732, Leonhard Euler offered the formula

$$n^2 - n + 41, \quad \text{Euler's formula}$$

which generates primes for n up to 40 and fails at $n = 41$. In 1879, E. B. Escott produced more primes with the formula

$$n^2 - 79n + 1601, \quad \text{Escott's formula}$$

which first fails at $n = 80$.

▮▮ **EXAMPLE 7** Finding Numbers Using Euler's and Escott's Formulas

Find the first five numbers produced by each of the polynomial formulas of Euler and Escott.

SOLUTION

Table 4 shows the required numbers.

Table 4 A Few Polynomial-Generated Prime Numbers

n	Euler formula $n^2 - n + 41$	Escott formula $n^2 - 79n + 1601$
1	41	1523
2	43	1447
3	47	1373
4	53	1301
5	61	1231

All values found here are primes. (Use **Table 1** to verify the Euler values.) ▮▮▮

Actually, it is not hard to prove that there can be no polynomial that will consistently generate primes. More complicated mathematical formulas exist for generating primes, but none produced so far can be practically applied in a reasonable amount of time, even using the fastest computers.

5.2 EXERCISES

Decide whether each statement is true *or* false.

1. Euclid's proof of the infinitude of primes is a proof by contradiction.

2. In the ancient times of Euclid, mathematicians had not achieved elegance in their proofs.

3. Every natural number of the form $4k + 1$ is prime.

4. Every natural number of the form $4k + 3$ is prime.

5. The number $2^{11} - 1$ is an example of a Mersenne prime.

6. As of early 2010, only five Fermat primes had ever been found.

7. Find the next two primes, of the form $4k + 1$, *not* listed specifically in **Example 3(a),** and express them as sums of squares.

8. Recall the first few perfect squares: 1, 4, 9, 16, 25. Try writing the numbers of the form $4k + 3$ listed in **Example 3(b)** as sums of two squares. Then complete this statement: The primes tested, of the form $4k + 3$, _____ be expressed as the sum of two squares. (Fermat claimed, but did not prove, that *no* prime of the form $4k + 3$ was the sum of two squares. Euler proved it 100 years later.)

9. Explain what is meant by a "proof by contradiction."

10. Does **Example 4** prove that every prime of the form $4k + 1$ can be expressed as a sum of two squares? Explain why or why not.

11. Verify that Euler's polynomial prime-generating formula $n^2 - n + 41$ fails to produce a prime for $n = 41$.

12. Evaluate Euler's polynomial formula for **(a)** $n = 42$, and **(b)** $n = 43$.

13. Choose the correct completion: For $n > 41$, Euler's formula produces a prime
    A. never. **B.** sometimes. **C.** always.
    (*Hint:* If no prime less than or equal to $\sqrt{n}$ divides n, then n is prime.)

14. Recall that Escott's formula, $n^2 - 79n + 1601$, fails to produce a prime for $n = 80$. Evaluate this formula for $n = 81$ and $n = 82$. Then complete the following statement: For $n > 80$, Escott's formula produces a prime
    A. never. **B.** sometimes. **C.** always.

15. **(a)** Evaluate the Fermat number F_4: $2^{2^n} + 1$ for $n = 4$.

    (b) In seeking possible prime factors of the Fermat number of part (a), what is the largest potential prime factor that one would have to try? (As stated in the text, this "fifth" Fermat number is in fact prime.)

16. **(a)** Verify the value given in the text for the "sixth" Fermat number (i.e., $2^{2^5} + 1$).

    (b) Divide this Fermat number by 641. (Euler discovered this factorization in 1732, proving that the sixth Fermat number is not prime.)

17. Write a short report on the Great Internet Mersenne Prime Search (GIMPS).

18. Write a short report identifying the 44th and 46th known Mersenne primes and how, when, and by whom they were found.

19. The Mersenne margin note on **page 187** cites a 1644 claim that was not totally resolved for some 300 years. Find out when, and by whom, Mersenne's five errors were demonstrated. (*Hint:* One was mentioned in the margin note on **page 181**.)

20. In Euclid's proof that there is no largest prime, we formed a number M by taking the product of primes and adding 1. Observe the pattern below.

$M = 2 + 1 = 3$	(3 is prime)
$M = 2 \cdot 3 + 1 = 7$	(7 is prime)
$M = 2 \cdot 3 \cdot 5 + 1 = 31$	(31 is prime)
$M = 2 \cdot 3 \cdot 5 \cdot 7 + 1 = 211$	(211 is prime)
$M = 2 \cdot 3 \cdot 5 \cdot 7 \cdot 11 + 1 = 2311$	(2311 is prime)

    It seems as though this pattern will always yield a prime number. Now evaluate

    $$M = 2 \cdot 3 \cdot 5 \cdot 7 \cdot 11 \cdot 13 + 1.$$

21. Is the final value of M computed in **Exercise 20** prime or composite? If it is composite, give its prime factorization.

22. Explain in your own words the proof by Euclid that there is no largest prime.

The text stated that the Mersenne number M_n is composite whenever n is composite. Exercises 23–26 develop one way you can always find a factor of such a Mersenne number.

23. For the composite number $n = 6$, find
    $$M_n = 2^n - 1.$$

24. Notice that $p = 3$ is a prime factor of $n = 6$. Find $2^p - 1$ for $p = 3$. Is $2^p - 1$ a factor of $2^n - 1$?

25. Complete this statement: If p is a prime factor of n, then _____ is a factor of the Mersenne number $2^n - 1$.

26. Find $M_n = 2^n - 1$ for $n = 10$.

27. Use the statement of **Exercise 25** to find two distinct factors of M_{10}.

28. Do you think this procedure will always produce *prime* factors of M_n for composite n? (*Hint:* Consider $n = 22$ and its prime factor $p = 11$, and recall the statement following **Example 5**.) Explain.

5.3 SELECTED TOPICS FROM NUMBER THEORY

Perfect Numbers • Deficient and Abundant Numbers • Amicable (Friendly) Numbers
• Goldbach's Conjecture • Twin Primes • Fermat's Last Theorem

Perfect Numbers

The mathematician **Albert Wilansky,** when phoning his brother-in-law, Mr. Smith, noticed an interesting property concerning Smith's phone number (493–7775). The number 4,937,775 is composite, and its prime factorization is

$$3 \cdot 5 \cdot 5 \cdot 65{,}837.$$

When the digits of the phone number are added, the result, 42, is equal to the sum of the digits in the prime factors: 3 + 5 + 5 + 6 + 5 + 8 + 3 + 7 = 42. Wilansky termed such a number a **Smith number.** In 1985 it was proved that there are infinitely many Smith numbers, but there still are many unanswered questions about them.

In **Chapter 1,** we introduced figurate numbers, a topic investigated by the Pythagoreans, a group of Greek mathematicians and musicians who held their meetings in secret. In this section we examine some of the other special numbers that fascinated the Pythagoreans and are still studied by mathematicians today.

Divisors of a natural number were covered in **Section 5.1.** The **proper divisors** of a natural number include all divisors of the number except the number itself. For example, the proper divisors of 8 are 1, 2, and 4. (8 is *not* a proper divisor of 8.)

> **Perfect Numbers**
>
> A natural number is said to be **perfect** if it is equal to the sum of its proper divisors.

Is 8 perfect? No, because $1 + 2 + 4 = 7$, and $7 \neq 8$. The least perfect number is 6, because the proper divisors of 6 are 1, 2, and 3, and

$$1 + 2 + 3 = 6. \quad \text{6 is perfect.}$$

▮▮ **EXAMPLE 1** Verifying a Perfect Number

Show that 28 is a perfect number.

SOLUTION

The proper divisors of 28 are 1, 2, 4, 7, and 14. The sum of these is 28:

$$1 + 2 + 4 + 7 + 14 = 28.$$

By the definition, 28 is perfect. ▮▮▮

The numbers 6 and 28 are the two least perfect numbers. The next two are 496 and 8128. The pattern of these first four perfect numbers led early writers to conjecture that

1. The *n*th perfect number contains exactly *n* digits.
2. The even perfect numbers end in the digits 6 and 8, alternately.

} Conjectures
NOT NECESSARILY
TRUE

(**Exercises 39–41** will help you evaluate these conjectures.)

There still are many unanswered questions about perfect numbers. Euclid showed that the following is true.

If $2^n - 1$ is prime, then $2^{n-1}(2^n - 1)$ is perfect, and conversely.

Because the prime values of $2^n - 1$ are the Mersenne primes (discussed in the previous section), this means that for every new Mersenne prime discovered, another perfect number is automatically revealed. (Hence, as of summer 2010, there were also 47 known perfect numbers.) It is also known that the following is true.

All even perfect numbers must take the form $2^{n-1}(2^n - 1)$.

It is strongly suspected that no odd perfect numbers exist. (Any odd one would have at least eight different prime factors and would have at least 300 decimal digits.) Therefore, Euclid and the early Greeks most likely identified the form of all perfect numbers.

Deficient and Abundant Numbers

Earlier we saw that 8 is not perfect because it is not equal to the sum of its proper divisors (8 ≠ 7). Next we define two alternative categories for natural numbers that are *not* perfect.

A number is said to be a **weird number** if it is abundant without being equal to the sum of any set of its own proper divisors. For example, 70 is weird because it is abundant (1 + 2 + 5 + 7 + 10 + 14 + 35 = 74 > 70), but the set of proper divisors

$$\{1, 2, 5, 7, 10, 14, 35\}$$

contains no subset whose elements add up to 70.

Deficient and Abundant Numbers

A natural number is **deficient** if it is greater than the sum of its proper divisors. It is **abundant** if it is less than the sum of its proper divisors.

Based on this definition, a *deficient number* is one with proper divisors that add up to less than the number itself, while an *abundant number* is one with proper divisors that add up to more than the number itself. For example, because the proper divisors of 8 (1, 2, and 4) add up to 7, which is less than 8, the number 8 is deficient.

■■ **EXAMPLE 2** Identifying Deficient and Abundant Numbers

Decide whether each number is deficient or abundant.

(a) 12   **(b)** 10

SOLUTION

(a) The proper divisors of 12 are 1, 2, 3, 4, and 6. The sum of these divisors is 16. Because 16 > 12, the number 12 is abundant.

(b) The proper divisors of 10 are 1, 2, and 5. Since 1 + 2 + 5 = 8, and 8 < 10, the number 10 is deficient.   ■■■

Amicable (Friendly) Numbers

Suppose that we add the proper divisors of 284.

$$1 + 2 + 4 + 71 + 142 = 220$$

Their sum is 220. Now, add the proper divisors of 220.

$$1 + 2 + 4 + 5 + 10 + 11 + 20 + 22 + 44 + 55 + 110 = 284$$

The sum of the proper divisors of 220 is 284, while the sum of the proper divisors of 284 is 220. Number pairs with this property are said to be *amicable*, or *friendly*.

An extension of the idea of amicable numbers results in **sociable numbers.** In a chain of sociable numbers, the sum of the proper divisors of each number is the next number in the chain, and the sum of the proper divisors of the last number in the chain is the first number. Here is a 5-link chain of sociable numbers:

12,496

14,288

15,472

14,536

14,264

The number 14,316 starts a 28-link chain of sociable numbers.

Amicable or Friendly Numbers

The natural numbers a and b are **amicable,** or **friendly,** if the sum of the proper divisors of a is b, and the sum of the proper divisors of b is a.

The smallest pair of amicable numbers, 220 and 284, was known to the Pythagoreans, but it was not until 1636 that Fermat found the next pair, 17,296 and 18,416. Many more pairs were found over the next few decades, but it took a 16-year-old Italian boy named Nicolo Paganini to discover in the year 1866 that the pair of amicable numbers 1184 and 1210 had been overlooked for centuries!

Today, powerful computers continually extend the lists of known amicable pairs. The last time we checked, nearly twelve million pairs were known. It still is unknown, however, if there are infinitely many such pairs. No one has found an amicable pair without prime factors in common, but the possibility of such a pair has not been eliminated.

A Dull Number? The Indian mathematician **Srinivasa Ramanujan** (1887–1920) developed many ideas in number theory. His friend and collaborator on occasion was G. H. Hardy, also a number theorist and professor at Cambridge University in England.

A story has been told about Ramanujan that illustrates his genius. Hardy once mentioned to Ramanujan that he had just taken a taxicab with a rather dull number: 1729. Ramanujan countered by saying that this number isn't dull at all; it is the smallest natural number that can be expressed as the sum of two cubes in two different ways:

$$1^3 + 12^3 = 1729$$
and $$9^3 + 10^3 = 1729.$$

Show that 85 can be written as the sum of two *squares* in two ways.

Goldbach's Conjecture

The mathematician Christian Goldbach (1690–1764) stated the following conjecture (guess), which is one of the most famous unsolved problems in mathematics.

> **Goldbach's Conjecture (Not Proved)**
>
> Every even number greater than 2 can be written as the sum of two prime numbers.
>
> *Examples:* $8 = 5 + 3$
>
> $10 = 5 + 5 \text{ (or } 10 = 7 + 3)$

Mathematicians have tried to prove the conjecture but have not succeeded. However, the conjecture has been verified (as of late 2010) for numbers up to 2×10^{18}.

▮▮ **EXAMPLE 3**   Expressing Numbers as Sums of Primes

Write each even number as the sum of two primes.

(a) 18   **(b)** 60

SOLUTION

(a) $18 = 5 + 13$. Another way of writing it is $7 + 11$. Notice that $1 + 17$ is *not* valid because by definition 1 is not a prime number.

(b) $60 = 7 + 53$. Can you find other ways? Why is $3 + 57$ not valid?   ▮▮▮

Twin Primes

Prime numbers that differ by 2 are called **twin primes.** Some twin prime pairs are 3 and 5, 5 and 7, 11 and 13, and so on. Like Goldbach's conjecture, the following conjecture about twin primes has never been proved.

> **Twin Prime Conjecture (Not Proved)**
>
> There are infinitely many pairs of twin primes.

Mathematics professor Gregory Larkin, played by Jeff Bridges, woos colleague Rose Morgan (Barbra Streisand) in the 1996 film *The Mirror Has Two Faces.* Larkin's research and book focus on the **twin prime conjecture,** which he correctly states in a dinner scene. He is amazed that his nonmathematician friend actually understands what he is talking about.

You may wish to verify that there are eight such pairs less than 100, using the Sieve of Eratosthenes in **Table 1.** As of summer 2010, the largest known twin primes were

$$65{,}516{,}468{,}355 \cdot 2^{333{,}333} \pm 1.   \text{Each contains 100,355 digits.}$$

Recall from **Section 5.2** that Euclid's proof of the infinitude of primes used numbers of the form

$$p_1 \cdot p_2 \cdot p_3 \cdots \cdot p_n + 1,$$

where all the ps are prime. It may seem that any such number must be prime, but that is not so. (See **Exercises 20 and 21** of **Section 5.2.**) However, this form often does produce primes (as does the same form with the plus replaced by a minus). When *all* the primes up to p_n are included, the resulting numbers, if prime, are called **primorial primes.** They are denoted

$$p\# \pm 1.$$

For example, $5\# + 1 = 2 \cdot 3 \cdot 5 + 1 = 31$ is a primorial prime. (In late 2010, the largest known primorial prime was $392{,}113\# + 1$, a number with 169,966 digits.) The primorial primes are a popular place to look for twin primes.

Sophie Germain (1776–1831) studied at the École Polytechnique in Paris in a day when female students were not admitted. A **Sophie Germain prime** is a prime p for which $2p + 1$ also is prime. Lately, large Sophie Germain primes have been discovered at the rate of one or more per year. As of late 2010, the largest one known was $183{,}027 \cdot 2^{265{,}440} - 1$, which has 79,911 digits.

Source: www.utm.edu

The popular animated television series *The Simpsons* provides not only humor and social commentary but also lessons in mathematics. One episode depicted the equation

$$1782^{12} + 1841^{12} = 1922^{12},$$

which, according to **Fermat's Last Theorem**, cannot be true. Your calculator may indicate that the equation is true, but this is because it cannot accurately display powers of this size. Actually, 1782^{12} must be an *even* number because *an even number to any power is even.* Also, 1841^{12} must be *odd*, because *an odd number to any power is odd.* So the sum on the left must be *odd*, because

$$even + odd = odd.$$

Similarly, 1922^{12} must be *even.* So the equation states that an odd number equals an even number, which is impossible. (See www.simpsonsmath.com)

▌▌ **EXAMPLE 4** Verifying Twin Primes

Verify that the primorial formula $p\# \pm 1$ produces twin prime pairs for both **(a)** $p = 3$ and **(b)** $p = 5$.

SOLUTION

(a) $3\# \pm 1 = 2 \cdot 3 \pm 1 = 6 \pm 1 = 5$ and 7 Twin primes

> Multiply, then add and subtract.

(b) $5\# \pm 1 = 2 \cdot 3 \cdot 5 \pm 1 = 30 \pm 1 = 29$ and 31 Twin primes   ▐▐▐

Fermat's Last Theorem

In any right triangle with shorter sides (legs) a and b, and longest side (hypotenuse) c, the equation $a^2 + b^2 = c^2$ will hold true. This is the famous Pythagorean theorem. For example,

$$3^2 + 4^2 = 5^2 \qquad a = 3, b = 4, c = 5$$
$$9 + 16 = 25 \qquad \text{Apply the exponents.}$$
$$25 = 25. \qquad \text{True}$$

It is known that there are infinitely many such triples (a, b, c) that satisfy the equation $a^2 + b^2 = c^2$. Is something similar true of the equation

$$a^n + b^n = c^n$$

for natural numbers $n \geq 3$? Pierre de Fermat, who is profiled in a margin note on **page 200,** thought that not only were there not infinitely many such triples, but that there were, in fact, none. He made the following claim in the 1600s.

> **Fermat's Last Theorem (Proved in the 1990s)**
>
> For *any* natural number $n \geq 3$, there are *no* triples (a, b, c) that satisfy the equation
>
> $$a^n + b^n = c^n.$$

Fermat's assertion was the object of some 350 years of attempts by mathematicians to provide a suitable proof. While it was verified for many specific cases (Fermat himself proved it for $n = 3$), a proof of the general case could not be found until the Princeton mathematician Andrew Wiles announced a proof in the spring of 1993. Although some flaws were discovered in his argument, Wiles was able, by the fall of 1994, to repair and even improve the proof.

There were probably about 100 mathematicians around the world qualified to understand the Wiles proof. ***Today Fermat's Last Theorem finally is regarded by the mathematics community as officially proved.***

▌▌ **EXAMPLE 5** Applying a Theorem Proved by Fermat

One of the theorems legitimately proved by Fermat is as follows:

> *Every odd prime can be expressed as the difference*
> *of two squares in one and only one way.*

Express each odd prime as the difference of two squares.

(a) 3   **(b)** 7

SOLUTION

(a) $3 = 4 - 1 = 2^2 - 1^2$ **(b)** $7 = 16 - 9 = 4^2 - 3^2$ ▐▐▐

For Further Thought

Curious and Interesting

One of the most remarkable books on number theory is *The Penguin Dictionary of Curious and Interesting Numbers* (1986) by David Wells. This book contains fascinating numbers and their properties, including the following.

- There are only three sets of three digits that form prime numbers in all possible arrangements: $\{1, 1, 3\}$, $\{1, 9, 9\}$, $\{3, 3, 7\}$.

- Find the sum of the cubes of the digits of 136:

$$1^3 + 3^3 + 6^3 = 244.$$

Repeat the process with the digits of 244:

$$2^3 + 4^3 + 4^3 = 136.$$

We're back to where we started.

- 635,318,657 is the least number that can be expressed as the sum of two fourth powers in two ways:

$$635{,}318{,}657 = 59^4 + 158^4 = 133^4 + 134^4.$$

- The number 24,678,050 has an interesting property:

$$24{,}678{,}050 = 2^8 + 4^8 + 6^8 + 7^8 + 8^8 + 0^8$$
$$+ 5^8 + 0^8.$$

- The number 54,748 has a similar interesting property:

$$54{,}748 = 5^5 + 4^5 + 7^5 + 4^5 + 8^5.$$

- The number 3435 has this property:

$$3435 = 3^3 + 4^4 + 3^3 + 5^5.$$

For anyone whose curiosity is piqued by such facts, this book is for you!

For Group or Individual Investigation

Have each student in the class choose a three-digit number that is a multiple of 3. Add the cubes of the digits. Repeat the process until the same number is obtained over and over. Then, have the students compare their results. What is curious and interesting about this process?

5.3 EXERCISES

Decide whether each statement in Exercises 1–10 is true *or* false.

1. There are infinitely many prime numbers.

2. The prime numbers 2 and 3 are twin primes.

3. There is no perfect number between 496 and 8128.

4. $2^n - 1$ is prime if and only if $2^{n-1}(2^n - 1)$ is perfect.

5. Any prime number must be deficient.

6. The equation $17 + 51 = 68$ verifies Goldbach's conjecture for the number 68.

7. There are more Mersenne primes known than there are perfect numbers.

8. The number 31 cannot be represented as the difference of two squares.

9. The number $2^6(2^7 - 1)$ is perfect.

10. Any natural number greater than 1 is one and only one of the following: perfect, deficient, or abundant.

11. The proper divisors of 496 are 1, 2, 4, 8, 16, 31, 62, 124, and 248. Use this information to verify that 496 is perfect.

12. The proper divisors of 8128 are 1, 2, 4, 8, 16, 32, 64, 127, 254, 508, 1016, 2032, and 4064. Use this information to verify that 8128 is perfect.

13. As mentioned in the text, when $2^n - 1$ is prime,

$$2^{n-1}(2^n - 1)$$

is perfect. By letting $n = 2, 3, 5$, and 7, we obtain the first four perfect numbers. Show that $2^n - 1$ is prime for $n = 13$, and then find the decimal digit representation for the fifth perfect number.

14. In the summer of 2010, the largest known prime number was $2^{43,112,609} - 1$. Use the formula in **Exercise 13** to write an expression for the perfect number generated by this prime number.

15. It has been proved that the reciprocals of *all* the positive divisors of a perfect number have a sum of 2. Verify this for the perfect number 6.

16. Consider the following equations.

$$6 = 1 + 2 + 3$$
$$28 = 1 + 2 + 3 + 4 + 5 + 6 + 7$$

Show that a similar equation is valid for the third perfect number, 496.

Determine whether each number is abundant *or* deficient.

17. 45   **18.** 48

19. 88   **20.** 64

21. There are four abundant numbers between 1 and 25. Find them. (*Hint:* They are all even, and no prime number is abundant.)

22. Explain why a prime number must be deficient.

23. The first odd abundant number is 945. Its proper divisors are 1, 3, 5, 7, 9, 15, 21, 27, 35, 45, 63, 105, 135, 189, and 315. Use this information to verify that 945 is abundant.

24. Explain in your own words the terms *perfect number, abundant number,* and *deficient number*.

25. Nicolo Paganini's numbers 1184 and 1210 are amicable. The proper divisors of 1184 are 1, 2, 4, 8, 16, 32, 37, 74, 148, 296, and 592. The proper divisors of 1210 are 1, 2, 5, 10, 11, 22, 55, 110, 121, 242, and 605. Use the definition of amicable (friendly) numbers to show that they are indeed amicable.

26. An Arabian mathematician of the ninth century stated the following.
   If the three numbers

$$x = 3 \cdot 2^{n-1} - 1,$$
$$y = 3 \cdot 2^n - 1,$$
and $$z = 9 \cdot 2^{2n-1} - 1$$

are all prime and $n \geq 2$, then $2^n xy$ and $2^n z$ are amicable numbers.

   (a) Use $n = 2$, and show that the result is the least pair of amicable numbers, namely 220 and 284.

   (b) Use $n = 4$ to obtain another pair of amicable numbers.

Write each even number as the sum of two primes. (There may be more than one way to do this.)

27. 16   **28.** 20

29. 30   **30.** 34

31. Joseph Louis Lagrange (1736–1813) conjectured that every odd natural number greater than 5 can be written as a sum $a + 2b$, where a and b are both primes.

   (a) Verify this for the odd natural number 11.

   (b) Verify that the odd natural number 17 can be written in this form in four different ways.

32. Another unproved conjecture in number theory states that every natural number multiple of 6 can be written as the difference of two primes. Verify this for 6, 12, and 18.

Find one pair of twin primes between the two numbers given.

33. 30, 50   **34.** 85, 105

While Pierre de Fermat probably is best known for his now famous "last theorem," he did provide proofs of many other theorems in number theory. Exercises 35–38 investigate some of these theorems.

35. If p is prime and the natural numbers a and p have no common factor except 1, then $a^{p-1} - 1$ is divisible by p.

   (a) Verify this for $p = 5$ and $a = 3$.

   (b) Verify this for $p = 7$ and $a = 2$.

36. Every odd prime can be expressed as the difference of two squares in one and only one way.

   (a) Find this one way for the prime number 5.

   (b) Find this one way for the prime number 11.

37. There is only one solution in natural numbers for $a^2 + 2 = b^3$, and it is $a = 5, b = 3$. Verify this solution.

38. There are only two solutions in integers for $a^2 + 4 = b^3$. One solution is $a = 2, b = 2$. Find the other solution.

The first four perfect numbers were identified in the text: 6, 28, 496, *and* 8128. *The next two are* 33,550,336 *and* 8,589,869,056. *Use this information about perfect numbers to work Exercises 39–41.*

39. Verify that each of these six perfect numbers ends in either 6 or 28. (In fact, this is true of all even perfect numbers.)

40. Is conjecture (1) in the text (that the nth perfect number contains exactly n digits) true or false? Explain.

41. Is conjecture (2) in the text (that the even perfect numbers end in the digits 6 and 8, alternately) true or false? Explain.

According to the Web site www.shyamsundergupta.com/amicable.htm, *a natural number is* **happy** *if the process of repeatedly summing the squares of its decimal digits finally ends in 1. For example, the least natural number (greater than 1) that is happy is 7, as shown here.*

$$7^2 = 49, \quad 4^2 + 9^2 = 97, \quad 9^2 + 7^2 = 130,$$
$$1^2 + 3^2 + 0^2 = 10, \quad 1^2 + 0^2 = 1.$$

An amicable pair is a **happy amicable pair** *if and only if both members of the pair are happy numbers. (The first 5000 amicable pairs include only 111 that are happy amicable pairs.) For each amicable pair, determine whether neither, one, or both of the members are happy, and whether the pair is a happy amicable pair.*

42. 220 and 284   **43.** 1184 and 1210

44. 10,572,550 and 10,854,650

45. 35,361,326 and 40,117,714

46. If the early Greeks knew the form of all even perfect numbers, namely $2^{n-1}(2^n - 1)$, then why did they not discover all the ones that are known today?

47. Explain why the primorial formula $p\# \pm 1$ does not result in a pair of twin primes for the prime value $p = 2$.

48. **(a)** What two numbers does the primorial formula produce for $p = 7$?

(b) Which, if either, of these numbers is prime?

49. Choose the correct completion: The primorial formula produces twin primes

A. never.   **B.** sometimes.   **C.** always.

*See the margin note (on **page 194**) defining a Sophie Germain prime, and complete this table.*

	p	$2p + 1$	Is p a Sophie Germain prime?
50.	2	_____	_____
51.	3	_____	_____
52.	5	_____	_____
53.	7	_____	_____
54.	11	_____	_____
55.	13	_____	_____

Factorial primes *are of the form* $n! \pm 1$ *for natural numbers* n. ($n!$ *denotes "n factorial," the product of* all *natural numbers up to n, not just the primes as in the primorial primes. For example,* $4! = 1 \cdot 2 \cdot 3 \cdot 4 = 24$.*) As of late 2010, the largest verified factorial prime was* $34{,}790! - 1$, *which has* 142,891 *digits. Find the missing entries in this table.*

	n	$n!$	$n! - 1$	$n! + 1$	Is $n! - 1$ prime?	Is $n! + 1$ prime?
	2	2	1	3	no	yes
56.	3	_____	_____	_____	_____	_____
57.	4	_____	_____	_____	_____	_____
58.	5	_____	_____	_____	_____	_____

59. Explain why the factorial prime formula does not give twin primes for $n = 2$.

Based on the preceding table, complete each statement with one of the following:

A. *never,*   **B.** *sometimes, or*   **C.** *always.*

When applied to particular values of n, the factorial prime formula $n! \pm 1$ produces

60. no primes _____   **61.** exactly one prime _____

62. twin primes _____

Greatest Common Factor • Least Common Multiple

Greatest Common Factor

The *greatest common factor* is defined as follows.

Greatest Common Factor

The **greatest common factor (GCF)** of a group of natural numbers is the largest natural number that is a factor of all the numbers in the group.

Examples: 18 is the GCF of 36 and 54, because 18 is the largest natural number that divides both 36 and 54.

1 is the GCF of 7 and 16.

The greatest common factor is often called the *greatest common divisor*, and may be symbolized GCD or gcd.

Greatest common factors can be found by using prime factorizations. To determine the GCF of 36 and 54, first write the prime factorization of each number (perhaps by using factor trees or repeated division).

$$36 = 2^2 \cdot 3^2$$
$$54 = 2^1 \cdot 3^3$$

The GCF is the product of the primes common to the factorizations, with each prime raised to the power indicated by the *least* exponent that it has in any factorization. Here, the prime 2 has 1 as the least exponent (in $54 = 2^1 \cdot 3^3$), while the prime 3 has 2 as the least exponent (in $36 = 2^2 \cdot 3^2$).

$$\text{GCF} = 2^1 \cdot 3^2 = 2 \cdot 9 = 18,$$

We summarize as follows.

Finding the Greatest Common Factor (Prime Factors Method)

Step 1 Write the prime factorization of each number.

Step 2 Choose all primes common to *all* factorizations, with each prime raised to the *least* exponent that it has in any factorization.

Step 3 Form the product of all the numbers in Step 2. This product is the greatest common factor.

▊▊ **EXAMPLE 1** Finding the Greatest Common Factor by the Prime Factors Method

Find the greatest common factor of 360 and 2700.

SOLUTION

The calculator shows that the greatest common divisor (factor) of 360 and 2700 is 180. Compare with **Example 1.**

Write the prime factorization of each number.

$$360 = 2^3 \cdot 3^2 \cdot 5 \qquad 2700 = 2^2 \cdot 3^3 \cdot 5^2$$

Find the primes common to both factorizations, with each prime having as its exponent the *least* exponent from either product.

Use the least exponents.

$$\text{GCF} = 2^2 \cdot 3^2 \cdot 5 = 180$$

The greatest common factor of 360 and 2700 is 180. ▊▊▊

▊▊ **EXAMPLE 2** Finding the Greatest Common Factor by the Prime Factors Method

Find the greatest common factor of 720, 1000, and 1800.

SOLUTION

Write the prime factorization for each number.

$$720 = 2^4 \cdot 3^2 \cdot 5$$
$$1000 = 2^3 \cdot 5^3$$
$$1800 = 2^3 \cdot 3^2 \cdot 5^2$$

Use the smallest exponent on each prime common to the factorizations.

$$\text{GCF} = 2^3 \cdot 5 = 40$$

(The prime 3 is not used in the greatest common factor because it does not appear in the prime factorization of 1000.) ▊▊▊

▮▮ **EXAMPLE 3** Finding the Greatest Common Factor by the Prime Factors Method

Find the greatest common factor of 80 and 63.

SOLUTION

$$80 = 2^4 \cdot 5$$
$$63 = 3^2 \cdot 7$$

There are no primes in common here, so the GCF is 1. The number 1 is the largest number that will divide into both 80 and 63. ▮▮▮

Two numbers, such as 80 and 63, with a greatest common factor of 1 are called **relatively prime numbers**—that is, they are prime *relative* to one another. (They have no common factors other than 1.)

Another method of finding the greatest common factor involves dividing the numbers by common prime factors.

Finding the Greatest Common Factor (Dividing by Prime Factors Method)

Step 1 Write the numbers in a row.

Step 2 Divide each of the numbers by a common prime factor. Try 2, then try 3, and so on.

Step 3 Divide the quotients by a common prime factor. Continue until no prime will divide into all the quotients.

Step 4 The product of the primes in Steps 2 and 3 is the greatest common factor.

▮▮ **EXAMPLE 4** Finding the Greatest Common Factor by Dividing by Prime Factors

Find the greatest common factor of 12, 18, and 60.

SOLUTION

Write the numbers in a row and divide by 2.

$$
\begin{array}{r|rrr}
2 & 12 & 18 & 60 \\
\hline
 & 6 & 9 & 30
\end{array}
$$

The numbers 6, 9, and 30 are not all divisible by 2, but they are divisible by 3.

$$
\begin{array}{r|rrr}
2 & 12 & 18 & 60 \\
\hline
3 & 6 & 9 & 30 \\
\hline
 & 2 & 3 & 10
\end{array}
$$

No prime divides into 2, 3, and 10, so the greatest common factor of the numbers 12, 18, and 60 is given by the product of the primes on the left, 2 and 3.

$$
\begin{array}{r|rrr}
2 & 12 & 18 & 60 \\
\hline
3 & 6 & 9 & 30 \\
\hline
 & 2 & 3 & 10
\end{array}
$$
$$2 \cdot 3 = 6$$

The GCF of 12, 18, and 60 is 6. ▮▮▮

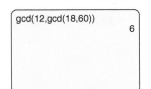

gcd(12,gcd(18,60))   6

This screen uses the fact that gcd(*a*, *b*, *c*) = gcd (*a*, gcd (*b*, *c*)). Compare with **Example 4.**

Pierre de Fermat (about 1601–1665), a government official who did not interest himself in mathematics until he was past 30, devoted leisure time to its study. He was a worthy scholar, best known for his work in number theory. His other major contributions involved certain applications in geometry and his original work in probability.

   Much of Fermat's best work survived only on loose sheets or jotted, without proof, in the margins of works that he read.

Another method of finding the greatest common factor of two numbers (but not more than two) is called the **Euclidean algorithm.***

EXAMPLE 5	Finding the Greatest Common Factor Using the Euclidean Algorithm

Use the Euclidean algorithm to find the greatest common factor of 90 and 168.

SOLUTION

Step 1 Begin by dividing the larger, 168, by the smaller, 90. Disregard the quotient, but note the remainder.

Step 2 Divide the smaller of the two numbers by the remainder obtained in Step 1. Once again, note the remainder.

Step 3 Continue dividing the successive remainders as many times as necessary to obtain a remainder of 0.

Step 4 The *last positive remainder* in this process is the greatest common factor of 90 and 168. It can be seen that their GCF is 6.

$$
\begin{array}{r}
1 \\
90\overline{)168} \\
90 \\
\hline
78
\end{array}
$$

$$
\begin{array}{r}
1 \\
78\overline{)90} \\
78 \\
\hline
12
\end{array}
$$

$$
\begin{array}{r}
6 \\
12\overline{)78} \\
72 \\
\hline
6
\end{array}
$$ Greatest common factor

$$
\begin{array}{r}
2 \\
6\overline{)12} \\
12 \\
\hline
0
\end{array}
$$

The Euclidean algorithm is particularly useful if the two numbers are difficult to factor into primes. We summarize the algorithm here.

Finding the Greatest Common Factor (Euclidean Algorithm)

To find the greatest common factor of two unequal numbers, divide the larger by the smaller. Note the remainder, and divide the previous divisor by this remainder. Continue the process until a remainder of 0 is obtained. The greatest common factor is the last positive remainder obtained.

Least Common Multiple

Closely related to the idea of the greatest common factor is the concept of the *least common multiple*.

Least Common Multiple

The **least common multiple (LCM)** of a group of natural numbers is the smallest natural number that is a multiple of all the numbers in the group.

Example: 30 is the LCM of 15 and 10 because 30 is the smallest number that appears in both sets of multiples.

Multiples of 15: {15, **30,** 45, 60, 75, 90, 105, . . . }

Multiples of 10: {10, 20, **30,** 40, 50, 60, 70, . . . }

---

*For a proof that this process does indeed give the greatest common factor, see *Elementary Introduction to Number Theory, Second Edition*, by Calvin T. Long, pp. 34–35.

The least common multiple of 15 and 10 is 30.

The set of natural numbers that are multiples of *both* 15 and 10 form the set of *common multiples:*

$$\{30, 60, 90, 120, \dots\}.$$

While there are infinitely many common multiples, the *least* common multiple is observed to be 30.

A method similar to the first one given for the greatest common factor may be used to find the least common multiple of a group of numbers.

Finding the Least Common Multiple (Prime Factors Method)

Step 1 Write the prime factorization of each number.

Step 2 Choose all primes belonging to *any* factorization, with each prime raised to the power indicated by the *greatest* exponent that it has in any factorization.

Step 3 Form the product of all the numbers in Step 2. This product is the least common multiple.

┃┃ EXAMPLE 6 Finding the Least Common Multiple by the Prime Factors Method

Find the least common multiple of 135, 280, and 300.

SOLUTION

Write the prime factorizations:

$$135 = 3^3 \cdot 5, \quad 280 = 2^3 \cdot 5 \cdot 7, \quad \text{and} \quad 300 = 2^2 \cdot 3 \cdot 5^2.$$

lcm(135,lcm(280,300))
37800

The least common multiple of 135, 280, and 300 is 37,800. Compare with **Example 6.**

Form the product of all the primes that appear in *any* of the factorizations. Use the *greatest* exponent from any factorization.

Use the greatest exponents.

$$\text{LCM} = 2^3 \cdot 3^3 \cdot 5^2 \cdot 7 = 37{,}800$$

The least natural number divisible by 135, 280, and 300 is 37,800.   ■ ■ ■

The least common multiple of a group of numbers can also be found by dividing by prime factors. The process is slightly different than that for finding the GCF.

Finding the Least Common Multiple (Dividing by Prime Factors Method)

Step 1 Write the numbers in a row.

Step 2 Divide each of the numbers by a common prime factor. Try 2, then try 3, and so on.

Step 3 Divide the quotients by a common prime factor. When no prime will divide all quotients, but a prime will divide some of them, divide where possible and bring any nondivisible quotients down. Continue until no prime will divide any two quotients.

Step 4 The product of all prime divisors from Steps 2 and 3 as well as all remaining quotients is the least common multiple.

▮▮ **EXAMPLE 7** Finding the Least Common Multiple by Dividing by Prime Factors

Find the least common multiple of 12, 18, and 60.

SOLUTION

Proceed just as in **Example 4** to obtain the following.

$$
\begin{array}{r|rrr}
2 & 12 & 18 & 60 \\ \hline
3 & 6 & 9 & 30 \\ \hline
 & 2 & 3 & 10 \\
\end{array}
$$

Now, even though no prime will divide 2, 3, and 10, the prime 2 will divide 2 and 10. Divide the 2 and the 10 and bring down the 3.

$$
\begin{array}{r|rrr}
2 & 12 & 18 & 60 \\ \hline
3 & 6 & 9 & 30 \\ \hline
2 & 2 & 3 & 10 \\ \hline
 & 1 & 3 & 5 \\
\end{array}
\qquad 2 \cdot 3 \cdot 2 \cdot 1 \cdot 3 \cdot 5 = 180
$$

The LCM of 12, 18, and 60 is 180. ▮▮▮

It is shown in more advanced courses that the least common multiple of two numbers m and n can be obtained by dividing their product by their greatest common factor.

Finding the Least Common Multiple (Formula)

The least common multiple of m and n can be computed as follows.

$$
LCM = \frac{m \cdot n}{\text{GCF of } m \text{ and } n}
$$

(This method works only for two numbers, not for more than two.)

▮▮ **EXAMPLE 8** Finding the Least Common Multiple by Formula

Use the formula to find the least common multiple of 90 and 168.

SOLUTION

In **Example 5** we used the Euclidean algorithm to find that the greatest common factor of 90 and 168 is 6. Therefore, the formula gives us

$$
\text{Least common multiple of 90 and 168} = \frac{90 \cdot 168}{6} = 2520.
$$
▮▮▮

(90*168)/gcd(90,168)

2520

This supports the result in **Example 8.**

PROBLEM-SOLVING HINT Problems that deal with questions such as "How many objects will there be in each group if each group contains the same number of objects?" and "When will two events occur at the same time?" can sometimes be solved using the ideas of greatest common factor and least common multiple.

▮▮ **EXAMPLE 9** Finding Common Starting Times of Movie Cycles

The King Theatre and the Star Theatre run movies continuously, and each starts its first feature at 1:00 P.M. If the movie shown at the King lasts 80 minutes and the movie shown at the Star lasts 2 hours, when will the two movies start again at the same time?

SOLUTION

First, convert 2 hours to 120 minutes. The question can be restated as follows: "What is the smallest number of minutes it will take for the two movies to start at the same time again?" This is equivalent to asking, "What is the least common multiple of 80 and 120?"

Using any of the methods described in this section, we find that the least common multiple of 80 and 120 is 240. Therefore, it will take 240 minutes, or $\frac{240}{60} = 4$ hours for the movies to start again at the same time. By adding 4 hours to 1:00 P.M., we find that they will start together again at 5:00 P.M.   ▮▮▮

▮▮ **EXAMPLE 10** Finding the Greatest Common Size of Stacks of Cards

Joshua Hornsby has 450 football cards and 840 baseball cards. He wants to place them in stacks on a table so that each stack has the same number of cards, and no stack has different types of cards within it. What is the greatest number of cards that he can have in each stack?

SOLUTION

Here, we are looking for the greatest number that will divide evenly into 450 and 840. This is, of course, the greatest common factor of 450 and 840. Using any of the methods described in this section, we find that

greatest common factor of 450 and 840 = 30.

Therefore, the greatest number of cards he can have in each stack is 30.   ▮▮▮

5.4 EXERCISES

Decide whether each statement is true *or* false.

1. Two even natural numbers cannot be relatively prime.

2. Two different prime numbers must be relatively prime.

3. If p is a prime number, then the greatest common factor of p and p^2 is p.

4. If p is a prime number, then the least common multiple of p and p^2 is p^3.

5. There is no prime number p such that the greatest common factor of p and 2 is 2.

6. The set of all common multiples of two given natural numbers is finite.

7. Two natural numbers must have at least one common factor.

8. The least common multiple of two different primes is their product.

9. Two composite numbers may be relatively prime.

10. The set of all common factors of two given natural numbers is finite.

Use the prime factors method to find the greatest common factor of each group of numbers.

11. 60 and 140
12. 400 and 110

13. 540 and 1200
14. 136 and 544

15. 52, 39, and 78
16. 138, 184, and 437

Use the method of dividing by prime factors to find the greatest common factor of each group of numbers.

17. 72 and 90
18. 166 and 415

19. 410 and 360
20. 384 and 222

21. 12, 18, and 36
22. 450, 1155, and 630

Use the Euclidean algorithm to find the greatest common factor of each group of numbers.

23. 32 and 56   **24.** 35 and 60

25. 24 and 108   **26.** 72 and 126

27. 480 and 400   **28.** 280 and 360

29. Explain in your own words how to find the greatest common factor of a group of numbers.

30. Explain in your own words how to find the least common multiple of a group of numbers.

Use the prime factors method to find the least common multiple of each group of numbers.

31. 54 and 30   **32.** 12 and 32

33. 90 and 50   **34.** 28 and 70

35. 30, 40, and 70   **36.** 24, 36, and 48

Use the method of dividing by prime factors to find the least common multiple of each group of numbers.

37. 24 and 32   **38.** 35 and 56

39. 45 and 75   **40.** 48, 54, and 60

41. 16, 120, and 216   **42.** 210, 385, and 2310

*Use the formula given in the text on **page 202** and the results of **Exercises 23–28** to find the least common multiple of each group of numbers.*

43. 32 and 56   **44.** 35 and 60

45. 24 and 108   **46.** 72 and 126

47. 480 and 400   **48.** 280 and 360

49. If p, q, and r are different primes, and a, b, and c are natural numbers such that $a > b > c$,

(a) what is the greatest common factor of $p^a q^c r^b$ and $p^b q^a r^c$?

(b) what is the least common multiple of $p^b q^a$, $q^b r^c$, and $p^a r^b$?

50. Find **(a)** the greatest common factor and **(b)** the least common multiple of $2^{31} \cdot 5^{17} \cdot 7^{21}$ and $2^{34} \cdot 5^{22} \cdot 7^{13}$. Leave your answers in prime factored form.

It is possible to extend the Euclidean algorithm in order to find the greatest common factor of more than two numbers. For example, if we wish to find the greatest common factor of 150, 210, and 240, we can first use the algorithm to find the greatest common factor of two of these (say, for example, 150 and 210). Then we find the greatest common factor of that result and the third number, 240. The final result is the greatest common factor of the original group of numbers.

Use the Euclidean algorithm as just described to find the greatest common factor of each group of numbers.

51. 150, 210, and 240   **52.** 12, 75, and 120

53. 90, 105, and 315   **54.** 48, 315, and 450

55. 144, 180, and 192   **56.** 180, 210, and 630

*If we allow repetitions of prime factors, we can use Venn diagrams (**Chapter 2**) to find the greatest common factor and the least common multiple of two numbers. For example, consider $36 = 2^2 \cdot 3^2$ and $45 = 3^2 \cdot 5$. Their greatest common factor is $3^2 = 9$, and their least common multiple is $2^2 \cdot 3^2 \cdot 5 = 180$.*

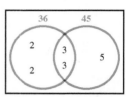

Intersection gives 3, 3.
Union gives 2, 2, 3, 3, 5.

*Use this method to find **(a)** the greatest common factor and **(b)** the least common multiple of the two numbers given.*

57. 12 and 18

58. 27 and 36

59. 54 and 72

60. Suppose that the least common multiple of p and q is q. What can we say about p and q?

61. Suppose that the least common multiple of p and q is pq. What can we say about p and q?

62. Suppose that the greatest common factor of p and q is p. What can we say about p and q?

63. Recall some of your early experiences in mathematics (for example, in the elementary grade classroom). What topic involving fractions required the use of the least common multiple? Give an example.

64. Recall some of your experiences in elementary algebra. What topics required the use of the greatest common factor? Give an example.

*Refer to **Examples 9 and 10** to solve each problem.*

65. *Inspecting Calculators* Karen Helfrich and Dorelle Less work on an assembly line, inspecting electronic calculators. Karen inspects the electronics of every sixteenth calculator, while Dorelle inspects the workmanship of every thirty-sixth calculator. If they both start working at the same time, which calculator will be the first that they both inspect?

66. *Night Off for Security Guards* Ross Craycraft and Jody Campbell work as security guards at a publishing company. Ross has every sixth night off, and Jody has every tenth night off. If both are off on July 1, what is the next night that they will both be off together?

67. Stacking Coins Lucy Bannister has 240 pennies and 288 nickels. She wants to place the pennies and nickels in stacks so that each stack has the same number of coins, and each stack contains only one denomination of coin. What is the largest number of coins that she can place in each stack?

68. Bicycle Racing Whitney Baer and Kim Davison are in a bicycle race, following a circular track. If they start at the same place and travel in the same direction, and Whitney completes a revolution every 40 seconds and Kim completes a revolution every 45 seconds, how long will it take them before they reach the starting point again simultaneously?

69. Selling Books Scott Day sold some books at $24 each, and used the money to buy some concert tickets at $50 each. He had no money left over after buying the tickets. What is the least amount of money he could have earned from selling the books? What is the least number of books he could have sold?

70. Sawing Lumber Terri Edwards has some pieces of two-by-four lumber. Some are 60 inches long, and some are 72 inches long. All of them must be sawn into shorter pieces. If all sawn pieces must be the same length, what is the longest such piece so that no lumber is left over?

EXTENSION Modern Cryptography

Basics of Cryptography • The Diffie-Hellman-Merkle Key Exchange Scheme
• RSA Public Key Cryptography

John Forbes Nash, Jr., profiled on **page 517**, was portrayed by Russell Crowe in the 2001 movie *A Beautiful Mind.* As a young American mathematician, Nash did brilliant work in several areas. One was real world code-breaking. An interactive session based on code-breaking, and more information on the movie, are available at www.abeautifulmind.com/main.html.

Basics of Cryptography **Cryptography** involves secret codes, ways of disguising information in order that a "sender" can transmit it to an intended "receiver" so that an "adversary" who somehow intercepts the transmission will be unable to discern its meaning. As is customary, we will refer to the sender and receiver (in either order) as Alice and Bob (A and B) and to the adversary as Eve (E). Converting a message to disguised form is called **encryption,** and converting it back to original form is called **decryption.**

Cryptography became more crucial as the extent of military, diplomatic, then industrial, and now even personal applications expanded. As the "code makers" became more adept at designing their systems, the "code breakers" became more adept at compromising those systems.

The basis of a cryptography system is normally some mathematical function, the "encryption algorithm," that encrypts (disguises) the message. (*Functions* are discussed in **Chapter 8.**) An example of a simple (and very insecure) encryption algorithm is the following:

> Replace every letter of the alphabet with the letter that *follows* it.
> (Replace z with a.)

Then the message "zebra" would be encrypted as "afcsb." Analyzing one or more intercepted messages encrypted using this function, and trying various possibilities, would enable an adversary to quickly determine the function, and its inverse, which would be the following:

> Replace every letter of the alphabet with the letter that *precedes* it.
> (Replace a with z.)

More advanced systems also use a **key,** which is some additional information needed to perform the algorithm correctly. By the middle of the twentieth century, state-of-the-art requirements for an effective cryptography system were as follows.

Basic Requirements of a Cryptography System

1. A *secret* algorithm (or function) for encrypting and decrypting data
2. A *secret* key that provides additional information necessary for a receiver to carry out the decrypting process

The difficulty with requirement 1 was that all encryption functions at the time were two-way functions. Once an adversary obtained the encryption algorithm, the inverse (that is, the decryption algorithm) could be deduced mathematically.

The difficulty with requirement 2 was that the security of the key frequently dropped off after a period of use. This meant that Bob and Alice must exchange a new key fairly often so that their communications would continue to be safe. But this measure may be self-defeating, because every key exchange may be vulnerable to interception. This dilemma became known as the **key exchange problem** (or the **key distribution problem** in the case of multiple intended receivers).

In the 1970s, researchers discovered how to construct a *one-way* function that overcame both difficulties. It is an *exponential function* (**Section 8.6**), and is given by

$$C = M^k \;(\textbf{mod } n),$$

with the calculation carried out modulo n. The achievement of an essentially one-way, rather than two-way, function is made possible by the theory of large prime numbers, the nature of modular arithmetic (introduced in the **Chapter 4 Extension**), and the present state of computer hardware and algorithms.

The Diffie-Hellman-Merkle Key Exchange Scheme First the key exchange problem was solved by the **Diffie-Hellman-Merkle key exchange scheme** (announced in 1976 and named for the Stanford University team of Whitfield Diffie, Martin Hellman, and Ralph Merkle). Basically, it works as follows.

The Diffie-Hellman-Merkle Key Exchange Scheme

Alice and Bob can establish a key (a number) that they both will know, but that Eve cannot find out, even if she observes the communications between Bob and Alice as they set up their key. Alice and Bob can agree to use the function $C = M^k$ (mod n) with specific values for M and n. (They can agree to all this by mail, telephone, e-mail, or even casual conversation. It won't matter if Eve finds out.) Then they carry out the following sequence of individual steps.

Alice's Actions	*Bob's Actions*
Step 1 Choose a value of a. (Keep this value secret.)	**Step 1** Choose a value of b. (Keep this value secret.)
Step 2 Compute $\alpha = M^a$ (mod n).	**Step 2** Compute $\beta = M^b$ (mod n).
Step 3 Send the value of α to Bob.	**Step 3** Send the value of β to Alice.
Step 4 Receive the value of β from Bob.	**Step 4** Receive the value of α from Alice.
Step 5 Compute the key: $$K = \beta^a \,(\textbf{mod } n).$$	**Step 5** Compute the key: $$K = \alpha^b \,(\textbf{mod } n).$$

By this procedure, Alice and Bob will arrive at the same key value K because

$$
\begin{aligned}
\beta^a &= (M^b)^a & &\beta = M^b \\
&= M^{ba} & &\text{Rule of exponents: } (a^m)^n = a^{mn} \\
&= M^{ab} & &\text{Commutative property: } ab = ba \\
&= (M^a)^b & &\text{Rule of exponents: } (a^m)^n = a^{mn} \\
&= \alpha^b. & &\alpha = M^a
\end{aligned}
$$

We illustrate the basic procedures using much smaller numbers than would be used in practice so that our computations can be done on a handheld calculator.

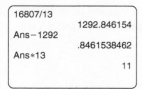

The display shows that the residue of 16,807, modulo 13, is 11.

Modular arithmetic, as discussed in the **Chapter 4 Extension,** will be essential here. Given a modulus n, every natural number a is "equivalent" (actually congruent) to the remainder obtained when a is divided by n. This remainder is called the **residue** of a, modulo n. To find the residue can be thought of as to "mod." In **Example 1** to follow, for instance, one of the calculations will be to find the residue of 16,807, modulo 13. The calculator routine from the **Chapter 4 Extension (page 172)** applies as follows.

Step 1 Divide 16,807 by 13, obtaining 1292.846154.

Step 2 Subtract the integer part of the quotient, obtaining 0.846154. . . .

Step 3 Multiply by 13, obtaining 11. (Round if necessary.)

So, we see that $16{,}807 \equiv 11 \pmod{13}$. We have shown that $16{,}807 = 1292 \cdot 13 + 11$.

(*Note:* In the work that follows, we carry out some lengthy sequences of modular arithmetic. We sometimes use the equals symbol, $=$, rather than the congruence symbol, $\equiv$, and when the modulus is understood, we sometimes omit the designation $\pmod{n}$.)

> **Calculator Routine for Finding the Residue of a, Modulo n**
>
> In a modular system, the residue modulo n for a number a can be found by completing these three steps, in turn.
>
> ***Step 1*** Divide a by the modulus n.
>
> ***Step 2*** Subtract the integer part of quotient to obtain only the fractional part.
>
> ***Step 3*** Multiply the fractional part of the quotient by n.
>
> The final result is the residue modulo n.

▌▌ **EXAMPLE 1** Using the Diffie-Hellman-Merkle Key Exchange Scheme

Establish a common key for Alice and Bob by using specific values for M, n, a, and b, and completing the steps outlined earlier for the Diffie-Hellman-Merkle key exchange scheme.

SOLUTION

Suppose Alice and Bob agree to use the values $M = 7$ and $n = 13$.

Alice's Actions

Step 1 Choose a value of a, say 5. (Alice keeps this value secret.)

Step 2 $\alpha = M^a \pmod{n}$
$= 7^5 \pmod{13}$
$= 16{,}807 \pmod{13}$
$= 11$

Step 3 Send $\alpha = 11$ to Bob.

Step 4 Receive $\beta = 3$.

Step 5 Compute the key:
$K = \beta^a \pmod{n}$
$= 3^5 \pmod{13}$
$= 243 \pmod{13}$
$= 9.$

Bob's Actions

Step 1 Choose a value of b, say 8. (Bob keeps this value secret.)

Step 2 $\beta = M^b \pmod{n}$
$= 7^8 \pmod{13}$
$= 5{,}764{,}801 \pmod{13}$
$= 3$

Step 3 Send $\beta = 3$ to Alice.

Step 4 Receive $\alpha = 11$.

Step 5 Compute the key:
$K = \alpha^b \pmod{n}$
$= 11^8 \pmod{13}$
$= 214{,}358{,}881 \pmod{13}$
$= 9.$

The display shows the calculation of K in the right column. (Ignore the tiny roundoff error.)

Both Alice and Bob arrived at the same key value, $K = 9$, which they can use for encrypting future communications to one another. ▮▮▮

When the **RSA code** was first introduced in 1977, Martin Gardner's "Mathematical Games" column in *Scientific American* challenged researchers to decode a message using an *n* with 129 digits. With the aid of number theory, it took 600 mathematicians in 25 different countries only 17 years to factor *n* into 64- and 65-digit prime factors, as shown here.

114,381,625,757,888,867,669,235,779,976,
146,612,010,218,296,721,242,362,562,561,
842,935,706,935,245,733,897,830,597,123,
563,958,705,058,989,075,147,599,290,026,
879,543,541 = 3,490,529,510,847,650,949,
147,849,619,903,898,133,417,764,638,493,
387,843,990,820,577 × 32,769,132,993,
266,709,549,961,988,190,834,461,413,177,
642,967,992,942,539,798,288,533

The decoded message said, "The magic words are squeamish ossifrage."

Today, RSA users select much larger values of *p* and *q*, resulting in an *n* of well over 300 digits. It is thought that breaking such an encryption would take all the computers in the world, working together, more time than the age of the universe.

Suppose, at Step 3 in **Example 1,** Eve intercepts Bob's transmission of the value $\beta = 3$ to Alice. This will not help her, because she cannot deduce Bob's value of *b* that generated β. In fact it could have been any of the values

$$8, 20, 32, 44, 56, \ldots,$$

an infinite list of possibilities. (In practice, all the numbers in this list would be vastly greater.) Also, Eve does not know what exponent Alice will apply to 3 to obtain the key. The value

$$a = 5$$

is Alice's secret, never communicated to anyone else, not even Bob, so Eve cannot know what key Alice will obtain. The same argument applies if Eve intercepts Alice's transmission to Bob of the value

$$\alpha = 11.$$

(She is stymied even if she intercepts both transmissions.)

RSA Public Key Cryptography At practically the same time that Diffie, Hellman, and Merkle solved the key exchange problem, another team of researchers, Ron Rivest, Adi Shamir, and Leonard Adleman, at MIT, used the same type of mathematical function to eliminate the need for key exchange. Their scheme, known as RSA (from their surnames), is called **public key cryptography.** Anyone who wants the capability of receiving encrypted data simply makes known their public key, which anyone else can then use to encrypt messages to them. The beauty of the system is that the receiver possesses another private key, necessary for decrypting but never released to anyone else.

What makes RSA successful is that we have the mathematical understanding to identify very large prime numbers, and to multiply them to obtain a product. But if the prime factors are large enough, it is impossible, given the present state of knowledge, for anyone to determine the two original factors, even using very powerful computers.

Using RSA, Alice can receive encrypted messages from Bob in such a way that Eve cannot discern their meaning even if she intercepts them. We show here a complete outline of all the basic procedures, from setting up the scheme to encrypting and then decrypting a message.

RSA Basics: A Public Key Cryptography Scheme

Alice (the receiver) completes the following steps.

Step 1 Choose two prime numbers, *p* and *q*, which she keeps secret.

Step 2 Compute the *modulus n* (which is the product $p \cdot q$).

Step 3 Compute $\ell = (p - 1)(q - 1)$.

Step 4 Choose the *encryption exponent e*, which can be any integer between 1 and ℓ that is relatively prime to ℓ, that is, has no common factors with ℓ.

Step 5 Find her *decryption exponent d*, a number satisfying

$$e \cdot d = 1 \ (\text{mod } \ell).$$

She keeps *d* secret.

Step 6 Provide Bob with her *public key*, which consists of the modulus *n* and the encryption exponent *e*.

(Bob's steps are on the next page.)

RSA Basics: A Public Key Cryptography Scheme (Cont.)

Now Bob (the sender) completes the following steps. (Recall that the purpose of all this is for Bob to be able to send Alice secure messages.)

Step 7   Convert the message to be sent to Alice into a number M (sometimes called the *plaintext*).

Step 8   Encrypt M, that is, use Alice's public key (n and e) to generate the encrypted message C (sometimes called the *ciphertext*) according to the formula

$$C = M^e \pmod{n}.$$

Step 9   Transmit C to Alice.

When Alice receives C, she completes the final step:

Step 10   Decrypt C, that is, use her private key, consisting of n (also part of her public key) and d, to reproduce the original plaintext message M according to the formula

$$M = C^d \pmod{n}.$$

▌▌ ▌ **EXAMPLE 2**   Devising a Public Encryption Key

Use the values $p = 7$ and $q = 13$ (arbitrarily chosen primes) to devise Alice's public key by completing Steps 2–4 of the above outline of RSA basics.

SOLUTION

Step 2 $n = p \cdot q = 7 \cdot 13 = 91$

Step 3 $\ell = (p - 1)(q - 1) = 6 \cdot 12 = 72$

Step 4   There are many choices here, but a prime less than 72 and relatively prime to 72 will meet the requirements. We arbitrarily choose $e = 11$.

Alice's public key is $n = 91, e = 11$. (Prime factors p and q must be kept secret.)

▀▀▀

A **brilliant number** (defined only in the last few years) is a product of two primes with equal numbers of digits. Is the product n in **Example 2** brilliant?

▌▌ ▌ **EXAMPLE 3**   Finding a Private Decryption Key

Complete Step 5 of the RSA basics outline to find Alice's private decryption key.

SOLUTION

Step 5   The decryption exponent d must satisfy

$$e \cdot d = 1 \pmod{\ell} \quad \text{or} \quad 11d = 1 \pmod{72}.$$

One way to satisfy this equation is to check the powers of 11 until we find one equal (actually congruent) to 1, modulo 72:

> Mod 72 congruences

$$11^1 = 11, \quad 11^2 = 121 = 49, \quad 11^3 = 1331 = 35,$$
$$11^4 = 14{,}641 = 25, \quad 11^5 = 161{,}051 = 59, \quad 11^6 = 1{,}771{,}561 = 1.$$

(The residues were found using the calculator routine given before **Example 1.**) Because we found that $11^6 = 1$, we take $d = 11^5 = 59$. This way,

$$e \cdot d = 11 \cdot 11^5 = 11^6 = 1, \quad \text{as required.}$$

Alice's private key is $n = 91, d = 59$.

▀▀▀

James Ellis, Clifford Cocks, and Malcolm Williamson all worked for Britain's Government Communications Headquarters in the 1970s. They actually discovered the mathematics of public key cryptography several years before the work at Stanford and MIT was announced (and subsequently patented). The British work was classified top secret and never came to light until some twenty years later, at approximately the same time that RSA Data Security, the company that had been built on U.S. RSA patents, was sold for $200 million.

▮▮ **EXAMPLE 4** Encrypting a Message for Transmission

Complete Steps 7 and 8 of the RSA basics outline to encrypt the message "HI" for Bob to send Alice. Use Alice's public key found in **Example 2:** $n = 91, e = 11$.

SOLUTION

Step 7 A simple way to convert "HI" to a number is to note that H and I are the 8th and 9th letters of the English alphabet. Simply let the plaintext message be $M = 89$.

Step 8 Now compute the ciphertext C: $C = M^e \pmod{n} = 89^{11} \pmod{91}$.

Here, 89^{11} is too large to be handled as we did the powers of 11 in **Example 3.** But we can use a trick here, expressing 11 as $1 + 2 + 8$. (1, 2, and 8 are the unique powers of 2 that sum to 11. So we are doing something like what we did when discussing the binary system in **Section 4.4**.) Now we can rewrite 89^{11} in terms of smaller powers and then make use of rules of exponents (**Section 7.5**).

$$89^{11} = 89^{1+2+8} \qquad 1 + 2 + 8 = 11$$
$$= 89^1 \cdot 89^2 \cdot 89^8 \qquad \text{Rule of exponents: } a^{n+m} = a^n \cdot a^m$$

Now we "mod before we multiply," in other words, we compute the residue of individual factors first, then multiply those results. This keeps the numbers smaller.

$$89^1 = \mathbf{89} \qquad\qquad \text{Definition of first power}$$
$$89^2 = 7921 = \mathbf{4} \qquad \text{Mod}$$
$$89^8 = 3.936588806\text{E}15 \quad \text{Calculator result}$$

This last factor is too large to handle like the others. Due to the way we "split up" the exponent, subsequent powers of 89 can be written as powers of earlier ones.

$$89^8 = (89^2)^4 \qquad \text{Rule of exponents: } a^{m \cdot n} = (a^m)^n$$
$$= 4^4 \qquad\quad 89^2 = 4 \text{ from above.}$$
$$= 256 \qquad \text{Evaluate } 4^4.$$
$$= \mathbf{74} \qquad\ \text{Mod}$$

Finally we obtain

$$89^{11} = \mathbf{89} \cdot \mathbf{4} \cdot \mathbf{74} \quad \text{Substitute.}$$
$$= 26{,}344 \qquad\quad \text{Multiply.}$$
$$= 45. \qquad\qquad\ \text{Mod}$$

The plaintext $M = 89$ (for the message "HI") has been converted to the ciphertext $C = 45$. ▮▮▮

Let's see if Alice can successfully decrypt the message 45 when she receives it.

▮▮ **EXAMPLE 5** Decrypting a Received Message

Complete Step 10 of the RSA basics outline to decrypt the message $C = 45$ from **Example 4.** Use Alice's private key, found in **Example 3:** $d = 59$ (also, $n = 91$).

SOLUTION

Step 10 The decryption formula gives

$$M = C^d \pmod{n}$$
$$= 45^{59} \pmod{91} \qquad\qquad\qquad\qquad \text{Substitute.}$$
$$= 45^{1+2+8+16+32} \pmod{91} \qquad\qquad \text{Use sum of powers of 2.}$$
$$= 45 \cdot 45^2 \cdot 45^8 \cdot 45^{16} \cdot 45^{32} \pmod{91}. \quad \text{Rule of exponents: } a^{m+n} = a^m \cdot a^n$$

Start with the smaller powers and "mod" each factor individually.

$$45^2 = 2025 = 23$$
$$45^8 = (45^2)^4 = 23^4 = 279{,}841 = 16$$
$$45^{16} = (45^8)^2 = 16^2 = 256 = 74$$
$$45^{32} = (45^{16})^2 = 74^2 = 5476 = 16$$

Inserting these values in the product for M, we get

$$M = 45 \cdot 23 \cdot 16 \cdot 74 \cdot 16$$
$$= 19{,}607{,}040$$
$$= 89.$$

We have correctly decrypted $C = 45$ to obtain

$$M = 89 = \text{HI}.$$

▮▮▮

EXTENSION EXERCISES

Find the residue in each case.

1. 45 (mod 6)   **2.** 67 (mod 10)

3. 225 (mod 13)   **4.** 418 (mod 15)

5. 5^9 (mod 12)   **6.** 4^{11} (mod 9)

7. 8^7 (mod 11)   **8.** 14^5 (mod 13)

9. 8^{27} (mod 17)   **10.** 45^7 (mod 23)

11. 11^{14} (mod 18)   **12.** 14^9 (mod 19)

Finding a Common Key *Find Alice and Bob's common key K by using the Diffie-Hellman-Merkle key exchange scheme with the given values of M, n, a, and b.*

	M	n	a	b
13.	5	13	7	6
14.	11	9	5	4
15.	5	11	6	7
16.	17	5	6	3

Apply the RSA scheme to find each missing value.

	p	q	n	ℓ
17.	5	11	___	___
18.	11	3	___	___
19.	5	13	___	___
20.	17	7	___	___

Encrypting Plaintext *Given the modulus n, the encryption exponent e, and the plaintext M, use RSA encryption to find the ciphertext C in each case.*

	n	e	M
21.	55	7	15
22.	33	7	8
23.	65	5	16
24.	119	11	12

Decrypting Ciphertext *Given the prime factors p and q, the encryption exponent e, and the ciphertext C, apply the RSA algorithm to find* **(a)** *the decryption exponent d and* **(b)** *the plaintext message M.*

	p	q	e	C
25.	5	11	3	30
26.	11	3	13	24
27.	5	13	35	17
28.	17	7	5	40

29. Describe the breakthrough represented by Diffie-Hellman-Merkle and RSA as opposed to all earlier forms of cryptography.

30. Explain why RSA would fail if mathematicians could (using computers) factor arbitrarily large numbers.

5.5 THE FIBONACCI SEQUENCE AND THE GOLDEN RATIO

The Fibonacci Sequence • The Golden Ratio

The Fibonacci Sequence

The solution of Fibonacci's rabbit problem is examined in **Chapter 1, pages 19–20.**

One of the most famous problems in elementary mathematics comes from the book *Liber Abaci*, written in 1202 by Leonardo of Pisa, a.k.a. Fibonacci. The problem is as follows:

> A man put a pair of rabbits in a cage. During the first month the rabbits produced no offspring, but each month thereafter produced one new pair of rabbits. If each new pair thus produced reproduces in the same manner, how many pairs of rabbits will there be at the end of one year?

The solution of this problem leads to a sequence of numbers known as the **Fibonacci sequence.** Here are the first fifteen terms of the Fibonacci sequence:

$$1, 1, 2, 3, 5, 8, 13, 21, 34, 55, 89, 144, 233, 377, 610.$$

After the first two terms (both 1) in the sequence, each term is obtained by adding the two previous terms. For example, the third term is obtained by adding $1 + 1$ to get 2, the fourth term is obtained by adding $1 + 2$ to get 3, and so on. This can be described by a mathematical formula known as a **recursion formula.**

If F_n represents the Fibonacci number in the nth position in the sequence, then

$$F_1 = 1$$
$$F_2 = 1$$
$$F_n = F_{n-2} + F_{n-1}, \quad \text{for } n \geq 3.$$

Using the recursion formula $F_n = F_{n-2} + F_{n-1}$, we obtain

$$F_3 = F_1 + F_2 = 1 + 1 = 2, \quad F_4 = F_2 + F_3 = 1 + 2 = 3, \quad \text{and so on.}$$

The **Fibonacci Association** is a research organization dedicated to investigation into the **Fibonacci sequence** and related topics. Check your library to see if it has the journal *Fibonacci Quarterly*. The first two journals of 1963 contain a basic introduction to the Fibonacci sequence.

The Fibonacci sequence exhibits many interesting patterns, and by inductive reasoning we can make many conjectures about these patterns. However, simply observing a finite number of examples does not provide a proof of a statement. Proofs of the properties of the Fibonacci sequence often involve mathematical induction (covered in college algebra texts). Here we simply observe the patterns and do not attempt to provide proofs.

▉▉ **EXAMPLE 1** Observing a Pattern of the Fibonacci Numbers

Find the sum of the squares of the first n Fibonacci numbers for $n = 1, 2, 3, 4, 5$, and examine the pattern. Generalize this relationship.

SOLUTION

$$1^2 = 1 = 1 \cdot 1 = F_1 \cdot F_2$$
$$1^2 + 1^2 = 2 = 1 \cdot 2 = F_2 \cdot F_3$$
$$1^2 + 1^2 + 2^2 = 6 = 2 \cdot 3 = F_3 \cdot F_4$$
$$1^2 + 1^2 + 2^2 + 3^2 = 15 = 3 \cdot 5 = F_4 \cdot F_5$$
$$1^2 + 1^2 + 2^2 + 3^2 + 5^2 = 40 = 5 \cdot 8 = F_5 \cdot F_6$$

The sum of the squares of the first n Fibonacci numbers seems to always be the product of F_n and F_{n+1}. This has been proved to be true, in general, using mathematical induction. ▉▉▉

The following program for the TI-83/84 Plus utilizes the *Binet form* of the *n*th Fibonacci number (see **Exercises 33–38**) to determine its value.

PROGRAM: FIB
: ClrHome
: Disp "WHICH TERM"
: Disp "OF THE"
: Disp "SEQUENCE DO"
: Disp "YOU WANT?"
: Input N
: $(1 + \sqrt{(5)})/2 \to A$
: $(1 - \sqrt{(5)})/2 \to B$
: $(A^\wedge N - B^\wedge N)/\sqrt{(5)} \to F$
: Disp F

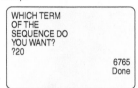

```
WHICH TERM
OF THE
SEQUENCE DO
YOU WANT?
?20
                    6765
                    Done
```

This screen indicates that the twentieth Fibonacci number is 6765.

Fibonacci Fun To observe one of the many interesting properties of the Fibonacci sequence, do the following.

1. Choose any term after the first and square it.
2. Multiply the terms before and after the term chosen in step 1.
3. Subtract the smaller value from the larger.
4. What is your result?

Try this procedure beginning with several different Fibonacci terms. **The result is always the same.**

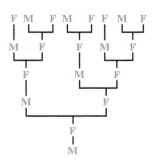

Figure 1

EXAMPLE 2 Observing the Fibonacci Sequence in a Long Division Problem

Observe the steps of the long division algorithm used to find the first few decimal places of the reciprocal of 89, the eleventh Fibonacci number. Locate occurrences of the terms of the Fibonacci sequence in the algorithm.

SOLUTION

$$
\begin{array}{r}
.011235\ldots \\
89{\overline{\smash{\big)}\,1.000000\ldots}} \\
\underline{89} \\
110 \\
\underline{89} \\
210 \\
\underline{178} \\
320 \\
\underline{267} \\
530 \\
\underline{445} \\
850\ldots
\end{array}
$$

Notice that after the 0 in the tenths place, the next five digits are the first five terms of the Fibonacci sequence. In addition, as indicated in color in the process, the digits 1, 1, 2, 3, 5, 8 appear in the division steps. Now, look at the digits next to the ones in color, beginning with the second "1"; they, too, are 1, 1, 2, 3, 5, ...

If the division process is continued past the final step shown above, the pattern seems to stop, since to ten decimal places, $\frac{1}{89} \approx 0.0112359551$. (The decimal representation actually begins to repeat later in the process, since $\frac{1}{89}$ is a rational number.) However, the sum below indicates how the Fibonacci numbers are actually "hidden" in this decimal.

$$
\begin{array}{l}
0.01 \\
0.001 \\
0.0002 \\
0.00003 \\
0.000005 \\
0.0000008 \\
0.00000013 \\
0.000000021 \\
0.0000000034 \\
0.00000000055 \\
\underline{0.000000000089} \\
\end{array}
$$

$\frac{1}{89} = 0.0112359550\ldots$ ▮▮▮

Fibonacci patterns have been found in numerous places in nature. For example, male honeybees (drones) hatch from eggs that have not been fertilized, so a male bee has only one parent, a female. On the other hand, female honeybees hatch from fertilized eggs, so a female has two parents, one male and one female. **Figure 1** shows several generations of ancestors for a male honeybee.

Notice that in the first generation, starting at the bottom, there is 1 bee, in the second there is 1 bee, in the third there are 2 bees, and so on. These are the terms of the Fibonacci sequence. Furthermore, beginning with the second generation, the numbers of female bees form the sequence, and beginning with the third generation, the numbers of male bees also form the sequence.

A fraction such as

$$1 + \cfrac{1}{1 + \cfrac{1}{1 + \cfrac{1}{1 + \cdots}}}$$

is called a **continued fraction.** This continued fraction can be evaluated as follows.

Let $\quad x = 1 + \cfrac{1}{1 + \cfrac{1}{1 + \cdots}}$

Then $\qquad x = 1 + \dfrac{1}{x}$

$\qquad\qquad x^2 = x + 1$

$\qquad x^2 - x - 1 = 0.$

By the quadratic formula from algebra,

$$x = \frac{1 \pm \sqrt{1 - 4(1)(-1)}}{2(1)}$$

$$x = \frac{1 \pm \sqrt{5}}{2}.$$

Notice that the positive solution is the **golden ratio.**

Successive terms in the Fibonacci sequence also appear in some plants. For example, the photo (below on the left) shows the double spiraling of a daisy head, with 21 clockwise spirals and 34 counterclockwise spirals. These numbers are successive terms in the sequence.

Most pineapples (see the photo below on the right) exhibit the Fibonacci sequence in the following way: Count the spirals formed by the "scales" of the cone, first counting from lower left to upper right. Then count the spirals from lower right to upper left. You should find that in one direction you get 8 spirals, and in the other you get 13 spirals, once again successive terms of the Fibonacci sequence. Many pinecones exhibit 5 and 8 spirals, and the cone of the giant sequoia has 3 and 5 spirals.

The Golden Ratio

If we consider the quotients of successive Fibonacci numbers, a pattern emerges.

$\dfrac{1}{1} = 1$	$\dfrac{5}{3} = 1.666\ldots$	$\dfrac{21}{13} \approx 1.615384615$	$\dfrac{89}{55} = 1.618181818\ldots$
$\dfrac{2}{1} = 2$	$\dfrac{8}{5} = 1.6$	$\dfrac{34}{21} \approx 1.619047619$	
$\dfrac{3}{2} = 1.5$	$\dfrac{13}{8} = 1.625$	$\dfrac{55}{34} \approx 1.617647059$	

These quotients seem to be approaching some "limiting value" close to 1.618. In fact, as we go farther into the sequence, these quotients approach the number

$$\mathbf{\frac{1 + \sqrt{5}}{2}}, \quad \text{Golden ratio}$$

known as the **golden ratio,** and often symbolized by ϕ, the Greek letter phi.

The golden ratio appears over and over in art, architecture, music, and nature. Its origins go back to the days of the ancient Greeks, who thought that a golden rectangle exhibited the most aesthetically pleasing proportion.

A **golden rectangle** is one that can be divided into a square and another (smaller) rectangle the same shape as the original rectangle. (See **Figure 2.**) If we let the smaller rectangle have length L and width W, as shown in the figure, then we see that the original rectangle has length $L + W$ and width L. Both rectangles (being "golden") have their lengths and widths in the golden ratio, ϕ, so we have

$$\frac{L}{W} = \frac{L + W}{L}$$

$$\frac{L}{W} = \frac{L}{L} + \frac{W}{L} \qquad \text{Write the right side as the sum of two fractions.}$$

Figure 2

$$\phi = 1 + \frac{1}{\phi} \qquad \text{Substitute } \frac{L}{W} = \phi, \frac{L}{L} = 1, \text{ and } \frac{W}{L} = \frac{1}{\phi}.$$

$$\phi^2 = \phi + 1 \qquad \text{Multiply both sides by } \phi.$$

$$\phi^2 - \phi - 1 = 0. \qquad \text{Write in standard quadratic form.}$$

Using the quadratic formula from algebra, the positive solution of this equation is found to be $\frac{1 + \sqrt{5}}{2} \approx 1.618033989$, the golden ratio.

The Parthenon (see the photo), built on the Acropolis in ancient Athens during the fifth century B.C., is an example of architecture exhibiting many distinct golden rectangles.

To see an interesting connection between the terms of the Fibonacci sequence, the golden ratio, and a phenomenon of nature, we can start with a rectangle measuring 89 by 55 units. (See **Figure 3**.) This is a very close approximation to a golden rectangle. Within this rectangle a square is then constructed, 55 units on a side. The remaining rectangle is also approximately a golden rectangle, measuring 55 units by 34 units. Each time this process is repeated, a square and an approximate golden rectangle are formed.

As indicated in **Figure 3**, vertices of the square may be joined by a smooth curve known as a *spiral*. This spiral resembles the outline of a cross section of the shell of the chambered nautilus, as shown in the photo.

A Golden Rectangle in Art The rectangle outlining the figure in *St. Jerome* by Leonardo da Vinci is an example of a golden rectangle.

Figure 3

For Further Thought

Mathematical Animation

The 1959 animated film *Donald in Mathmagic Land* has endured for over 50 years as a classic. It provides a 25-minute trip with Donald Duck, led by the Spirit of Mathematics, through the world of mathematics. Several minutes of the film are devoted to the golden ratio (or, as it is termed there, the golden section).

Disney provides animation to explain the golden ratio in a way that the printed word simply cannot do. The golden ratio is seen in architecture, nature, and the human body.

For Group or Individual Investigation

1. Verify the following Fibonacci pattern in the conifer family. Obtain a pineapple, and count spirals formed by the "scales" of the cone, first counting from lower left to upper right. Then count the spirals from lower right to upper left. What do you find?

2. Two popular sizes of index cards are 3″ by 5″ and 5″ by 8″. Why do you think that these are industry-standard sizes?

3. Divide your height by the height to your navel. Find a class average. What value does this come close to?

5.5 EXERCISES

Answer each question concerning the Fibonacci sequence or the golden ratio.

1. The sixteenth Fibonacci number is 987 and the seventeenth Fibonacci number is 1597. What is the value of the eighteenth Fibonacci number?

2. Recall that F_n represents the Fibonacci number in the *n*th position in the sequence. What are the only two values of *n* such that $F_n = n$?

3. $F_{22} = 17,711$ and $F_{24} = 46,368$. What is the value of F_{23}?

4. If two successive terms of the Fibonacci sequence are both odd, is the next term even or odd?

5. What is the exact value of the golden ratio?

6. What is the approximate value of the golden ratio to the nearest thousandth?

In each of Exercises 7–14, a pattern is established involving terms of the Fibonacci sequence. Use inductive reasoning to make a conjecture concerning the next equation in the pattern, and verify it. You may wish to refer to the first few terms of the sequence given in the text.

7. $1 = 2 - 1$
   $1 + 1 = 3 - 1$
   $1 + 1 + 2 = 5 - 1$
   $1 + 1 + 2 + 3 = 8 - 1$
   $1 + 1 + 2 + 3 + 5 = 13 - 1$

8. $1 = 2 - 1$
   $1 + 3 = 5 - 1$
   $1 + 3 + 8 = 13 - 1$
   $1 + 3 + 8 + 21 = 34 - 1$
   $1 + 3 + 8 + 21 + 55 = 89 - 1$

9. $1 = 1$
   $1 + 2 = 3$
   $1 + 2 + 5 = 8$
   $1 + 2 + 5 + 13 = 21$
   $1 + 2 + 5 + 13 + 34 = 55$

10. $1^2 + 1^2 = 2$
    $1^2 + 2^2 = 5$
    $2^2 + 3^2 = 13$
    $3^2 + 5^2 = 34$
    $5^2 + 8^2 = 89$

11. $2^2 - 1^2 = 3$
    $3^2 - 1^2 = 8$
    $5^2 - 2^2 = 21$
    $8^2 - 3^2 = 55$

12. $2^3 + 1^3 - 1^3 = 8$
    $3^3 + 2^3 - 1^3 = 34$
    $5^3 + 3^3 - 2^3 = 144$
    $8^3 + 5^3 - 3^3 = 610$

13. $1 = 1^2$
    $1 - 2 = -1^2$
    $1 - 2 + 5 = 2^2$
    $1 - 2 + 5 - 13 = -3^2$
    $1 - 2 + 5 - 13 + 34 = 5^2$

14. $1 - 1 = -1 + 1$
    $1 - 1 + 2 = 1 + 1$
    $1 - 1 + 2 - 3 = -2 + 1$
    $1 - 1 + 2 - 3 + 5 = 3 + 1$
    $1 - 1 + 2 - 3 + 5 - 8 = -5 + 1$

15. Every natural number can be expressed as a sum of Fibonacci numbers, where no number is used more than once. For example, $25 = 21 + 3 + 1$. Express each of the following in this way.
    (a) 37 **(b)** 40 **(c)** 52

16. It has been shown that if *m* divides *n*, then F_m is a factor of F_n. Show that this is true for the following values of *m* and *n*.
    (a) $m = 2, n = 6$ **(b)** $m = 3, n = 9$
    (c) $m = 4, n = 8$

17. It has been shown that if the greatest common factor of *m* and *n* is *r*, then the greatest common factor of F_m and F_n is F_r. Show that this is true for the following values of *m* and *n*.
    (a) $m = 10, n = 4$ **(b)** $m = 12, n = 6$
    (c) $m = 14, n = 6$

18. For any prime number *p* except 2 or 5, either F_{p+1} or F_{p-1} is divisible by *p*. Show that this is true for the following values of *p*.
    (a) $p = 3$ **(b)** $p = 7$ **(c)** $p = 11$

19. Earlier we saw that if a term of the Fibonacci sequence is squared and then the product of the terms on each side of the term is found, there will always be a difference of 1. Follow the steps below, choosing the seventh Fibonacci number, 13.

    (a) Square 13. Multiply the terms of the sequence two positions away from 13 (i.e., 5 and 34). Subtract the smaller result from the larger, and record your answer.

    (b) Square 13. Multiply the terms of the sequence three positions away from 13. Once again, subtract the smaller result from the larger, and record your answer.

    (c) Repeat the process, moving four terms away from 13.

    (d) Make a conjecture about what will happen when you repeat the process, moving five terms away. Verify your answer.

20. A Number Trick Here is a number trick that you can perform. Ask someone to pick any two numbers at random and to write them down. Ask the person to determine a third number by adding the first and second, a fourth number by adding the second and third, and so on, until ten numbers are determined. Then ask the person to add these ten numbers. You will be able to give the sum before the person even completes the list, because the sum will always be 11 times the seventh number in the list. Verify that this is true, by using x and y as the first two numbers arbitrarily chosen. (*Hint:* Remember the distributive property from algebra.)

*Another Fibonacci-type sequence that has been studied by mathematicians is the **Lucas sequence,** named after a French mathematician of the nineteenth century. The first ten terms of the Lucas sequence are*

$$1, 3, 4, 7, 11, 18, 29, 47, 76, 123.$$

21. What is the eleventh term of the Lucas sequence?

22. Choose any term of the Lucas sequence and square it. Then multiply the terms on either side of the one you chose. Subtract the smaller result from the larger. Repeat this for a different term of the sequence. Do you get the same result? Make a conjecture about this pattern.

23. The first term of the Lucas sequence is 1. Add the first and third terms. Record your answer. Now add the first, third, and fifth terms and record your answer. Continue this pattern, each time adding another term that is in an *odd* position in the sequence. What do you notice about all of your sums?

24. The second term of the Lucas sequence is 3. Add the second and fourth terms. Record your answer. Now add the second, fourth, and sixth terms and record your answer. Continue this pattern, each time adding another term that is in an *even* position of the sequence. What do you notice about all of your sums?

25. Many interesting patterns exist among the terms of the Fibonacci sequence and the Lucas sequence. Make a conjecture about the next equation that would appear in each of the lists and then verify it.

(a) $1 \cdot 1 = 1$
$1 \cdot 3 = 3$
$2 \cdot 4 = 8$
$3 \cdot 7 = 21$
$5 \cdot 11 = 55$

(b) $1 + 2 = 3$
$1 + 3 = 4$
$2 + 5 = 7$
$3 + 8 = 11$
$5 + 13 = 18$

(c) $1 + 1 = 2 \cdot 1$
$1 + 3 = 2 \cdot 2$
$2 + 4 = 2 \cdot 3$
$3 + 7 = 2 \cdot 5$
$5 + 11 = 2 \cdot 8$

(d) $1 + 4 = 5 \cdot 1$
$3 + 7 = 5 \cdot 2$
$4 + 11 = 5 \cdot 3$
$7 + 18 = 5 \cdot 5$
$11 + 29 = 5 \cdot 8$

26. In the text we illustrate that the quotients of successive terms of the Fibonacci sequence approach the golden ratio. Make a similar observation for the terms of the Lucas sequence; that is, find the decimal approximations for the quotients

$$\frac{3}{1}, \frac{4}{3}, \frac{7}{4}, \frac{11}{7}, \frac{18}{11}, \frac{29}{18},$$

and so on, using a calculator. Then make a conjecture about what seems to be happening.

*Recall the **Pythagorean theorem** from geometry: If a right triangle has legs of lengths a and b and hypotenuse of length c, then*

$$a^2 + b^2 = c^2.$$

*Suppose that we choose any four successive terms of the Fibonacci sequence. Multiply the first and fourth. Double the product of the second and third. Add the squares of the second and third. The three results obtained form a **Pythagorean triple** (three numbers that satisfy the equation $a^2 + b^2 = c^2$). Find the Pythagorean triple obtained this way using the four given successive terms of the Fibonacci sequence.*

27. 1, 1, 2, 3   **28.** 1, 2, 3, 5   **29.** 2, 3, 5, 8

30. Look at the values of the hypotenuse (c) in the answers to **Exercises 27–29.** What do you notice about each of them?

31. The following array of numbers is called **Pascal's triangle.**

```
              1
            1   1
          1   2   1
        1   3   3   1
      1   4   6   4   1
    1   5  10  10   5   1
  1   6  15  20  15   6   1
```

This array is important in the study of counting techniques and probability (see later chapters) and appears in algebra in the binomial theorem. If the triangular array is written in a different form, as follows, and the sums along the diagonals as indicated by the dashed lines are found, there is an interesting occurrence. What do you find when the numbers are added?

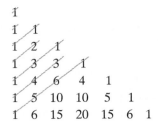

32. Write a paragraph explaining some of the occurrences of the Fibonacci sequence and the golden ratio in your everyday surroundings.

Exercises 33–38 require a scientific calculator.

33. The positive solution of the equation $x^2 - x - 1 = 0$ is $\frac{1 + \sqrt{5}}{2}$, as indicated in the text. The negative solution is $\frac{1 - \sqrt{5}}{2}$. Find the decimal approximations for both. What similarity do you notice between the two decimals?

34. In some cases, writers define the golden ratio to be the *reciprocal* of $\frac{1 + \sqrt{5}}{2}$. Find a decimal approximation for the reciprocal of $\frac{1 + \sqrt{5}}{2}$. What similarity do you notice between the decimals for $\frac{1 + \sqrt{5}}{2}$ and its reciprocal?

A remarkable relationship exists between the two solutions of $x^2 - x - 1 = 0$,

$$\phi = \frac{1 + \sqrt{5}}{2} \quad and \quad \overline{\phi} = \frac{1 - \sqrt{5}}{2},$$

and the Fibonacci numbers. To find the nth Fibonacci number without using the recursion formula, use a calculator to evaluate

$$\frac{\phi^n - \overline{\phi}^n}{\sqrt{5}}.$$

For example, to find the thirteenth Fibonacci number, evaluate

$$\frac{\left(\frac{1 + \sqrt{5}}{2}\right)^{13} - \left(\frac{1 - \sqrt{5}}{2}\right)^{13}}{\sqrt{5}}$$

*This form is known as the **Binet form** of the nth Fibonacci number. Use the Binet form and a calculator to find the nth Fibonacci number for each of the following values of n.*

35. $n = 14$ **36.** $n = 20$

37. $n = 22$ **38.** $n = 25$

COLLABORATIVE INVESTIGATION

Investigating an Interesting Property of Number Squares

In this group activity we will investigate a property of certain square arrangements of numbers. Begin by dividing up the class into groups of three or four students. Each student in the group should prepare a square of numbers like the one that follows:

1	2	3	4	5
6	7	8	9	10
11	12	13	14	15
16	17	18	19	20
21	22	23	24	25

Topics for Discussion

1. Each student should do the following individually:

Choose any number in the first row. Circle it, and cross out all entries in the column below it. (For example, if you circle 4, cross out 9, 14, 19, and 24.) Now circle any remaining number in the second row, and cross out all entries in the column below it.

Repeat this procedure for the third and fourth rows, and then circle the final remaining number in the fifth row.

Now each student in the group should add the circled numbers and compare his or her sum with all others in the group. What do you notice?

2. Verify that the sum in **Exercise 1** is equal to

$$\frac{1}{5}(1 + 2 + 3 + 4 + \cdots + 5^2).$$

3. Suppose **Exercise 1** was done as shown here:

1	②	3	4	5
6	̷7̷	⑧	9	10
11	̷1̷2̷	̷1̷3̷	14	⑮
⑯	̷1̷7̷	̷1̷8̷	19	̷2̷0̷
̷2̷1̷	̷2̷2̷	̷2̷3̷	㉔	̷2̷5̷

Notice that summing the circled entries is just like summing

$$1 + 2 + 3 + 4 + 5,$$

except that

3 is replaced by $3 + 5$,
5 is replaced by $5 + 10$,
1 is replaced by $1 + 15$,
4 is replaced by $4 + 20$.

We can express this as

$$\begin{aligned}
\text{sum} &= (1 + 2 + 3 + 4 + 5) \\
&\quad + (5 + 10 + 15 + 20) \\
&= 15 + 50, \quad \text{or} \quad 65.
\end{aligned}$$

4. Explain why, whatever entries you choose to circle in the various rows, the sum is always the same.

5. Prepare a similar square of the natural numbers 1 through 36. Then repeat **Exercise 1.** Discuss your results. Verify that the sum is equal to

$$\frac{1}{6}(1 + 2 + 3 + 4 + \cdots + 6^2).$$

6. As a group, fill in the entries in this equation for the 6 by 6 square.

sum = (_____ + _____ + _____ + _____ + _____ + _____)
+ (_____ + _____ + _____ + _____ + _____)

7. As a group, predict the sum of the circled numbers in a 7 by 7 square by expressing it as follows. (Do not actually construct the square. Just generalize the pattern observed in the 5 by 5 and 6 by 6 cases.)

sum = (_____ + _____ + _____ + _____ + _____ + _____
+ _____) + (_____ + _____ + _____ + _____ +
_____ + _____)

Verify that the sum is equal to

$$\frac{1}{7}(1 + 2 + 3 + 4 + \cdots + 7^2).$$

8. Each individual should now prepare another 5 by 5 square and repeat **Exercise 1,** except this time start with a number in the first *column* and cross out remaining numbers in *rows.* In your group, discuss and explain what you observe. In particular, how do the individuals' answers compare, and how do they compare with the **Exercise 1** answers?

CHAPTER 5 TEST

In Exercises 1–6, decide whether each statement is true *or* false.

1. No two prime numbers differ by 1.

2. There are infinitely many prime numbers.

3. If a natural number is divisible by 9, then it must also be divisible by 3.

4. If p and q are different primes, 1 is their greatest common factor and pq is their least common multiple.

5. For all natural numbers n, 1 is a factor of n and n is a multiple of n.

6. If a natural number is not perfect, then it must be abundant.

7. Use divisibility tests to determine whether the number

656,723,600

is divisible by each of the following.
(a) 2   (b) 3   (c) 4
(d) 5   (e) 6   (f) 8
(g) 9   (h) 10   (i) 12

8. Decide whether each number is prime, composite, or neither.
(a) 87   (b) 97   (c) 1

9. Give the prime factorization of 2520.

10. In your own words state the Fundamental Theorem of Arithmetic.

11. Decide whether each number is perfect, deficient, or abundant.
(a) 36   (b) 8   (c) 28

12. Which of the following statements is false?
A. There are no known odd perfect numbers.
B. Every even perfect number must end in 6 or 28.
C. Goldbach's Conjecture for the number 8 is illustrated by the equation $8 = 7 + 1$.

13. Give a pair of twin primes between 50 and 70.

14. Find the greatest common factor of 135 and 216.

15. Find the least common multiple of 15, 45, and 50.

16. *Day Off for Fast-food Workers* Both Katherine Chong and Josh Dunlap work at a fast-food outlet. Katherine has every sixth day off and Josh has every fourth day off. If they are both off on Wednesday of this week, what will be the day of the week that they are next off together?

17. The twenty-third Fibonacci number is 28,657 and the twenty-fourth Fibonacci number is 46,368. What is the twenty-fifth Fibonacci number?

18. Make a conjecture about the next equation in the following list, and verify it.
$$8 - (1 + 1 + 2 + 3) = 1$$
$$13 - (1 + 2 + 3 + 5) = 2$$
$$21 - (2 + 3 + 5 + 8) = 3$$
$$34 - (3 + 5 + 8 + 13) = 5$$
$$55 - (5 + 8 + 13 + 21) = 8$$

19. Choose the correct completion of this statement: If p is a prime number, then $2^p - 1$ is prime

A. never   **B.** sometimes   **C.** always.

20. Give the first eight terms of a Fibonacci-type sequence with first term 1 and second term 5.

21. Choose any term after the first in the sequence of **Exercise 20.** Square it. Multiply the two terms on either side of it. Subtract the smaller result from the larger. Now repeat the process with a different term. Make a conjecture about what this process will yield for any term of the sequence.

22. Which one of the following is the *exact* value of the golden ratio?

A. $\dfrac{1 + \sqrt{5}}{2}$ **B.** $\dfrac{1 - \sqrt{5}}{2}$ **C.** 1.6   **D.** 1.618

23. Briefly state what Fermat's Last Theorem says, and describe the circumstances of its proof, including the approximate time interval involved.

24. Write a brief explanation of the acronym GIMPS. Include a definition and several examples of the term represented by the letters MP.

THE REAL NUMBERS AND THEIR REPRESENTATIONS

6

The 1997 film *Smilla's Sense of Snow* stars Julia Ormond as a brilliant young scientist who has a passion for snow and mathematics. In a conversation, she speaks of her love of numbers.

> To me, the number system is like human life. First you have the natural numbers, the ones that are whole and positive, like the numbers of a small child. Consciousness expands and a child discovers longing. Do you know the mathematical expression for longing? Negative numbers, the formalization of the feeling that you're missing something. Then the child discovers the in-between spaces, between stones, between people, between numbers, and that produces fractions. But it's like a kind of madness, because it doesn't even stop there. It never stops. There are numbers that we can't even begin to comprehend. Mathematics is a vast, open landscape. . . .

In this chapter we study the rational and the irrational numbers, which together form the real number system.

6.1 REAL NUMBERS, ORDER, AND ABSOLUTE VALUE

Sets of Real Numbers • Order in the Real Numbers • Additive Inverses and Absolute Value • Applications

Sets of Real Numbers

The mathematician Leopold Kronecker (1823–1891) once made the statement, "God made the integers, all the rest is the work of man." The *natural numbers* are those numbers with which we count discrete objects. By including 0 in the set, we obtain the set of *whole numbers*.

Natural Numbers

$\{1, 2, 3, 4, \ldots\}$ is the set of **natural numbers.**

Whole Numbers

$\{0, 1, 2, 3, \ldots\}$ is the set of **whole numbers.**

These numbers, along with many others, can be represented on **number lines** like the one pictured in **Figure 1**. We draw a number line by locating any point on the line and calling it 0. Choose any point to the right of 0 and call it 1. The distance between 0 and 1 gives a unit of measure used to locate other points, as shown in **Figure 1**. The numbers labeled and those continuing in the same way to the right correspond to the set of whole numbers.

Figure 1

All the whole numbers starting with 1 are located to the right of 0 on the number line. But numbers may also be placed to the left of 0. These numbers, written $-1, -2, -3$, and so on, are shown in **Figure 2**. (The negative sign is used to show that the numbers are located to the *left* of 0.)

Figure 2

The history of the concept of zero is told in ***Zero: The Biography of a Dangerous Idea***, by Charles Seife.

The numbers to the *left* of 0 are **negative numbers.** The numbers to the *right* of 0 are **positive numbers.** Positive numbers and negative numbers are called **signed numbers.** The number 0 itself is neither positive nor negative.

There are many practical applications of negative numbers. For example, temperatures sometimes fall below zero. The lowest temperature ever recorded in meteorological records was $-128.6°F$ at Vostok, Antarctica, on July 22, 1983. Altitudes below sea level can be represented by negative numbers. The shore surrounding the Dead Sea is 1312 feet below sea level. This can be represented as -1312 feet.

The whole numbers, their negatives, and zero make up the set of *integers.*

Integers

$\{\ldots, -3, -2, -1, 0, 1, 2, 3, \ldots\}$ is the set of **integers.**

Not all numbers are integers. For example, $\frac{1}{2}$ is a number *halfway* between the integers 0 and 1. Several numbers that are not integers are *graphed* in **Figure 3**. The **graph** of a number is a point on the number line representing that number. Think of the graph of a set of numbers as a "picture" of the set. All the numbers in **Figure 3** can be written as quotients of integers and are examples of *rational numbers.*

Figure 3

An integer, such as 2, is also a rational number. This is true because $2 = \frac{2}{1}$.

Rational Numbers

$\{x \mid x$ is a quotient of two integers, with denominator not equal to 0$\}$ is the set of **rational numbers.**

(Read the part in the braces as "the set of all numbers x such that x is a quotient of two integers, with denominator not equal to 0.")

The set symbolism used in the definition of rational numbers,

$$\{x \mid x \textbf{ has a certain property}\},$$

is called **set-builder notation.** This notation is convenient to use when it is not possible, or practical, to list all the elements of the set.
   There are other numbers on the number line that are not rational. For example, a square that measures one unit on a side has a diagonal whose length is the square root of 2, written $\sqrt{2}$. See **Figure 4**. It will be shown later that $\sqrt{2}$ cannot be written as a quotient of integers. Because of this, $\sqrt{2}$ is an *irrational number.*

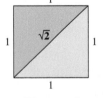

Figure 4

Irrational Numbers

$\{x \mid x$ is a number on the number line that is not rational$\}$ is the set of **irrational numbers.**

Irrational numbers include $\sqrt{3}, \sqrt{7}, -\sqrt{10}$, and π, which is the ratio of the distance around a circle (its *circumference*) to the distance across it (its *diameter*). All numbers that can be represented by points on the number line (the union of the sets of rational and irrational numbers) are called *real numbers.*

Real Numbers

$\{x \mid x$ is a number that can be represented by a point on the number line$\}$ is the set of **real numbers.**

Real numbers can be written as decimal numbers. Any rational number can be written as a decimal that will come to an end (terminate), or repeat in a fixed "block" of digits. For example, $\frac{2}{5} = 0.4$ and $\frac{27}{100} = 0.27$ are rational numbers with terminating decimals; $\frac{1}{3} = 0.3333\ldots$ and $\frac{3}{11} = 0.27272727\ldots$ are repeating decimals.

The decimal representation of an irrational number will neither terminate nor repeat. Decimal representations of rational and irrational numbers will be discussed further later in this chapter.

Figure 5 illustrates two ways to represent the relationships among the various sets of real numbers.

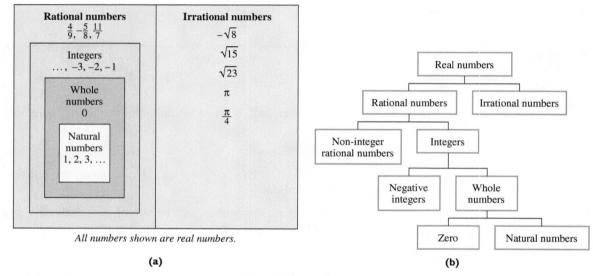

All numbers shown are real numbers.

(a)

(b)

Figure 5

▋▋ **EXAMPLE 1** Identifying Elements of a Set of Numbers

List the numbers in the set that belong to each set of numbers.

$$\left\{ -5, -\frac{2}{3}, 0, \sqrt{2}, \frac{13}{4}, 5, 5.8 \right\}$$

(a) natural numbers   **(b)** whole numbers   **(c)** integers

(d) rational numbers   **(e)** irrational numbers   **(f)** real numbers

SOLUTION

(a) The only natural number in the set is 5.

(b) The whole numbers consist of the natural numbers and 0. So, the elements of the set that are whole numbers are 0 and 5.

(c) The integers in the set are -5, 0, and 5.

(d) The rational numbers are -5, $-\frac{2}{3}$, 0, $\frac{13}{4}$, 5, and 5.8, because each of these numbers *can* be written as the quotient of two integers. For example, $5.8 = \frac{58}{10} = \frac{29}{5}$.

(e) The only irrational number in the set is $\sqrt{2}$.

(f) All the numbers in the set are real numbers.   ▋▋▋

The TI-83/84 Plus calculator will convert a decimal to a fraction. See **Example 1(d)**.

Order in the Real Numbers

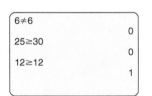

7 < 8   1

8 > 2   1

5 ≤ 9   1

The calculator returns a 1 for each of these statements of inequality, signifying that each is true.

The symbol for equality, =, was first introduced by the Englishman Robert Recorde in his 1557 algebra text *The Whetstone of Witte.* He used two parallel line segments, because, he claimed, no two things can be more equal.

The symbols for order relationships, < and >, were first used by Thomas Harriot (1560–1621), another Englishman. These symbols were not immediately adopted by other mathematicians.

Suppose that a and b represent two real numbers. If their graphs on the number line are the same point, they are **equal.** If the graph of a lies to the left of b, a **is less than** b, and if the graph of a lies to the right of b, a **is greater than** b. The **law of trichotomy** says that for two numbers a and b, one and only one of the following is true.

$$a = b, \quad a < b, \quad \text{or} \quad a > b$$

When read from left to right, the symbol $<$ means "is less than."

$$7 < 8 \qquad \text{7 is less than 8.}$$

The symbol $>$ means "is greater than."

$$8 > 2 \qquad \text{8 is greater than 2.}$$

Notice that the symbol always points to the lesser number.

Lesser number ⟶ $8 < 15$

The symbol $\leq$ means "is less than or equal to."

$$5 \leq 9 \qquad \text{5 is less than or equal to 9.}$$

This statement is true, since $5 < 9$ is true. *If either the $<$ part or the $=$ part is true, then the inequality $\leq$ is true.* Also, $8 \leq 8$ is true since $8 = 8$ is true. But it is not true that $13 \leq 9$ because neither $13 < 9$ nor $13 = 9$ is true.

The symbol $\geq$ means "is greater than or equal to."

$$9 \geq 5 \qquad \text{9 is greater than or equal to 5.}$$

This statement is true because $9 > 5$ is true.

■‖ EXAMPLE 2 Comparing Real Numbers

Determine whether each statement is *true* or *false.*

(a) $6 \neq 6$ **(b)** $5 < 19$ **(c)** $15 \leq 20$ **(d)** $25 \geq 30$ **(e)** $12 \geq 12$

6 ≠ 6   0

25 ≥ 30   0

12 ≥ 12   1

The inequalities in **Example 2(a) and (d)** are false, as signified by the 0. The statement in **Example 2(e)** is true.

SOLUTION

(a) The statement $6 \neq 6$ is false, because 6 *is equal to* 6.

(b) Since 5 is indeed less than 19, this statement is true.

(c) The statement $15 \leq 20$ is true, since $15 < 20$.

(d) Both $25 > 30$ and $25 = 30$ are false, so $25 \geq 30$ is false.

(e) Since $12 = 12$, the statement $12 \geq 12$ is true.   ■■■

Additive Inverses and Absolute Value

For any nonzero real number x, there is exactly one number on the number line the same distance from 0 as x but on the opposite side of 0. In **Figure 6**, the numbers 3 and -3 are the same distance from 0 but are on opposite sides of 0. Thus, 3 and -3 are called **additive inverses, negatives,** or **opposites,** of each other.

Figure 6

The TI-83/84 Plus distinguishes between the negative symbol (⁻) and the operation of subtraction.

The additive inverse of the number 0 is 0 itself. This makes 0 the only real number that is its own additive inverse. Other additive inverses occur in pairs. For example, 4 and −4, and 5 and −5, are additive inverses of each other. Several pairs of additive inverses are shown in **Figure 7**.

Figure 7

The additive inverse of a number can be indicated by writing the symbol − in front of the number. With this symbol, the additive inverse of 7 is written −7. The additive inverse of −4 is written −(−4) and can be read "the opposite of −4" or "the negative of −4." **Figure 7** suggests that 4 is an additive inverse of −4. Since a number can have only one additive inverse, the symbols 4 and −(−4) must represent the same number, which means that

$$-(-4) = 4.$$

Double Negative Rule

For any real number x, the following is true.

$$-(-x) = x$$

Table 1 shows several numbers and their additive inverses. An important property of additive inverses will be studied later in this chapter:

$$a + (-a) = (-a) + a = 0, \quad \text{for all real numbers } a.$$

As mentioned above, additive inverses are numbers that are the same distance from 0 (but in opposite directions) on the number line. See **Figure 7**. This idea can also be expressed by saying that a number and its additive inverse have the same absolute value. The **absolute value** of a real number can be defined as the distance between 0 and the number on the number line.

The symbol for the absolute value of the number x is $|x|$, read **"the absolute value of x."** For example, the distance between 2 and 0 on the number line is 2 units, so

$$|2| = 2.$$

Because the distance between −2 and 0 on the number line is also 2 units,

$$|-2| = 2.$$

Since distance is a physical measurement, which is never negative, ***the absolute value of a number is never negative.*** Since 0 is a distance of 0 units from 0, $|0| = 0.$

Formal Definition of Absolute Value

For any real number x, the absolute value of x is defined as follows.

$$|x| = \begin{cases} x & \text{if } x \geq 0 \\ -x & \text{if } x < 0 \end{cases}$$

If x is a positive number or 0, then its absolute value is x itself. For example, since 8 is a positive number, $|8| = 8$. ***If x is a negative number, then its absolute value is the additive inverse of x.*** For example, if $x = -9$, then $|-9| = -(-9) = 9$, since the additive inverse of −9 is 9.

Table 1

Number	Additive Inverse
−4	−(−4) or 4
0	0
19	−19
$-\dfrac{2}{3}$	$\dfrac{2}{3}$

The formal definition of absolute value can be confusing if it is not read carefully. The "$-x$" in the second part of the definition *does not* represent a negative number. Since x is negative in the second part, $-x$ represents the opposite of a negative number, that is, a positive number.

■■ EXAMPLE 3   Using Absolute Value

Simplify by finding the absolute value.

(a) $|5|$ **(b)** $|-5|$ **(c)** $-|5|$

(d) $-|-14|$ **(e)** $|8-2|$ **(f)** $-|8-2|$

SOLUTION

(a) $|5| = 5$

(b) $|-5| = -(-5) = 5$

(c) $-|5| = -(5) = -5$

(d) $-|-14| = -(14) = -14$

(e) $|8-2| = |6| = 6$

(f) $-|8-2| = -|6| = -6$ ■■■

```
|(-5)|
                5
-|-14|
               -14
-|8-2|
               -6
```

This screen supports the results of
Example 3(b), (d), and (f).

Example 3(e) shows that absolute value bars also serve as grouping symbols. *Perform any operations that appear inside absolute value symbols before finding the absolute value.*

Applications

■■ EXAMPLE 4   Interpreting Change Using a Table

The projected annual rates of change in employment (in percent) in some of the fastest growing and in some of the most rapidly declining industries from 2002 through 2012 are shown in **Table 2**. What industry in the list is expected to see the greatest change? the least change?

Table 2

Industry (2002–2012)	Annual Rate of Change (in percent)
Software publishers	5.3
Care services for the elderly	4.5
Child day-care services	3.6
Cut-and-sew apparel manufacturing	−12.2
Fabric mills	−5.9
Metal ore mining	−4.8

Source: U.S. Bureau of Labor Statistics.

SOLUTION

We want the greatest *change*, without regard to whether the change is an increase or a decrease. Look for the number in the list with the greatest absolute value. That number is found in cut-and-sew apparel manufacturing, since

$$|-12.2| = 12.2.$$

Similarly, the least change is in the child day-care services industry:

$$|3.6| = 3.6.$$ ■■■

6.1 EXERCISES

Give a number that satisfies the given condition.

1. An integer between 4.5 and 5.5

2. A rational number between 2.8 and 2.9

3. A whole number that is not positive and is less than 1

4. A whole number greater than 4.5

5. An irrational number that is between $\sqrt{13}$ and $\sqrt{15}$

6. A real number that is neither negative nor positive

Decide whether each statement is true *or* false.

7. Every natural number is positive.

8. Every whole number is positive.

9. Every integer is a rational number.

10. Every rational number is a real number.

List all numbers from each set that are **(a)** *natural numbers;* **(b)** *whole numbers;* **(c)** *integers;* **(d)** *rational numbers;* **(e)** *irrational numbers;* **(f)** *real numbers.*

11. $\left\{ -9, -\sqrt{7}, -1\frac{1}{4}, -\frac{3}{5}, 0, \sqrt{5}, 3, 5.9, 7 \right\}$

12. $\left\{ -5.3, -5, -\sqrt{3}, -1, -\frac{1}{9}, 0, 1.2, 1.8, 3, \sqrt{11} \right\}$

13. Explain the different sets of numbers introduced in this section, and give an example of each kind.

14. What two possible situations exist for the decimal representation of a rational number?

Use an integer to express each number in boldface print representing a change or measurement in the following applications.

15. *Height of the New York Times Tower* The New York Times Tower is **1046** feet high. (*Source:* Council on Tall Buildings and Urban Habitat.)

16. *Population of North Dakota* Between 1990 and 2000, the population of North Dakota increased by **3400.** (*Source:* U.S. Census Bureau.)

17. *Height of Mt. Arenal* The height of Mt. Arenal, an active volcano in Costa Rica, is **5436** feet above sea level. (*Source: The New York Times Almanac.*)

18. *Boiling Point of Chlorine* The boiling point of chlorine is approximately **30°** below 0° Fahrenheit.

19. *Melting Point of Fluorine* The melting point of fluorine gas is **220°** below 0° Celsius.

20. *Population of D.C.* Between 1990 and 2000, the population of the District of Columbia decreased by **31,841.** (*Source:* U.S. Census Bureau.)

21. *Windchill* When the wind speed is **30** miles per hour and the actual temperature is **15°** Fahrenheit, the windchill factor is **5°** below 0° Fahrenheit.

22. *Elevation of New Orleans* The city of New Orleans lies **8** feet below sea level. (*Source:* U.S. Geological Survey, *Elevations and Distances in the United States.*)

23. *Depths and Heights of Seas and Mountains* The chart gives selected depths and heights of bodies of water and mountains.

Bodies of Water	Average Depth in Feet (as a negative number)	Mountains	Altitude in Feet (as a positive number)
Pacific Ocean	−12,925	McKinley	20,320
South China Sea	−4802	Point Success	14,150
Gulf of California	−2375	Matlalcueyetl	14,636
Caribbean Sea	−8448	Ranier	14,410
Indian Ocean	−12,598	Steele	16,644

Source: The World Almanac and Book of Facts.

(a) List the bodies of water in order, starting with the deepest and ending with the shallowest.

(b) List the mountains in order, starting with the lowest and ending with the highest.

(c) *True or false:* The absolute value of the depth of the Pacific Ocean is greater than the absolute value of the depth of the Indian Ocean.

(d) *True or false:* The absolute value of the depth of the Gulf of California is greater than the absolute value of the depth of the Caribbean Sea.

24. *Percent Change* The graph shows the percent change in domestic car sales from January 2004 to January 2005 for various automakers.

(a) Which automaker had the greatest change in sales? What was that change?

(b) Which automaker had the least change in sales? What was the change?

(c) *True* or *false:* The absolute value of the percent change for Ford was greater than the absolute value of the percent change for General Motors.

(d) *True* or *false:* The percent change for Toyota was more than four times greater than the percent change for Mazda.

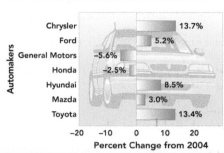

CAR SALES, 2005

Source: Chicago Tribune.

Graph each group of numbers on a number line.

25. $-2, -6, -4, 3, 4$

26. $-5, -3, -2, 0, 4$

27. $\frac{1}{4}, 2\frac{1}{2}, -3\frac{4}{5}, -4, -1\frac{5}{8}$

28. $5\frac{1}{4}, 4\frac{5}{9}, -2\frac{1}{3}, 0, -3\frac{2}{5}$

29. Match each expression in Column I with its value in Column II. Some choices in Column II may not be used.

I	II
(a) $\lvert -7 \rvert$	**A.** 7
(b) $-(-7)$	**B.** -7
(c) $-\lvert -7 \rvert$	**C.** neither A nor B
(d) $-\lvert -(-7) \rvert$	**D.** both A and B

30. Fill in the blanks with the correct values: The opposite of -2 is _____, while the absolute value of -2 is _____. The additive inverse of -2 is _____, while the additive inverse of the absolute value of -2 is _____.

Find **(a)** *the additive inverse (or opposite) of each number and* **(b)** *the absolute value of each number.*

31. -2

32. -8

33. 6

34. 11

35. $7 - 4$

36. $8 - 3$

37. $7 - 7$

38. $3 - 3$

39. Use the results of **Exercises 35 and 36** to complete the following: If $a - b > 0$, then the absolute value of $a - b$ in terms of a and b is _____.

40. Look at **Exercises 37 and 38** and use the results to complete the following: If $a - b = 0$, then the absolute value of $a - b$ is _____.

Select the lesser of the two given numbers.

41. $-12, -4$

42. $-9, -14$

43. $-8, -1$

44. $-15, -16$

45. $3, \lvert -4 \rvert$

46. $5, \lvert -2 \rvert$

47. $\lvert -3 \rvert, \lvert -4 \rvert$

48. $\lvert -8 \rvert, \lvert -9 \rvert$

49. $-\lvert -6 \rvert, -\lvert -4 \rvert$

50. $-\lvert -2 \rvert, -\lvert -3 \rvert$

51. $\lvert 5 - 3 \rvert, \lvert 6 - 2 \rvert$

52. $\lvert 7 - 2 \rvert, \lvert 8 - 1 \rvert$

Decide whether each statement is true *or* false.

53. $6 > -(-2)$

54. $-8 > -(-2)$

55. $-4 \le -(-5)$

56. $-6 \le -(-3)$

57. $\lvert -6 \rvert < \lvert -9 \rvert$

58. $\lvert -12 \rvert < \lvert -20 \rvert$

59. $-\lvert 8 \rvert > \lvert -9 \rvert$

60. $-\lvert 12 \rvert > \lvert -15 \rvert$

61. $-\lvert -5 \rvert \ge -\lvert -9 \rvert$

62. $-\lvert -12 \rvert \le -\lvert -15 \rvert$

63. $\lvert 6 - 5 \rvert \ge \lvert 6 - 2 \rvert$

64. $\lvert 13 - 8 \rvert \le \lvert 7 - 4 \rvert$

65. *Population Change* The table shows the percent change in population from 2000 through 2006 for selected states.

(a) Which state had the greatest change in population? What was this change? Was it an increase or a decrease?

State	Percent Change
Alabama	3.4
Iowa	1.9
Louisiana	-4.1
Michigan	1.6
North Dakota	-1.0
West Virginia	0.6

Source: U.S. Census Bureau.

(b) Which state had the least change in population? What was this change? Was it an increase or a decrease?

66. **Balance of Trade** The table gives the net trade balance, in millions of dollars, for selected U.S. trade partners for January 2006.

Country	Trade Balance (in millions of dollars)
India	−1257
China	−17,911
Netherlands	756
France	−85
Turkey	−78

Source: U.S. Census Bureau.

A negative balance means that imports to the United States exceeded exports from the United States, while a positive balance means that exports exceeded imports.

(a) Which country had the greatest discrepancy between exports and imports? Explain.

(b) Which country had the least discrepancy between exports and imports? Explain.

67. **Comparing Employment Data** Refer to the table in **Example 4.** Of the fabric mills and software publishing industries, which annual employment rate shows the greater change (without regard to sign)?

68. Students often say "Absolute value is always positive." Is this true? If not, explain why.

Give three numbers between −6 and 6 that satisfy each given condition.

69. Positive real numbers but not integers

70. Real numbers but not positive numbers

71. Real numbers but not whole numbers

72. Rational numbers but not integers

73. Real numbers but not rational numbers

74. Rational numbers but not negative numbers

6.2 OPERATIONS, PROPERTIES, AND APPLICATIONS OF REAL NUMBERS

Operations • Order of Operations • Properties of Addition and Multiplication of Real Numbers • Applications of Real Numbers

Operations

The result of adding two numbers is called their **sum.** The numbers being added are called **addends** (or **terms**).

Adding Real Numbers

Like Signs Add two numbers with the *same* sign by adding their absolute values. The sign of the sum (either + or −) is the same as the sign of the two numbers.

Unlike Signs Add two numbers with *different* signs by subtracting the lesser absolute value from the greater to find the absolute value of the sum. The sum is positive if the positive number has the greater absolute value. The sum is negative if the negative number has the greater absolute value.

For example, to add −12 and −8, first find their absolute values.

$$|-12| = 12 \quad \text{and} \quad |-8| = 8$$

Since −12 and −8 have the *same* sign, add their absolute values: 12 + 8 = 20. Give the sum the sign of the two numbers. Since both numbers are negative, the sum is negative and

$$-12 + (-8) = -20.$$

Find $-17 + 11$ by subtracting the absolute values, because these numbers have different signs.

$$|-17| = 17 \quad \text{and} \quad |11| = 11$$
$$17 - 11 = 6$$

Give the result the sign of the number with the larger absolute value.

$$-17 + 11 = -6$$

Negative since $|-17| > |11|$

▮▮ **EXAMPLE 1** Adding Signed Numbers

Find each sum.

(a) $-6 + (-3)$ **(b)** $-12 + (-4)$ **(c)** $4 + (-1)$

(d) $-9 + 16$ **(e)** $-16 + 12$ **(f)** $-4 + 4$

SOLUTION

(a) $-6 + (-3) = -(6 + 3) = -9$ **(b)** $-12 + (-4) = -(12 + 4) = -16$

(c) $4 + (-1) = 3$ **(d)** $-9 + 16 = 7$

(e) $-16 + 12 = -4$ **(f)** $-4 + 4 = 0$ The sum of additive inverses is 0. ▮▮▮

The calculator supports the results of **Example 1(a), (c), and (e).**

The result of subtracting two numbers is called their **difference.** In $a - b$, a is called the **minuend,** and b is called the **subtrahend.** Compare the two statements below.

$$7 - 5 = 2 \quad \text{and} \quad 7 + (-5) = 2$$

In a similar way, $9 - 3 = 9 + (-3)$. That is, to subtract 3 from 9, add the additive inverse of 3 to 9. These examples suggest the following rule for subtraction.

Definition of Subtraction

For all real numbers a and b,

$$a - b = a + (-b).$$

(Change the sign of the subtrahend and add.)

▮▮ **EXAMPLE 2** Subtracting Signed Numbers

Find each difference.

(a) $6 - 8$ **(b)** $-12 - 4$ **(c)** $-10 - (-7)$ **(d)** $15 - (-3)$

SOLUTION

Change to addition.

Change sign of the subtrahend and add.

(a) $6 - 8 = 6 + (-8) = -2$

Change to addition.

Sign is changed.

(b) $-12 - 4 = -12 + (-4) = -16$

The calculator supports the results of **Example 2(a), (b), and (c).**

Practical Arithmetic From the time of Egyptian and Babylonian merchants, practical aspects of arithmetic complemented mystical (or "Pythagorean") tendencies. This was certainly true in the time of **Adam Riese** (1489–1559), a "reckon master" influential when commerce was growing in Northern Europe. He championed new methods of reckoning using Hindu-Arabic numerals and quill pens. (The Roman methods then in common use moved counters on a ruled board.) Riese thus fulfilled Fibonacci's efforts 300 years earlier to supplant Roman numerals and methods.

(c) $-10 - (-7) = -10 + [-(-7)]$ This step can be omitted.

$$= -10 + 7$$
$$= -3$$

(d) $15 - (-3) = 15 + 3 = 18$ ▮▮▮

The result of multiplying two numbers is called their **product.** The two numbers being multiplied are called **factors.** Any rules for multiplication with negative real numbers should be consistent with the usual rules for multiplication of positive real numbers and zero. To inductively obtain a rule for multiplying a positive real number and a negative real number, observe the pattern of products below.

$$4 \cdot 5 = 20$$
$$4 \cdot 4 = 16$$
$$4 \cdot 3 = 12$$
$$4 \cdot 2 = 8$$
$$4 \cdot 1 = 4$$
$$4 \cdot 0 = 0$$
$$4 \cdot (-1) = ?$$

What number must be assigned as the product $4 \cdot (-1)$ so that the pattern is maintained? The numbers just to the left of the equality signs decrease by 1 each time, and the products to the right decrease by 4 each time. To maintain the pattern, the number to the right in the bottom equation must be 4 less than 0, which is -4, so

$$4 \cdot (-1) = -4.$$

The pattern continues with

$$4 \cdot (-2) = -8$$
$$4 \cdot (-3) = -12$$
$$4 \cdot (-4) = -16,$$

and so on. In the same way,

$$-4 \cdot 2 = -8$$
$$-4 \cdot 3 = -12$$
$$-4 \cdot 4 = -16,$$

and so on. A similar observation can be made about the product of two negative real numbers. Look at the pattern that follows.

$$-5 \cdot 4 = -20$$
$$-5 \cdot 3 = -15$$
$$-5 \cdot 2 = -10$$
$$-5 \cdot 1 = -5$$
$$-5 \cdot 0 = 0$$
$$-5 \cdot (-1) = ?$$

The numbers just to the left of the equality signs decrease by 1 each time. The products on the right increase by 5 each time. To maintain the pattern, the product $-5 \cdot (-1)$ must be 5 more than 0, so it seems reasonable for the following to be true.

$$-5 \cdot (-1) = 5$$

Continuing this pattern gives the following.

$$-5 \cdot (-2) = 10$$
$$-5 \cdot (-3) = 15$$
$$-5 \cdot (-4) = 20$$
$$\vdots$$

These observations lead to the following rules for multiplication.

$(+) \cdot (+) = +$
$(-) \cdot (-) = +$
$(+) \cdot (-) = -$
$(-) \cdot (+) = -$

Multiplying Real Numbers

Like Signs Multiply two numbers with the *same* sign by multiplying their absolute values to find the absolute value of the product. The product is positive.

Unlike Signs Multiply two numbers with *different* signs by multiplying their absolute values to find the absolute value of the product. The product is negative.

▐▌ EXAMPLE 3 Multiplying Signed Numbers

Find each product.

(a) $-9 \cdot 7$ **(b)** $14 \cdot (-5)$ **(c)** $-8 \cdot (-4)$

SOLUTION

(a) $-9 \cdot 7 = -63$ **(b)** $14 \cdot (-5) = -70$ **(c)** $-8 \cdot (-4) = 32$ ███

```
-9*7
                    -63
14*-5
                    -70
-8*-4
                     32
```

The symbol (∗) represents multiplication on this screen. The display supports the results of **Example 3**.

The result of dividing two numbers is called their **quotient.** In the quotient $a \div b$ (or $\frac{a}{b}$), where $b \neq 0$, a is called the **dividend** (or numerator), and b is called the **divisor** (or denominator). For real numbers a, b, and c,

$$\text{if} \quad \frac{a}{b} = c, \quad \text{then} \quad a = b \cdot c.$$

To illustrate this, consider the quotient $\frac{10}{-2}$. The value of this quotient is obtained by asking, "What number multiplied by -2 gives 10?" From our discussion of multiplication, the answer to this question must be "-5." Therefore,

$$\frac{10}{-2} = -5, \quad \text{because} \quad 10 = -2 \cdot (-5).$$

Similarly,

$$\frac{-10}{2} = -5 \quad \text{and} \quad \frac{-10}{-2} = 5.$$

These facts, along with the fact that the quotient of two positive numbers is positive, lead to the following rules for division.

$(+)/(+) = +$
$(-)/(-) = +$
$(+)/(-) = -$
$(-)/(+) = -$

Dividing Real Numbers

Like Signs Divide two numbers with the *same* sign by dividing their absolute values to find the absolute value of the quotient. The quotient is positive.

Unlike Signs Divide two numbers with *different* signs by dividing their absolute values to find the absolute value of the quotient. The quotient is negative.

▌▌ **EXAMPLE 4** Dividing Signed Numbers

Find each quotient.

(a) $\dfrac{15}{-5}$ **(b)** $\dfrac{-100}{-25}$ **(c)** $\dfrac{-60}{3}$

SOLUTION

(a) $\dfrac{15}{-5} = -3$ This is true because $-5 \cdot (-3) = 15$.

(b) $\dfrac{-100}{-25} = 4$ **(c)** $\dfrac{-60}{3} = -20$ ▌▌▌

If 0 is divided by a nonzero number, the quotient is 0.

$$\frac{0}{a} = 0, \quad \text{for } a \neq 0$$

This is true because $a \cdot 0 = 0$. However, we cannot divide by 0. There is a good reason for this. Whenever a division is performed, we want to obtain one and only one quotient. Now consider this division problem.

$$\frac{7}{0}$$

We must ask ourselves "What number multiplied by 0 gives 7?" There is no such number, since the product of 0 and any number is zero. Now consider this quotient.

$$\frac{0}{0}$$

There are infinitely many answers to the question, "What number multiplied by 0 gives 0?" Since division by 0 does not yield a *unique* quotient, it is not permitted.

> **Division by Zero**
>
> ***Division by 0 is undefined.***

Order of Operations

Given a problem such as $5 + 2 \cdot 3$, should 5 and 2 be added first or should 2 and 3 be multiplied first? When a problem involves more than one operation, we use the following rules for **order of operations.**

> **Order of Operations**
>
> *If parentheses or square brackets are present:*
>
> **Step 1** Work separately above and below any **fraction bar.**
>
> **Step 2** Use the rules below within each set of **parentheses or square brackets.** Start with the innermost set and work outward.
>
> *If no parentheses or brackets are present:*
>
> **Step 1** Apply any **exponents.**
>
> **Step 2** Do any **multiplications or divisions** in the order in which they occur, working from left to right.
>
> **Step 3** Do any **additions or subtractions** in the order in which they occur, working from left to right.

15/-5
                         -3
-100/-25
                          4
-60/3
                        -20

The division operation is represented by a slash (/). This screen supports the results of **Example 4.**

ERR:DIVIDE BY 0
1: Quit
2: Goto

Dividing by zero leads to this message on the TI-83/84 Plus.

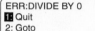
5+2*3

What result does the calculator give? The order of operations determines the answer. (See **Example 5(a).**)

The sentence **"Please excuse my dear Aunt Sally"** is often used to help us remember the rule for order of operations. The letters **P, E, M, D, A, S** are the first letters of the words of the sentence, and they stand for *parentheses, exponents, multiply, divide, add, subtract.* (*Remember also that M and D have equal priority, as do A and S. Operations with equal priority are performed in order from left to right.*)

When evaluating an exponential expression that involves a negative sign, be aware that $(-a)^n$ and $-a^n$ do not necessarily represent the same quantity. For example, if $a = 2$ and $n = 6$,

$$(-2)^6 = (-2)(-2)(-2)(-2)(-2)(-2) = 64 \qquad \text{The base is } -2.$$

while $\qquad -2^6 = -(2 \cdot 2 \cdot 2 \cdot 2 \cdot 2 \cdot 2) = -64. \qquad$ The base is 2.

$(-2)^6$	
	64
-2^6	
	-64

Notice the difference in the two expressions. This supports $(-2)^6 \neq -2^6$.

▮▮ **EXAMPLE 5** Using the Order of Operations

Use the order of operations to simplify each expression.

(a) $5 + 2 \cdot 3$
(b) $4 \cdot 3^2 + 7 - (2 + 8)$
(c) $\dfrac{2(8 - 12) - 11(4)}{5(-2) - 3}$
(d) -4^4
(e) $(-4)^4$
(f) $(-8)(-3) - [4 - (3 - 6)]$

SOLUTION

(a) $5 + 2 \cdot 3 = 5 + 6 \qquad$ Multiply.

$\qquad\qquad\qquad = 11 \qquad$ Add.

Be careful! Multiply first.

(b) $4 \cdot 3^2 + 7 - (2 + 8) = 4 \cdot 3^2 + 7 - 10 \qquad$ Work within parentheses first.

3^2 means $3 \cdot 3$, not $3 \cdot 2$.

$\qquad\qquad\qquad\qquad\qquad = 4 \cdot 9 + 7 - 10 \qquad$ Apply the exponent.

$\qquad\qquad\qquad\qquad\qquad = 36 + 7 - 10 \qquad$ Multiply.

$\qquad\qquad\qquad\qquad\qquad = 43 - 10 \qquad$ Add.

$\qquad\qquad\qquad\qquad\qquad = 33 \qquad$ Subtract.

(c) $\dfrac{2(8 - 12) - 11(4)}{5(-2) - 3} = \dfrac{2(-4) - 11(4)}{5(-2) - 3} \qquad$ Work separately above and below fraction bar.

$\qquad\qquad\qquad\qquad\qquad = \dfrac{-8 - 44}{-10 - 3} \qquad$ Multiply.

$\qquad\qquad\qquad\qquad\qquad = \dfrac{-52}{-13} \qquad$ Subtract.

$\qquad\qquad\qquad\qquad\qquad = 4 \qquad$ Divide.

(d) $-4^4 = -(4 \cdot 4 \cdot 4 \cdot 4) = -256$

The base is 4, not -4.

(e) $(-4)^4 = (-4)(-4)(-4)(-4) = 256$

The base is -4 here.

$5+2*3$	
	11
-4^4	
	-256
$-8*-3-(4-(3-6))$	
	17

The calculator supports the results in **Example 5(a), (d), and (f).**

(f) $-8(-3) - [4 - (3 - 6)] = -8(-3) - [4 - (-3)] \qquad$ Work within parentheses.

Start here.

$\qquad\qquad\qquad\qquad\qquad = -8(-3) - [4 + 3] \qquad$ Definition of subtraction

$\qquad\qquad\qquad\qquad\qquad = -8(-3) - 7 \qquad$ Work within brackets.

$\qquad\qquad\qquad\qquad\qquad = 24 - 7 \qquad$ Multiply.

$\qquad\qquad\qquad\qquad\qquad = 17 \qquad$ Subtract. ▮▮▮

Properties of Addition and Multiplication of Real Numbers

Properties of Addition and Multiplication

For real numbers a, b, and c, the following properties hold.

Closure Properties	$a + b$ and ab **are real numbers.**
Commutative Properties	$a + b = b + a$ $ab = ba$
Associative Properties	$(a + b) + c = a + (b + c)$
	$(ab)c = a(bc)$
Identity Properties	There is a real number 0 such that
	$a + 0 = a$ and $0 + a = a.$
	There is a real number 1 such that
	$a \cdot 1 = a$ and $1 \cdot a = a.$
Inverse Properties	For each real number a, there is a single real number $-a$ such that
	$a + (-a) = 0$ and $(-a) + a = 0.$
	For each nonzero real number a, there is a single real number $\frac{1}{a}$ such that
	$a \cdot \dfrac{1}{a} = 1$ and $\dfrac{1}{a} \cdot a = 1.$
Distributive Property of Multiplication with Respect to Addition	$a(b + c) = ab + ac$
	$(b + c)a = ba + ca$

The set of real numbers is said to be closed with respect to the operations of addition and multiplication. This means that the sum of two real numbers and the product of two real numbers are themselves real numbers. The commutative properties state that two real numbers may be added or multiplied in either order without affecting the result. The associative properties allow us to group terms or factors in any manner we wish without affecting the result.

The number 0 is the **identity element for addition.** It may be added to any real number to obtain that real number. Similarly, 1 is the **identity element for multiplication.** Multiplying a real number by 1 will always yield that real number.

Each real number a has an **additive inverse,** $-a$, such that the sum of a and its additive inverse is the additive identity element 0. Each nonzero real number a has a **multiplicative inverse,** or **reciprocal,** $\frac{1}{a}$, such that the product of a and its multiplicative inverse is the multiplicative identity element 1.

The distributive property allows us to change certain products to sums and certain sums to products.

```
X+Y=Y+X
                    1
X+(Y+Z)=(X+Y)+Z
                    1
5(X+Y)=5X+5Y
                    1
```

No matter what values are stored in X, Y, and Z, the commutative, associative, and distributive properties assure us that these statements are true.

▐▌ **EXAMPLE 6** Identifying Properties of Addition and Multiplication

Identify the property of addition or multiplication illustrated in each statement.

(a) $5 + 7$ is a real number.

(b) $5 + (6 + 8) = (5 + 6) + 8$

(c) $8 + 0 = 8$

(d) $-4\left(-\dfrac{1}{4}\right) = 1$

(e) $4 + (3 + 9) = 4 + (9 + 3)$

(f) $5(x + y) = 5x + 5y$

SOLUTION

(a) The statement that the sum of two real numbers is also a real number is an example of the *closure property of addition*.

(b) Because the grouping of the terms is different on the two sides of the equation, this illustrates the *associative property of addition*.

(c) Adding 0 to a number yields the number itself. This is an example of the *identity property of addition*.

(d) Multiplying a number by its reciprocal yields 1, and this illustrates the *inverse property of multiplication*.

(e) The order of the addends (terms) 3 and 9 is different, so this is justified by the *commutative property of addition*.

(f) The factor 5 is distributed to the terms x and y. This is an example of the *distributive property of multiplication with respect to addition*.   ▌▌▌

Applications of Real Numbers

The usefulness of negative numbers can be seen by considering situations that arise in everyday life. For example, we need negative numbers to express the temperatures on January days in Anchorage, Alaska, where they often drop below zero. The phrases "in the red" and "in the black" mean losing money and making money, respectively. These descriptions go back to the days when bookkeepers used red ink to represent losses and black ink to represent gains.

> **PROBLEM-SOLVING HINT** When problems deal with gains and losses, the gains may be interpreted as positive numbers and the losses as negative numbers. Temperatures below 0° are negative, and those above 0° are positive. Altitudes above sea level are considered positive, and those below sea level are considered negative.

▌▌ **EXAMPLE 7**   Analyzing Change in Annual Returns

Figure 8 shows annual returns in percent for Class A shares of the AIM Charter Fund.

Source: AIM.

Figure 8

Use a signed number to represent the change in the percent returns, shown in **Figure 8** on the preceding page, for the following years.

(a) 2002 to 2003   **(b)** 2003 to 2004

SOLUTION

(a) To find this change, we start with the percent from 2003 and subtract from it the percent from 2002.

$$\underbrace{23.99}_{\text{The 2003 percent}} - \underbrace{(-16.14)}_{\text{The 2002 percent}} = \underbrace{\mathbf{40.13}}_{\substack{\text{A positive number} \\ \text{indicates an increase.}}}$$

(b) Use the same procedure as in part (a).

$$\underbrace{8.67}_{\text{The 2004 percent}} - \underbrace{23.99}_{\text{The 2003 percent}} = \underbrace{-\mathbf{15.32}}_{\substack{\text{A negative number} \\ \text{indicates a decrease.}}}$$

▌▌▌

▌▌ **EXAMPLE 8** Determining Difference of Temperatures

The record high temperature in the United States was 134° Fahrenheit, recorded at Death Valley, California, in 1913. The record low was −80°F, at Prospect Creek, Alaska, in 1971. See **Figure 9**. How much greater was the highest temperature than the lowest temperature? (*Source: The World Almanac and Book of Facts.*)

SOLUTION

We must subtract the lower temperature from the higher temperature.

$$134 - (-80) = 134 + 80 \quad \text{Use the definition of subtraction.}$$
$$= 214 \quad \text{Add.}$$

The difference of the two temperatures is 214°F.

▌▌▌

Figure 9

Fill in each blank with the correct response.

1. The sum of two negative numbers will always be a _____ number.
      (positive/negative)

2. The sum of a number and its opposite will always be ____ .

3. To simplify the expression $8 + [-2 + (-3 + 5)]$, I should begin by adding _____ and _____, according to the rules for order of operations.

4. If I am adding a positive number and a negative number, and the negative number has the larger absolute value, the sum will be a _____ number.
      (positive/negative)

5. Explain in words how to add signed numbers. Consider the various cases and give examples.

6. Explain in words how to multiply signed numbers.

Perform the indicated operations, using the order of operations as necessary.

7. $-12 + (-8)$ **8.** $-5 + (-2)$

9. $12 + (-16)$ **10.** $-6 + 17$

11. $-12 - (-1)$ **12.** $-3 - (-8)$

13. $-5 + 11 + 3$ **14.** $-9 + 16 + 5$

15. $12 - (-3) - (-5)$ **16.** $15 - (-6) - (-8)$

17. $-9 - (-11) - (4 - 6)$

18. $-4 - (-13) + (-5 + 10)$

19. $(-12)(-2)$ **20.** $(-3)(-5)$

21. $9(-12)(-4)(-1)(3)$ **22.** $-5(-17)(2)(-2)(4)$

23. $\dfrac{-18}{-3}$ **24.** $\dfrac{-100}{-50}$ **25.** $\dfrac{36}{-6}$

26. $\dfrac{52}{-13}$ **27.** $\dfrac{0}{12}$ **28.** $\dfrac{0}{-7}$

29. $-6 + [5 - (3 + 2)]$ **30.** $-8[4 + (7 - 8)]$

31. $-4 - 3(-2) + 5^2$ **32.** $-6 - 5(-8) + 3^2$

33. $(-8 - 5)(-2 - 1)$ **34.** $\dfrac{(-10 + 4) \cdot (-3)}{-7 - 2}$

35. $-8(-2) - [(4^2) + (7 - 3)]$

36. $-7(-3) - [2^3 - (3 - 4)]$

37. $\dfrac{(-6 + 3) \cdot (-4)}{-5 - 1}$

38. $\dfrac{2(-5 + 3)}{-2^2} - \dfrac{(-3^2 + 2)(3)}{3 - (-4)}$

39. $\dfrac{2(-5) + (-3)(-2^2)}{-3^2 + 9}$ **40.** $\dfrac{3(-4) + (-5)(-2)}{2^3 - 2 + (-6)}$

41. $-\dfrac{1}{4}[3(-5) + 7(-5) + 1(-2)]$

42. $\dfrac{5 - 3\left(\dfrac{-5 - 9}{-7}\right) - 6}{-9 - 11 + 3 \cdot 7}$

43. Which of the following expressions are undefined?

    A. $\dfrac{8}{0}$ **B.** $\dfrac{9}{6 - 6}$ **C.** $\dfrac{4 - 4}{5 - 5}$ **D.** $\dfrac{0}{-1}$

44. If you have no money in your pocket and you divide it equally among your three siblings, how much does each get? Use this situation to explain division of zero by a positive integer.

Identify the property illustrated by each statement.

45. $6 + 9 = 9 + 6$ **46.** $8 \cdot 4 = 4 \cdot 8$

47. $9 + (-9) = 0$ **48.** $12 + 0 = 12$

49. $9 \cdot 1 = 9$ **50.** $\left(\dfrac{1}{-3}\right) \cdot (-3) = 1$

51. $7 + (2 + 5) = (7 + 2) + 5$

52. $(3 \cdot 5) \cdot 4 = 4 \cdot (3 \cdot 5)$

53. $0 + 283 = 283$

54. $6 \cdot (4 \cdot 2) = (6 \cdot 4) \cdot 2$

55. $2 \cdot (4 + 3) = 2 \cdot 4 + 2 \cdot 3$

56. $9 \cdot 6 + 9 \cdot 8 = 9 \cdot (6 + 8)$

57. $0 = -8 + 8$

58. $19 + 12$ is a real number.

59. $19 \cdot 12$ is a real number.

60. One of the authors received an email message from an old friend, Frank Capek. Frank said that his grandson had to evaluate $9 + 15 \div 3$. Frank and his wife, Barbara, said that the answer is 8, but the grandson said that the correct answer is 14. The grandson's reasoning is "There is a rule called the Order of Process so that you proceed from right to left rather than from left to right."

    (a) What is the correct answer?

    (b) Is the grandson's reasoning correct? Explain.

Exercises 61–68 are designed to explore the properties of real numbers in further detail.

61. (a) Evaluate $6 - 8$ and $8 - 6$.

    (b) By the results of part (a), we may conclude that subtraction is not a(n) _____ operation.

    (c) Are there *any* real numbers a and b for which $a - b = b - a$? If so, give an example.

62. (a) Evaluate $4 \div 8$ and $8 \div 4$.

    (b) By the results of part (a), we may conclude that division is not a(n) _____ operation.

    (c) Are there *any* real numbers a and b for which $a \div b = b \div a$? If so, give an example.

63. Many everyday occurrences can be thought of as operations that have opposites or inverses. For example, the inverse operation for "going to sleep" is "waking up." For each of the given activities, specify its inverse activity.

    (a) cleaning up your room

    (b) earning money

    (c) increasing the volume on your MP3 player

64. Many everyday activities are commutative; that is, the order in which they occur does not affect the outcome. For example, "putting on your shirt" and "putting on your pants" are commutative operations. Decide whether the given activities are commutative.

    (a) putting on your shoes; putting on your socks

    (b) getting dressed; taking a shower

    (c) combing your hair; brushing your teeth

65. The following conversation actually took place between one of the authors of this text and his son, Jack, when Jack was four years old.

DADDY: "Jack, what is $3 + 0$?"
JACK: "3"
DADDY: "Jack, what is $4 + 0$?"
JACK: "4 . . . and Daddy, *string* plus zero equals *string!*"
What property of addition of real numbers did Jack recognize?

66. The phrase *defective merchandise counter* is an example of a phrase that can have different meanings depending upon how the words are grouped (think of the associative properties). For example, (*defective merchandise*) *counter* is a location at which we would return an item that does not work, while *defective* (*merchandise counter*) is a broken place where items are bought and sold. For each of the following phrases, determine why the associative property does not hold.

(a) difficult test question

(b) woman fearing husband

(c) man biting dog

67. The distributive property holds for multiplication with respect to addition. Does the distributive property hold for addition with respect to multiplication? That is, is $a + (b \cdot c) = (a + b) \cdot (a + c)$ true for all values of a, b, and c? (*Hint:* Let $a = 2$, $b = 3$, and $c = 4$.)

68. Suppose that a student shows you the following work.

$$-3(4 - 6) = -3(4) - 3(6) = -12 - 18 = -30$$

The student has made a very common **error** in applying the distributive property. Explain the student's mistake, and work the problem correctly.

Each expression in Exercises 69–76 is equal to either 81 *or* −81. *Decide which of these is the correct value.*

69. -3^4 **70.** $-(3^4)$ **71.** $(-3)^4$

72. $-(-3^4)$ **73.** $-(-3)^4$ **74.** $[-(-3)]^4$

75. $-[-(-3)]^4$ **76.** $-[-(-3^4)]$

77. *Federal Budget Outlays* The bar graph shows federal budget outlays for the U.S. Treasury Department for the years 2006 through 2009. Use a signed number to represent the change in outlay for each time period.

(a) 2006 to 2007

(b) 2007 to 2008

(c) 2008 to 2009

(d) 2006 to 2009

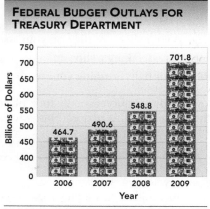

FEDERAL BUDGET OUTLAYS FOR TREASURY DEPARTMENT

Source: U.S. Office of Management and Budget.

78. *Heights of Mountains and Depths of Trenches* The chart shows the heights in feet of some selected mountains and the depths in feet (as negative numbers) of some selected ocean trenches.

Mountain	Height	Trench	Depth
Foraker	17,400	Philippine	−32,995
Wilson	14,246	Cayman	−24,721
Pikes Peak	14,110	Java	−23,376

Source: The World Almanac and Book of Facts.

(a) How much higher is Mt. Foraker than the bottom of the Philippine Trench?

(b) What is the difference between the height of Pikes Peak and the depth of the Java Trench?

(c) How much deeper is the Cayman Trench than the Java Trench?

(d) How much deeper is the Philippine Trench than the Cayman Trench?

79. *Social Security Finances* The table shows Social Security tax revenue and cost of benefits (in billions of dollars).

Year	Tax Revenue	Cost of Benefits
2000	538	409
2010*	916	710
2020*	1479	1405
2030*	2041	2542

*Projected
Source: Social Security Board of Trustees.

(a) Find the difference between Social Security tax revenue and cost of benefits for each year shown in the table.

(b) Interpret your answer for 2030.

80. *House of Representatives* Based on census population projections for 2020, New York will lose 5 seats in the U.S. House of Representatives, Pennsylvania will lose 4 seats, and Ohio will lose 3. Write a signed number that represents the total projected change in the number of seats for these three states. (*Source:* Population Reference Bureau.)

81. *House of Representatives* Michigan is projected to lose 3 seats in the U.S. House of Representatives and Illinois 2 in 2020. The states projected to gain the most seats are California with 9, Texas with 5, Florida with 3, Georgia with 2, and Arizona with 2. Write a signed number that represents the algebraic sum of these changes. (*Source:* Population Reference Bureau.)

82. *Checking Account Balance* Christine MacKrell's checking account balance is $54.00. She then takes a gamble by writing a check for $89.00. What is her new balance? (Write the balance as a signed number.)

83. **Checking Account Balance** In August, Kimberly Manzi began with a checking account balance of $904.89. Her checks and deposits for August are given below:

Checks	Deposits
$35.84	$85.00
$26.14	$120.76
$3.12	

Assuming no other transactions, what was her account balance at the end of August?

84. **Checking Account Balance** In September, David Lopez began with a checking account balance of $904.89. His checks and deposits for September are given below:

Checks	Deposits
$41.29	$80.59
$13.66	$276.13
$84.40	

Assuming no other transactions, what was his account balance at the end of September?

85. **Difference in Elevations** The top of Mt. Whitney, visible from Death Valley, has an altitude of 14,494 feet above sea level. The bottom of Death Valley is 282 feet below sea level. Using 0 as sea level, find the difference of these two elevations. (*Source: World Almanac and Book of Facts.*)

86. **Altitude of Hikers** The surface, or rim, of a canyon is at altitude 0. On a hike down into the canyon, a party of hikers stops for a rest at 130 meters below the surface. They then descend another 54 meters. What is their new altitude? (Write the altitude as a signed number.)

87. **Drastic Temperature Change** On January 23, 1943, the temperature rose 49°F in two minutes in Spearfish, South Dakota. If the starting temperature was −4°F, what was the temperature two minutes later? (*Source: Guinness World Records.*)

88. **Drastic Temperature Change** The greatest change in temperature ever recorded within a 24-hour period occurred in Browning, Montana, on January 23–24, 1916. The temperature fell 100°F from a starting temperature of 44°F. What was the low temperature during this period? (*Source: Guinness World Records.*)

89. **Extreme Temperatures in Alabama** The lowest temperature ever recorded in Alabama was −27°F. The highest temperature ever recorded there was 139°F more than the lowest. What was this highest temperature? (*Source:* National Climatic Data Center.)

90. **Extreme Temperatures in Iowa** The lowest temperature ever recorded in Iowa was −47°F. The highest temperature ever recorded there was 165°F more than the lowest temperature. What was this highest temperature? (*Source:* National Climatic Data Center.)

91. **Low Temperatures in Illinois and Minnesota** The lowest temperature recorded in Illinois was −36°F in 1999. The record low in Minnesota was set in 1996 and was 24°F lower than −36°F. What was the record low in Minnesota? (*Source: The World Almanac and Book of Facts.*)

92. **Low Temperatures in New Mexico and Utah** The lowest temperature ever recorded in New Mexico was −50°F in 1951. The lowest temperature ever recorded in Utah was in 1985 and was 19°F lower than New Mexico's record low. What is the record low temperature for Utah? (*Source:* National Climatic Data Center.)

93. **Breaching of Humpback Whales** Mark and Debbie noticed that one of their favorite whales, "Pineapple," breached 15 feet above the surface of the ocean while her mate cruised 12 feet below the surface. What is the difference between these two levels?

94. **Highest Point in Louisiana** The highest point in Louisiana is Driskill Mountain, at an altitude of 535 feet. The lowest point is at Spanish Fort, 8 feet below sea level. Using zero as sea level, find the difference between these two elevations. (*Source: The World Almanac and Book of Facts.*)

95. **Birth Date of a Greek Mathematician** A certain Greek mathematician was born in 428 B.C. Her father was born 41 years earlier. In what year was her father born?

96. **Birth Date of a Roman Philosopher** A certain Roman philosopher was born in 325 B.C. Her mother was born 35 years earlier. In what year was her mother born?

Home Prices *Median sales prices for existing single-family homes in the United States for the years 2003 through 2007 are shown in the table. Complete the table, determining the change from one year to the next by subtraction.*

	Year	Median Sales Price	Change from Previous Year
	2003	$180,200	
97.	2004	$195,200	
98.	2005	$219,000	
99.	2006	$221,900	
100.	2007	$217,900	

Source: National Association of Realtors.

6.3 RATIONAL NUMBERS AND DECIMAL REPRESENTATION

Definition and the Fundamental Property • Operations with Rational Numbers • Density and the Arithmetic Mean • Decimal Form of Rational Numbers

Definition and the Fundamental Property

Benjamin Banneker (1731–1806) spent the first half of his life tending a farm in Maryland. He gained a reputation locally for his mechanical skills and abilities in mathematical problem solving. In 1772 he acquired astronomy books from a neighbor and devoted himself to learning astronomy, observing the skies, and making calculations. In 1789 Banneker joined the team that surveyed what is now the District of Columbia.

Banneker published almanacs yearly from 1792 to 1802. He sent a copy of his first almanac to Thomas Jefferson along with an impassioned letter against slavery. Jefferson subsequently championed the cause of this early African-American mathematician.

The set of real numbers is composed of two important mutually exclusive subsets: the rational numbers and the irrational numbers. (Two sets are *mutually exclusive* if they contain no elements in common.)

Recall from **Section 6.1** that quotients of integers are called **rational numbers.** Think of the rational numbers as being made up of all the fractions (quotients of integers with denominator not equal to zero) and all the integers. Any integer can be written as the quotient of two integers. For example, the integer 9 can be written as the quotient $\frac{9}{1}$, or $\frac{18}{2}$, or $\frac{27}{3}$, and so on. Also, -5 can be expressed as a quotient of integers as $\frac{-5}{1}$ or $\frac{-10}{2}$, and so on. (How can the integer 0 be written as a quotient of integers?)

> **Rational Numbers**
>
> **Rational numbers** = $\{x \mid x \text{ is a quotient of two integers, with denominator not } 0\}$

A rational number is said to be in **lowest terms** if the greatest common factor of the numerator (top number) and the denominator (bottom number) is 1. Rational numbers are written in lowest terms by using the *fundamental property of rational numbers.*

> **Fundamental Property of Rational Numbers**
>
> If a, b, and k are integers with $b \neq 0$ and $k \neq 0$, then the following is true.
>
> $$\frac{a \cdot k}{b \cdot k} = \frac{a}{b}$$

▌▌ **EXAMPLE 1**   Writing a Fraction in Lowest Terms

Write $\frac{36}{54}$ in lowest terms.

SOLUTION

The greatest common factor of 36 and 54 is 18.

$$\frac{36}{54} = \frac{2 \cdot 18}{3 \cdot 18} = \frac{2}{3}$$

Use the fundamental property with $k = 18$.

▬▬▬

The calculator gives 36/54 in lowest terms, as illustrated in **Example 1.**

In **Example 1,** we see that $\frac{36}{54} = \frac{2}{3}$. If we multiply the numerator of the fraction on the left by the denominator of the fraction on the right, we obtain $36 \cdot 3 = 108$. If we multiply the denominator of the fraction on the left by the numerator of the fraction on the right, we obtain $54 \cdot 2 = 108$. The result is the same in both cases.

One way of determining whether two fractions are equal is to perform this test. If the product of the **"extremes"** (36 and 3 in this case) equals the product of the **"means"** (54 and 2), the fractions are equal. This test for equality of rational numbers is called the **cross-product test.**

Cross-Product Test for Equality of Rational Numbers

For rational numbers $\frac{a}{b}$ and $\frac{c}{d}$, $b \neq 0$, $d \neq 0$, the following is true.

$$\frac{a}{b} = \frac{c}{d} \quad \text{if and only if} \quad a \cdot d = b \cdot c$$

Operations with Rational Numbers

The operation of addition of rational numbers can be illustrated by the sketches in **Figure 10.** The rectangle at the top left is divided into three equal portions, with one of the portions in color. The rectangle at the top right is divided into five equal parts, with two of them in color.

The total of the areas in color is represented by the sum

$$\frac{1}{3} + \frac{2}{5}.$$

To evaluate this sum, the areas in color must be redrawn in terms of a common unit. Since the least common multiple of 3 and 5 is 15, redraw both rectangles with 15 parts. See **Figure 11.** In the figure, 11 of the small rectangles are in color, so

$$\frac{1}{3} + \frac{2}{5} = \frac{5}{15} + \frac{6}{15} = \frac{11}{15}.$$

Figure 10

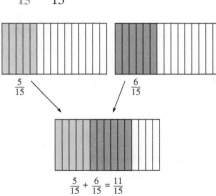

Figure 11

A similar example could be given for the difference of rational numbers.

Adding and Subtracting Rational Numbers

If $\frac{a}{b}$ and $\frac{c}{d}$ are rational numbers, then the following are true.

$$\frac{a}{b} + \frac{c}{d} = \frac{ad + bc}{bd} \quad \text{and} \quad \frac{a}{b} - \frac{c}{d} = \frac{ad - bc}{bd}$$

This formal definition is seldom used in practice. We usually first rewrite the fractions with the least common multiple of their denominators, called the **least common denominator (LCD).**

▌▌ **EXAMPLE 2** Adding and Subtracting Rational Numbers

Perform each operation.

(a) $\dfrac{2}{15} + \dfrac{1}{10}$ **(b)** $\dfrac{173}{180} - \dfrac{69}{1200}$

SOLUTION

(a) Since $30 \div 15 = 2$, $\dfrac{2}{15} = \dfrac{2 \cdot 2}{15 \cdot 2} = \dfrac{4}{30}$

and since $30 \div 10 = 3$, $\dfrac{1}{10} = \dfrac{1 \cdot 3}{10 \cdot 3} = \dfrac{3}{30}.$ *The LCD is 30.*

Thus, $\dfrac{2}{15} + \dfrac{1}{10} = \dfrac{4}{30} + \dfrac{3}{30} = \dfrac{7}{30}.$

(b) The least common multiple of 180 and 1200 is 3600.

$$\frac{173}{180} - \frac{69}{1200} = \frac{3460}{3600} - \frac{207}{3600} = \frac{3460 - 207}{3600} = \frac{3253}{3600}$$

▌▌▌

```
2/15+1/10▶Frac
                 7
                ──
                30
173/180−69/1200▶Frac
               3253
               ────
               3600
```

The results of **Example 2** are illustrated in this screen.

Multiplying Rational Numbers

If $\frac{a}{b}$ and $\frac{c}{d}$ are rational numbers, then the following is true.

$$\frac{a}{b} \cdot \frac{c}{d} = \frac{ac}{bd}$$

▌▌ **EXAMPLE 3** Multiplying Rational Numbers

Find each product.

(a) $\dfrac{3}{4} \cdot \dfrac{7}{10}$ **(b)** $\dfrac{5}{18} \cdot \dfrac{3}{10}$

SOLUTION

(a) $\dfrac{3}{4} \cdot \dfrac{7}{10} = \dfrac{3 \cdot 7}{4 \cdot 10} = \dfrac{21}{40}$

(b) $\dfrac{5}{18} \cdot \dfrac{3}{10} = \dfrac{5 \cdot 3}{18 \cdot 10} = \dfrac{15}{180} = \dfrac{1 \cdot 15}{12 \cdot 15} = \dfrac{1}{12}$

```
(3/4)*(7/10)▶Frac
                 21
                ──
                40
(5/18)*(3/10)▶Frac
                 1
                ──
                12
```

To illustrate the results of **Example 3,** we use parentheses around the fraction factors.

In practice, a multiplication problem such as

$$\frac{5}{18} \cdot \frac{3}{10}$$

in part (b) is often solved by using slash marks to indicate that common factors have been divided out of the numerator and denominator.

$$\frac{\overset{1}{\cancel{5}}}{\underset{6}{\cancel{18}}} \cdot \frac{\overset{1}{\cancel{3}}}{\underset{2}{\cancel{10}}} = \frac{1}{6} \cdot \frac{1}{2} \quad \begin{array}{l} \text{3 is divided out of 3 and 18.} \\ \text{5 is divided out of 5 and 10.} \end{array}$$

$$= \frac{1}{12}$$

▮▮▮

In a fraction, the fraction bar indicates the operation of division. The multiplicative inverse of the nonzero number b is $\frac{1}{b}$. We define division using multiplicative inverses.

> **Definition of Division**
>
> If a and b are real numbers, $b \neq 0$, then the following is true.
>
> $$\frac{a}{b} = a \cdot \frac{1}{b}$$

You probably have heard the rule, "To divide fractions, invert the divisor and multiply." To illustrate this rule, suppose that you have $\frac{7}{8}$ of a gallon of milk and you wish to find how many quarts you have. Since a quart is $\frac{1}{4}$ of a gallon, you must ask yourself, "How many $\frac{1}{4}$s are there in $\frac{7}{8}$?" This would be interpreted as

$$\frac{7}{8} \div \frac{1}{4}, \quad \text{or} \quad \frac{\frac{7}{8}}{\frac{1}{4}}.$$

The fundamental property of rational numbers can be extended to rational number values of a, b, and k.

$$\frac{a}{b} = \frac{a \cdot k}{b \cdot k} = \frac{\frac{7}{8} \cdot 4}{\frac{1}{4} \cdot 4} = \frac{\frac{7}{8} \cdot 4}{1} = \frac{7}{8} \cdot \frac{4}{1} \quad \text{Let } a = \tfrac{7}{8}, b = \tfrac{1}{4}, \text{ and } k = 4 \left(\text{the reciprocal of } b = \tfrac{1}{4}\right).$$

We began with the division problem $\frac{7}{8} \div \frac{1}{4}$, which, through a series of equivalent expressions, led to the multiplication problem $\frac{7}{8} \cdot \frac{4}{1}$. So dividing by $\frac{1}{4}$ is equivalent to multiplying by its reciprocal, $\frac{4}{1}$.

$$\frac{7}{8} \cdot \frac{4}{1} = \frac{28}{8} = \frac{7}{2} \quad \text{Definition of multiplication of fractions}$$

Thus there are $\frac{7}{2}$, or $3\frac{1}{2}$, quarts in $\frac{7}{8}$ gallon.*

Early U.S. cents and **half cents** used fractions to denote their denominations. The half cent used $\frac{1}{200}$ and the cent used $\frac{1}{100}$. (See **Exercise 18** for a photo of an interesting error coin.)

The coins shown here were part of the collection of Louis E. Eliasberg, Sr. **Louis Eliasberg** was the only person ever to assemble a complete collection of United States coins. The Eliasberg gold coins were auctioned in 1982, while the copper, nickel, and silver coins were auctioned in two sales in 1996 and 1997. The half cent pictured sold for $506,000 and the cent sold for $27,500. The cent shown in **Exercise 18** went for a mere $2970.

---

*$3\frac{1}{2}$ is a **mixed number.** Mixed numbers are covered in the exercises for this section.

Dividing Rational Numbers

If $\frac{a}{b}$ and $\frac{c}{d}$ are rational numbers, where $\frac{c}{d} \neq 0$, then the following is true.

$$\frac{a}{b} \div \frac{c}{d} = \frac{a}{b} \cdot \frac{d}{c} = \frac{ad}{bc}$$

▮▮ **EXAMPLE 4** Dividing Rational Numbers

Find each quotient.

(a) $\dfrac{3}{5} \div \dfrac{7}{15}$ **(b)** $\dfrac{-4}{7} \div \dfrac{3}{14}$ **(c)** $\dfrac{2}{9} \div 4$ **(d)** $-9 \div \dfrac{3}{5}$

SOLUTION

(a) $\dfrac{3}{5} \div \dfrac{7}{15} = \dfrac{3}{5} \cdot \dfrac{15}{7} = \dfrac{45}{35} = \dfrac{9 \cdot 5}{7 \cdot 5} = \dfrac{9}{7}$

(b) $\dfrac{-4}{7} \div \dfrac{3}{14} = \dfrac{-4}{7} \cdot \dfrac{14}{3} = \dfrac{-56}{21} = \dfrac{-8 \cdot 7}{3 \cdot 7} = \dfrac{-8}{3} = -\dfrac{8}{3}$

> $\dfrac{-a}{b}, \dfrac{a}{-b},$ and $-\dfrac{a}{b}$ are all equal.

(c) $\dfrac{2}{9} \div 4 = \dfrac{2}{9} \div \dfrac{4}{1} = \dfrac{2}{9} \cdot \dfrac{1}{4} = \dfrac{\overset{1}{2}}{9} \cdot \dfrac{1}{\underset{2}{4}} = \dfrac{1}{18}$

(d) $-9 \div \dfrac{3}{5} = \dfrac{\overset{-3}{-9}}{1} \cdot \dfrac{5}{\underset{1}{3}} = -15$ ▮▮▮

(-4/7)/(3/14)▶Frac
$-\frac{8}{3}$

(2/9)/4▶Frac
$\frac{1}{18}$

This screen supports the results in
Example 4(b) and (c).

Density and the Arithmetic Mean

There is no integer between two consecutive integers, such as 3 and 4. However, a rational number can always be found between any two distinct rational numbers. For this reason, the set of rational numbers is said to be *dense*.

Density Property of the Rational Numbers

If r and t are distinct rational numbers, with $r < t$, then there exists a rational number s such that

$$r < s < t.$$

Repeated applications of the density property lead to the following conclusion.

> *There are infinitely many rational numbers between two distinct rational numbers.*

One example of a rational number that is between two distinct rational numbers is the *arithmetic mean*. To find the **arithmetic mean,** or **average,** of n numbers, we add the numbers and then divide the sum by n. For two numbers, the number that lies halfway between them is their average.

▌▌ EXAMPLE 5 Finding the Arithmetic Mean (Average)

Find the rational number halfway between $\frac{2}{3}$ and $\frac{5}{6}$ (that is, their arithmetic mean, or average).

SOLUTION

First, find their sum.

> Find a common denominator.

$$\frac{2}{3} + \frac{5}{6} = \frac{4}{6} + \frac{5}{6} = \frac{9}{6}, \quad \text{or} \quad \frac{3}{2}$$

Now divide the sum, $\frac{3}{2}$, by 2.

$$\frac{3}{2} \div 2 = \frac{3}{2} \cdot \frac{1}{2} = \frac{3}{4} \qquad \text{To divide, multiply by the reciprocal of the divisor.}$$

The number $\frac{3}{4}$ is halfway between $\frac{2}{3}$ and $\frac{5}{6}$. ███

▌▌ EXAMPLE 6 Finding the Arithmetic Mean (Average)

Table 3 shows the number of female civilian workers, in thousands, for some selected states. What is the average number, in thousands, for this group of states?

SOLUTION

To find this average, divide the sum by the number of states, 6.

$$\frac{2918 + 320 + 2016 + 869 + 571 + 1427}{6} = \frac{8121}{6} = 1353.5$$

The average number of female civilian workers for the group of states is about 1354 thousand (or 1,354,000). ███

It is also true that between any two *real* numbers there is another *real* number. Thus, as in the case of the rational numbers, the set of real numbers is dense.

Decimal Form of Rational Numbers

Rational numbers can be expressed as decimals. Decimal numerals have place values that are powers of 10. The place values are as shown here.

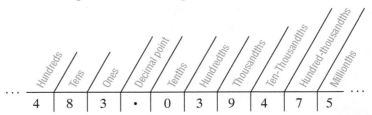

The decimal numeral 483.039475 is read "four hundred eighty-three and thirty-nine thousand, four hundred seventy-five millionths."

A rational number in the form $\frac{a}{b}$ can be expressed as a decimal most easily by entering it into a calculator. For example, to write $\frac{3}{8}$ as a decimal, enter 3, then enter the operation of division, then enter 8. Press the equals key to find the following equivalence.

$$\frac{3}{8} = 0.375$$

This same result may be obtained by long division, as shown in the margin. By this result, the rational number $\frac{3}{8}$ is the same as the decimal 0.375. A decimal such as 0.375, which stops, is called a **terminating decimal.**

$$\frac{1}{4} = 0.25, \quad \frac{7}{10} = 0.7, \quad \text{and} \quad \frac{89}{1000} = 0.089 \qquad \text{Examples of terminating decimals}$$

Table 3

State	Number (in thousands)
Illinois	2918
Maine	320
North Carolina	2016
Oregon	869
Utah	571
Wisconsin	1427

Source: U.S. Bureau of Labor Statistics.

```
        0.375              0.3636 ...
   8) 3.000          11) 4.00000 ...
      24                  33
      ──                  ──
      60                  70
      56                  66
      ──                  ──
      40                  40
      40                  33
      ──                  ──
       0                  70
                          66
                          ──
                          40
```

While 2/3 has a repeating decimal representation (2/3 = $0.\overline{6}$), the calculator rounds off in the final decimal place displayed.

Not all rational numbers can be represented by terminating decimals. For example, convert $\frac{4}{11}$ into a decimal by dividing 11 into 4 using a calculator. The display shows

$$0.3636363636, \quad \text{or perhaps} \quad 0.363636364.$$

However, we see that the long division process, shown in the margin on the previous page, indicates that we will actually get 0.3636 . . . , with the digits 36 repeating over and over indefinitely. To indicate this, we write a bar (called a *vinculum*) over the "block" of digits that repeats.

$$\frac{4}{11} = 0.\overline{36} \quad \text{0.}\overline{36}\text{ means 0.3636....}$$

A decimal such as $0.\overline{36}$, which continues indefinitely, is called a **repeating decimal.**

$$\frac{5}{11} = 0.\overline{45}, \quad \frac{1}{3} = 0.\overline{3}, \quad \text{and} \quad \frac{5}{6} = 0.8\overline{3} \quad \text{Examples of repeating decimals}$$

Because of the limitations of the display of a calculator, and because some rational numbers have repeating decimals, it is important to be able to interpret calculator results accordingly when obtaining repeating decimals.

While we distinguish between *terminating* and *repeating* decimals in this book, some mathematicians prefer to consider all rational numbers as repeating decimals. This can be justified by thinking this way: if the division process leads to a remainder of 0, then zeros repeat without end in the decimal form. For example, we can consider the decimal form of $\frac{3}{4}$ as follows.

$$\frac{3}{4} = 0.75\overline{0}$$

By considering the possible remainders that may be obtained when converting a quotient of integers to a decimal, we can draw an important conclusion about the decimal form of rational numbers. If the remainder is never zero, the division will produce a repeating decimal. This happens because each step of the division process must produce a remainder that is less than the divisor. Since the number of different possible remainders is less than the divisor, the remainders must eventually begin to repeat. This makes the digits of the quotient repeat, producing a repeating decimal.

Although only ten decimal digits are shown, all three fractions have decimals that repeat endlessly.

Decimal Representation of Rational Numbers

Any rational number can be expressed as either a terminating decimal or a repeating decimal.

To determine whether the decimal form of a quotient of integers will terminate or repeat, we use the following rule.

Criteria for Terminating and Repeating Decimals

A rational number $\frac{a}{b}$ *in lowest terms* results in a **terminating decimal** if the only prime factor of the denominator is 2 or 5 (or both).

A rational number $\frac{a}{b}$ *in lowest terms* results in a **repeating decimal** if a prime other than 2 or 5 appears in the prime factorization of the denominator.

Simon Stevin (1548–1620) worked as a bookkeeper in Belgium and became an engineer in the Netherlands army. He is usually given credit for the development of **decimals.**

Justification of this rule is based on the fact that the prime factors of 10 are 2 and 5, and the decimal system uses ten as its base.

To find a baseball player's batting average, we divide the number of hits by the number of at-bats. A surprising paradox exists concerning averages. It is possible for Player *A* to have a higher batting average than Player *B* in each of two successive years, yet for the two-year period, Player *B* can have a higher total batting average. Look at the chart.

Year	Joe Shlabotnik	Scott Bailes
1998	$\frac{20}{40} = .500$	$\frac{90}{200} = .450$
1999	$\frac{60}{200} = .300$	$\frac{10}{40} = .250$
Two-year total	$\frac{80}{240} = .333$	$\frac{100}{240} = .417$

In both individual years, Shlabotnik had a higher average, but for the two-year period, Bailes had the higher average. This is an example of **Simpson's paradox** from statistics. (See also the **Chapter 12** opener, on **page 629.**)

▮▮ **EXAMPLE 7** Determining Whether a Decimal Terminates or Repeats

Determine whether the decimal form terminates or repeats.

(a) $\frac{7}{8}$ **(b)** $\frac{13}{150}$ **(c)** $\frac{6}{75}$

SOLUTION

(a) The rational number $\frac{7}{8}$ is in lowest terms. Its denominator is 8, and since 8 factors as 2^3, the decimal form will terminate. No primes other than 2 or 5 divide the denominator.

(b) The rational number $\frac{13}{150}$ is in lowest terms with denominator $150 = 2 \cdot 3 \cdot 5^2$. Since 3 appears as a prime factor of the denominator, the decimal form will repeat.

(c) First write the rational number $\frac{6}{75}$ in lowest terms.

$$\frac{6}{75} = \frac{2}{25} \qquad \text{Denominator is 25.}$$

Since $25 = 5^2$, the decimal form will terminate.   ▮▮▮

We have seen that a rational number will be represented by either a terminating or a repeating decimal. Must a terminating decimal or a repeating decimal represent a rational number? The answer is *yes*. For example, the terminating decimal 0.6 represents a rational number.

$$0.6 = \frac{6}{10} = \frac{3}{5}$$

▮▮ **EXAMPLE 8** Writing Terminating Decimals as Quotients of Integers

Write each terminating decimal as a quotient of integers.

(a) 0.437   **(b)** 8.2

SOLUTION

(a) $0.437 = \dfrac{437}{1000}$ Read as "four hundred thirty-seven thousandths" and then write as a fraction.

(b) $8.2 = 8 + \dfrac{2}{10} = \dfrac{82}{10} = \dfrac{41}{5}$ Read as a decimal, write as a sum, and then add.   ▮▮▮

.437▶Frac
$\frac{437}{1000}$

8.2▶Frac
$\frac{41}{5}$

The results of **Example 8** are supported in this screen.

We now show how to convert a repeating decimal to a quotient of integers.

▮▮ **EXAMPLE 9** Writing a Repeating Decimal as a Quotient of Integers

Find a quotient of two integers equal to $0.\overline{85}$.

SOLUTION

Step 1   Let $x = 0.\overline{85}$, so $x = 0.858585\ldots$.

Step 2   Multiply both sides of the equation $x = 0.858585\ldots$ by 100. (Use 100 since there are **two** digits in the part that repeats, and $100 = 10^2$.)

$$x = 0.858585\ldots$$
$$100x = 100(0.858585\ldots)$$
$$100x = 85.858585\ldots$$

$1 = 0.999999999999...$

Terminating or Repeating? One of the most baffling truths of elementary mathematics is the following:

$$1 = 0.9999....$$

Most people believe that $0.\overline{9}$ has to be less than 1, but this is not the case. The following argument shows why. Let $x = 0.9999....$ Then

$$10x = 9.9999...$$
$$\underline{x = 0.9999...}$$
$$9x = 9 \qquad \text{Subtract.}$$
$$x = 1. \qquad \text{Divide.}$$

Therefore, $1 = 0.9999....$ Similarly, it can be shown that any terminating decimal can be represented as a repeating decimal with an endless string of 9s. For example, $0.5 = 0.49999...$ and $2.6 = 2.59999....$ This is a way of justifying that any rational number may be represented as a repeating decimal.

Step 3 Subtract the expressions in Step 1 from the final expressions in Step 2.

$$100x = 85.858585... \qquad \text{(Recall that } x = 1x \text{ and}$$
$$\underline{x = 0.858585...} \qquad \quad 100x - x = 99x.)$$
$$99x = 85 \qquad \qquad \text{Subtract.}$$

Step 4 Solve the equation $99x = 85$ by dividing both sides by 99.

$$99x = 85$$
$$\frac{99x}{99} = \frac{85}{99} \qquad \text{Divide by 99.}$$
$$x = \frac{85}{99} \qquad \frac{99x}{99} = x$$
$$0.\overline{85} = \frac{85}{99} \qquad x = 0.\overline{85}$$

When checking with a calculator, remember that the calculator will only show a finite number of decimal places and may round off in the final decimal place shown. ▊▊▊

For Further Thought

The Influence of Spanish Coinage on Stock Prices

Until August 28, 2000, when decimalization of the U.S. stock market began, market prices were reported with fractions having denominators with powers of 2, such as $17\frac{3}{4}$ and $112\frac{5}{8}$. Did you ever wonder why this was done?

During the early years of the United States, prior to the minting of its own coinage, the Spanish eight-reales coin, also known as the Spanish milled dollar, circulated freely in the states. Its fractional parts, the four reales, two reales, and one real, were known as **pieces of eight,** and were described as such in pirate and treasure lore. When the New York Stock Exchange was founded in 1792, it chose to use the Spanish milled dollar as its price basis, rather than the decimal base as proposed by Thomas Jefferson that same year.

In the September 1997 issue of *COINage*, Tom Delorey's article "The End of 'Pieces of Eight'" gives the following account:

As the Spanish dollar and its fractions continued to be legal tender in America alongside the decimal coins until 1857, there was no urgency to change the system—and by the time the Spanish-American money was withdrawn

in 1857, pricing stocks in eighths of a dollar—and no less—was a tradition carved in stone. Being somewhat a conservative organization, the NYSE saw no need to fix what was not broken.

All prices on the U.S. stock markets are now reported in decimals. (*Source:* "Stock price tables go to decimal listings," *The Times Picayune,* June 27, 2000.)

For Group or Individual Investigation

Consider this: Have you ever heard this old cheer? "Two bits, four bits, six bits, a dollar. All for the (home team), stand up and holler." The term **two bits** refers to 25 cents. Discuss how this cheer is based on the Spanish eight-reales coin.

6.3 EXERCISES

Choose the expression(s) that is (are) equivalent to the given rational number.

1. $\dfrac{4}{8}$

   A. $\dfrac{1}{2}$ **B.** $\dfrac{8}{4}$ **C.** 0.5 **D.** $0.5\overline{0}$ **E.** $0.\overline{55}$

2. $\dfrac{2}{3}$

   A. 0.67 **B.** $0.\overline{6}$ **C.** $\dfrac{20}{30}$ **D.** $0.666\ldots$ **E.** 0.6

3. $\dfrac{5}{9}$

   A. 0.56 **B.** 0.55 **C.** $0.\overline{5}$ **D.** $\dfrac{9}{5}$ **E.** $1\dfrac{4}{5}$

4. $\dfrac{1}{4}$

   A. 0.25 **B.** $0.24\overline{9}$ **C.** $\dfrac{25}{100}$ **D.** 4 **E.** $\dfrac{10}{400}$

Write each fraction in lowest terms.

5. $\dfrac{16}{48}$ **6.** $\dfrac{21}{28}$ **7.** $-\dfrac{15}{35}$ **8.** $-\dfrac{8}{48}$

Write each fraction in three other ways.

9. $\dfrac{3}{8}$ **10.** $\dfrac{9}{10}$

11. $-\dfrac{5}{7}$ **12.** $-\dfrac{7}{12}$

13. Write a fraction in lowest terms that represents the portion of each figure that is in color.

  (a)   **(b)**

  (c)   **(d)**

14. Write a fraction in lowest terms that represents the region described in parts (a)–(d).

(a) the dots in the rectangle as a part of the dots in the entire figure

(b) the dots in the triangle as a part of the dots in the entire figure

(c) the dots in the rectangle as a part of the dots in the union of the triangle and the rectangle

(d) the dots in the intersection of the triangle and the rectangle as a part of the dots in the union of the triangle and the rectangle

15. Refer to the figure for **Exercise 14** and write a description of the region that is represented by the fraction $\frac{1}{12}$.

16. *Batting Averages* In a softball league, Paul Lewis got 8 hits in 20 at-bats, and Josh LaRoche got 12 hits in 30 at-bats. Which player (if either) had the higher batting average?

17. *Batting Averages* After ten games, the following statistics were obtained.

Player	At-bats	Hits	Home Runs
Anne Kelly	40	9	2
Christine O'Brien	36	12	3
Leah Goldberg	11	5	1
Otis Taylor	16	8	0
Carol Britz	20	10	2

Answer using estimation skills as necessary.

(a) Which player got a hit in exactly $\frac{1}{3}$ of his or her at-bats?

(b) Which player got a hit in just less than $\frac{1}{2}$ of his or her at-bats?

(c) Which player got a home run in just less than $\frac{1}{10}$ of his or her at-bats?

(d) Which player got a hit in just less than $\frac{1}{4}$ of his or her at-bats?

(e) Which two players got hits in exactly the same fractional parts of their at-bats? What was the fractional part, reduced to lowest terms?

18. Refer to the margin note discussing the use of common fractions on early U.S. copper coinage. The photo here shows an error near the bottom that occurred on an 1802 large cent. Discuss the error and how it represents a mathematical impossibility.

Perform the indicated operations and express answers in lowest terms. Use the order of operations as necessary.

19. $\dfrac{3}{8} + \dfrac{1}{8}$ **20.** $\dfrac{7}{9} + \dfrac{1}{9}$ **21.** $\dfrac{5}{16} + \dfrac{7}{12}$

22. $\dfrac{1}{15} + \dfrac{7}{18}$ **23.** $\dfrac{2}{3} - \dfrac{7}{8}$ **24.** $\dfrac{13}{20} - \dfrac{5}{12}$

25. $\dfrac{5}{8} - \dfrac{3}{14}$ **26.** $\dfrac{19}{15} - \dfrac{7}{12}$ **27.** $\dfrac{3}{4} \cdot \dfrac{9}{5}$

28. $\dfrac{3}{8} \cdot \dfrac{2}{7}$ **29.** $-\dfrac{2}{3} \cdot -\dfrac{5}{8}$ **30.** $-\dfrac{2}{4} \cdot \dfrac{3}{9}$

31. $\dfrac{5}{12} \div \dfrac{15}{4}$ **32.** $\dfrac{15}{16} \div \dfrac{30}{8}$

33. $-\dfrac{9}{16} \div -\dfrac{3}{8}$ **34.** $-\dfrac{3}{8} \div \dfrac{5}{4}$

35. $\left(\dfrac{1}{3} \div \dfrac{1}{2}\right) + \dfrac{5}{6}$ **36.** $\dfrac{2}{5} \div \left(-\dfrac{4}{5} \div \dfrac{3}{10}\right)$

37. *Recipe for Grits* The following chart appears on a package of Quaker® Quick Grits.

	Microwave	Stove Top		
Servings	**1**	**1**	**4**	**6**
Water	$\frac{3}{4}$ cup	1 cup	3 cups	4 cups
Grits	3 Tbsp	3 Tbsp	$\frac{3}{4}$ cup	1 cup
Salt (optional)	dash	dash	$\frac{1}{4}$ tsp	$\frac{1}{2}$ tsp

(a) How many cups of water would be needed for 6 microwave servings?

(b) How many cups of grits would be needed for 5 stove-top servings? (*Hint:* 5 is halfway between 4 and 6.)

38. *U.S. Immigrants* Approximately 34 million people living in the United States in 2004 were born in other countries.

U.S. Immigrants by Region of Birth

Source: U.S. Census Bureau.

The circle graph in the previous column gives the fractional number from each region of birth for these immigrants.

(a) What fractional part of the immigrants were from other regions?

(b) What fractional part of the immigrants were from Latin America or Asia?

(c) How many (in millions) were from Europe?

*The **mixed number** $2\frac{5}{8}$ represents the sum $2 + \frac{5}{8}$. We can convert $2\frac{5}{8}$ to a fraction as follows:*

$$2\frac{5}{8} = 2 + \frac{5}{8} = \frac{2}{1} + \frac{5}{8} = \frac{16}{8} + \frac{5}{8} = \frac{21}{8}.$$

The fraction $\frac{21}{8}$ can be converted back to a mixed number by dividing 8 into 21. The quotient is 2, the remainder is 5, and the divisor is 8.

Convert each mixed number to a fraction, and convert each fraction to a mixed number.

39. $4\dfrac{1}{3}$ **40.** $3\dfrac{7}{8}$ **41.** $2\dfrac{9}{10}$

42. $\dfrac{18}{5}$ **43.** $\dfrac{27}{4}$ **44.** $\dfrac{19}{3}$

It is possible to add mixed numbers by first converting them to fractions, adding, and then converting the sum back to a mixed number. For example,

$$2\frac{1}{3} + 3\frac{1}{2} = \frac{7}{3} + \frac{7}{2} = \frac{14}{6} + \frac{21}{6} = \frac{35}{6} = 5\frac{5}{6}.$$

The other operations with mixed numbers may be performed in a similar manner.

Perform each operation and express your answer as a mixed number.

45. $3\dfrac{1}{4} + 2\dfrac{7}{8}$ **46.** $6\dfrac{1}{5} - 2\dfrac{7}{15}$

47. $-4\dfrac{7}{8} \cdot 3\dfrac{2}{3}$ **48.** $-4\dfrac{1}{6} \div 1\dfrac{2}{3}$

Solve each problem.

49. *Socket Wrench Measurements* A hardware store sells a 22-piece socket wrench set. The measure of the largest socket is $\frac{3}{4}$ in., while the measure of the smallest socket is $\frac{3}{16}$ in. What is the difference between these measures?

50. *Swiss Cheese Hole Sizes*   Under existing standards, most of the holes in Swiss cheese must have diameters between $\frac{11}{16}$ and $\frac{13}{16}$ in. To accommodate new high-speed slicing machines, the USDA wants to reduce the minimum size to $\frac{3}{8}$ in. How much smaller is $\frac{3}{8}$ in. than $\frac{11}{16}$ in.? (*Source:* U.S. Department of Agriculture.)

*A quotient of quantities containing fractions (with denominators not zero) is called a **complex fraction.** There are two methods that are used to simplify a complex fraction.*

Method 1   *Simplify the numerator and denominator separately. Then rewrite as a division problem, and proceed as you would when dividing fractions.*

Method 2   *Multiply both the numerator and denominator by the least common denominator of all the fractions found within the complex fraction. (This is, in effect, multiplying the fraction by 1, which does not change its value.) Apply the distributive property, if necessary, and simplify.*

Use one of the methods above to simplify each complex fraction.

51. $\dfrac{\frac{1}{2}+\frac{1}{4}}{\frac{1}{2}-\frac{1}{4}}$

52. $\dfrac{\frac{2}{3}+\frac{1}{6}}{\frac{2}{3}-\frac{1}{6}}$

53. $\dfrac{\frac{5}{8}-\frac{1}{4}}{\frac{1}{8}+\frac{3}{4}}$

54. $\dfrac{\frac{3}{16}-\frac{1}{2}}{\frac{5}{16}+\frac{1}{8}}$

55. $\dfrac{\frac{7}{11}+\frac{3}{10}}{\frac{1}{11}-\frac{9}{10}}$

56. $\dfrac{\frac{11}{15}+\frac{1}{9}}{\frac{13}{15}-\frac{2}{3}}$

*The expressions in Exercises 57 and 58 are called **continued fractions.** Write each in the form $\frac{p}{q}$ reduced to lowest terms. (Hint: Start at the bottom and work up.)*

57. $2 + \dfrac{1}{1 + \dfrac{1}{3 + \frac{1}{2}}}$

58. $4 + \dfrac{1}{2 + \dfrac{1}{1 + \frac{1}{3}}}$

Find the rational number halfway between the two given rational numbers.

59. $\dfrac{1}{2}, \dfrac{3}{4}$

60. $\dfrac{1}{3}, \dfrac{5}{12}$

61. $\dfrac{3}{5}, \dfrac{2}{3}$

62. $\dfrac{7}{12}, \dfrac{5}{8}$

63. $-\dfrac{2}{3}, -\dfrac{5}{6}$

64. $-3, -\dfrac{5}{2}$

Solve each problem.

65. *Average Annual Salary*   The table shows the average annual salary in the eight highest-paying metropolitan areas in the United States. Find the average of these amounts to the nearest dollar.

Metropolitan Area	Average Annual Salary
San Jose, CA	$63,056
New York, NY	$57,708
San Francisco, CA	$56,602
New Haven, CT, area	$51,170
Middlesex, NJ, area	$50,457
Jersey City, NJ	$49,562
Newark, NJ	$48,781
Washington, DC, area	$48,430

Source: Bureau of Labor Statistics.

66. *Tourism Earnings*   The top five countries for tourism earnings in 2007 are shown in the table. Find the average of these figures.

Country	Receipts (in billions of dollars)
U.S.	96.7
Spain	57.6
France	54.3
Italy	42.7
China	37.2

Source: World Tourism Organization.

In the March 1973 issue of The Mathematics Teacher *there appeared an article by Laurence Sherzer, an eighth-grade mathematics teacher, that immortalized one of his students, Robert McKay. To find a number (not necessarily their average) between two positive rational numbers $\frac{a}{b}$ and $\frac{c}{d}$, McKay claimed, simply add the numerators and add the denominators.*

*For example, to find a rational number between $\frac{1}{3}$ and $\frac{1}{4}$, add $1 + 1 = 2$ to get the numerator and $3 + 4 = 7$ to get the denominator. Therefore, by **McKay's theorem,** $\frac{2}{7}$ is between $\frac{1}{3}$ and $\frac{1}{4}$. Sherzer provided a proof of this method in the article. In Exercises 67–74 on the next page, use McKay's theorem to find a rational number between the two given rational numbers.*

67. $\frac{5}{6}$ and $\frac{9}{13}$

68. $\frac{10}{11}$ and $\frac{13}{19}$

69. $\frac{4}{13}$ and $\frac{9}{16}$

70. $\frac{6}{11}$ and $\frac{13}{14}$

71. $\frac{7}{6}$ and $\frac{9}{8}$

72. $\frac{11}{5}$ and $\frac{12}{11}$

73. 2 and 3

74. 3 and 4

75. Apply McKay's theorem to any pair of consecutive integers, and make a conjecture about what always happens in this case.

76. Explain in your own words how to find the rational number that is one-fourth of the way between two different rational numbers.

Convert each rational number into either a repeating or a terminating decimal. Use a calculator if your instructor so allows.

77. $\frac{3}{4}$

78. $\frac{7}{8}$

79. $\frac{3}{16}$

80. $\frac{9}{32}$

81. $\frac{3}{11}$

82. $\frac{9}{11}$

83. $\frac{2}{7}$

84. $\frac{11}{15}$

Convert each terminating decimal into a quotient of integers. Write each in lowest terms.

85. 0.4

86. 0.9

87. 0.85

88. 0.105

89. 0.934

90. 0.7984

*Use the method of **Example 7** to decide whether each rational number would yield a repeating or a terminating decimal. (Hint: Write in lowest terms before trying to decide.)*

91. $\frac{8}{15}$

92. $\frac{8}{35}$

93. $\frac{13}{125}$

94. $\frac{3}{24}$

95. $\frac{22}{55}$

96. $\frac{24}{75}$

97. Follow through on all parts of this exercise in order.

(a) Find the decimal for $\frac{1}{3}$.

(b) Find the decimal for $\frac{2}{3}$.

(c) By adding the decimal expressions obtained in parts (a) and (b), obtain a decimal expression for $\frac{1}{3} + \frac{2}{3} = \frac{3}{3} = 1$.

(d) State your result. Read the margin note on terminating and repeating decimals in this section, which refers to this idea.

98. It is a fact that $\frac{1}{3} = 0.333\ldots$. Multiply both sides of this equation by 3. Does your answer bother you? See the margin note on terminating and repeating decimals in this section.

*Use the method of **Example 9** to write each rational number as a quotient of integers in lowest terms.*

99. (a) 0.8 **(b)** $0.7\overline{9}$ **100. (a)** 0.75 **(b)** $0.74\overline{9}$

101. (a) 0.66 **(b)** $0.65\overline{9}$

102. Based on your results in **Exercises 99–101,** predict the lowest terms form of the rational number $0.4\overline{9}$.

6.4 IRRATIONAL NUMBERS AND DECIMAL REPRESENTATION

Definition and Basic Concepts • Irrationality of $\sqrt{2}$ and Proof by Contradiction • Operations with Square Roots • The Irrational Numbers π, ϕ, and e

Definition and Basic Concepts

Every rational number has a decimal form that terminates or repeats, and every repeating or terminating decimal represents a rational number. However,

$$0.102001000200001000002\ldots$$

does not terminate and does not repeat. (It is true that there is a pattern in this decimal, but no single block of digits repeats indefinitely.)*

*In this section, we will assume that the digits of a number such as this continue indefinitely in the pattern established. The next few digits would be 000000100000002, and so on.

Tsu Ch'ung-chih (about 500 A.D.), the Chinese mathematician honored on the above stamp, investigated the digits of π. Aryabhata, his Indian contemporary, gave 3.1416 as the value.

Irrational Numbers

Irrational numbers = $\{x \mid x$ is a number represented by a nonrepeating, non-terminating decimal$\}$

As the name implies, an irrational number cannot be represented as a quotient of integers.

The decimal number mentioned at the bottom of the previous page is an irrational number. Other irrational numbers include $\sqrt{2}$, $\frac{1+\sqrt{5}}{2}$ (ϕ, from **Section 5.5**), π (the ratio of the circumference of a circle to its diameter), and e (a constant *approximately equal to* 2.71828). There are infinitely many irrational numbers.

Irrationality of $\sqrt{2}$ and Proof by Contradiction

Figure 12 illustrates how a point with coordinate $\sqrt{2}$ can be located on a number line.

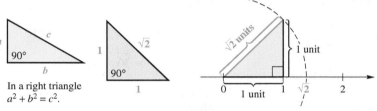

In a right triangle $a^2 + b^2 = c^2$.

Figure 12

The proof that $\sqrt{2}$ is irrational is a classic example of a **proof by contradiction.** We begin by assuming that $\sqrt{2}$ is rational, which leads to a contradiction, or absurdity. The method is also called **reductio ad absurdum** (Latin for "reduce to the absurd"). In order to understand the proof, we consider three preliminary facts:

1. When a rational number is written in lowest terms, the greatest common factor of the numerator and denominator is 1.

2. If an integer is even, then it has 2 as a factor and may be written in the form $2k$, where k is an integer.

3. If a perfect square is even, then its square root is even.

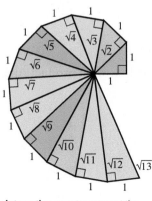

An interesting way to represent the lengths corresponding to $\sqrt{2}$, $\sqrt{3}$, $\sqrt{4}$, $\sqrt{5}$, and so on, is shown in the figure. Use the **Pythagorean theorem** to verify the lengths in the figure.

▮▮ **THEOREM**

Statement: $\sqrt{2}$ is an irrational number.

Proof: Assume that $\sqrt{2}$ is a rational number. Then by definition,

$$\sqrt{2} = \frac{p}{q}, \quad \text{for some integers } p \text{ and } q.$$

Furthermore, assume that $\frac{p}{q}$ is the form of $\sqrt{2}$ that is written in lowest terms, so the greatest common factor of p and q is 1.

$$2 = \frac{p^2}{q^2} \quad \text{Square both sides of the equation.}$$

$$2q^2 = p^2 \quad \text{Multiply by } q^2.$$

The last equation, $2q^2 = p^2$, indicates that 2 is a factor of p^2. So p^2 is even, and thus p is even. Since p is even, it may be written in the form $2k$, where k is an integer.

Now, substitute $2k$ for p in the last equation and simplify.

$$2q^2 = (2k)^2 \quad \text{Let } p = 2k.$$

$$2q^2 = 4k^2 \quad (2k)^2 = 2k \cdot 2k = 4k^2$$

$$q^2 = 2k^2 \quad \text{Divide by 2.}$$

Since q^2 has 2 as a factor, q^2 must be even, and thus q must be even. This leads to a contradiction: p and q cannot both be even because they would then have a common factor of 2. It was assumed that their greatest common factor is 1.

Therefore, since the original assumption that $\sqrt{2}$ is rational has led to a contradiction, it must follow that $\sqrt{2}$ is irrational. ▮▮▮

Operations with Square Roots

In everyday mathematical work, nearly all of our calculations deal with rational numbers, usually in decimal form. However, we must sometimes perform operations with irrational numbers.

$$\sqrt{2}, \quad \sqrt{3}, \quad \text{and} \quad \sqrt{13} \quad \text{Examples of square roots that are irrational}$$

$$\sqrt{4} = 2, \quad \sqrt{36} = 6, \quad \text{and} \quad \sqrt{100} = 10 \quad \text{Examples of square roots that are rational}$$

If n is a positive integer that is not the square of an integer, then $\sqrt{n}$ is an irrational number.

A calculator with a square root key can give approximations of square roots of numbers that are not perfect squares. To show that they are approximations, we use the $\approx$ symbol to indicate "is approximately equal to." Some such calculator approximations are as follows.

$$\sqrt{2} \approx 1.414213562, \quad \sqrt{6} \approx 2.449489743, \quad \text{and} \quad \sqrt{1949} \approx 44.14748011$$

Recall that $\sqrt{a}$, for $a \geq 0$, is the nonnegative number whose square is a. That is, $\left(\sqrt{a}\right)^2 = a$. We will now look at some simple operations with square roots.

Notice that

$$\sqrt{4} \cdot \sqrt{9} = 2 \cdot 3 = 6$$

and

$$\sqrt{4 \cdot 9} = \sqrt{36} = 6.$$

Thus, $\sqrt{4} \cdot \sqrt{9} = \sqrt{4 \cdot 9}$. This is a particular case of the following product rule.

Northern Exposure ran between 1990 and 1995 on the CBS network. In the episode "Nothing's Perfect" (10/12/92), the local disc jockey Chris Stevens (played by John Corbett) meets and develops a relationship with a mathematician (played by Wendel Meldrum) after accidentally running over her dog. Her area of research is **computation of the decimal digits of pi.** She mentions that a string of eight 8s appears in the decimal relatively early in the expansion. This string starts at position 46,663,520 counting from the first digit after the decimal point.

> **Product Rule for Square Roots**
>
> For nonnegative real numbers a and b, the following is true.
> $$\sqrt{a} \cdot \sqrt{b} = \sqrt{a \cdot b}$$

Just as every rational number $\frac{a}{b}$ can be written in *lowest terms* (by using the fundamental property of rational numbers), every square root radical has a *simplified form*.

> **Conditions Necessary for the Simplified Form of a Square Root Radical**
>
> A square root radical is in **simplified form** if the following three conditions are met.
>
> **1.** The number under the radical **(radicand)** has no factor (except 1) that is a perfect square.
> **2.** The radicand has no fractions.
> **3.** No denominator contains a radical.

▮▮ **EXAMPLE 1** Simplifying a Square Root Radical (Product Rule)

Simplify $\sqrt{27}$.

SOLUTION

Since 9 is a factor of 27 and 9 is a perfect square, $\sqrt{27}$ is not in simplified form. The first condition of simplified form is not met. We simplify as follows.

$$\sqrt{27} = \sqrt{9 \cdot 3}$$
$$= \sqrt{9} \cdot \sqrt{3} \quad \text{Use the product rule.}$$
Simplified form $\quad = 3\sqrt{3} \quad \sqrt{9} = 3 \text{ since } 3^2 = 9.$ ▮▮▮

Near the end of the 2008 movie *Harold & Kumar Escape From Guantanamo Bay,* Kumar (Kal Penn), an excellent **mathematics student,** is involved in an incident at the wedding of his former girlfriend Vanessa (Danneel Harris), greatly embarrassing her. When she confronts him, he asks if he could do something to embarrass himself to make her feel better. She says that nothing could do so, but he goes on to recite a "nerdy" yet beautiful poem dealing with the square root of three, written by the late David Feinberg. The text of the poem can be found on the internet by searching "David Feinberg Square Root of 3." There are references to irrational numbers, integers, an approximation for the square root of 3, and the product rule for square root radicals.

Expressions such as $\sqrt{27}$ and $3\sqrt{3}$ represent the *exact value* of the square root of 27. If we use the square root key of a calculator, we find

$$\sqrt{27} \approx 5.196152423.$$

If we find $\sqrt{3}$ and then multiply the result by 3, we get

$$3\sqrt{3} \approx 3(1.732050808) \approx 5.196152423.$$

Notice that these approximations are the same, as we would expect. The work in **Example 1** provides the mathematical justification that they are indeed equal.

> **Quotient Rule for Square Roots**
>
> For nonnegative real numbers a and positive real numbers b, the following is true.
>
> $$\frac{\sqrt{a}}{\sqrt{b}} = \sqrt{\frac{a}{b}}$$

▮▮ **EXAMPLE 2** Simplifying Square Root Radicals (Quotient Rule)

Simplify each radical.

(a) $\sqrt{\dfrac{25}{9}}$ **(b)** $\sqrt{\dfrac{3}{4}}$ **(c)** $\sqrt{\dfrac{1}{2}}$

SOLUTION

(a) Because the radicand contains a fraction, the radical expression is not simplified.

$$\sqrt{\frac{25}{9}} = \frac{\sqrt{25}}{\sqrt{9}} = \frac{5}{3} \quad \text{Use the quotient rule.}$$

In the second season of the original *Star Trek* series, the episode "Wolf in the Fold" told the story of an alien entity that had taken over the computer of the starship *Enterprise*. To drive the entity out of the computer, Captain Kirk suggested the following to Mr. Spock:

KIRK: Spock, don't you have a compulsory scan unit built into the computer banks?
SPOCK: Yes we do, Captain, but with the entity in control . . . .
KIRK: Well aren't there certain mathematical problems which simply cannot be solved?
SPOCK: Indeed. If we can focus the attention of the computer on one of them . . . .
KIRK: That ought to do it.

Later, they are able to do just that:

SPOCK: Ready?
KIRK: Implement.
SPOCK: Computer, this is a class "A" compulsory directive. Compute to the last digit the value of pi.
COMPUTER: No, no, no, no, no, ...
SPOCK (TO KIRK): As we know, the value of pi is a transcendental figure without resolution. The computer banks will work on this problem to the exclusion of all else until we order it to stop.
KIRK: Yes, that should keep that thing busy for a while.

The alien could not comply, because pi (π) is an irrational number, and its decimal representation has no last digit. As a result, ingenuity and mathematics saved the *Enterprise*.

(b) $\sqrt{\dfrac{3}{4}} = \dfrac{\sqrt{3}}{\sqrt{4}} = \dfrac{\sqrt{3}}{2}$ Use the quotient rule.

(c) $\sqrt{\dfrac{1}{2}} = \dfrac{\sqrt{1}}{\sqrt{2}} = \dfrac{1}{\sqrt{2}}$ This is not yet simplified.

This expression is not simplified, since condition 3 of simplified form is not met. To give an equivalent expression with no radical in the denominator, we use a procedure called **rationalizing the denominator.** Multiply $\frac{1}{\sqrt{2}}$ by $\frac{\sqrt{2}}{\sqrt{2}}$, which is a form of 1, the identity element for multiplication.

$$\frac{1}{\sqrt{2}} = \frac{1}{\sqrt{2}} \cdot \frac{\sqrt{2}}{\sqrt{2}} = \frac{\sqrt{2}}{2} \quad \sqrt{2} \cdot \sqrt{2} = 2$$

This is the simplified form of $\sqrt{\frac{1}{2}}$. ▌▌▌

Is $\sqrt{4} + \sqrt{9} = \sqrt{4 + 9}$ a true statement? The answer is *no*, since

$$\sqrt{4} + \sqrt{9} = 2 + 3 = 5, \quad \text{while} \quad \sqrt{4 + 9} = \sqrt{13}, \quad \text{and} \quad 5 \neq \sqrt{13}.$$

Square root radicals may be combined, however, if they have the same radicand. Such radicals are **like radicals.** We add (and subtract) like radicals using the distributive property.

▌▌ **EXAMPLE 3** Adding and Subtracting Square Root Radicals

Add or subtract as indicated.

(a) $3\sqrt{6} + 4\sqrt{6}$ **(b)** $\sqrt{18} - \sqrt{32}$

SOLUTION

(a) Since both terms contain $\sqrt{6}$, they are like radicals, and may be combined.

$$3\sqrt{6} + 4\sqrt{6} = (3 + 4)\sqrt{6} \quad \text{Distributive property}$$
$$= 7\sqrt{6} \quad \text{Add.}$$

(b) If we simplify $\sqrt{18}$ and $\sqrt{32}$, then this operation can be performed.

$$\sqrt{18} - \sqrt{32} = \sqrt{9 \cdot 2} - \sqrt{16 \cdot 2} \quad \text{Factor so that perfect squares are in the radicands.}$$
$$= \sqrt{9} \cdot \sqrt{2} - \sqrt{16} \cdot \sqrt{2} \quad \text{Product rule}$$
$$= 3\sqrt{2} - 4\sqrt{2} \quad \text{Take square roots.}$$
$$= (3 - 4)\sqrt{2} \quad \text{Distributive property}$$
$$= -1\sqrt{2} \quad \text{Subtract.}$$
$$= -\sqrt{2} \quad -1 \cdot a = -a$$ ▌▌▌

From **Example 3,** we see that like radicals may be added or subtracted by adding or subtracting their coefficients (the numbers by which they are multiplied) and keeping the same radical. Observe these examples.

$$9\sqrt{7} + 8\sqrt{7} = 17\sqrt{7} \quad (\text{since } 9 + 8 = 17)$$
$$4\sqrt{3} - 12\sqrt{3} = -8\sqrt{3} \quad (\text{since } 4 - 12 = -8)$$

In the statements of the product and quotient rules for square roots, the radicands could not be negative. While $-\sqrt{2}$ is a real number, for example, $\sqrt{-2}$ is not. There is no real number whose square is -2. The same may be said for any negative radicand. In order to handle this situation, mathematicians have extended our number system to include *complex numbers,* discussed in the **Extension** at the end of this chapter.

The Irrational Numbers π, ϕ, and e

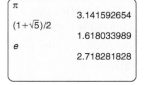

π	3.141592654
$(1+\sqrt{5})/2$	
	1.618033989
e	
	2.718281828

Figure 13

Figure 13 shows approximations for three of the most interesting and important irrational numbers in mathematics. The first of these, π, represents the ratio of the circumference of a circle to its diameter. The second, ϕ, is the Golden Ratio, covered in detail in **Section 5.5.** Its exact value is $\dfrac{1 + \sqrt{5}}{2}$. The third is e, a fundamental number in our universe. It is the base of the *natural exponential* and *natural logarithmic* functions, as seen in **Section 8.6.** The letter e was chosen to honor Leonhard Euler, who published extensive research on the number in 1746.

Pi (π)

$$\pi \approx 3.14159265358979323846264643383279$$

The computation of the digits of π has fascinated mathematicians since ancient times. Archimedes was the first to explore it extensively, and as of October 20, 2005, its value had been computed to 1,241,100,000,000 decimal digits. Yasumasa Kanada of the University of Tokyo and the brothers Gregory and David Chudnovsky are among today's foremost pi researchers. The book *A History of π* by Petr Beckmann is a classic and now in its third edition. Numerous Web sites, including the following, are devoted to the history and methods of computation of pi.

> www.joyofpi.com/
> www.math.utah.edu/~alfeld/Archimedes/Archimedes.html
> www.super-computing.org/
> www.pbs.org/wgbh/nova/sciencenow/3210/04.html

One of the methods of computing pi involves the topic of *infinite series*.

This poem, dedicated to **Archimedes** ("the immortal Syracusan"), allows us to learn the first 31 digits of the decimal representation of π. By replacing each word with the number of letters it contains, with a decimal point following the initial 3, the decimal is found. The poem was written by A. C. Orr, and appeared in the *Literary Digest* in 1906.

Now I, even I, would celebrate
In rhymes unapt, the great
Immortal Syracusan, rivaled nevermore,
Who in his wondrous lore
Passed on before,
Left men his guidance
How to circles mensurate.

▮▮ **EXAMPLE 4**   Computing the Digits of Pi Using an Infinite Series

It is shown in higher mathematics that the *infinite series*

$$1 - \frac{1}{3} + \frac{1}{5} - \frac{1}{7} + \frac{1}{9} + \dots \text{ ``converges'' to } \frac{\pi}{4}.$$

That is, as more and more terms are considered, its value becomes closer and closer to $\frac{\pi}{4}$. With a calculator, approximate the value of pi using twenty-one terms of this series.

SOLUTION

Figure 14 on the next page shows the necessary calculation on the TI-83/84 Plus calculator. The sum of the first twenty-one terms is multiplied by 4, to obtain the approximation 3.189184782. (This series converges slowly. While this is only correct to the first decimal place, better approximations are obtained using more terms of the series.)

In 1767 **J. H. Lambert** proved that π is irrational (and thus its decimal will never terminate and never repeat). Nevertheless, the 1897 Indiana state legislature considered a bill that would have *legislated* the value of π. In one part of the bill, the value was stated to be 4, and in another part, 3.2. Amazingly, the bill passed the House, but the Senate postponed action on the bill indefinitely.

Figure 14 ▌▌▌

A rectangle that satisfies the condition that the ratio of its length to its width is equal to the ratio of the sum of its length and width to its length is called a **Golden Rectangle.** This ratio is called the **Golden Ratio.** Its exact value is the irrational number $\frac{1 + \sqrt{5}}{2}$. It is represented by the Greek letter ϕ (phi).

Phi (ϕ)

$$\phi = \frac{1 + \sqrt{5}}{2} \approx 1.61803398874989484820458683436 5$$

Two readily accessible books on phi are *The Divine Proportion, A Study in Mathematical Beauty* by H. E. Huntley, and the more recent *The Golden Ratio* by Mario Livio. Some popular Web sites devoted to this irrational number are the following.

www.mcs.surrey.ac.uk/Personal/R.Knott/Fibonacci/

www.goldennumber.net/

www.mathforum.org/dr.math/faq/faq.golden.ratio.html

www.geom.uiuc.edu/~demo5337/s97b/art.htm

▌▌ **EXAMPLE 5** Computing the Digits of Phi Using the Fibonacci Sequence

The first twelve terms of the Fibonacci sequence are

$$1, 1, 2, 3, 5, 8, 13, 21, 34, 55, 89, 144.$$

Each term after the first two terms is obtained by adding the two previous terms. Thus, the thirteenth term is $89 + 144 = 233$. As one goes farther and farther out in the sequence, the ratio of a term to its predecessor gets closer and closer to ϕ. How far out must one go in order to approximate ϕ so that the first five decimal places agree?

SOLUTION

After 144, the next three Fibonacci numbers are 233, 377, and 610. **Figure 15** shows that $\frac{610}{377} \approx 1.618037135$, which agrees with ϕ to the fifth decimal place. ▌▌▌

The irrational number e is a fundamental constant in mathematics. In **Section 8.6,** e is the base of exponential and logarithmic functions.

233/144	
	1.618055556
377/233	
	1.618025751
610/377	
	1.618037135

Figure 15

e

$$e \approx 2.71828182845904523536028747135 3$$

The nature of *e* has made it less understood by the layman than π (or even ϕ, for that matter). The 1994 book *e: The Story of a Number* by Eli Maor has attempted to rectify this situation. The following Web sites also give information on *e*.

> www.mathforum.org/dr.math/faq/faq.e.html
>
> www-groups.dcs.st-and.ac.uk/~history/HistTopics/e.html
>
> http://antwrp.gsfc.nasa.gov/htmltest/gifcity/e.1mil
>
> www.math.toronto.edu/mathnet/answers/ereal.html

Example 6 illustrates another infinite series, this one converging to *e*.

▋▋ EXAMPLE 6 Computing the Digits of *e* Using an Infinite Series

The infinite series

$$2 + \frac{1}{1 \cdot 2} + \frac{1}{1 \cdot 2 \cdot 3} + \frac{1}{1 \cdot 2 \cdot 3 \cdot 4} + \ldots \text{ converges to } e.$$

Use a calculator to approximate *e* using the first seven terms of this series.

SOLUTION

Figure 16 shows the sum of the first seven terms. (The denominators have all been multiplied out.) The sum is 2.718253968, which agrees with *e* to four decimal places. This series converges more rapidly than the one for π in **Example 4**.   ▮▮▮

Scrolled Equation

2+1/2+1/6+1/24+1/120+1/720 ▸
◂ +1/5040

2.718253968

Figure 16

6.4 EXERCISES

Identify each number as rational *or* irrational.

1. $\dfrac{4}{9}$ 2. $\dfrac{7}{8}$ 3. $\sqrt{10}$

4. $\sqrt{14}$ 5. 1.618   6. 2.718

7. $0.\overline{41}$ 8. $0.\overline{32}$ 9. π

10. *e*   11. 3.14159   12. $\dfrac{22}{7}$

13. 0.878778777877778 . . .   14. $\dfrac{1 + \sqrt{5}}{2}$

15. **(a)** Find the sum.

> 0.272772777277772 . . .
>
> +0.616116111611116 . . .

(b) Based on the result of part (a), we can conclude that the sum of two _____ numbers may be a(n) _____ number.

16. **(a)** Find the sum.

> 0.010110111011110 . . .
>
> +0.252552555255552 . . .

(b) Based on the result of part (a), we can conclude that the sum of two _____ numbers may be a(n) _____ number.

Use a calculator to find a rational decimal approximation for each irrational number. Give as many places as your calculator shows.

17. $\sqrt{39}$ 18. $\sqrt{44}$ 19. $\sqrt{15.1}$ 20. $\sqrt{33.6}$

21. $\sqrt{884}$ 22. $\sqrt{643}$ 23. $\sqrt{\dfrac{9}{8}}$ 24. $\sqrt{\dfrac{6}{5}}$

*Use the methods of **Examples 1 and 2** to simplify each expression. Then, use a calculator to approximate both the given expression and the simplified expression. (Both should be the same.)*

25. $\sqrt{50}$ 26. $\sqrt{32}$

27. $\sqrt{75}$ 28. $\sqrt{150}$

29. $\sqrt{288}$ 30. $\sqrt{200}$

31. $\dfrac{5}{\sqrt{6}}$ 32. $\dfrac{3}{\sqrt{2}}$

33. $\sqrt{\dfrac{7}{4}}$ 34. $\sqrt{\dfrac{8}{9}}$

35. $\sqrt{\dfrac{7}{3}}$ 36. $\sqrt{\dfrac{14}{5}}$

*Use the method of **Example 3** to perform the indicated operations.*

37. $\sqrt{17} + 2\sqrt{17}$ **38.** $3\sqrt{19} + \sqrt{19}$

39. $5\sqrt{7} - \sqrt{7}$ **40.** $3\sqrt{27} - \sqrt{27}$

41. $3\sqrt{18} + \sqrt{2}$ **42.** $2\sqrt{48} - \sqrt{3}$

43. $-\sqrt{12} + \sqrt{75}$ **44.** $2\sqrt{27} - \sqrt{300}$

Exercises 45–58 deal with π, ϕ, or e. Use a calculator or computer as necessary.

45. Move one matchstick to make the equation approximately true. (*Source:* www.joyofpi.com)

46. Find the square root of $\frac{2143}{22}$ using a calculator. Then find the square root of that result. Compare your result to the decimal given for π in the margin note. What do you notice?

47. Use a calculator to find the first eight digits in the decimal for $\frac{355}{113}$. Compare the result to the decimal for π given in the text. What do you notice?

48. You may have seen the statements "use $\frac{22}{7}$ for π" and "use 3.14 for π." Since $\frac{22}{7}$ is the quotient of two integers, and 3.14 is a terminating decimal, do these statements suggest that π is rational?

49. In the Bible (I Kings 7:23), a verse describes a circular pool at King Solomon's temple, about 1000 B.C. The pool is said to be ten cubits across, "and a line of 30 cubits did compass it round about." What value of π does this imply?

50. The ancient Egyptians used a method for finding the area of a circle that is equivalent to a value of 3.1605 for π. Write this decimal as a mixed number.

51. The computation of π has fascinated mathematicians and laymen for centuries. In the nineteenth century, the British mathematician William Shanks spent many years of his life calculating π to 707 decimal places. It turned out that only the first 527 were correct. Use an Internet search to find the 528th decimal digit of π (following the whole number part 3.).

52. One of the reasons for computing so many digits of π is to determine how often each digit appears and to identify any interesting patterns among the digits. Gregory and David Chudnovsky have spent a great deal of time looking for patterns in the digits. For example, six 9s in a row appear relatively early in the decimal, within the first 800 decimal places. Use an Internet search to find the positions of these six 9s in a row.

53. The expression $\frac{2 \cdot 2 \cdot 4 \cdot 4 \cdot 6 \cdot 6 \cdot 8 \cdots}{1 \cdot 3 \cdot 3 \cdot 5 \cdot 5 \cdot 7 \cdot 7 \cdots}$ converges to $\frac{\pi}{2}$. Use a calculator to evaluate only the digits of the expression as shown here, and then multiply by 2. What value for an approximation for π does this give (to one decimal place)?

54. A **mnemonic device** is a scheme whereby one is able to recall facts by memorizing something completely unrelated to the facts. One way of learning the first few digits of the decimal for π is to memorize a sentence (or several sentences) and count the letters in each word of the sentence. For example, "See, I know a digit," will give the first 5 digits of π: "See" has 3 letters, "I" has 1 letter, "know" has 4 letters, "a" has 1 letter, and "digit" has 5 letters. So the first five digits are 3.1415.

Verify that the following mnemonic devices work.

(a) "May I have a large container of coffee?"

(b) "See, I have a rhyme assisting my feeble brain, its tasks ofttimes resisting."

(c) "How I want a drink, alcoholic of course, after the heavy lectures involving quantum mechanics."

55. Use a calculator to find the decimal approximations for $\phi = \frac{1 + \sqrt{5}}{2}$ and its **conjugate,** $\frac{1 - \sqrt{5}}{2}$. Comment on the similarities and differences in the two decimals.

56. In some literature, the Golden Ratio is defined to be the reciprocal of $\frac{1 + \sqrt{5}}{2}$, which is $\frac{2}{1 + \sqrt{5}}$. Use a calculator to find a decimal approximation for $\frac{2}{1 + \sqrt{5}}$ and compare it to ϕ as defined in this text. What do you observe?

57. An approximation for e is 2.718281828. A student noticed that there seems to be a repetition of four digits in this number (1, 8, 2, 8) and concluded that e is rational, because repeating decimals represent rational numbers. Was the student correct? Why or why not?

58. Use a calculator with an exponential key to find values for the following: $(1.1)^{10}$, $(1.01)^{100}$, $(1.001)^{1000}$, $(1.0001)^{10,000}$, and $(1.00001)^{100,000}$. Compare your results to the approximation given for e in this section. What do you find?

Solve each problem. Use a calculator as necessary, and give approximations to the nearest tenth unless specified otherwise.

59. *Period of a Pendulum* The period of a pendulum in seconds depends on its length, *L,* in feet, and is given by the formula

$$P = 2\pi\sqrt{\frac{L}{32}}.$$

If a pendulum is 5.1 feet long, what is its period? Use 3.14 for π.

60. Radius of an Aluminum Can The radius of the circular top or bottom of an aluminum can with surface area S and height h is given by

$$r = \frac{-h + \sqrt{h^2 + 0.64S}}{2}.$$

What radius should be used to make a can with height 12 inches and surface area 400 square inches?

61. Distance to the Horizon Jack Adrian, a friend of one of the authors of this text, has a beautiful 14th floor condo, with a stunning view, in downtown Chicago. The floor is 150 feet above the ground. Knowing that this author is a mathematics teacher, Jack emailed the author and told him that he recalled once having studied a formula for calculating the distance to the horizon, but could not remember it. He wanted to know how far he can see from his condo. The author responded:

> *To find the distance to the horizon in miles, take the square root of the height of your view and multiply that result by 1.224. That will give you the number of miles to the horizon.*

Assuming Jack's eyes are 6 feet above his floor, the total height from the ground is $150 + 6 = 156$ feet. To the nearest tenth of a mile, how far can he see to the horizon?

62. Electronics Formula The formula $I = \sqrt{\dfrac{2P}{L}}$ relates the coefficient of self-induction L (in henrys), the energy P stored in an electronic circuit (in joules), and the current I (in amps). Find the value of I if $P = 120$ joules and $L = 80$ henrys.

63. Area of the Bermuda Triangle **Heron's formula** gives a method of finding the area of a triangle if the lengths of its sides are known. Suppose that a, b, and c are the lengths of the sides. Let s denote one-half of the perimeter of the triangle (called the **semiperimeter**); that is,

$$s = \frac{1}{2}(a + b + c).$$

Then the area A of the triangle is given by

$$A = \sqrt{s(s - a)(s - b)(s - c)}.$$

Find the area of the Bermuda Triangle, if the "sides" of this triangle measure approximately 850 miles, 925 miles, and 1300 miles. Give your answer to the nearest thousand square miles.

64. Area Enclosed by the Vietnam Veterans' Memorial The Vietnam Veterans' Memorial in Washington, D.C., is in the shape of an unenclosed isosceles triangle with equal sides of length 246.75 feet. If the triangle were enclosed, the third side would have length 438.14 feet. Use Heron's formula from the previous exercise to find the area of this enclosure to the nearest hundred square feet. (*Source:* Information pamphlet obtained at the Vietnam Veterans' Memorial.)

65. Perfect Triangles A **perfect triangle** is a triangle whose sides have whole number lengths and whose area is numerically equal to its perimeter. Use Heron's formula to show that the triangle with sides of length 9, 10, and 17 is perfect.

66. Heron Triangles A **Heron triangle** is a triangle having integer sides and area. Use Heron's formula to show that each of the following is a Heron triangle.

(a) $a = 11, b = 13, c = 20$

(b) $a = 13, b = 14, c = 15$

(c) $a = 7, b = 15, c = 20$

67. Diagonal of a Box The length of the diagonal of a box is given by

$$D = \sqrt{L^2 + W^2 + H^2},$$

where L, W, and H are the length, the width, and the height of the box. Find the length of the diagonal, D, of a box that is 4 feet long, 3 feet wide, and 2 feet high.

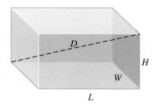

68. Rate of Return on an Investment If an investment of P dollars grows to A dollars in two years, the annual rate of return on the investment is given by

$$r = \frac{\sqrt{A} - \sqrt{P}}{\sqrt{P}}.$$

First rationalize the denominator and then find the annual rate of return (as a decimal) if $50,000 increases to $58,320.

69. Accident Reconstruction Police sometimes use the following procedure to estimate the speed at which a car was traveling at the time of an accident. A police officer drives the car involved in the accident under conditions similar to those during which the accident took place and then skids to a stop. If the car is driven at 30 miles per hour, then the speed at the time of the accident is given by

$$s = 30\sqrt{\frac{a}{p}}.$$

Here, a is the length of the skid marks left at the time of the accident and p is the length of the skid marks in the police test. Find s for the following values of a and p.

(a) $a = 862$ feet; $p = 156$ feet

(b) $a = 382$ feet; $p = 96$ feet

(c) $a = 84$ feet; $p = 26$ feet

70. **Law of Tensions** In the study of sound, one version of the law of tensions is

$$f_1 = f_2 \sqrt{\frac{F_1}{F_2}}.$$

Find f_1 to the nearest unit if $F_1 = 300$, $F_2 = 60$, and $f_2 = 260$.

*The concept of square (second) root can be extended to **cube (third) root, fourth root,** and so on. If $n \geq 2$ and a is a nonnegative number, $\sqrt[n]{a}$ represents the nonnegative number whose nth power is a. For example,*

$$\sqrt[3]{8} = 2 \quad because \quad 2^3 = 8,$$
$$\sqrt[3]{1000} = 10 \quad because \quad 10^3 = 1000,$$
$$\sqrt[4]{81} = 3 \quad because \quad 3^4 = 81, \quad and\ so\ on.$$

Find each root.

71. $\sqrt[3]{64}$ 72. $\sqrt[3]{125}$

73. $\sqrt[3]{343}$ 74. $\sqrt[3]{729}$

75. $\sqrt[3]{216}$ 76. $\sqrt[3]{512}$

77. $\sqrt[4]{1}$ 78. $\sqrt[4]{16}$

79. $\sqrt[4]{256}$ 80. $\sqrt[4]{625}$

81. $\sqrt[4]{4096}$ 82. $\sqrt[4]{2401}$

Use a calculator to approximate each root. Give as many places as your calculator shows. (Hint: To find the fourth root, find the square root of the square root.)

83. $\sqrt[3]{43}$ 84. $\sqrt[3]{87}$

85. $\sqrt[3]{198}$ 86. $\sqrt[4]{2107}$

87. $\sqrt[4]{10,265.2}$ 88. $\sqrt[4]{863.5}$

89. $\sqrt[4]{968.1}$ 90. $\sqrt[4]{12,966.4}$

6.5 APPLICATIONS OF DECIMALS AND PERCENTS

Operations with Decimals • Rounding Decimals • Percent • Applications

Operations with Decimals

Because calculators have, for the most part, replaced paper-and-pencil methods for operations with decimals and percent, we will only briefly mention these latter methods. *We strongly suggest that the work in this section be done with a calculator at hand.*

Addition and Subtraction of Decimals

To add or subtract decimal numbers, line up the decimal points in a column and perform the operation.

▮▮ **EXAMPLE 1** Adding and Subtracting Decimal Numbers

Find each of the following.

(a) $0.46 + 3.9 + 12.58$ (b) $12.1 - 8.723$

SOLUTION

(a)
```
   0.46      Line up decimal points.
   3.90      Attach a zero as a placeholder.
 +12.58
 ─────
  16.94    ← Sum
```

(b)
```
  12.100     Attach zeros.
  −8.723
  ─────
   3.377   ← Difference
```

```
.46+3.9+12.58
              16.94
12.1−8.723
               3.377
```

This screen supports the results in **Example 1.**

▮▮▮

Recall that when two numbers are multiplied, the numbers are called **factors** and the answer is called the **product.** When two numbers are divided, the number being divided is called the **dividend,** the number doing the dividing is called the **divisor,** and the answer is called the **quotient.**

Multiplication and Division of Decimals

Multiplication   To multiply decimals, multiply in the same manner as integers are multiplied. The number of decimal places to the right of the decimal point in the product is the *sum* of the numbers of places to the right of the decimal points in the factors.

Division   To divide decimals, move the decimal point to the right the same number of places in the divisor and the dividend so as to obtain a whole number in the divisor. Divide in the same manner as integers are divided. The number of decimal places to the right of the decimal point in the quotient is the same as the number of places to the right in the dividend.

Here the TI-83/84 Plus is set to round the answer to two decimal places.

▌▌ EXAMPLE 2   Multiplying and Dividing Decimal Numbers

Find each of the following.

(a) 4.613×2.52 **(b)** $65.175 \div 8.25$

SOLUTION

(a)
$$
\begin{array}{r}
4.613 \quad \leftarrow \text{3 decimal places} \\
\times \quad 2.52 \quad \leftarrow \text{2 decimal places} \\
\hline
9226 \\
23065 \\
9226 \\
\hline
11.62476 \quad \leftarrow \text{3 + 2 = 5 decimal places}
\end{array}
$$

(b) $8.25\overline{)65.175} \rightarrow$
$$
\begin{array}{r}
7.9 \\
825\overline{)6517.5} \\
5775 \\
\hline
7425 \\
7425 \\
\hline
0
\end{array}
$$

Bring the decimal point straight up in the answer.

▌▌▌

Rounding Decimals

▌▌ EXAMPLE 3   Rounding a Decimal Number

Round 3.917 to the nearest hundredth.

SOLUTION

The hundredths place in 3.917 contains the digit 1.

3.917
↑ Hundredths place

To round this decimal, locate 3.91 and 3.92 on a number line as in **Figure 17**.

Figure 17

The calculator rounds 3.917 to the nearest hundredth.

The distance from 3.91 to 3.92 is divided into ten equal parts. The seventh of these ten parts locates the number 3.917. As the number line shows, 3.917 is closer to 3.92 than it is to 3.91, so 3.917 rounded to the nearest hundredth is 3.92.   ▌▌▌

3.915   3.92

The calculator rounds 3.915 *up* to 3.92.

If the number line method of **Example 3** were used to round 3.915 to the nearest hundredth, a problem would develop—the number 3.915 is exactly halfway between 3.91 and 3.92. An arbitrary decision is then made to round *up*: 3.915 rounded to the nearest hundredth is 3.92. (Some disciplines have guidelines so that in certain cases, a *downward* roundoff is made. We will not investigate these.)

Rules for Rounding Decimals

Step 1 Locate the **place** to which the number is being rounded.

Step 2 Look at the next **digit to the right** of the place to which the number is being rounded.

Step 3A If this digit is **less than 5,** drop all digits to the right of the place to which the number is being rounded. Do *not change* the digit in the place to which the number is being rounded.

Step 3B If this digit is **5 or greater,** drop all digits to the right of the place to which the number is being rounded. *Add one* to the digit in the place to which the number is being rounded.

▌▌ **EXAMPLE 4** Rounding a Decimal Number

Round 14.39656 to the nearest thousandth.

SOLUTION

Step 1 Use an arrow to locate the place to which the number is being rounded.

$$14.39656$$

Thousandths place

Step 2 Check to see if the first digit to the right of the arrow is 5 or greater.

14.396 ⑤ 6   Digit to the right of the arrow is 5.

Step 3 Since the digit to the right of the arrow is 5 or greater, increase by 1 the digit to which the arrow is pointing. Drop all digits to the right of the arrow.

14.39656   Drop.

14.397   Increase by 1.

14.39656
        14.397

With the calculator set to round to three decimal places, the result of **Example 4** is supported.

Finally, 14.39656 rounded to the nearest thousandth is 14.397.   ▌▌▌

Percent

One of the main applications of decimals comes from problems involving percents. The word **percent** means **"per hundred."** The symbol % represents "percent."

Percent

$$1\% = \frac{1}{100} = 0.01$$

In *The Producers*, Leo Bloom (Gene Wilder) and Max Bialystock (Zero Mostel) scheme to make a fortune by overfinancing what they think will be a Broadway flop. After enumerating the **percent** of profits all of Max's little old ladies have been offered in the production, reality sets in.

MAX: Leo, how much percentage of a play can there be altogether?

LEO: Max, you can only sell 100% of anything.

MAX: And how much for *Springtime for Hitler* have we sold?

LEO: 25,000%.

MAX (reaching for Leo's blue security blanket): 25,000% . . . . Give me that blue thing.

In *Willy Wonka and the Chocolate Factory*, upon preparing a mixture in his laboratory, Wilder delivers the following impossible **percent** analysis as he drinks his latest concoction.

WILLY WONKA: Invention, my dear friends, is 93% perspiration, 6% electricity, 4% evaporation, and 2% butterscotch ripple.

FEMALE VOICE: That's 105%.

MALE VOICE: Any good?

WILLY WONKA: Yes!

▮▮ **EXAMPLE 5** Converting Percents to Decimals

Convert each percent to a decimal.

(a) 98%   **(b)** 3.4%   **(c)** 0.2%   **(d)** 150%

SOLUTION

(a) $98\% = 98(1\%) = 98(0.01) = 0.98$

(b) $3.4\% = 3.4(1\%) = 3.4(0.01) = 0.034$

(c) $0.2\% = 0.2(1\%) = 0.2(0.01) = 0.002$

(d) $150\% = 150(1\%) = 150(0.01) = 1.5$ ▮▮▮

▮▮ **EXAMPLE 6** Converting Decimals to Percents

Convert each decimal to a percent.

(a) 0.13   **(b)** 0.532   **(c)** 2.3   **(d)** 0.07

SOLUTION

(a) $0.13 = 13(0.01) = 13(1\%) = 13\%$

(b) $0.532 = 53.2(0.01) = 53.2(1\%) = 53.2\%$

(c) $2.3 = 230(0.01) = 230(1\%) = 230\%$

(d) $0.07 = 7(0.01) = 7(1\%) = 7\%$ ▮▮▮

Converting between Decimals and Percents

To convert a percent to a decimal, drop the percent symbol (%) and move the decimal point two places to the left, inserting zeros as placeholders if necessary.

To convert a decimal to a percent, move the decimal point two places to the right, inserting zeros as placeholders if necessary, and attach the percent symbol (%).

▮▮ **EXAMPLE 7** Converting Fractions to Percents

Convert each fraction to a percent.

(a) $\dfrac{3}{5}$ **(b)** $\dfrac{14}{25}$

SOLUTION

(a) First write $\frac{3}{5}$ as a decimal. Dividing 3 by 5 gives $\frac{3}{5} = 0.6 = 60\%$.

(b) $\dfrac{14}{25} = \dfrac{14 \cdot 4}{25 \cdot 4} = \dfrac{56}{100} = 0.56 = 56\%$ ▮▮▮

Converting a Fraction to a Percent

To convert a fraction to a percent, convert the fraction to a decimal, and then convert the decimal to a percent.

The percent symbol, %, probably evolved from a symbol introduced in an Italian manuscript of 1425. Instead of "per 100," "P 100," or "P cento," which were common at that time, the author used "Pͬ." By about 1650 the ͬ had become $\frac{0}{0}$, so "per $\frac{0}{0}$" was often used. Finally the "per" was dropped, leaving $\frac{0}{0}$ or %.

Source: Historical Topics for the Mathematics Classroom, the Thirty-first Yearbook of the National Council of Teachers of Mathematics, 1969.

In the following examples involving percents, three methods are shown. The second method in each case involves using cross-products. The third method involves the percent key of a basic calculator. (Keystrokes may vary among models.)

▮▮ **EXAMPLE 8** Finding a Percent of a Number

Find 18% of 250.

SOLUTION

Method 1 The key word "of" translates as "times."

$$(18\%)(250) = (0.18)(250) = 45$$

Method 2 Think "18 is to 100 as what (x) is to 250?" This translates as follows.

$$\frac{18}{100} = \frac{x}{250}$$

$$100x = 18 \cdot 250 \qquad \frac{a}{b} = \frac{c}{d} \text{ if and only if } ad = bc.$$

$$x = \frac{18 \cdot 250}{100} \qquad \text{Divide by 100.}$$

$$x = 45 \qquad \text{Simplify.}$$

Method 3 Use the percent key on a calculator with the following keystrokes.

With any of these methods, we find that 18% of 250 is 45. ▮▮▮

▮▮ **EXAMPLE 9** Finding What Percent One Number Is of Another

What percent of 500 is 75?

SOLUTION

Method 1 Let the phrase "what percent" be represented by $x \cdot 1\%$ or $0.01x$. Again the word "of" translates as "times," while "is" translates as "equals."

$$0.01x \cdot 500 = 75$$

$$5x = 75 \qquad \text{Multiply on the left side.}$$

$$x = 15 \qquad \text{Divide by 5.}$$

Method 2 Think "What (x) is to 100 as 75 is to 500?"

$$\frac{x}{100} = \frac{75}{500}$$

$$500x = 7500 \qquad \text{Cross-products}$$

$$x = 15 \qquad \text{Divide by 500.}$$

Method 3 Use the following keystrokes on a calculator.

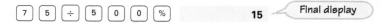

In each case, 15 is the percent, so we conclude that 75 is 15% of 500. ▮▮▮

▮▮ **EXAMPLE 10** Finding a Number of Which a Given Number Is a Given Percent

38 is 5% of what number?

SOLUTION

Method 1

$$38 = 0.05x$$

$$x = \frac{38}{0.05} \quad \text{Divide by 0.05.}$$

$$x = 760 \quad \text{Simplify.}$$

Method 2 Think "38 is to what number (x) as 5 is to 100?"

$$\frac{38}{x} = \frac{5}{100}$$

$$5x = 3800 \quad \text{Cross-products}$$

$$x = 760 \quad \text{Divide by 5.}$$

Method 3 Use the following keystrokes on a calculator.

⟨3⟩ ⟨8⟩ ⟨÷⟩ ⟨5⟩ ⟨%⟩　　　760 ⟵ Final display

Each method shows us that 38 is 5% of 760. ▮▮▮

There are various shortcuts that can be used to work with percents. Suppose that you need to compute 20% of 50. Here are two such shortcuts.

1. You think "20% means $\frac{1}{5}$, and to find $\frac{1}{5}$ of something I divide by 5, so 50 divided by 5 is 10. The answer is 10."

2. You think "20% is twice 10%, and to find 10% of something I move the decimal point one place to the left. So, 10% of 50 is 5, and 20% is twice 5, or 10. The answer is 10."

Applications

▮▮ **EXAMPLE 11** Interpreting Percents from a Graph

In 2007, Americans spent about $41.2 billion on their pets. Use the graph in **Figure 18** to determine how much of this amount was spent on pet food.

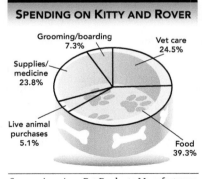

SPENDING ON KITTY AND ROVER

Grooming/boarding 7.3%
Vet care 24.5%
Supplies/medicine 23.8%
Live animal purchases 5.1%
Food 39.3%

Source: American Pet Products Manufacturers Association, Inc.

Figure 18

Dotty

SOLUTION

According to the graph on the preceding page, 39.3% was spent on food. Let x represent this amount in billions of dollars. We use Method 2 of **Example 8.**

$$\frac{x}{41.2} = 0.393 \qquad \text{39.3\% = 0.393}$$

$$x = 41.2(0.393) \quad \text{Multiply by 41.2.}$$

$$x \approx 16.2 \qquad \text{Nearest tenth}$$

Therefore, about $16.2 billion was spent on pet food.   ▌▌▌

In many applications we are asked to find the percent increase or percent decrease from one quantity to another. The following guidelines are helpful.

Finding Percent Increase or Decrease

1. To find the **percent increase from a to b,** where $b > a$, subtract a from b, and divide this result by a. Convert to a percent.

   Example: The percent increase from 4 to 7 is $\frac{7-4}{4} = \frac{3}{4} = 75\%$.

2. To find the **percent decrease from a to b,** where $b < a$, subtract b from a, and divide this result by a. Convert to a percent.

   Example: The percent decrease from 8 to 6 is $\frac{8-6}{8} = \frac{2}{8} = \frac{1}{4} = 25\%$.

▌▌ **EXAMPLE 12** Solving Problems about Percent Increase or Decrease

(a) An electronics store marked up a laptop computer from their cost of $1200 to a selling price of $1464. What was the percent markup?

(b) The enrollment in a community college declined from 12,750 during one school year to 11,350 the following year. Find the percent decrease to the nearest tenth.

SOLUTION

(a) "Markup" is a name for an increase. Let x = the percent increase (as a decimal).

> Subtract to find the amount of increase.

$$x = \frac{1464 - 1200}{1200} \quad \text{Substitute the given values.}$$

> Use the original cost.

$$x = \frac{264}{1200}$$

$$x = 0.22 \qquad \text{Use a calculator.}$$

The computer was marked up 22%.

(b) Let x = the percent decrease (as a decimal).

$$\text{percent decrease} = \frac{\text{amount of decrease}}{\text{original amount}}$$

> Subtract to find the amount of decrease.

$$x = \frac{12{,}750 - 11{,}350}{12{,}750} \quad \text{Substitute the given values.}$$

> Use the original enrollment.

$$x = \frac{1400}{12{,}750}$$

$$x \approx 0.11 \qquad \text{Use a calculator.}$$

The college enrollment decreased by about 11%.   ▌▌▌

When calculating a percent increase or a percent decrease, be sure to use the original number (**before** *the increase or decrease*) *as the base.* A common error is to use the final number (*after* the increase or decrease) in the denominator of the fraction.

For Further Thought

It's Time to End Decimal Point Abuse

Using a decimal point erroneously with a ¢ symbol is seen almost on a daily basis. Think about it . . . $.99 represents $\frac{99}{100}$ of a dollar, or 99 cents, while 99¢ also represents 99 cents (since ¢ is the symbol for *cent*). So what does .99¢ represent? That's right, $\frac{99}{100}$ of one cent!

Look at the photos provided by one of the authors. An order of spicy nuggets at Wendy's is advertised for .99¢. What do you think would happen if you gave the clerk a dime and asked for ten orders and change? You would most likely get a dumbfounded look. A similar response would probably be forthcoming if you asked for Sierra Mist, which costs even less: .79¢. To vacuum your car, it costs .50¢, a mere half cent. At The Floor Place, fabulous floors really do cost less . . . a lot less: less than half a cent per square foot for Berber flooring. Now here's a deal: a 2-liter bottle of Coca Cola for .09¢! (No doubt, the 1 preceding the decimal point fell off. Even then, one such bottle would cost only a tiny bit more than one penny.) At Winn Dixie, one pound of bananas costs .69¢.

For Group or Individual Investigation

Assume that the products shown in the photos are actually being sold for the indicated prices. Answer each of the following.

1. How many orders of spicy nuggets should you get for $1.00? How much change would Wendy's owe you?

2. How much does one ounce of Sierra Mist cost?

3. If you deposit two quarters to have your car vacuumed, how many times should you be able to vacuum?

4. You want to cover your room area with 400 square feet of Berber flooring. How much will this cost?

5. How many 2 liter bottles of Coca Cola would nine cents get you?

6. If 3 bananas weigh a total of 1 pound, how many can you get for a penny?

6.5 EXERCISES

Decide whether each statement is true *or* false.

1. 300% of 12 is 36.

2. 25% of a quantity is the same as $\frac{1}{4}$ of that quantity.

3. When 759.367 is rounded to the nearest hundredth, the result is 759.40.

4. When 759.367 is rounded to the nearest hundred, the result is 759.37.

5. To find 50% of a quantity, we may simply divide the quantity by 2.

6. A soccer team that has won 12 games and lost 8 games has a winning percentage of 60%.

7. If 70% is the lowest passing grade on a quiz that has 50 items of equal value, then answering at least 35 items correctly will assure you of a passing grade.

8. 30 is more than 40% of 120.

9. .99¢ = 99 cents

10. If an item usually costs $70.00 and it is discounted 10%, then the discount price is $7.00.

Calculate each of the following using either a calculator or paper-and-pencil methods, as directed by your instructor.

11. 8.53 + 2.785

12. 9.358 + 7.2137

13. 8.74 − 12.955

14. 2.41 − 3.997

15. 25.7 × 0.032

16. 45.1 × 8.344

17. 1019.825 ÷ 21.47

18. −262.563 ÷ 125.03

19. $\dfrac{118.5}{1.45 + 2.3}$

20. 2.45(1.2 + 3.4 − 5.6)

Government Spending   *For 2005, total U.S. government spending was about $2500 billion (or $2.5 trillion). The circle graph shows how the spending was divided.*

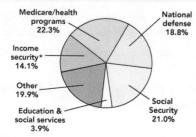

2005 U.S. GOVERNMENT SPENDING

Medicare/health programs 22.3%

National defense 18.8%

Income security* 14.1%

Other 19.9%

Education & social services 3.9%

Social Security 21.0%

*Includes pensions for government workers, unemployment compensation, food stamps, and other such programs.

Source: Office of Management and Budget.

21. About how much was spent on Social Security?

22. About how much did the U.S. government spend on education and social services in 2005?

Postage Stamp Pricing   *Refer to* **For Further Thought** *on decimal point abuse. At one time, the United States Postal Service sold rolls of 33-cent stamps that featured fruit berries. One such stamp is shown on the left. On the right is a photo of the pricing information found on the cellophane wrapper of such a roll.*

100 STAMPS PSA
.33¢ ea. TOTAL $33.00
FRUIT BERRIES
ITEM 7757
BCA

23. Look at the second line of the pricing information. According to the price listed *per stamp*, how many stamps should you be able to purchase for one cent?

24. The total price listed is the amount the Postal Service actually charges. If you were to multiply the listed price *per stamp* by the number of stamps, what should the total price be?

Pricing of Pie and Coffee   *The photos here were taken at a flea market near Natchez, MS. The handwritten signs indicate that a piece of pie costs .10¢ and a cup of coffee ("ffee") costs .5¢. Assuming these are the actual prices, answer the questions in Exercises 25–28.*

25. How much will 10 pieces of pie and 10 cups of coffee cost?

26. How much will 20 pieces of pie and 10 cups of coffee cost?

27. How many pieces of pie can you get for $1.00?

28. How many cups of coffee can you get for $1.00?

Exercises 29–32 are based on formulas found in Auto Math Handbook: Mathematical Calculations, Theory, and Formulas for Automotive Enthusiasts, *by John Lawlor (1991, HP Books).*

29. *Blood Alcohol Concentration* The Blood Alcohol Concentration (BAC) of a person who has been drinking is given by the formula

$$BAC = \frac{(\text{ounces} \times \text{percent alcohol} \times 0.075)}{\text{body weight in lb}}$$
$$- (\text{hours of drinking} \times 0.015).$$

Suppose a policeman stops a 190-pound man who, in two hours, has ingested four 12-ounce beers, each having a 3.2 percent alcohol content. The formula would then read

$$BAC = \frac{[(4 \times 12) \times 3.2 \times 0.075]}{190} - (2 \times 0.015).$$

(a) Find this BAC.

(b) Find the BAC for a 135-pound woman who, in three hours, has drunk three 12-ounce beers, each having a 4.0 percent alcohol content.

30. *Approximate Automobile Speed* The approximate speed of an automobile in miles per hour (MPH) can be found in terms of the engine's revolutions per minute (rpm), the tire diameter in inches, and the overall gear ratio by the formula

$$MPH = \frac{\text{rpm} \times \text{tire diameter}}{\text{gear ratio} \times 336}.$$

If a certain automobile has an rpm of 5600, a tire diameter of 26 inches, and a gear ratio of 3.12, what is its approximate speed (MPH)?

31. *Engine Horsepower* Horsepower can be found from indicated mean effective pressure (mep) in pounds per square inch, engine displacement in cubic inches, and revolutions per minute (rpm) using the formula

$$\text{Horsepower} = \frac{\text{mep} \times \text{displacement} \times \text{rpm}}{792{,}000}.$$

Suppose that an engine has displacement of 302 cubic inches and indicated mep of 195 pounds per square inch at 4000 rpm. What is its approximate horsepower?

32. *Torque Approximation* To determine the torque at a given value of rpm, the formula below applies:

$$\text{Torque} = \frac{5252 \times \text{horsepower}}{\text{rpm}}.$$

If the horsepower of a certain vehicle is 400 at 4500 rpm, what is the approximate torque?

Round each number to the nearest **(a)** *tenth;* **(b)** *hundredth. Always round from the original number.*

33. 78.414   **34.** 3689.537   **35.** 0.0837

36. 0.0658   **37.** 12.68925   **38.** 43.99613

Convert each decimal to a percent.

39. 0.42   **40.** 0.87   **41.** 0.365   **42.** 0.792

43. 0.008   **44.** 0.0093   **45.** 2.1   **46.** 8.9

Convert each fraction to a percent.

47. $\frac{1}{5}$ **48.** $\frac{2}{5}$ **49.** $\frac{1}{100}$ **50.** $\frac{1}{50}$

51. $\frac{3}{8}$ **52.** $\frac{5}{6}$ **53.** $\frac{3}{2}$ **54.** $\frac{7}{4}$

55. Explain the difference between $\frac{1}{2}$ of a quantity and $\frac{1}{2}\%$ of the quantity.

56. Group I shows some common percents, found in many everyday situations. In Group II are fractional equivalents of these percents. Match the fractions in Group II with their equivalent percents in Group I.

I		II	
(a) 25%	**(b)** 10%	**A.** $\frac{1}{3}$	**B.** $\frac{1}{50}$
(c) 2%	**(d)** 20%	**C.** $\frac{3}{4}$	**D.** $\frac{1}{10}$
(e) 75%	**(f)** $33\frac{1}{3}\%$	**E.** $\frac{1}{4}$	**F.** $\frac{1}{5}$

57. Fill in each blank with the correct numerical response.

(a) 5% means _____ in every 100.

(b) 25% means 6 in every _____.

(c) 200% means _____ for every 4.

(d) 0.5% means _____ in every 100.

(e) _____ % means 12 for every 2.

58. The Venn diagram shows the number of elements in the four regions formed.

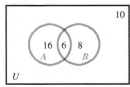

(a) What percent of the elements in the universe are in $A \cap B$?

(b) What percent of the elements in the universe are in A but not in B?

(c) What percent of the elements in $A \cup B$ are in $A \cap B$?

(d) What percent of the elements in the universe are in neither A nor B?

59. *Discount and Markup* Suppose that an item regularly costs $60.00 and it is discounted 20%. If it is then marked up 20%, is the resulting price $60.00? If not, what is it?

60. The figures in **Exercise 13** of **Section 6.3** are reproduced here. Express the fractional parts represented by the shaded areas as percents.

(a)

(b)

(c)

(d)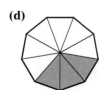

Win-Loss Record *Exercises 61 and 62 deal with winning percentage in the standings of sports teams.*

61. At the end of the regular 2009 Major League Baseball season, the standings of the East Division of the American League were as shown. Winning percentage is commonly expressed as a decimal rounded to the nearest thousandth. To find the winning percentage of a team, divide the number of wins (W) by the total number of games played (W + L). Find the winning percentage of each team.

Team	W	L	Pct.
New York Yankees	103	59	.636
Boston	95	67	
Tampa Bay	84	78	
Toronto	75	87	
Baltimore	64	98	

Source: World Almanac and Book of Facts.

(a) Boston   **(b)** Tampa Bay
(c) Toronto   **(d)** Baltimore

62. Repeat **Exercise 61** for the following standings for the East Division of the National League.

Team	W	L	Pct.
Philadelphia	93	69	
Florida	87	75	.537
Atlanta	86	76	
New York Mets	70	92	
Washington	59	103	

Source: World Almanac and Book of Facts.

(a) Philadelphia   **(b)** Atlanta
(c) New York Mets   **(d)** Washington

Work each problem involving percent.

63. What is 26% of 480?

64. Find 38% of 12.

65. Find 10.5% of 28.

66. What is 48.6% of 19?

67. What percent of 30 is 45?

68. What percent of 48 is 20?

69. 25% of what number is 150?

70. 12% of what number is 3600?

71. 0.392 is what percent of 28?

72. 78.84 is what percent of 292?

Solve each problem involving percent increase or decrease.

73. **Percent Increase** After 1 year on the job, Grady got a raise from $10.50 per hour to $11.34 per hour. What was the percent increase in his hourly wage?

74. **Percent Discount** Clayton bought a ticket to a rock concert at a discount. The regular price of the ticket was $70.00, but he paid only $59.50. What was the percent discount?

75. **Percent Decrease** Between July 1, 2000, and July 1, 2007, the estimated population of Pittsfield, Massachusetts declined from 134,953 to 129,798. What was the percent decrease to the nearest tenth? (*Source:* U.S. Census Bureau.)

76. **Percent Increase** Between July 1, 2000, and July 1, 2007, the estimated population of Anchorage, Alaska grew from 320,391 to 362,340. What was the percent increase to the nearest tenth? (*Source:* U.S. Census Bureau.)

77. **Percent Discount** In April 2008, the audio CD of the Original Broadway Cast Recording of the musical *Wicked* was available at www.amazon.com for $9.97. The list price (full price) of this CD was $18.98. To the nearest tenth, what was the percent discount? (*Source:* www.amazon.com)

78. **Percent Discount** In April 2008, the DVD of the movie *Alvin and the Chipmunks* was released. This DVD had a list price of $29.99 and was for sale at www.amazon.com at $15.99. To the nearest tenth, what was the percent discount? (*Source:* www.amazon.com)

Use mental techniques to answer the questions in Exercises 79–82. Try to avoid using paper and pencil or a calculator.

79. **Allowance Increase** Carly Murray's allowance was raised from $4.00 per week to $5.00 per week. What was the percent of the increase?
    A. 25%   **B.** 20%   **C.** 50%   **D.** 30%

80. **Boat Purchase and Sale** Susan Nassy bought a boat five years ago for $5000 and sold it this year for $2000. What percent of her original purchase did she lose on the sale?
    A. 40%   **B.** 50%   **C.** 20%   **D.** 60%

81. *Population of Alabama* The 2000 U.S. census showed that the population of Alabama was 4,447,000, with 26.0% represented by African Americans. What is the best estimate of the African American population in Alabama? (*Source:* U.S. Census Bureau.)

A. 500,000   **B.** 1,500,000

C. 1,100,000   **D.** 750,000

82. *Population of Hawaii* The 2000 U.S. census showed that the population of Hawaii was 1,212,000, with 21.4% of the population being of two or more races. What is the best estimate of this population of Hawaii? (*Source:* U.S. Census Bureau.)

A. 240,000   **B.** 300,000

C. 21,400   **D.** 24,000

Gasoline Prices *The line graph shows the average price, adjusted for inflation, that Americans have paid for a gallon of gasoline for selected years between 1958 and 2008. Use this information in Exercises 83 and 84.*

AVERAGE GASOLINE PRICES

Source: www.inflationdata.com

83. By what percent did prices increase from 1998 to 2008?

84. By what percent did prices decrease from 1978 to 1988?

Metabolic Units *One way to measure a person's cardio fitness is to calculate how many METs, or metabolic units, he or she can reach at peak exertion. One MET is the amount of energy used when sitting quietly. To calculate ideal METs, we can use one of the following expressions.*

$$14.7 - age \cdot 0.13 \quad \text{For women}$$

$$14.7 - age \cdot 0.11 \quad \text{For men}$$

(*Source: New England Journal of Medicine,* August, 2005.)

85. A 40-year-old woman wishes to calculate her ideal MET.

  (a) Write the expression using her age.

  (b) Calculate her ideal MET. (*Hint:* Use the order of operations.)

  (c) Researchers recommend that a person reach approximately 85% of their MET when exercising. Calculate 85% of the ideal MET from part (b). Then refer to the following table. What activity can the woman do that is approximately this value?

Activity	METs	Activity	METs
Golf (with cart)	2.5	Skiing (water or downhill)	6.8
Walking (3 mph)	3.3	Swimming	7.0
Mowing lawn (power mower)	4.5	Walking (5 mph)	8.0
Ballroom or square dancing	5.5	Jogging	10.2
Cycling	5.7	Rope skipping	12.0

Source: Harvard School of Public Health.

86. Repeat parts **(a)–(c)** of **Exercise 85** for a 55-year-old man.

87. *Value of 1916-D Mercury Dime* The 1916 Mercury dime minted in Denver is quite rare. In 1979 its value in Extremely Fine condition was $625. The 2010 value had increased to $6200. What was the percent increase in the value of this coin from 1979 to 2010? (*Sources: A Guide Book of United States Coins; Coin World Coin Values.*)

88. *Value of 1903-O Morgan Dollar* In 1963, the value of a 1903 Morgan dollar minted in New Orleans in typical Uncirculated condition was $1500. Due to a discovery of a large hoard of these dollars late that year, the value plummeted. Its value in 2010 was $550. What was the percent decrease in its value from 1963 to 2010? (*Sources: A Guide Book of United States Coins; Coin World Coin Values.*)

Tipping Procedure It is customary in our society to "tip" waiters and waitresses when dining in restaurants. One common rate for tipping is 15%. A quick way of figuring a tip that will give a close approximation of 15% is as follows:

Step 1 Round off the bill to the nearest dollar.

Step 2 Find 10% of this amount by moving the decimal point one place to the left.

Step 3 Take half of the amount obtained in Step 2 and add it to the result of Step 2.

This will give you approximately 15% *of the bill. The amount obtained in Step 3 is 5%, and* 10% + 5% = 15%. *Use the method above to find an approximation of* 15% *for each restaurant bill.*

89. $29.57   **90.** $38.32

91. $5.15   **92.** $7.89

Suppose that you get extremely good service and decide to tip 20%. You can use the first two steps listed, and then in Step 3, double the amount you obtained in Step 2. Use this method to find an approximation of 20% for each restaurant bill.

93. $59.96   **94.** $40.24

95. $180.43   **96.** $199.86

97. Say Again? A television reporter once asked a professional wrist-wrestler what percent of his sport was physical and what percent was mental. The athlete responded "I would say it's 50% physical and 90% mental." Comment on this response.

98. Are You Sure? According to *The Yogi Book,* consisting of quotations by baseball Hall-of-Famer Yogi Berra, he claims that "90% of the game is half mental." Comment on this statement.

EXTENSION Complex Numbers

Basic Concepts and the Imaginary Unit • Products and Quotients
• Complex Numbers and Powers of *i*

Basic Concepts and the Imaginary Unit Numbers such as $\sqrt{-5}$ and $\sqrt{-16}$ were called *imaginary* by early mathematicians. Eventually, their use made it necessary to expand the set of real numbers to form the set of **complex numbers.**

Consider the equation $z^2 + 1 = 0$. It has no real number solution, since any solution must be a number whose square is -1. In the set of real numbers all squares are nonnegative numbers, because the product of either two positive numbers or two negative numbers is positive and $0^2 = 0$. To provide a solution for the equation $z^2 + 1 = 0$, a new number i is defined so that the following is true.

$$i^2 = -1, \text{ which implies that } i = \sqrt{-1}.$$

The number i is called the **imaginary unit.** This definition of i makes it possible to define the square root of any negative number as follows.

Gauss and the Complex Numbers In about 1831 **Carl Gauss** was able to show that numbers of the form $a + bi$ can be represented as points on the plane just as real numbers are. He shared this contribution with **Robert Argand,** a bookkeeper in Paris, who wrote an essay on the geometry of the complex numbers in 1806. This went unnoticed at the time.

$\sqrt{-b}$

For any positive real number b, $\sqrt{-b} = i\sqrt{b}.$

▮▮ **EXAMPLE 1** Writing Square Roots Using *i*

Write each number as a product of a real number and i.

(a) $\sqrt{-100}$ **(b)** $\sqrt{-2}$

SOLUTION

(a) $\sqrt{-100} = i\sqrt{100} = 10i$ **(b)** $\sqrt{-2} = \sqrt{2}i = i\sqrt{2}$ ▮▮▮

An Imaginary Tale: The Story of $\sqrt{-1}$
by Paul J. Nahin provides a historical
account of the development of complex
numbers.

In **Example 1(b)**, it is easy to mistake $\sqrt{2}i$ for $\sqrt{2i}$, with the *i* under the radical. For this reason, it is common to write $\sqrt{2}\,i$ as $i\sqrt{2}$.

Products and Quotients When finding a product such as $\sqrt{-4} \cdot \sqrt{-9}$, the product rule for radicals cannot be used, since that rule applies only when both radicals represent real numbers. For this reason, always change $\sqrt{-b}$ (where $b > 0$) to the form $i\sqrt{b}$ before performing any multiplications or divisions.

$$\sqrt{-4} \cdot \sqrt{-9} = i\sqrt{4} \cdot i\sqrt{9} = i \cdot 2 \cdot i \cdot 3 = 6i^2$$

Since $i^2 = -1$,

$$6i^2 = 6(-1) = -6.$$

An ***incorrect*** use of the product rule for radicals would give a wrong answer.

$$\sqrt{-4} \cdot \sqrt{-9} = \sqrt{(-4)(-9)} = \sqrt{36} = 6 \quad \text{Incorrect}$$

This same reasoning holds for quotients as well.

When the TI-83/84 Plus calculator is in
complex mode, denoted by $a + bi$, it will
perform complex number arithmetic.

▮▮ **EXAMPLE 2** Multiplying Expressions Involving *i*

Multiply.

(a) $\sqrt{-3} \cdot \sqrt{-7}$ **(b)** $\sqrt{-2} \cdot \sqrt{-8}$ **(c)** $\sqrt{-5} \cdot \sqrt{6}$

SOLUTION

(a) $\sqrt{-3} \cdot \sqrt{-7} = i\sqrt{3} \cdot i\sqrt{7} = i^2\sqrt{3 \cdot 7} = (-1)\sqrt{21} = -\sqrt{21}$

(b) $\sqrt{-2} \cdot \sqrt{-8} = i\sqrt{2} \cdot i\sqrt{8} = i^2\sqrt{2 \cdot 8} = (-1)\sqrt{16} = (-1)4 = -4$

(c) $\sqrt{-5} \cdot \sqrt{6} = i\sqrt{5} \cdot \sqrt{6} = i\sqrt{30}$ ▮▮▮

▮▮ **EXAMPLE 3** Dividing Expressions Involving *i*

Divide.

(a) $\dfrac{\sqrt{-75}}{\sqrt{-3}}$ **(b)** $\dfrac{\sqrt{-32}}{\sqrt{8}}$

This screen supports the results of
Examples 2(b), 3(a), and 3(b).

SOLUTION

(a) $\dfrac{\sqrt{-75}}{\sqrt{-3}} = \dfrac{i\sqrt{75}}{i\sqrt{3}} = \sqrt{\dfrac{75}{3}} = \sqrt{25} = 5$

(b) $\dfrac{\sqrt{-32}}{\sqrt{8}} = \dfrac{i\sqrt{32}}{\sqrt{8}} = i\sqrt{\dfrac{32}{8}} = i\sqrt{4} = 2i$ ▮▮▮

Complex Numbers and Powers of *i* *Complex numbers* are defined as follows.

> **Complex Numbers**
>
> If *a* and *b* are real numbers, then any number of the form $a + bi$ is called a **complex number.**

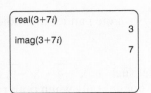

The TI-83/84 Plus calculator identifies the real and imaginary parts of $3 + 7i$.

In the complex number $a + bi$, the number a is called the **real part** and b is called the **imaginary part.*** When $b = 0$, $a + bi$ is a real number, so the real numbers are a subset of the complex numbers. Complex numbers of the form bi, where $b \neq 0$, are called **pure imaginary numbers.** In spite of their name, such numbers are very useful in applications, particularly in work with electricity.

An interesting pattern emerges when we consider various powers of i. By definition, $i^0 = 1$, and $i^1 = i$. We have seen that $i^2 = -1$, and greater powers of i can be found as shown in the following list.

$$i^3 = i \cdot i^2 = i(-1) = -i \qquad i^6 = i^2 \cdot i^4 = (-1) \cdot 1 = -1$$

$$i^4 = i^2 \cdot i^2 = (-1)(-1) = 1 \qquad i^7 = i^3 \cdot i^4 = (-i) \cdot 1 = -i$$

$$i^5 = i \cdot i^4 = i \cdot 1 = i \qquad i^8 = i^4 \cdot i^4 = 1 \cdot 1 = 1$$

A few powers of i are listed here.

The calculator computes powers of i. Compare to the powers in the chart.

Powers of i			
$i^1 = i$	$i^5 = i$	$i^9 = i$	$i^{13} = i$
$i^2 = -1$	$i^6 = -1$	$i^{10} = -1$	$i^{14} = -1$
$i^3 = -i$	$i^7 = -i$	$i^{11} = -i$	$i^{15} = -i$
$i^4 = 1$	$i^8 = 1$	$i^{12} = 1$	$i^{16} = 1$

The powers of i rotate through the four numbers i, -1, $-i$, and 1. Larger powers of i can be simplified by using the fact that $i^4 = 1$. For example, consider i^{75}.

$$i^{75} = (i^4)^{18} \cdot i^3 = 1^{18} \cdot i^3 = 1 \cdot i^3 = -i$$

Simplifying Large Powers of i

Step 1 Divide the exponent by 4.

Step 2 Observe the remainder obtained in Step 1. The large power of i is the same as i raised to the power determined by this remainder. Refer to the previous chart to complete the simplification. (If the remainder is 0, the power simplifies to $i^0 = 1$.)

▮▮ **EXAMPLE 4** Simplifying Powers of i

Simplify each power of i.

(a) i^{12} **(b)** i^{39}

SOLUTION

(a) $i^{12} = (i^4)^3 = 1^3 = 1$

(b) To find i^{39}, start by dividing 39 by 4 (Step 1), as shown in the margin. The remainder is 3. So $i^{39} = i^3 = -i$ (Step 2).

Another way to simplify i^{39} is as follows.

$$i^{39} = i^{36} \cdot i^3 = (i^4)^9 \cdot i^3 = 1^9 \cdot (-i) = -i$$ ▮▮▮

$$\begin{array}{r} 9 \\ 4\,\overline{)39} \\ \underline{36} \\ 3 \end{array} \longleftarrow \text{Remainder}$$

---

*In some texts, bi is called the imaginary part.

EXTENSION EXERCISES

*Use the method of **Examples 1–3** to write each expression as a real number or a product of a real number and i.*

1. $\sqrt{-144}$ **2.** $\sqrt{-196}$ **3.** $-\sqrt{-225}$

4. $-\sqrt{-400}$ **5.** $\sqrt{-3}$ **6.** $\sqrt{-19}$

7. $\sqrt{-75}$ **8.** $\sqrt{-125}$

9. $\sqrt{-5} \cdot \sqrt{-5}$ **10.** $\sqrt{-3} \cdot \sqrt{-3}$

11. $\sqrt{-9} \cdot \sqrt{-36}$ **12.** $\sqrt{-4} \cdot \sqrt{-81}$

13. $\sqrt{-16} \cdot \sqrt{-100}$ **14.** $\sqrt{-81} \cdot \sqrt{-121}$

15. $\dfrac{\sqrt{-200}}{\sqrt{-100}}$ **16.** $\dfrac{\sqrt{-50}}{\sqrt{-2}}$

17. $\dfrac{\sqrt{-54}}{\sqrt{6}}$ **18.** $\dfrac{\sqrt{-90}}{\sqrt{10}}$

19. $\dfrac{\sqrt{-288}}{\sqrt{-8}}$ **20.** $\dfrac{\sqrt{-48} \cdot \sqrt{-3}}{\sqrt{-2}}$

*Use the method of **Example 4** to simplify each power of i.*

21. i^8 **22.** i^{16} **23.** i^{42} **24.** i^{86}

25. i^{47} **26.** i^{63} **27.** i^{101} **28.** i^{141}

COLLABORATIVE INVESTIGATION

Budgeting to Buy a Car

You are shopping for a sports car and have put aside a certain amount of money each month for a car payment. Your instructor will assign this amount to you. After looking through a variety of resources, you have narrowed your choices to the cars listed in the table.

Year/Make/ Model	Retail Price	Fuel Tank Size (in gallons)	Miles per Gallon (city)	Miles per Gallon (highway)
2010 Ford Mustang	$31,395	16.0	16	24
2010 Ford Taurus SEL	$29,220	19.0	17	25
2010 Toyota Camry Hybrid	$26,150	17.2	33	34
2010 Mazda MX-5 Miata	$26,250	12.7	21	28
2010 Honda CR-V EX-L	$26,495	15.3	21	28
2010 Chevrolet Malibu Hybrid	$25,555	16.0	26	34

Source: www.edmunds.com

As a group, work through the following steps to determine which car you can afford to buy.

A. Decide which cars you think are within your budget.

B. Select one of the cars you identified in part A. Have each member of the group calculate the monthly payment for this car using a different financing option. Use the formula given below, where P is principal, r is interest rate, and m is the number of monthly payments, along with the financing options table.

Financing Options

Time (in years)	Interest Rate
4	2.0%
5	3.5%
6	5.0%

$$\text{Monthly Payment} = \frac{\dfrac{Pr}{12}}{1 - \left(\dfrac{12}{12 + r}\right)^m}$$

C. Have each group member determine the amount of money paid in interest over the duration of the loan for his or her financing option.

D. Consider fuel expenses.

　1. Assume you will travel an average of 75 miles in the city and 400 miles on the highway each week. How many gallons of gas will you need to buy each month?

　2. Using typical prices for gas in your area at this time, how much money will you need to have available for buying gas?

E. Repeat parts B–D as necessary until your group can reach a consensus on the car you will buy and the financing option you will use. Write a paragraph to explain your choices.

CHAPTER 6 TEST

1. Consider $\{-4, -\sqrt{5}, -\frac{3}{2}, -0.5, 0, \sqrt{3}, 4.1, 12\}$. List the elements of the set that belong to each of the following.
   (a) natural numbers
   (b) whole numbers
   (c) integers
   (d) rational numbers
   (e) irrational numbers
   (f) real numbers

2. Match each set in (a)–(d) with the correct set-builder notation description in A–D.
   (a) $\{\ldots, -4, -3, -2, -1\}$
   (b) $\{3, 4, 5, 6, \ldots\}$
   (c) $\{1, 2, 3, 4, \ldots\}$
   (d) $\{-12, \ldots, -2, -1, 0, 1, 2, \ldots, 12\}$

   A. $\{x \mid x$ is an integer with absolute value less than or equal to 12$\}$
   B. $\{x \mid x$ is an integer greater than 2.5$\}$
   C. $\{x \mid x$ is a negative integer$\}$
   D. $\{x \mid x$ is a positive integer$\}$

3. Decide whether each statement is *true* or *false*.
   (a) The absolute value of a number must be positive.
   (b) $|-7| = -(-7)$
   (c) $\frac{2}{5}$ is an example of a real number that is not an integer.
   (d) Every real number is either positive or negative.

Perform the indicated operations. Use the order of operations as necessary.

4. $6^2 - 4(9 - 1)$

5. $\dfrac{(-8 + 3) - (5 + 10)}{7 - 9}$

6. $(-3)(-2) - [5 + (8 - 10)]$

7. **Changes in Foreclosures**   The graph shows the percent change in U.S. foreclosure filings from 2008 to 2009 for various states. Use this graph to answer parts (a)–(d) at the top of the next column. (Consider absolute value.)

PERCENT CHANGE IN FORECLOSURES

Connecticut −31.18%
Ohio −14.76%
Indiana −10.77%
Maine 10.63%
Minnesota 52.74%
Louisiana 34.38%
Texas −14.38%

−40 −30 −20 −10 0 10 20 30 40 50
Percent Change

Source: Realty Trac, Inc.

(a) Which state had the greatest change in foreclosures? What was that change?
(b) Which state had the least change in foreclosures? What was that change?
(c) *True* or *false:* The absolute value of the percent change for Texas was greater than the absolute value of the percent change for Ohio.
(d) *True* or *false:* The percent change for Minnesota was more than four times greater than the percent change for Maine.

8. **Altitude of a Plane**   The surface of the Dead Sea has altitude 1299 ft below sea level. Victoria LoCascio is flying 80 ft above that surface. How much altitude must she gain to clear a 3852 ft pass by 225 ft? (*Source: The World Almanac and Book of Facts.*)

9. **Median Home Prices**   Median pricings for existing homes in the United States for the years 2004 through 2009 are shown in the table. Complete the table, determining the change from one year to the next by subtraction.

	Year	Median-Priced Existing Homes	Change from Previous Year
	2004	$195,200	
	2005	$219,000	$23,800
(a)	2006	$221,900	
(b)	2007	$217,900	
(c)	2008	$196,600	
(d)	2009	$177,500	

Source: National Association of Realtors.

10. Match each statement in (a)–(f) with the property that justifies it in A–F.
    (a) $7 \cdot (8 \cdot 5) = (7 \cdot 8) \cdot 5$
    (b) $3x + 3y = 3(x + y)$
    (c) $8 \cdot 1 = 1 \cdot 8 = 8$
    (d) $7 + (6 + 9) = (6 + 9) + 7$
    (e) $9 + (-9) = -9 + 9 = 0$
    (f) $5 \cdot 8$ is a real number.

    A. Distributive property
    B. Identity property
    C. Closure property
    D. Commutative property
    E. Associative property
    F. Inverse property

11. **Basketball Shot Statistics**   Six players on the local high school basketball team had shooting statistics as shown in the table on the next page. Answer each question, using estimation skills as necessary.

Player	Field Goal Attempts	Field Goals Made
Ed Moura	40	13
Jack Pritchard	10	4
Chuck Miller	20	8
Ben Whitney	6	4
Charlie Dawkins	7	2
Jason McElwain ("J-Mac")	7	6

(a) Which players made more than half of their attempts?

(b) Which players made just less than $\frac{1}{3}$ of their attempts?

(c) Which player made exactly $\frac{2}{3}$ of his attempts?

(d) Which two players made the same fractional parts of their attempts? What was the fractional part, reduced to lowest terms?

(e) Which player made the greatest fractional part of his attempts?

Perform each operation. Write your answer in lowest terms.

12. $\frac{3}{16} + \frac{1}{2}$

13. $\frac{9}{20} - \frac{3}{32}$

14. $\frac{3}{8} \cdot \left(-\frac{16}{15}\right)$

15. $\frac{7}{9} \div \frac{14}{27}$

16. Convert each rational number into a repeating or terminating decimal. Use a calculator if your instructor so allows.

(a) $\frac{9}{20}$

(b) $\frac{5}{12}$

17. Convert each decimal into a quotient of integers, reduced to lowest terms.

(a) 0.72

(b) $0.\overline{58}$

18. Identify each number as rational or irrational.

(a) $\sqrt{10}$

(b) $\sqrt{16}$

(c) 0.01

(d) $0.\overline{01}$

(e) 0.0101101110...

(f) π

*For each of the following, **(a)** use a calculator to find a decimal approximation and **(b)** simplify the radical according to the guidelines in this chapter.*

19. $\sqrt{150}$

20. $\frac{13}{\sqrt{7}}$

21. $2\sqrt{32} - 5\sqrt{128}$

22. A student using her powerful new calculator states that the *exact* value of $\sqrt{65}$ is 8.062257748. Is she correct? If not, explain.

23. Work each of the following using either a calculator or paper-and-pencil methods, as directed by your instructor.

(a) $4.6 + 9.21$

(b) $12 - 3.725 - 8.59$

(c) $86(0.45)$

(d) $236.439 \div (-9.73)$

24. Round 9.0449 to the following place values:

(a) hundredths

(b) thousandths.

25. (a) Find 18.5% of 90.

(b) What number is 145% of 70?

26. Consider the figure.

(a) What percent of the total number of shapes are circles?

(b) What percent of the total number of shapes are not stars?

27. *Sales of Books* Use estimation techniques to answer the following: In 2008, Carol Merrigan sold $300,000 worth of books. In 2009, she sold $900,000. Her 2009 sales were _____ of her 2008 sales.

A. 30%   **B.** $33\frac{1}{3}$%   **C.** 200%   **D.** 300%

28. *Creature Comforts* From a list of "everyday items" often taken for granted, adults were recently surveyed as to those items they wouldn't want to live without. Complete the results shown in the table if 2400 adults were surveyed.

Item	Percent That Wouldn't Want to Live Without	Number That Wouldn't Want to Live Without
Toilet paper	69%	
Zipper	42%	
Frozen Food		384
Self-stick note pads		144

(Other items included tape, hairspray, pantyhose, paper clips, and Velcro.)

Source: Market Facts for Kleenex Cottonelle.

29. *Composition of U.S. Workforce*   The U.S. Bureau of Labor Statistics reported the composition of the U.S. workforce for the year 2006. The total number of people in the workforce for that year was 148,847,000. To the nearest thousand, how many of these were in the Hispanic category?

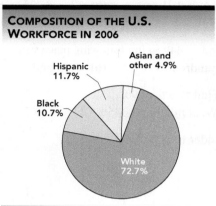

Source: U.S. Bureau of Labor Statistics.

30. *Medicare Funding*   Projections have indicated that funding for Medicare will not cover its costs unless the program changes. The line graph shows projections for the years 2004 through 2013. What signed number represents how much the funding will have changed from 2004 to 2013?

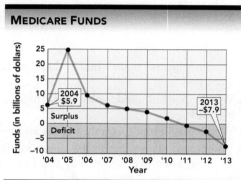

Source: Centers for Medicare and Medicaid Services.

PROBABILITY

11

Suppose you're on a game show, and you're given the choice of three doors: Behind one of the doors is a car, and behind the other doors, goats. Of course, you want to win the car. You pick one of the doors, say Door 1, and the host, who knows what's behind the other doors, opens another door, say Door 3, to reveal a goat. He then says to you, "Do you want to change your choice?" Is it to your advantage to switch to Door 2?

This question appeared in *Parade* magazine in a column written by Marilyn vos Savant in the early 1990s. This probability problem, known as the Monty Hall Problem, was named after the host of the popular game show *Let's Make a Deal*. Marilyn's answer caused an incredible amount of discussion and argument among the general public at that time.

The answer and its justification can also be found at the interactive Web site www.math.ucsd.edu/~crypto/Monty/monty .html. *Would YOU switch doors?* (See page 613 for the answer.)

11.1 BASIC CONCEPTS

Historical Background • Probability • The Law of Large Numbers
• Probability in Genetics • Odds

If the **Pascal–Fermat correspondence** of 1654 marks the birth of probability theory, it wasn't an easy birth. In his 2010 book, *The Unfinished Game: Pascal, Fermat, and the Seventeenth-Century Letter that Made the World Modern* (see the photo above), Keith Devlin describes how the two "struggled for several weeks" to solve the unfinished game problem. In fact, this is no exception, but rather the rule, even for the greatest mathematicians. The reams of scratch work behind the elegant results are seldom seen and rarely published.

Historical Background

The modern mathematical theory of probability came mainly from the Russian scholars P. L. Chebyshev (1821–1922), A. A. Markov (1856–1922), and Andrei Nikolaevich Kolmogorov (1903–1987). But the basic ideas arose much earlier, mostly in questions of games and gambling. In 1654, two French mathematicians, Pierre de Fermat (about 1601–1665) and Blaise Pascal (1623–1662), corresponded with each other regarding a problem posed by the Chevalier de Méré, a gambler and member of the aristocracy.

> *If the two players of a game are forced to quit before the game is finished, how should the pot be divided?*

Pascal and Fermat solved the problem by developing basic methods of determining each player's chance, or probability, of winning.

The Dutch mathematician and scientist Christiaan Huygens (1629–1695) wrote a formal treatise on probability. It appeared in 1657 and was based on the Pascal–Fermat correspondence.

One of the first to apply probability to matters other than gambling was the French mathematician Pierre Simon de Laplace (1749–1827), who is usually credited with being the "father" of probability theory.

Probability

If you go to a supermarket and select five pounds of peaches at 89¢ per pound, you can easily predict the amount you will be charged at the checkout counter.

$$5 \cdot \$0.89 = \$4.45.$$

This is an example of a **deterministic phenomenon.** It can be predicted exactly on the basis of obtainable information, namely, in this case, number of pounds and cost per pound.

On the other hand, consider the problem faced by the produce manager of the market, who must order peaches to have on hand each day without knowing exactly how many pounds customers will buy during the day. Customer demand is an example of a **random phenomenon.** It fluctuates in such a way that its value (on a given day) cannot be predicted exactly with obtainable information.

The study of probability is concerned with such random phenomena. Even though we cannot be certain whether a given result will occur, we often can obtain a good measure of its *likelihood*, or **probability.** This chapter discusses various ways of finding and using probabilities.

Any observation, or measurement, of a random phenomenon is an **experiment.** The possible results of the experiment are **outcomes,** and the set of all possible outcomes is the **sample space.**

Usually we are interested in some particular collection of the possible outcomes. Any such subset of the sample space is an **event.** Outcomes that belong to the event are "favorable outcomes," or "successes." Any time a success is observed, we say that the event has "occurred." The probability of an event, being a numerical measure of the event's likelihood, is determined in one of two ways, either *theoretically* (mathematically) or *empirically* (experimentally).

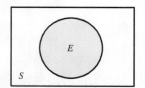

Every event is a subset of the sample space.

▮▮ **EXAMPLE 1** Finding Probability When Tossing a Coin

If a single coin is tossed, find the probability that it will land heads up.

SOLUTION

There is no apparent reason for one side of a coin to land up any more often than the other (in the long run), so we assume that heads and tails are equally likely.

The experiment here is the tossing of a single fair coin, the sample space is $S = \{h, t\}$, and the event whose probability we seek is $E = \{h\}$. Since one of the two equally likely outcomes is a head, the probability of heads is the quotient of 1 and 2.

$$\text{Probability (heads)} = \frac{1}{2}, \quad \text{written} \quad P(h) = \frac{1}{2} \quad \text{or} \quad P(E) = \frac{1}{2}.$$ ▮▮▮

▮▮ **EXAMPLE 2** Finding Probability When Tossing a Cup

If a Styrofoam cup is tossed, find the probability that it will land on its top.

SOLUTION

Intuitively, it seems that such a cup will land on its side much more often than on its top or its bottom. But just how much more often is not clear. To get an idea, we performed the experiment of tossing such a cup 50 times. It landed on its side 44 times, on its top 5 times, and on its bottom just 1 time. By the frequency of "success" in this experiment, we concluded for the cup we used that

$$P(\text{top}) \approx \frac{5}{50} = \frac{1}{10}.$$ Write in lowest terms.   ▮▮▮

In **Example 1** involving the tossing of a fair coin, the number of possible outcomes was obviously two, both were equally likely, and one of the outcomes was a head. No actual experiment was required. The desired probability was obtained *theoretically*. Theoretical probabilities apply to dice rolling, card games, roulette, lotteries, and so on, and apparently to many phenomena in nature.

Laplace, in his famous *Analytic Theory of Probability*, published in 1812, gave a formula that applies to any such theoretical probability, as long as the sample space S is finite and all outcomes are equally likely. (It is sometimes referred to as the *classical definition of probability*.)

> **Theoretical Probability Formula**
>
> If all outcomes in a sample space S are equally likely, and E is an event within that sample space, then the **theoretical probability** of event E is given by the following formula.
>
> $$P(E) = \frac{\text{number of favorable outcomes}}{\text{total number of outcomes}} = \frac{n(E)}{n(S)}$$

On the other hand, **Example 2** involved the tossing of a cup, where the likelihoods of the various outcomes were not intuitively clear. It took an actual experiment to arrive at a probability value of $\frac{1}{10}$, and that value, based on a portion of all possible tosses of the cup, should be regarded as an approximation of the true theoretical probability. The value was found according to the *experimental*, or *empirical*, probability formula.

"But is it probable," asked Pascal, "that probability gives assurance? Nothing gives certainty but truth; nothing gives rest but the sincere search for truth." When Pascal wrote that, he had gone to live at the Jansenist convent of Port-Royal after a carriage accident in 1654.

Pascal's notes on Christianity were collected after his death in the *Pensées* (thoughts). The above quotation is included. Another develops Pascal's "rule of the wager": If you bet God exists and live accordingly, you will have gained much even if God does not exist; if you bet the opposite and God does exist, you will have lost the reason for living right—hence everything.

In 1827, **Robert Brown** (1773–1858), a Scottish physician and botanist, described the irregular motion of microscopic pollen grains suspended in water. Such "Brownian motion," as it came to be called, was not understood until 1905 when Albert Einstein explained it by treating molecular motion as a random phenomenon.

Empirical Probability Formula

If E is an event that may happen when an experiment is performed, then an **empirical probability** of event E is given by the following formula.

$$P(E) = \frac{\text{number of times event } E \text{ occurred}}{\text{number of times the experiment was performed}}$$

Usually it is clear in applications which probability formula should be used.

▮▮ **EXAMPLE 3** Finding the Probability of Having Daughters

Kathy Campbell wants to have exactly two daughters. Assuming that boy and girl babies are equally likely, find her probability of success if

(a) she has a total of two children. **(b)** she has a total of three children.

SOLUTION

(a) The equal likelihood assumption allows the use of theoretical probability. But how can we determine the number of favorable outcomes and the total number of possible outcomes?

One way is to use a tree diagram (see **Section 10.1**) to enumerate the possibilities, as shown in **Figure 1**. From the outcome column we obtain the sample space $S = \{gg, gb, bg, bb\}$. Only one outcome, marked with an arrow, is favorable to the event of exactly two daughters: $E = \{gg\}$.

$$P(E) = \frac{n(E)}{n(S)} = \frac{1}{4} \quad \text{Theoretical probability formula}$$

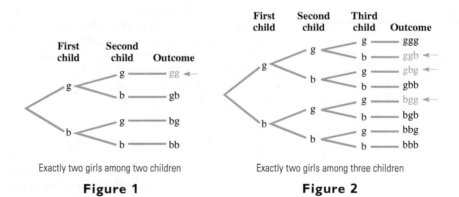

Exactly two girls among two children

Figure 1

Exactly two girls among three children

Figure 2

(b) For three children altogether, we construct another tree diagram, as shown in **Figure 2**. In this case, we see that

$$S = \{ggg, ggb, gbg, gbb, bgg, bgb, bbg, bbb\} \quad \text{and} \quad E = \{ggb, gbg, bgg\},$$

so $P(E) = \frac{3}{8}$. ▮▮▮

When dealing (or drawing) cards, as in the next example, the dealing is generally done "without replacement." Once dealt, a card is *not* replaced in the deck. So all cards in a hand are distinct. (Repetitions are *not* allowed.) In many cases, such as building three-digit numbers, repetition of digits *is* allowed. For example, 255 is a legitimate three-digit number. So digit selection is done "with replacement."

EXAMPLE 4 Finding Probability When Dealing Cards

Find the probability of being dealt each of the following hands in five-card poker. Use a calculator to obtain answers to eight decimal places.

(a) a full house (three of one denomination and two of another)

(b) a royal flush (the five highest cards—ace, king, queen, jack, ten—of a single suit)

SOLUTION

(a) Table 1 summarizes the various possible kinds of five-card hands. (For more on card hands, see **Section 10.3.**) Since the 2,598,960 possible individual hands all are equally likely, we can enter the appropriate numbers from the table into the theoretical probability formula.

$$P(\text{full house}) = \frac{3744}{2,598,960} = \frac{6}{4165} \approx 0.00144058$$

(b) The table shows that there are four royal flushes, one for each suit.

$$P(\text{royal flush}) = \frac{4}{2,598,960} = \frac{1}{649,740} \approx 0.00000154$$ ■■■

Table 1	Number of Poker Hands in 5-Card Poker; Nothing Wild
Event E	**Number of Outcomes Favorable to E**
Royal flush	4
Straight flush	36
Four of a kind	624
Full house	3744
Flush	5108
Straight	10,200
Three of a kind	54,912
Two pairs	123,552
One pair	1,098,240
No pair	1,302,540
Total	2,598,960

Examples 3 and 4 both utilized the theoretical probability formula because we were able to enumerate all possible outcomes and all were equally likely. In **Example 3,** however, the equal likelihood of girl and boy babies was *assumed.* In fact, male births typically occur a little more frequently. (At the same time, there usually are more females living at any given time, due to higher infant mortality rates among males and longer female life expectancy in general.) **Example 5** shows a way of incorporating such empirical information.

EXAMPLE 5 Finding the Probability of the Gender of a Resident

According to *Pocket World in Figures,* 2009 edition, published by *The Economist,* the U.S. population at the end of 2006 included 148.2 million males and 152.8 million females. If a person were selected randomly from the population in that year, what is the probability that the person would be a male?

SOLUTION

In this case, we calculate the empirical probability from the given experimental data.

$$P(\text{male}) = \frac{\text{number of males}}{\text{total number of persons}}$$

$$= \frac{148.2 \text{ million}}{148.2 \text{ million} + 152.8 \text{ million}}$$

$$\approx 0.492$$ ■■■

The Law of Large Numbers

Recall the cup of **Example 2.** If we tossed it 50 more times, we would have 100 total tosses upon which to base an empirical probability of the cup landing on its top. The new value would likely be (at least slightly) different from what we obtained before. It would still be an empirical probability, but it would be "better" in the sense that it is based upon a larger set of outcomes.

The **law of large numbers** also can be stated as follows.

A theoretical probability really says nothing about one, or even a few, repetitions of an experiment, but only about the proportion of successes we would expect over the long run.

If, as we increase the number of tosses, the resulting empirical probability values approach some particular number, that number can be defined as the theoretical probability of that particular cup landing on its top. We could determine this "limiting" value only as the actual number of observed tosses approaches the total number of possible tosses of the cup. Since there are potentially an infinite number of possible tosses, we could never actually find the theoretical probability. But we can still assume such a number exists. And as the number of actual observed tosses increases, the resulting empirical probabilities should tend ever closer to the theoretical value.

This very important principle is known as the **law of large numbers** (or sometimes as the "law of averages").

> **Law of Large Numbers**
>
> As an experiment is repeated more and more times, the proportion of outcomes favorable to any particular event will tend to come closer and closer to the theoretical probability of that event.

▮▮ **EXAMPLE 6** Graphing a Sequence of Proportions

A fair coin was tossed 35 times, producing the following sequence of outcomes.

tthhh, ttthh, hthtt, hhthh, ttthh, thttt, hhthh

Calculate the ratio of heads to total tosses after the first toss, the second toss, and so on through all 35 tosses, and plot these ratios on a graph.

SOLUTION

After the first toss, we have 0 heads out of 1 toss, for a ratio of $\frac{0}{1} = 0.00$. After two tosses, we have $\frac{0}{2} = 0.00$. After three tosses, we have $\frac{1}{3} \approx 0.33$. Verify that the first six ratios are

0.00, 0.00, 0.33, 0.50, 0.60, 0.50.

The thirty-five ratios are plotted as points in **Figure 3**. The fluctuations away from 0.50 become smaller as the number of tosses increases, and the ratios appear to approach 0.50 toward the right side of the graph, in keeping with the law of large numbers.

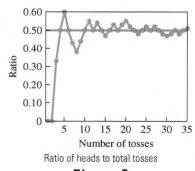

Ratio of heads to total tosses

Figure 3

▮▮▮

> **Comparing Empirical and Theoretical Probabilities**
>
> A series of repeated experiments provides an *empirical probability* for an event, which, by *inductive reasoning*, is an *estimate* of the event's *theoretical probability*. (Increasing the number of repetitions increases the reliability of the estimate.)
>
> Likewise, an established *theoretical probability* for an event enables us, by *deductive reasoning*, to *predict* the proportion of times the event will occur in a series of repeated experiments. (The prediction should be more accurate for larger numbers of repetitions.)

Probability in Genetics

Probabilities, both empirical and theoretical, have been valuable tools in many areas of science. An important early example was the work of the Austrian monk Gregor Mendel, who used the idea of randomness to help establish the study of genetics.

In an effort to understand the mechanism of character transmittal from one generation to the next in plants, Mendel counted the number of occurrences of various characteristics. He found that the flower color in certain pea plants obeyed this scheme:

Pure red crossed with pure white produces red.

Mendel theorized that red is "dominant" (symbolized with the capital letter R), while white is "recessive" (symbolized with the lowercase letter r). The pure red parent carried only genes for red (R), and the pure white parent carried only genes for white (r). The offspring would receive one gene from each parent, hence one of the four combinations shown in the body of **Table 2**. Because every offspring receives one gene for red, that characteristic dominates and the offspring exhibits the color red.

Gregor Johann Mendel (1822–1884) came from a peasant family who managed to send him to school. By 1847 he had been ordained and was teaching at the Abbey of St. Thomas. He finished his education at the University of Vienna and returned to the abbey to teach mathematics and natural science.

Mendel began to carry out experiments on plants in the abbey garden, notably pea plants, whose distinct traits (unit characters) he had puzzled over. In 1865 he published his results. His work was not appreciated at the time even though he had laid the foundation of **classical genetics.**

Table 2	**First to Second Generation**	Second Parent	
		r	**r**
First Parent	**R**	Rr	Rr
	R	Rr	Rr

Table 3	**Second to Third Generation**	Second Parent	
		R	**r**
First Parent	**R**	RR	Rr
	r	rR	rr

Now each of these second-generation offspring, though exhibiting the color red, still carries one of each gene. So when two of them are crossed, each third-generation offspring will receive one of the gene combinations shown in **Table 3**. Mendel theorized that each of these four possibilities would be equally likely and produced experimental counts that were close enough to support this hypothesis.

▮▮ **EXAMPLE 7** Finding Probabilities of Flower Colors

Referring to **Table 3**, determine the probability that a third-generation offspring will exhibit each flower color. Base the probabilities on the sample space of equally likely outcomes: $S = \{RR, Rr, rR, rr\}$.

(a) red   **(b)** white

SOLUTION

(a) Since red dominates white, any combination with at least one gene for red (R) will result in red flowers. Since three of the four possibilities meet this criterion, $P(\text{red}) = \frac{3}{4}$.

(b) Only the combination rr has no gene for red, so $P(\text{white}) = \frac{1}{4}$.   ▮▮▮

Odds

Whereas probability compares the number of favorable outcomes to the total number of outcomes, **odds** compare the number of favorable outcomes to the number of unfavorable outcomes. Odds are commonly quoted, rather than probabilities, in horse racing, lotteries, and most other gambling situations. And the odds quoted normally are odds "against" rather than odds "in favor."

Smoking 1.4 cigarettes
Spending 1 hour in a coal mine
Living 2 days in New York or Boston
Eating 40 teaspoons of peanut butter
Living 2 months with a cigarette smoker
Flying 1000 miles in a jet
Traveling 300 miles in a car
Riding 10 miles on a bicycle

Risk is the probability that a harmful event will occur. Almost every action or substance exposes a person to some risk, and the assessment and reduction of risk accounts for a great deal of study and effort in our world. The list above, from *Calculated Risk*, by J. Rodricks, contains activities that carry an annual increased risk of death by one chance in a million.

Odds

If all outcomes in a sample space are equally likely, a of them are favorable to the event E, and the remaining b outcomes are unfavorable to E, then the **odds in favor** of E are a to b, and the **odds against** E are b to a.

▍▍ **EXAMPLE 8** Finding the Odds of Getting an Intern Position

Theresa Cortesini has been promised one of six jobs, three of which would be intern positions at the state capitol. If she has equal chances for all six jobs, find the odds that she will get one of the intern positions.

SOLUTION

Since three possibilities are favorable and three are not, the odds of becoming an intern at the capitol are 3 to 3 (or 1 to 1 in reduced terms). Odds of 1 to 1 are often termed "even odds," or a "50–50 chance." ▍▍▍

▍▍ **EXAMPLE 9** Finding the Odds of Winning a Raffle

Bob Barickman has purchased 12 tickets for an office raffle in which the winner will receive an iPad. If 104 tickets were sold altogether and each has an equal chance of winning, what are the odds against Bob's winning the iPad?

SOLUTION

Bob has 12 chances to win and $104 - 12 = 92$ chances to lose, so the odds against winning are 92 to 12, or 23 to 3. (Divide both 92 and 12 by 4.) ▍▍▍

Converting between Probability and Odds

Let E be an event.

1. If $P(E) = \frac{a}{b}$, then the odds in favor of E are a to $(b - a)$.

2. If the odds in favor of E are a to b, then $P(E) = \frac{a}{a + b}$.

▍▍ **EXAMPLE 10** Converting from Probability to Odds

There is a 30% chance of rain tomorrow. Give this information in terms of odds.

SOLUTION

$$P(\text{rain}) = 0.30 = \frac{30}{100} = \frac{3}{10}$$

> Convert the decimal fraction to a quotient of integers and reduce.

By conversion formula 1 above, the odds in favor of rain are 3 to $10 - 3$, or 3 to 7. Or, we can say the odds are 7 to 3 against rain tomorrow. ▍▍▍

▍▍ **EXAMPLE 11** Converting from Odds to Probability

In a certain sweepstakes, your odds of winning are 1 to 99,999. What is the probability that you will win?

SOLUTION

$$P(\text{win}) = \frac{1}{1 + 99,999} = \frac{1}{100,000} = 0.00001 \quad \text{Conversion formula 2}$$ ▍▍▍

11.1 EXERCISES

In Exercises 1–4, give the probability that the spinner shown would land on **(a)** *red,* **(b)** *yellow,* **(c)** *blue.*

1.

2.

3.

4.

Solve each probability problem.

5. *Using Spinners to Generate Numbers* Suppose the spinner shown here is spun once, to determine a single-digit number, and we are interested in the event E that the resulting number is odd. Give each of the following.

(a) the sample space

(b) the number of favorable outcomes

(c) the number of unfavorable outcomes

(d) the total number of possible outcomes

(e) the probability of an odd number

(f) the odds in favor of an odd number

6. *Lining Up Preschool Children* Kim Lenaghan's group of preschool children includes nine girls and seven boys. If Kim randomly selects one child to be first in line, with E being the event that the one selected is a girl, give each of the following.

(a) the total number of possible outcomes

(b) the number of favorable outcomes

(c) the number of unfavorable outcomes

(d) the probability of event E

(e) the odds in favor of event E

7. *Using Spinners to Generate Numbers* The spinner of **Exercise 5** is spun twice in succession to determine a two-digit number. Give each of the following.

(a) the sample space

(b) the probability of an odd number

(c) the probability of a number with repeated digits

(d) the probability of a number greater than 30

(e) the probability of a prime number

8. *Probabilities in Coin Tossing* Two fair coins are tossed (say a dime and a quarter). Give each of the following.

(a) the sample space

(b) the probability of heads on the dime

(c) the probability of heads on the quarter

(d) the probability of getting both heads

(e) the probability of getting the same outcome on both coins

9. *Drawing Balls from an Urn* Anne Kelly randomly chooses a single ball from the urn shown here. Find the odds against each event.

(a) red   **(b)** yellow   **(c)** blue

10. *Random Selection of Club Officers* Five people (Alan, Bill, Cathy, David, and Evelyn) form a club $N = \{A, B, C, D, E\}$. If they choose a president randomly, find the odds against each result.

(a) Cathy   **(b)** a woman

(c) a person whose name begins with a consonant

11. *Random Selection of Fifties Music* Butch LeBeau has fifty hit singles from the fifties, including exactly one by Smiley Lewis, two by The Drifters, three by Bobby Darin, four by The Coasters, and five by Fats Domino. If Butch randomly selects one hit from his collection of fifty, find the probability it will be by each of the following.

(a) Smiley Lewis   **(b)** The Drifters

(c) Bobby Darin   **(d)** The Coasters

(e) Fats Domino

12. *Probabilities in Coin Tossing* Three fair coins are tossed.

(a) Write out the sample space.

Determine the probability of each event.

(b) no heads   **(c)** exactly one head

(d) exactly two heads   **(e)** three heads

13. *Number Sums for Rolling Two Dice* The sample space for the rolling of two fair dice appeared in **Table 2** of **Section 10.1**. Reproduce that table, but replace each of the 36 equally likely ordered pairs with its corresponding sum (for the two dice). Then find the probability of rolling each sum.

(a) 2   **(b)** 3   **(c)** 4

(d) 5   **(e)** 6   **(f)** 7

(g) 8   **(h)** 9   **(i)** 10

(j) 11   **(k)** 12

In Exercises 14 and 15, give answers to three decimal places.

14. *Probability of Seed Germination* In a hybrid corn research project, 200 seeds were planted, and 175 of them germinated. Find the empirical probability that any particular seed of this type will germinate.

15. *Probability of Forest Land in California* According to *The World Almanac and Book of Facts 2010,* California has 155,959 square miles of land area, 51,250 square miles of which are forested. Find the probability that a randomly selected location in California will be forested.

16. *Probabilities of Two Daughters Among Four Children* In **Example 3,** what would be Kathy's probability of having exactly two daughters if she were to have four children altogether? (You may want to use a tree diagram to construct the sample space.)

17. *Rolling Altered Dice* A six-sided die has been altered so that the side that had been a single dot is now a blank face. Another die has a blank face instead of the face with four dots. What is the probability that a sum of 7 is rolled when the two dice are thrown? (*Mathematics Teacher* calendar problem)

18. *Probability of Location in a Tunnel* Mr. Davis is driving through a tunnel that is eight miles long. At this instant, what is the probability that he is at least six miles from one end of the tunnel? (*Mathematics Teacher* calendar problem)

Genetics in Snapdragons Mendel found no dominance in snapdragons (in contrast to peas) with respect to red and white flower color. When pure red and pure white parents are crossed (see **Table 2**), *the resulting* Rr *combination (one of each gene) produces second-generation offspring with* pink *flowers. These second-generation pinks, however, still carry one red and one white gene, so when they are crossed the third generation is still governed by* **Table 3**.
Find each probability for third-generation snapdragons.

19. *P*(red)   **20.** *P*(pink)   **21.** *P*(white)

Genetics in Pea Plants   Mendel also investigated various characteristics besides flower color. For example, round peas are dominant over recessive wrinkled peas. First, second, and third generations can again be analyzed using **Tables 2 and 3**, *where* R *represents round and* r *represents wrinkled.*

22. Explain why crossing pure round and pure wrinkled first-generation parents will always produce round peas in the second-generation offspring.

23. When second-generation round pea plants (each of which carries both R and r genes) are crossed, find the probability that a third-generation offspring will have

(a) round peas,   (b) wrinkled peas.

Genetics of Cystic Fibrosis Cystic fibrosis *is one of the most common inherited diseases in North America (including the United States), occurring in about 1 of every 2000 Caucasian births and about 1 of every 250,000 non-Caucasian births. Even with modern treatment, victims usually die from lung damage by their early twenties.*
If we denote a cystic fibrosis gene with a c *and a disease-free gene with a* C *(since the disease is recessive), then only a* cc *person will actually have the disease. Such persons would ordinarily die before parenting children, but a child can also inherit the disease from two* Cc *parents (who themselves are healthy, that is, have no symptoms but are "carriers" of the disease). This is like a pea plant inheriting white flowers from two red-flowered parents that both carry genes for white.*

24. Find the empirical probability (to four decimal places) that cystic fibrosis will occur in a randomly selected infant birth among U.S. Caucasians.

25. Find the empirical probability (to six decimal places) that cystic fibrosis will occur in a randomly selected infant birth among U.S. non-Caucasians.

26. Among 150,000 North American Caucasian births, about how many occurrences of cystic fibrosis would you expect?

Suppose that both partners in a marriage are cystic fibrosis carriers (a rare occurrence). Construct a chart similar to **Table 3** *and determine the probability of each of the following events.*

27. Their first child will have the disease.

28. Their first child will be a carrier.

29. Their first child will neither have nor carry the disease.

Suppose a child is born to one cystic fibrosis carrier parent and one non-carrier parent. Find the probability of each of the following events.

30. The child will have cystic fibrosis.

31. The child will be a healthy cystic fibrosis carrier.

32. The child will neither have nor carry the disease.

Genetics of Sickle-Cell Anemia Sickle-cell anemia *occurs in about 1 of every 500 black baby births and about 1 of every 160,000 non-black baby births. It is ordinarily fatal in early childhood. There is a test to identify carriers. Unlike cystic fibrosis, which is recessive, sickle-cell anemia is* **codominant.** *This means that inheriting two sickle-cell genes causes the disease, while inheriting just one sickle-cell gene causes a mild (non-fatal) version (which is called* **sickle-cell trait**). *This is similar to a snapdragon plant manifesting pink flowers by inheriting one red gene and one white gene.*
In Exercises 33 and 34, find the empirical probabilities of the given events.

33. A randomly selected black baby will have sickle-cell anemia. (Give your answer to three decimal places.)

34. A randomly selected non-black baby will have sickle-cell anemia. (Give your answer to six decimal places.)

35. Among 80,000 births of black babies, about how many occurrences of sickle-cell anemia would you expect?

Find the theoretical probability of each condition in a child both of whose parents have sickle-cell trait.

36. The child will have sickle-cell anemia.

37. The child will have sickle-cell trait.

38. The child will be healthy.

39. *Women's 100-Meter Run* In the history of track and field, no woman has broken the 10-second barrier in the 100-meter run.

   (a) From the statement above, find the empirical probability that a woman runner will break the 10-second barrier next year.

   (b) Can you find the theoretical probability for the event of part (a)?

   (c) Is it possible that the event of part (a) will occur?

40. Is there any way a coin could fail to be "fair"? Explain.

41. On page 27 of their book *Descartes' Dream*, Philip Davis and Reuben Hersh ask the question, "Is probability real or is it just a cover-up for ignorance?" What do you think? Are some things truly random, or is everything potentially deterministic?

42. If $P(E) = 0.37$, find

   (a) the odds in favor of E,   **(b)** the odds against E.

43. If the odds in favor of event E are 12 to 19, find $P(E)$.

44. If the odds against event E are 10 to 3, find $P(E)$.

Probabilities of Poker Hands *In 5-card poker, find the probability of being dealt each of the following. Give each answer to eight decimal places. (Refer to* **Table 1**.*)*

45. a straight flush   **46.** two pairs

47. four of a kind   **48.** four queens

49. a hearts flush (*not* a royal flush or a straight flush)

50. *Probabilities in Dart Throwing* If a dart hits the square target shown here at random, what is the probability that it will hit in a colored region? (*Hint:* Compare the area of the colored regions to the total area of the target.)

51. *Probabilities in Olympic Curling* In the Olympic event of curling, the scoring area (shown here) consists of four concentric circles on the ice with radii of 6 inches, 2 feet, 4 feet, and 6 feet.

If a team member lands a (43-pound) stone *randomly* within the scoring area, find the probability that it ends up centered on

   (a) red,   **(b)** white,   **(c)** blue.

52. *Drawing Cards* When drawing cards without replacement from a standard 52-card deck, find the maximum number of cards you could possibly draw and still get

   (a) fewer than three black cards,

   (b) fewer than six spades,

   (c) fewer than four face cards,

   (d) fewer than two kings.

The remaining exercises require careful thought to determine n(E) and n(S). (In some cases, you may want to employ counting methods from Chapter 10, such as the fundamental counting principle, permutations, or combinations.)

Probabilities of Seating Arrangements *Six people (three married couples) arrange themselves randomly in six consecutive seats in a row. Find the probability of each event in Exercises 53–56. (Hint: In each case the denominator of the probability fraction will be 6! = 720, the total number of ways to arrange six items.)*

53. Each man will sit immediately to the left of his wife.

54. Each man will sit immediately to the left of a woman.

55. The women will be in three adjacent seats.

56. The women will be in three adjacent seats, as will the men.

57. *Selecting Slopes* If two distinct numbers are chosen randomly from the set $\{-2, -\frac{4}{3}, -\frac{1}{2}, 0, \frac{1}{2}, \frac{3}{4}, 3\}$, find the probability that they will be the slopes of two perpendicular lines. (See **Section 8.2**.)

58. *Racing Bets* At most horse-racing tracks, the "trifecta" is a particular race in which you win if you correctly pick the "win," "place," and "show" horses (the first-, second-, and third-place winners), in their proper order. If five horses of equal ability are entered in today's trifecta race, and Tracy Light selects an entry, what is the probability that she will be a winner?

59. *Probabilities of Student Course Schedules* Suppose you plan to take three courses next term. If you select them randomly from a listing of twelve courses, five of which are science courses, what is the probability that all three courses you select will be science courses?

60. *Selecting Symphony Performances* Rhonda Goedeker randomly selects three symphony performances to attend this season, choosing from a schedule of ten performances, three of which will feature works by Beethoven. Find the probability that Rhonda will select all of the Beethoven programs.

Selecting Class Reports Assuming that Ben, Jill, and Pam are three of the 26 members of the class, and that three of the class members will be chosen randomly to deliver their reports during the next class meeting, find the probability (to six decimal places) of each event.

61. Ben, Jill, and Pam are selected, in that order.

62. Ben, Jill, and Pam are selected, in any order.

63. *Random Selection of Prime Numbers* If two distinct prime numbers are randomly selected from among the first eight prime numbers, what is the probability that their sum will be 24?

64. *Building Numbers from Sets of Digits* The digits 1, 2, 3, 4, and 5 are randomly arranged to form a five-digit number. Find the probability of each event.

(a) The number is even.

(b) The first and last digits of the number both are even.

65. *Random Sums* Two integers are randomly selected from the set $\{1, 2, 3, 4, 5, 6, 7, 8, 9\}$ and are added together. Find the probability that their sum is 11 if they are selected

(a) with replacement,   (b) without replacement.

66. *Random Sums and Products* Tamika selects two different numbers at random from the set $\{8, 9, 10\}$ and adds them. Carlos takes two different numbers at random from the set $\{3, 5, 6\}$ and multiplies them. What is the probability that Tamika's result is greater than Carlos's result? (*Mathematics Teacher* calendar problem)

67. *Divisibility of Random Products* When a fair six-sided die is tossed on a tabletop, the bottom face cannot be seen. What is the probability that the product of the numbers on the five faces that can be seen is divisible by 6? (*Mathematics Teacher* calendar problem)

68. *Building Fractions with Dice* Lisa has one red die and one green die, which she rolls to make up fractions. The green die is the numerator, and the red die is the denominator. Some of the fractions have terminating decimal representations. How many different terminating decimal results can these two dice represent? What is the probability of rolling a fraction with a terminating decimal representation? (*Mathematics Teacher* calendar problem)

*Finding Palindromic Numbers Numbers that are **palindromes** read the same forward and backward. For example, 30203 is a five-digit palindrome. If a single number is chosen randomly from each of the following sets, find the probability that it will be palindromic.*

69. the set of all two-digit numbers

70. the set of all three-digit numbers

Six people, call them A, B, C, D, E, and F, are randomly divided into three groups of two. Find the probability of each event. (Do not impose unwanted ordering among groups.)

71. *A* and *B* are in the same group, as are *C* and *D*.

72. *E* and *F* are in the same group.

11.2 EVENTS INVOLVING "NOT" AND "OR"

Properties of Probability • Events Involving "Not" • Events Involving "Or"

Properties of Probability

Recall that an empirical probability, based upon experimental observation, may be the best value available but still is only an approximation to the ("true") theoretical probability. For example, no human has ever been known to jump higher than 8.5 feet vertically, so the empirical probability of such an event is zero. Observing the rate at which high jump records have been broken, we suspect that the event is, in fact, possible and may one day occur. Hence it must have some nonzero theoretical probability, even though we have no way of assessing its exact value.

Recall also that the theoretical probability formula,

$$P(E) = \frac{n(E)}{n(S)},$$

is valid only when all outcomes in the sample space S are equally likely. For the experiment of tossing two fair coins, we can write $S = \{hh, ht, th, tt\}$ and compute

$$P(\text{both heads}) = \frac{1}{4}, \quad \text{which is } \textit{correct,}$$

whereas if we define the sample space with non-equally likely outcomes as $S = \{\text{both heads, both tails, one of each}\}$, we are led to

$$P(\text{both heads}) = \frac{1}{3}, \quad \text{which is } \textit{incorrect.}$$

(To convince yourself that $\frac{1}{4}$ is a better value than $\frac{1}{3}$, toss two fair coins 100 times or so to see what the empirical fraction seems to approach.)

For any event E within a sample space S, we know that $0 \le n(E) \le n(S)$. Dividing all members of this inequality by $n(S)$ gives

$$\frac{0}{n(S)} \le \frac{n(E)}{n(S)} \le \frac{n(S)}{n(S)}, \quad \text{or} \quad \mathbf{0 \le P(E) \le 1.}$$

In words, the probability of any event is a number from 0 through 1, inclusive.

If event E is *impossible* (cannot happen), then $n(E)$ must be 0 (E is the empty set), so $P(E) = 0$. If event E is *certain* (cannot help but happen), then $n(E) = n(S)$, so

$$P(E) = \frac{n(E)}{n(S)} = \frac{n(S)}{n(S)} = 1.$$

Pierre Simon de Laplace (1749–1827) began in 1773 to solve the problem of why Jupiter's orbit seems to shrink and Saturn's orbit seems to expand. Eventually Laplace worked out a complete theory of the solar system. *Celestial Mechanics* resulted from almost a lifetime of work. In five volumes, it was published between 1799 and 1825 and gained for Laplace the reputation "Newton of France."

Laplace's work on probability was actually an adjunct to his celestial mechanics. He needed to demonstrate that probability is useful in interpreting scientific data.

Properties of Probability

Let E be an event within the sample space S. That is, E is a subset of S. Then the following properties hold.

1. $0 \le P(E) \le 1$ (The probability of an event is a number from 0 through 1, inclusive.)

2. $P(\emptyset) = 0$ (The probability of an impossible event is 0.)

3. $P(S) = 1$ (The probability of a certain event is 1.)

■ ■ EXAMPLE 1 Finding Probability When Rolling a Die

When a single fair die is rolled, find the probability of each event.

(a) the number 2 is rolled   **(b)** a number other than 2 is rolled

(c) the number 7 is rolled   **(d)** a number less than 7 is rolled

SOLUTION

(a) Since one of the six possibilities is a 2, $P(2) = \frac{1}{6}$.

(b) There are five such numbers, 1, 3, 4, 5, and 6, so $P(\text{a number other than 2}) = \frac{5}{6}$.

(c) None of the possible outcomes is 7. Thus, $P(7) = \frac{0}{6} = 0$.

(d) Since all six of the possible outcomes are less than 7,

$$P(\text{a number less than 7}) = \frac{6}{6} = 1. \qquad \blacksquare\blacksquare\blacksquare$$

No probability in **Example 1** was less than 0 or greater than 1, which illustrates probability property 1. The "impossible" event of part (c) had probability 0, illustrating property 2. The "certain" event of part (d) had probability 1, illustrating property 3.

Events Involving "Not"

Table 4 repeats the information of **Table 8** of **Section 10.5,** with a third correspondence added in row 3. These correspondences are the basis for the probability rules. For example, the probability of an event *not* happening involves the *complement* and *subtraction,* according to row 1 of the table.

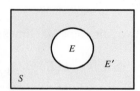

The logical connective "not" corresponds to "complement" in set theory.

$$P(not\,E) = P(S) - P(E)$$
$$= 1 - P(E)$$

Figure 4

Table 4   Set Theory/Logic/Arithmetic Correspondences

	Set Theory	Logic	Arithmetic
1. Operation or Connective (Symbol)	Complement (′)	Not (~)	Subtraction (−)
2. Operation or Connective (Symbol)	Union (∪)	Or (∨)	Addition (+)
3. Operation or Connective (Symbol)	Intersection (∩)	And (∧)	Multiplication (·)

The rule for the probability of a complement follows and is illustrated in **Figure 4.**

Probability of a Complement (for Not *E*)

The probability that an event *E* will *not* occur is equal to one minus the probability that it *will* occur.

$$P(\textbf{not } E) = 1 - P(E)$$

Notice that the events of **Examples 1(a) and (b),** namely "2" and "not 2," are complements of one another, and that their probabilities add up to 1. This illustrates the above probability rule. The equation

$$P(E) + P(E') = 1$$

is a rearrangement of the formula for the probability of a complement. Another form of the equation that is also useful at times follows.

$$P(E) = 1 - P(E')$$

▋▋ **EXAMPLE 2** Finding the Probability of a Complement

When a single card is drawn from a standard 52-card deck, what is the probability that it will not be a king?

SOLUTION

$$P(\text{not a king}) = 1 - P(\text{king}) = 1 - \frac{4}{52} = \frac{48}{52} = \frac{12}{13}$$

Remember to write in lowest terms.

▋▋▋

▮▮ **EXAMPLE 3** Finding the Probability of a Complement

If five fair coins are tossed, find the probability of obtaining at least two heads.

SOLUTION

There are $2^5 = 32$ possible outcomes for the experiment of tossing five fair coins. Most include at least two heads. In fact, only the outcomes

ttttt, htttt, thttt, tthtt, tttht, and tttth

do *not* include at least two heads. If E denotes the event "at least two heads," then E' is the event "not at least two heads,"

$$P(E) = 1 - P(E') = 1 - \frac{6}{32} = \frac{26}{32} = \frac{13}{16}$$ ▮▮▮

Mary Somerville (1780–1872) is associated with Laplace because of her brilliant exposition of his *Celestial Mechanics.*

    Somerville studied Euclid thoroughly and perfected her Latin so she could read Newton's *Principia.* In about 1816 she went to London and soon became part of its literary and scientific circles.

    Somerville's book on Laplace's theories came out in 1831 with great acclaim. Then followed a panoramic book, *Connection of the Physical Sciences* (1834). A statement in one of its editions suggested that irregularities in the orbit of Uranus might indicate that a more remote planet, not yet seen, existed. This caught the eye of the scientists who worked out the calculations for Neptune's orbit.

Events Involving "Or"

Examples 2 and 3 showed how the probability of an event can be approached *indirectly,* by first considering the complement of the event. Another indirect approach is to break the event into simpler component events. Row 2 of **Table 4** indicates that the probability of one event *or* another should involve the *union* and *addition.*

▮▮ **EXAMPLE 4** Selecting From a Set of Numbers

If one number is selected randomly from the set $\{1, 2, 3, 4, 5, 6, 7, 8, 9, 10\}$, find the probability that it will be

(a) odd or a multiple of 4   **(b)** odd or a multiple of 3.

SOLUTION

Define the following events:

$$\begin{aligned} S &= \{1, 2, 3, 4, 5, 6, 7, 8, 9, 10\} && \text{Sample space} \\ A &= \{1, 3, 5, 7, 9\} && \text{Odd outcomes} \\ B &= \{4, 8\} && \text{Multiples of 4} \\ C &= \{3, 6, 9\} && \text{Multiples of 3} \end{aligned}$$

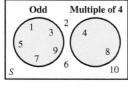

Figure 5

(a) **Figure 5** shows the positioning of the 10 integers within the sample space and within the pertinent sets A and B. The composite event "A or B" corresponds to the set $A \cup B = \{1, 3, 4, 5, 7, 8, 9\}$. By the theoretical probability formula,

$$P(A \text{ or } B) = \frac{7}{10}.$$ Of 10 total outcomes, 7 are favorable.

(b) **Figure 6** shows the situation.

Of 10 total outcomes, 6 are favorable.

$$P(A \text{ or } C) = \frac{6}{10} = \frac{3}{5}$$ ▮▮▮

Figure 6

Would an addition formula have worked in **Example 4**? Let's check.

Part (a): $P(A \text{ or } B) = P(A) + P(B) = \dfrac{5}{10} + \dfrac{2}{10} = \dfrac{7}{10}$ Correct

Part (b): $P(A \text{ or } C) = P(A) + P(C) = \dfrac{5}{10} + \dfrac{3}{10} = \dfrac{8}{10} = \dfrac{4}{5}$ Incorrect

The trouble in part (b) is that A and C are not disjoint sets. They have outcomes in common. Just as with the additive counting principle in **Chapter 10,** an adjustment must be made here to compensate for counting the common outcomes twice.

$$P(A \text{ or } C) = P(A) + P(C) - P(A \text{ and } C)$$
$$= \frac{5}{10} + \frac{3}{10} - \frac{2}{10} = \frac{6}{10} = \frac{3}{5} \qquad \text{Correct}$$

In probability theory, events that are disjoint sets are called *mutually exclusive events.*

Mutually Exclusive Events

Two events A and B are **mutually exclusive events** if they have no outcomes in common. (Mutually exclusive events cannot occur simultaneously.)

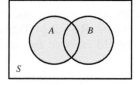

The logical connective "or" corresponds to "union" in set theory.

$P(A \text{ or } B)$
$= P(A) + P(B) - P(A \text{ and } B)$

Figure 7

The results observed in **Example 4** are generalized as follows. The two possibilities are illustrated in **Figures 7 and 8**.

Addition Rule of Probability (for A or B)

If A and B are any two events, then

$$P(A \text{ or } B) = P(A) + P(B) - P(A \text{ and } B).$$

If A and B are mutually exclusive, then

$$P(A \text{ or } B) = P(A) + P(B).$$

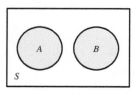

When A and B are mutually exclusive,
$P(A \text{ or } B) = P(A) + P(B)$.

Figure 8

Actually, the first formula in the addition rule applies in all cases. (The third term on the right drops out when A and B are mutually exclusive, because $P(A \text{ and } B) = 0$.) Still it is good to remember the second formula in the preceding box for the many cases where the component events are mutually exclusive. In this section, we consider only cases where the event "A and B" is simple. We deal with more involved composites involving "and" in the next section.

▮▮ **EXAMPLE 5** Finding the Probability of an Event Involving "Or"

If a single card is drawn from a standard 52-card deck, what is the probability that it will be a spade or a red card?

SOLUTION

First note that "spade" and "red" cannot both occur, because there are no red spades. (All spades are black.) Therefore, we can use the formula for mutually exclusive events. There are 13 spades and 26 red cards in the deck.

$$P(\text{spade or red}) = P(\text{spade}) + P(\text{red}) = \frac{13}{52} + \frac{26}{52} = \frac{39}{52} = \frac{3}{4} \qquad ▮▮▮$$

We often need to consider composites of more than two events. When each event involved is mutually exclusive of all the others, we extend the addition rule to the appropriate number of components.

▮▮ **EXAMPLE 6** Treating Unions of Several Components

Amy Hogan plans to spend from 1 to 6 hours on her homework. If x represents the number of hours to be spent, then the probabilities of the various values of x, rounded to the nearest hour, are shown in **Table 5**. Find the probabilities that Amy will spend

(a) fewer than 3 hours **(b)** more than 2 hours

(c) more than 1 but no more than 5 hours **(d)** fewer than 5 hours.

SOLUTION

Because the time periods in **Table 5** are mutually exclusive of one another, we can simply add the appropriate component probabilities.

Table 5

x	$P(x)$
1	0.05
2	0.10
3	0.20
4	0.40
5	0.10
6	0.15

(a) $P(\text{fewer than } 3) = P(1 \text{ or } 2)$ Fewer than 3 means 1 or 2.

$\qquad\qquad\qquad\quad = P(1) + P(2)$ Addition rule

$\qquad\qquad\qquad\quad = 0.05 + 0.10$ Substitute values from **Table 5**.

$\qquad\qquad\qquad\quad = 0.15$

(b) $P(\text{more than } 2) = P(3 \text{ or } 4 \text{ or } 5 \text{ or } 6)$ More than 2 means 3, 4, 5, or 6.

$\qquad\qquad\qquad\quad = P(3) + P(4) + P(5) + P(6)$ Addition rule

$\qquad\qquad\qquad\quad = 0.20 + 0.40 + 0.10 + 0.15$ Substitute values from **Table 5**.

$\qquad\qquad\qquad\quad = 0.85$

(c) $P(\text{more than 1 but no more than 5})$

$\qquad\qquad\quad = P(2 \text{ or } 3 \text{ or } 4 \text{ or } 5)$ 2, 3, 4, and 5 are more than 1 and no more than 5.

$\qquad\qquad\quad = P(2) + P(3) + P(4) + P(5)$ Addition rule

$\qquad\qquad\quad = 0.10 + 0.20 + 0.40 + 0.10$ Substitute values from **Table 5**.

$\qquad\qquad\quad = 0.80$

(d) Although we could take a direct approach here, as in parts (a), (b), and (c), we will combine the complement rule with the addition rule.

$P(\text{fewer than } 5) = 1 - P(\text{not fewer than } 5)$ Complement rule

$\qquad\qquad\qquad = 1 - P(5 \text{ or more})$ 5 or more is equivalent to not fewer than 5.

$\qquad\qquad\qquad = 1 - P(5 \text{ or } 6)$ 5 or more means 5 or 6.

$\qquad\qquad\qquad = 1 - [P(5) + P(6)]$ Addition rule

$\qquad\qquad\qquad = 1 - (0.10 + 0.15)$ Substitute values from **Table 5**.

$\qquad\qquad\qquad = 1 - 0.25$ Add inside the parentheses first.

$\qquad\qquad\qquad = 0.75$ ▮▮▮

Table 5 in **Example 6** lists all possible time intervals so the corresponding probabilities add up to 1, a necessary condition for the way part (d) was done. The time spent on homework here is an example of a **random variable.** (It is "random" since we cannot predict which of its possible values will occur.)

A listing like **Table 5**, which shows all possible values of a random variable, along with the probabilities that those values will occur, is called a **probability distribution** for that random variable. Since *all* possible values are listed, they make up the entire sample space, and so the listed probabilities must add up to 1 (by probability property 3). Probability distributions will occur in **Exercises 32 and 33** of this section and will be discussed further in later sections.

■■ EXAMPLE 7   Finding the Probability of an Event Involving "Or"

Find the probability that a single card drawn from a standard 52-card deck will be a diamond or a face card.

SOLUTION

The component events "diamond" and "face card" can occur simultaneously. (The jack, queen, and king of diamonds belong to both events.) So, we must use the first formula of the addition rule. We let D denote "diamond" and F denote "face card."

$$P(D \text{ or } F) = P(D) + P(F) - P(D \text{ and } F) \quad \text{Addition rule}$$

$$= \frac{13}{52} + \frac{12}{52} - \frac{3}{52} \quad \begin{array}{l}\text{There are 13 diamonds, 12 face cards,} \\ \text{and 3 that are both.}\end{array}$$

$$= \frac{22}{52} \quad \text{Add and subtract.}$$

$$= \frac{11}{26} \quad \text{Write in lowest terms.} \quad ■■■$$

■■ EXAMPLE 8   Finding the Probability of an Event Involving "Or"

Of 20 elective courses, Emily Horowitz plans to enroll in one, which she will choose by throwing a dart at the schedule of courses. If 8 of the courses are recreational, 9 are interesting, and 3 are both recreational and interesting, find the probability that the course Emily chooses will have at least one of these two attributes.

SOLUTION

If R denotes "recreational" and I denotes "interesting," then $P(R) = \frac{8}{20}$, $P(I) = \frac{9}{20}$, and $P(R \text{ and } I) = \frac{3}{20}$. R and I are not mutually exclusive.

$$P(R \text{ or } I) = \frac{8}{20} + \frac{9}{20} - \frac{3}{20} = \frac{14}{20} = \frac{7}{10} \quad \text{Addition rule; lowest terms} \quad ■■■$$

11.2 EXERCISES

1. *Determining Whether Events Are Mutually Exclusive* Amanda Crotts has three office assistants. If A is the event that at least two of them are men and B is the event that at least two of them are women, are A and B mutually exclusive?

2. *Determining Whether Events Are Mutually Exclusive* Jeanne Jalufka earned her college degree several years ago. Consider the following four events.

   Her alma mater is in the East.
   Her alma mater is a private college.
   Her alma mater is in the Northwest.
   Her alma mater is in the South.

   Are these events all mutually exclusive of one another?

3. Explain the difference between the two formulas in the addition rule of probability on **page 592,** illustrating each one with an appropriate example.

Probabilities for Rolling a Die For the experiment of rolling a single fair die, find the probability of each event.

4. not less than 2

5. not prime

6. odd or less than 5

7. even or prime

8. odd or even

9. less than 3 or greater than 4

Probability and Odds for Drawing a Card For the experiment of drawing a single card from a standard 52-card deck, find (a) the probability, and (b) the odds in favor, of each event.

10. not an ace

11. king or queen

12. club or heart

13. spade or face card

14. not a heart, or a 7

15. neither a heart nor a 7

Number Sums for Rolling a Pair of Dice *For the experiment of rolling an ordinary pair of dice, find the probability that the sum will be each of the following. (You may want to use a table showing the sum for each of the 36 equally likely outcomes.)*

16. 11 or 12

17. even or a multiple of 3

18. odd or greater than 9

19. less than 3 or greater than 9

20. Find the probability of getting a prime number in each case.

   (a) A number is chosen randomly from the set $\{1, 2, 3, 4, \ldots, 12\}$.

   (b) Two dice are rolled and the sum is observed.

21. Suppose, for a given experiment, A, B, C, and D are events, all mutually exclusive of one another, such that $A \cup B \cup C \cup D = S$ (the sample space). By extending the addition rule of probability on **page 592** to this case, and utilizing probability property 3, what statement can you make?

Probabilities of Poker Hands *If you are dealt a 5-card hand (this implies without replacement) from a standard 52-card deck, find the probability of getting each of the following. Refer to **Table 1** of **Section 11.1**, and give answers to six decimal places.*

22. a flush or three of a kind

23. a full house or a straight

24. a black flush or two pairs

25. nothing any better than two pairs

Probabilities in Golf Scoring *The table gives golfer Brian Donahue's probabilities of scoring in various ranges on a par-70 course. In a given round, find the probability of each event in Exercises 26–30.*

26. 95 or higher

27. par or above

28. in the 80s

29. less than 90

30. not in the 70s, 80s, or 90s

31. What are the odds of Brian's scoring below par?

x	$P(x)$
Below 60	0.04
60–64	0.06
65–69	0.14
70–74	0.30
75–79	0.23
80–84	0.09
85–89	0.06
90–94	0.04
95–99	0.03
100 or above	0.01

32. ***Drawing Balls from an Urn*** Anne Kelly randomly chooses a single ball from the urn shown here, and x represents the color of the ball chosen. Construct a complete probability distribution for the random variable x.

33. Let x denote the sum of two distinct numbers selected randomly from the set $\{1, 2, 3, 4, 5\}$. Construct the probability distribution for the random variable x.

34. ***Comparing Empirical and Theoretical Probabilities for Rolling Dice*** Roll a pair of dice 50 times, keeping track of the number of times the sum is "less than 3 or greater than 9" (that is 2, 10, 11, or 12).

   (a) From your results, calculate an empirical probability for the event "less than 3 or greater than 9."

   (b) By how much does your answer differ from the *theoretical* probability of **Exercise 19?**

For Exercises 35–38, let A be an event within the sample space S, and let $n(A) = a$ and $n(S) = s$.

35. Use the complements principle of counting to find an expression for $n(A')$.

36. Use the theoretical probability formula to express $P(A)$ and $P(A')$.

37. Evaluate, and simplify, $P(A) + P(A')$.

38. What rule have you proved?

The remaining exercises require careful thought for the determination of n(E) and n(S). (In some cases, you may want to employ counting methods from Chapter 10, such as the fundamental counting principle, permutations, or combinations.)

Building Numbers from Sets of Digits *Suppose we want to form three-digit numbers using the set of digits*

$$\{0, 1, 2, 3, 4, 5\}.$$

For example, 501 *and* 224 *are such numbers but* 035 *is not.*

39. How many such numbers are possible?

40. How many of these numbers are multiples of 5?

41. If one three-digit number is chosen at random from all those that can be made from the above set of digits, find the probability that the one chosen is not a multiple of 5.

42. *Multiplying Numbers Generated by Spinners* An experiment consists of spinning both spinners shown here and multiplying the resulting numbers together. Find the probability that the resulting product will be even.

43. *Drawing Colored Marbles from Boxes* A bag contains fifty blue and fifty green marbles. Two marbles at a time are randomly selected. If both are green, they are placed in box A; if both are blue, in box B; if one is green and the other is blue, in box C. After all marbles are drawn, what is the probability that the numbers of marbles in box A and box B are the same? (*Mathematics Teacher* calendar problem)

44. *Random Births on the Same Day of the Week* What is the probability that, of three people selected at random, at least two were born on the same day of the week? (*Mathematics Teacher* calendar problem)

11.3 CONDITIONAL PROBABILITY; EVENTS INVOLVING "AND"

Conditional Probability • Events Involving "And"

Even **a rare occurrence** can sometimes cause widespread controversy. When Mattel Toys marketed a new talking Barbie doll a few years ago, some of the Barbies were programmed to say "Math class is tough." The National Council of Teachers of Mathematics (NCTM), the American Association of University Women (AAUW), and numerous consumers voiced complaints about the damage such a message could do to the self-confidence of children and to their attitudes toward school and mathematics. Mattel subsequently agreed to erase the phrase from the microchip to be used in future doll production.

Each Barbie was programmed to say four different statements, randomly selected from a pool of 270 prerecorded statements. Therefore, the probability of getting one that said "Math class is tough" was only

$$\frac{1 \cdot {}_{269}C_3}{{}_{270}C_4} \approx 0.015.$$

Other messages included in the pool were "I love school, don't you?," "I'm studying to be a doctor," and "Let's study for the quiz."

Conditional Probability

Sometimes the probability of an event must be computed using the knowledge that some other event has happened (or is happening, or will happen—the timing is not important). This type of probability is called *conditional probability*.

> **Conditional Probability**
>
> The probability of event B, computed on the assumption that event A has happened, is called the **conditional probability of B given A**, and is denoted
>
> $$P(B|A).$$

▌▌ **EXAMPLE 1** Selecting from a Set of Numbers

From the sample space $S = \{1, 2, 3, 4, 5, 6, 7, 8, 9, 10\}$, a single number is to be selected randomly. Find each probability given the events

A: The selected number is odd, and B: The selected number is a multiple of 3.

(a) $P(B)$ **(b)** $P(A \text{ and } B)$ **(c)** $P(B|A)$

SOLUTION

(a) $B = \{3, 6, 9\}$, so $P(B) = \frac{n(B)}{n(S)} = \frac{3}{10}$.

(b) A and B is the set $A \cap B = \{1, 3, 5, 7, 9\} \cap \{3, 6, 9\} = \{3, 9\}$.

$$P(A \text{ and } B) = \frac{n(A \cap B)}{n(S)} = \frac{2}{10} = \frac{1}{5}$$

(c) The given condition, that A occurs, effectively reduces the sample space from S to A, and the elements of the new sample space A that are also in B are the elements of $A \cap B$.

$$P(B|A) = \frac{n(A \cap B)}{n(A)} = \frac{2}{5}$$

▌▌▌

A **cosmic impact,** the collision of a meteor, comet, or asteroid with Earth, could be as catastrophic as full-scale nuclear war, killing a billion or more people. The Web site www.impact.arc .nasa.gov reports that a large enough object (1 kilometer or more in diameter) could even put the human species at risk of annihilation by causing drastic climate changes and destroying food crops.

The Spaceguard Survey has discovered more than half of the estimated number of near-Earth asteroids (NEAs) in this size range and hopes to locate 90% of them in the next decade. Although the risk of finding one on a collision course with the Earth is slight, it is anticipated that, if we did, we would be able to deflect it before impact.

The photo above shows a crater in Arizona, 4000 feet in diameter and 570 feet deep, thought to have been formed 20,000 to 50,000 years ago by a meteorite about 50 meters across, hitting the ground at several kilometers per second. (See http://en.wikipedia.org/wiki/ Meteor_Crater.)

Example 1 illustrates some important points. First, because

$$\frac{n(A \cap B)}{n(A)} = \frac{\frac{n(A \cap B)}{n(S)}}{\frac{n(A)}{n(S)}} \quad \text{Multiply numerator and denominator by } \frac{1}{n(S)}.$$

$$= \frac{P(A \cap B)}{P(A)}, \quad \text{Theoretical probability formula}$$

the final line of the example gives the following convenient formula.

> **Conditional Probability Formula**
>
> The **conditional probability of B given A** is calculated as follows.
>
> $$P(B|A) = \frac{P(A \cap B)}{P(A)} = \frac{P(A \text{ and } B)}{P(A)}$$

A second observation from **Example 1** is that the conditional probability of B, given A, was $\frac{2}{5}$, whereas the "unconditional" probability of B (with no condition given) was $\frac{3}{10}$, so the condition did make a difference.

▌ **EXAMPLE 2** Finding Probabilities of Boys and Girls in a Family

Given a family with two children, find the probabilities that

(a) both are girls, given that at least one is a girl, and

(b) both are girls, given that the older child is a girl.

(Assume boys and girls are equally likely.)

SOLUTION

We define the following events.

$$\begin{aligned}
S &= \{gg, gb, bg, bb\} \quad &\text{Sample space} \\
A &= \{gg\} \quad &\text{Both are girls.} \\
B &= \{gg, gb, bg\} \quad &\text{At least one is a girl.} \\
C &= \{gg, gb\} \quad &\text{The older one is a girl.}
\end{aligned}$$

Note that $A \cap B = \{gg\}$.

(a) $P(A|B) = \dfrac{P(A \text{ and } B)}{P(B)} = \dfrac{\frac{1}{4}}{\frac{3}{4}} = \dfrac{1}{4} \div \dfrac{3}{4} = \dfrac{1}{4} \cdot \dfrac{4}{3} = \dfrac{1}{3}$

(b) $P(A|C) = \dfrac{P(A \text{ and } C)}{P(C)} = \dfrac{\frac{1}{4}}{\frac{2}{4}} = \dfrac{1}{4} \div \dfrac{2}{4} = \dfrac{1}{4} \cdot \dfrac{4}{2} = \dfrac{1}{2}$ ▌▌▌

Sometimes a conditional probability is no different than the corresponding unconditional probability, in which case we call the two events *independent*.

> **Independent Events**
>
> Two events A and B are called **independent events** if knowledge about the occurrence of one of them has no effect on the probability of the other one, that is, if
>
> $$P(B|A) = P(B), \quad \text{or, equivalently,} \quad P(A|B) = P(A).$$

▎▎ **EXAMPLE 3** Checking Events for Independence

A single card is to be drawn from a standard 52-card deck. (The sample space S has 52 elements.) Given the events

A: The selected card is a face card,   and B: The selected card is black,

(a) Find $P(B)$.

(b) Find $P(B|A)$.

(c) Determine whether events A and B are independent.

SOLUTION

(a) There are 26 black cards in the 52-card deck.

$$P(B) = \frac{26}{52} = \frac{1}{2} \quad \text{Theoretical probability formula}$$

(b) $P(B|A) = \dfrac{P(B \text{ and } A)}{P(A)}$ Conditional probability formula

$= \dfrac{\frac{6}{52}}{\frac{12}{52}}$ Of 52 cards, 12 are face cards and 6 are black face cards.

$= \dfrac{6}{52} \cdot \dfrac{52}{12}$ To divide, multiply by the reciprocal.

$= \dfrac{1}{2}$ Calculate and write in lowest terms.

(c) Because $P(B|A) = P(B)$, events A and B are independent.   ▎▎▎

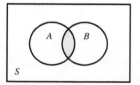

The logical connective "and" corresponds to "intersection" in set theory.

$P(A \text{ and } B) = P(A) \cdot P(B|A)$

Figure 9

Events Involving "And"

If we multiply both sides of the conditional probability formula by $P(A)$, we obtain an expression for $P(A \cap B)$, which applies to events of the form "A and B." The resulting formula is related to the fundamental counting principle of **Chapter 10.** It is illustrated in **Figure 9**.

Just as the calculation of $P(A \text{ or } B)$ is simpler when A and B are mutually exclusive, the calculation of $P(A \text{ and } B)$ is simpler when A and B are independent.

Multiplication Rule of Probability (for A and B)

If A and B are any two events, then

$$P(A \text{ and } B) = P(A) \cdot P(B|A).$$

If A and B are independent, then

$$P(A \text{ and } B) = P(A) \cdot P(B).$$

The first formula in the multiplication rule actually applies in all cases. ($P(B|A) = P(B)$ when A and B are independent.) Still, the independence of the component events is clear in many cases, so it is good to remember the second formula as well.

▮▮ **EXAMPLE 4** Selecting from a Set of Books

Each year, Jacqui Carper adds to her book collection a number of new publications that she believes will be of lasting value and interest. She has categorized each of her twenty acquisitions for 2011 as hardcover or paperback and as fiction or nonfiction. The numbers of books in the various categories are shown in **Table 6**.

Table 6 Year 2011 Books

	Fiction (F)	Nonfiction (N)	Totals
Hardcover (H)	3	5	8
Paperback (P)	8	4	12
Totals	11	9	20

If Jacqui randomly chooses one of these 20 books, find the probability it will be

(a) hardcover, **(b)** fiction, given it is hardcover, **(c)** hardcover and fiction.

SOLUTION

(a) Eight of the 20 books are hardcover, so $P(H) = \frac{8}{20} = \frac{2}{5}$.

(b) The given condition that the book is hardcover reduces the sample space to eight books. Of those eight, just three are fiction, so $P(F|H) = \frac{3}{8}$.

(c) $P(H \text{ and } F) = P(H) \cdot P(F|H) = \frac{2}{5} \cdot \frac{3}{8} = \frac{3}{20}$ Multiplication rule

It is easier here if we simply notice, directly from **Table 6**, that 3 of the 20 books are "hardcover and fiction." This verifies that the general multiplication rule of probability did give us the correct answer. ▮▮▮

▮▮ **EXAMPLE 5** Selecting from a Set of Planets

Table 7 lists the eight planets of our solar system together with their mean distances from the sun, in millions of kilometers. (Data is from *The World Almanac and Book of Facts 2010*.) Carrie Ayers must choose two distinct planets to cover in her astronomy report. If she selects randomly, find the probability that the first one selected is closer to the sun than Mars and the second is closer than Saturn.

SOLUTION

We define the events

A: The first is closer than Mars, and B: The second is closer than Saturn.

Then $P(A) = \frac{3}{8}$. (Three of the original eight choices are favorable.) If the planet selected first is closer than Mars, it is also closer than Saturn, and since that planet is no longer available, $P(B|A) = \frac{4}{7}$. (Four of the remaining seven are favorable.)

$$P(A \text{ and } B) = P(A) \cdot P(B|A) = \frac{3}{8} \cdot \frac{4}{7} = \frac{3}{14} \approx 0.214 \quad \text{Multiplication rule} \quad ▮▮▮$$

In **Example 5,** the condition that A had occurred changed the probability of B, since the selection was done, in effect, without replacement. (Repetitions were not allowed.) Events A and B were not independent. On the other hand, in the next example, the same events, A and B, will be independent.

Table 7 Mean Distance of Planets from the Sun

Mercury	58
Venus	108
Earth	150
Mars	228
Jupiter	778
Saturn	1430
Uranus	2870
Neptune	4500

∎∎ EXAMPLE 6   Selecting from a Set of Planets

Carrie must again select two planets, but this time one is for an oral report, the other is for a written report, and they need not be distinct. (The same planet may be selected for both reports.) Again find the probability that, if she selects randomly, the first is closer than Mars and the second is closer than Saturn.

SOLUTION

Defining events A and B as in **Example 5,** we have $P(A) = \frac{3}{8}$, just as before. But the selection is now done *with* replacement. (Repetitions *are* allowed.) Event B is independent of event A, so we can use the second form of the multiplication rule.

$$P(A \text{ and } B) = P(A) \cdot P(B) = \frac{3}{8} \cdot \frac{5}{8} = \frac{15}{64} \approx 0.234 \quad \text{Answer is different than in Example 5.} \quad ∎∎∎$$

∎∎ EXAMPLE 7   Selecting from a Deck of Cards

A single card is drawn from a standard 52-card deck. Let B denote the event that the card is black, and let D denote the event that it is a diamond. Are events B and D

(a) independent?   **(b)** mutually exclusive?

SOLUTION

(a) For the unconditional probability of D, we get $P(D) = \frac{13}{52} = \frac{1}{4}$. (Thirteen of the 52 cards are diamonds.) But for the conditional probability of D, given B, we have $P(D|B) = \frac{0}{26} = 0$. (None of the 26 black cards are diamonds.) Since the conditional probability $P(D|B)$ is different than the unconditional probability $P(D)$, B and D are not independent.

(b) Mutually exclusive events are events that cannot both occur for a given performance of an experiment. Since no card in the deck is both black and a diamond, B and D are mutually exclusive.   ∎∎∎

∎∎ EXAMPLE 8   Selecting from an Urn of Balls

Anne is still drawing balls from the same urn (shown at the side). This time she draws three balls, without replacement. Find the probability that she gets red, yellow, and blue balls, in that order.

SOLUTION

Using appropriate letters to denote the colors, and subscripts to indicate first, second, and third draws, the event can be symbolized R_1 and Y_2 and B_3.

$$P(R_1 \text{ and } Y_2 \text{ and } B_3) = P(R_1) \cdot P(Y_2|R_1) \cdot P(B_3|R_1 \text{ and } Y_2)$$

$$= \frac{4}{11} \cdot \frac{5}{10} \cdot \frac{2}{9} = \frac{4}{99} \approx 0.0404 \quad ∎∎∎$$

∎∎ EXAMPLE 9   Selecting from a Deck of Cards

If five cards are drawn without replacement from a standard 52-card deck, find the probability that they all are hearts.

SOLUTION

Each time a heart is drawn, the number of available cards decreases by one and the number of hearts decreases by one.

$$P(\text{all hearts}) = \frac{13}{52} \cdot \frac{12}{51} \cdot \frac{11}{50} \cdot \frac{10}{49} \cdot \frac{9}{48} = \frac{33}{66{,}640} \approx 0.000495 \quad ∎∎∎$$

The **search for extraterrestrial intelligence (SETI)** may have begun in earnest as early as 1961 when Dr. Frank Drake presented an equation for estimating the number of possible civilizations in the Milky Way galaxy whose communications we might detect. Over the years, the effort has been advanced by many scientists, including the late astronomer and exobiologist Carl Sagan, who popularized the issue in TV appearances and in his book *The Cosmic Connection: An Extraterrestrial Perspective* (Dell Paperback). "There must be other starfolk," said Sagan. In fact, some astronomers have estimated the odds against life on Earth being the only life in the universe at one hundred billion billion to one.

Other experts disagree. Freeman Dyson, a noted mathematical physicist and astronomer, says in his book *Disturbing the Universe* that after considering the same evidence and arguments, he believes it is just as likely as not (even odds) that there never was any other intelligent life out there.

If you studied counting methods (**Chapter 10**), you may prefer to solve the problem of **Example 9** by using the theoretical probability formula and combinations. The total possible number of 5-card hands, drawn without replacement, is $_{52}C_5$, and the number of those containing only hearts is $_{13}C_5$.

$$P(\text{all hearts}) = \frac{_{13}C_5}{_{52}C_5} = \frac{\dfrac{13!}{5!8!}}{\dfrac{52!}{5!47!}} \approx 0.000495 \quad \text{Use a calculator.}$$

▌▌ **EXAMPLE 10**   Using Both Addition and Multiplication Rules

The local garage employs two mechanics, Arnie and Burt. Your consumer club has found that Arnie does twice as many jobs as Burt, Arnie does a good job three out of four times, and Burt does a good job only two out of five times. If you plan to take your car in for repairs, find the probability that a good job will be done.

SOLUTION

We define the events

A: work done by Arnie; B: work done by Burt; G: good job done.

Since Arnie does twice as many jobs as Burt, the (unconditional) probabilities of events A and B are, respectively, $\frac{2}{3}$ and $\frac{1}{3}$. Since Arnie does a good job three out of four times, the probability of a good job, given that Arnie did the work, is $\frac{3}{4}$. And since Burt does well two out of five times, the probability of a good job, given that Burt did the work, is $\frac{2}{5}$. (These last two probabilities are conditional.) These four values can be summarized.

$$P(A) = \frac{2}{3}, \quad P(B) = \frac{1}{3}, \quad P(G|A) = \frac{3}{4}, \quad \text{and} \quad P(G|B) = \frac{2}{5}.$$

Event G can occur in two mutually exclusive ways: Arnie could do the work and do a good job ($A \cap G$), or Burt could do the work and do a good job ($B \cap G$).

$$\begin{aligned} P(G) &= P(A \cap G) + P(B \cap G) && \text{Addition rule} \\ &= P(A) \cdot P(G|A) + P(B) \cdot P(G|B) && \text{Multiplication rule} \\ &= \frac{2}{3} \cdot \frac{3}{4} + \frac{1}{3} \cdot \frac{2}{5} && \text{Substitute the values.} \\ &= \frac{1}{2} + \frac{2}{15} = \frac{19}{30} \approx 0.633 \end{aligned}$$

Multiply first, then add.

■■■

The tree diagram in **Figure 10** shows a graphical way to organize the work of **Example 10.** Use the given information to draw the tree diagram, then find the probability of a good job by adding the probabilities from the indicated branches of the tree.

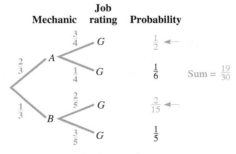

Garage mechanics experiment

Figure 10

▮▮ **EXAMPLE 11** Selecting Door Prizes

Rob Brown is among five door prize winners at a Christmas party. The five winners are asked to choose, without looking, from a bag which, they are told, contains five tokens, four of them redeemable for candy canes and one specific token redeemable for a $100 gift certificate. Can Rob improve his chance of getting the gift certificate by drawing first among the five people?

SOLUTION

We denote candy cane by C, gift certificate by G, and first draw, second draw, and so on by subscripts $1, 2, \ldots$. Then if Rob draws first, his probability of getting the gift certificate is

$$P(G_1) = \frac{1}{5}.$$

If he draws second, his probability of getting the gift certificate is

$$
\begin{aligned}
P(G_2) &= P(C_1 \text{ and } G_2) \\
&= P(C_1) \cdot P(G_2 | C_1) \\
&= \frac{4}{5} \cdot \frac{1}{4} = \frac{1}{5}. \qquad \text{Same result as above}
\end{aligned}
$$

For the third draw,

$$
\begin{aligned}
P(G_3) &= P(C_1 \text{ and } C_2 \text{ and } G_3) \\
&= P(C_1) \cdot P(C_2 | C_1) \cdot P(G_3 | C_1 \text{ and } C_2) \\
&= \frac{4}{5} \cdot \frac{3}{4} \cdot \frac{1}{3} = \frac{1}{5}. \qquad \text{Same result as above}
\end{aligned}
$$

The probability of getting the gift certificate is $\frac{1}{5}$ when drawing fourth or fifth. The order in which the five winners draw does not affect Rob's chances. ▮▮▮

The **search for extraterrestrial intelligence (SETI)** has been mainly accomplished over the last decade through **SETI@HOME,** the largest distributed computing program on Earth. Most of the data are collected by the world's largest radio telescope, built into a 20-acre natural bowl in Aricebo, Puerto Rico (pictured above), and processed by millions of personal computers around the world.

To learn more, or for a chance to be the first to "contact" an extraterrestrial civilization, check out www.setiathome.ssl.berkeley.edu.

For Further Thought

The Birthday Problem

A classic problem (with a surprising result) involves the probability that a given group of people will include at least one pair of people with the same birthday (the same day of the year, not necessarily the same year). This problem can be analyzed using the probability of a complement formula (**Section 11.2**) and the multiplication rule of probability from this section. Suppose there are three people in the group.

P(at least one duplication of birthdays)

$= 1 - P$(no duplications) Complement formula

$= 1 - P$(2nd is different than 1st and 3rd is different than 1st and 2nd)

$= 1 - \dfrac{364}{365} \cdot \dfrac{363}{365}$ Multiplication rule

$\approx 1 - 0.992$

$= 0.008$

(To simplify the calculations, we have assumed 365 possible birth dates, ignoring February 29.)

By doing more calculations like the one above, we find that the smaller the group, the smaller the probability of a duplication. The larger the group, the larger the probability of a duplication. The table on the next page shows the probability of at least one duplication for numbers of people from 2 through 52.

For Group or Individual Investigation

1. Based on the data shown in the table, what are the odds in favor of a duplication in a group of 30 people?

2. Estimate from the table the least number of people for which the probability of duplication is at least $\frac{1}{2}$.

3. How small a group is required for the probability of a duplication to be *exactly* 0?

4. How large a group is required for the probability of a duplication to be *exactly* 1?

Number of People	Probability of at Least One Duplication	Number of People	Probability of at Least One Duplication	Number of People	Probability of at Least One Duplication
2	0.003	19	0.379	36	0.832
3	0.008	20	0.411	37	0.849
4	0.016	21	0.444	38	0.864
5	0.027	22	0.476	39	0.878
6	0.040	23	0.507	40	0.891
7	0.056	24	0.538	41	0.903
8	0.074	25	0.569	42	0.914
9	0.095	26	0.598	43	0.924
10	0.117	27	0.627	44	0.933
11	0.141	28	0.654	45	0.941
12	0.167	29	0.681	46	0.948
13	0.194	30	0.706	47	0.955
14	0.223	31	0.730	48	0.961
15	0.253	32	0.753	49	0.966
16	0.284	33	0.775	50	0.970
17	0.315	34	0.795	51	0.974
18	0.347	35	0.814	52	0.978

11.3 EXERCISES

For each experiment, determine whether the two given events are independent.

1. **Tossing Coins** A fair coin is tossed twice. The events are "head on the first" and "head on the second."

2. **Rolling Dice** A pair of dice are rolled. The events are "even on the first" and "odd on the second."

3. **Comparing Planets' Mean Distances from the Sun** Two planets are selected, without replacement, from the list in **Table 7**. The events are "the first selected planet is closer than Jupiter" and "the second selected planet is farther than Mars."

4. **Comparing Mean Distances from the Sun** Two celestial bodies are selected, with replacement, from the list in **Table 7**. The events are "the first selected body is closer than Earth" and "the second selected body is farther than Uranus."

5. **Guessing Answers on a Multiple-choice Test** The answers are all guessed on a twenty-question multiple-choice test. The events are "the first answer is correct" and "the last answer is correct."

6. **Selecting Committees of U.S. Senators** A committee of five is randomly selected from the 100 U.S. Senators. The events are "the first member selected is a Republican" and "the second member selected is a Republican." (Assume that there are both Republicans and non-Republicans in the Senate.)

Comparing Gender and Career Motivation of College Students One hundred college seniors attending a career fair at a university were categorized according to gender and according to primary career motivation, as summarized here.

	Primary Career Motivation			
	Money	Allowed to be Creative	Sense of Giving to Society	Total
Male	19	15	14	48
Female	12	23	17	52
Total	31	38	31	100

If one of these students is to be selected at random, find the probability that the student selected will satisfy each condition in Exercises 7–12.

7. female

8. motivated primarily by creativity

9. not motivated primarily by money

10. male and motivated primarily by money

11. male, given that primary motivation is a sense of giving to society

12. motivated primarily by money or creativity, given that the student is female

Selecting Pets *A pet store has seven puppies, including four poodles, two terriers, and one retriever. If Rebecka and Aaron, in that order, each select one puppy at random,* with replacement *(they may both select the same one), find the probability of each event in Exercises 13–16.*

13. both select a poodle

14. Rebecka selects a retriever, Aaron selects a terrier

15. Rebecka selects a terrier, Aaron selects a retriever

16. both select a retriever

Selecting Pets *Suppose two puppies are selected as earlier, but this time* without replacement *(Rebecka and Aaron cannot both select the same puppy). Find the probability of each event in Exercises 17–22.*

17. both select a poodle

18. Aaron selects a terrier, given Rebecka selects a poodle

19. Aaron selects a retriever, given Rebecka selects a poodle

20. Rebecka selects a retriever

21. Aaron selects a retriever, given Rebecka selects a retriever

22. both select a retriever

Dealing Cards *Let two cards be dealt successively, without replacement, from a standard 52-card deck. Find the probability of each event in Exercises 23–27.*

23. spade second, given spade first

24. club second, given diamond first

25. two face cards

26. no face cards

27. The first card is a jack and the second is a face card.

28. Given events A and B within the sample space S, the following sequence of steps establishes formulas that can be used to compute conditional probabilities. Justify each statement.

(a) $P(A \text{ and } B) = P(A) \cdot P(B|A)$

(b) Therefore, $P(B|A) = \dfrac{P(A \text{ and } B)}{P(A)}$.

(c) Therefore, $P(B|A) = \dfrac{n(A \text{ and } B)/n(S)}{n(A)/n(S)}$.

(d) Therefore, $P(B|A) = \dfrac{n(A \text{ and } B)}{n(A)}$.

Considering Conditions in Card Drawing *Use the results of* **Exercise 28** *to find each probability when a single card is drawn from a standard 52-card deck.*

29. $P(\text{queen} \,|\, \text{face card})$

30. $P(\text{face card} \,|\, \text{queen})$

31. $P(\text{red} \,|\, \text{diamond})$

32. $P(\text{diamond} \,|\, \text{red})$

Investigating P(A and B) *Complete Exercises 33 and 34 to discover a general property of the probability of an event of the form A and B.*

33. If one number is chosen randomly from the integers 1 through 10, the probability of getting a number that is *odd and prime,* by the multiplication rule, is

$$P(\text{odd}) \cdot P(\text{prime} \,|\, \text{odd}) = \frac{5}{10} \cdot \frac{3}{5} = \frac{3}{10}.$$

Compute the product $P(\text{prime}) \cdot P(\text{odd} \,|\, \text{prime})$, and compare to the product above.

34. What does **Exercise 33** imply, in general, about the probability of an event of the form A and B?

35. **Gender in Sequences of Babies** Two authors of this book each have three sons and no daughters. Assuming boy and girl babies are equally likely, what is the probability of this event?

36. **Rolling Dice** Three dice are tossed. What is the probability that the numbers shown will all be different? (*Mathematics Teacher* calendar problem)

The remaining exercises, and groups of exercises, may require concepts from earlier sections, such as the complements principle of counting and addition rules, as well as the multiplication rule of this section.

Probabilities in Warehouse Grocery Shopping *Therese Felser manages a grocery warehouse which encourages volume shopping on the part of its customers. Therese has discovered that, on any given weekday, 70 percent of the customer sales amount to more than $100. That is, any given sale on such a day has a probability of 0.70 of being for more than $100. (Actually, the conditional probabilities throughout the day would change slightly, depending on earlier sales, but this effect would be negligible for the first several sales of the day, so we can treat them as independent.)*
Find the probability of each event in Exercises 37–40. (Give answers to three decimal places.)

37. The first two sales on Wednesday are both for more than $100.

38. The first three sales on Wednesday are all for more than $100.

39. None of the first three sales on Wednesday is for more than $100.

40. Exactly one of the first three sales on Wednesday is for more than $100.

Pollution from the Space Shuttle Launch Site *One problem encountered by developers of the space shuttle program is air pollution in the area surrounding the launch site. A certain direction from the launch site is considered critical in terms of hydrogen chloride pollution from the exhaust cloud. It has been determined that weather conditions would cause emission cloud movement in the critical direction only 5% of the time.*

In Exercises 41–44, find the probability for each event. Assume that probabilities for a particular launch in no way depend on the probabilities for other launches. (Give answers to two decimal places.)

41. A given launch will not result in cloud movement in the critical direction.

42. No cloud movement in the critical direction will occur during any of 5 launches.

43. Any 5 launches will result in at least one cloud movement in the critical direction.

44. Any 10 launches will result in at least one cloud movement in the critical direction.

Ordering Job Interviews *Three men and three women are waiting to be interviewed for jobs. If they are all selected in random order, find the probability of each event in Exercises 45–47.*

45. All the women will be interviewed first.

46. The first three interviewees will all be the same sex.

47. No man will be interviewed until at least two women have been interviewed.

48. ***Cutting Up a Cube*** A $4'' \times 4'' \times 4''$ cube is painted and then cut into sixty-four $1'' \times 1'' \times 1''$ cubes. A unit cube is then randomly selected and rolled. What is the probability that the top face of the rolled cube is painted? Express your answer as a common fraction. (*Mathematics Teacher* calendar problem)

49. ***Tossing a Two-Headed Coin?*** A gambler has two coins in his pocket—one fair coin and one two-headed coin. He selects a coin at random and flips it twice. If he gets two heads, what is the probability that he selected the fair coin? (*Mathematics Teacher* calendar problem)

50. In **Example 8,** where Anne draws three balls without replacement, what would be her probability of getting one of each color, where the order does not matter?

51. ***Gender in Sequences of Babies*** Assuming boy and girl babies are equally likely, find the probability that it would take

(a) at least three births to obtain two girls,

(b) at least four births to obtain two girls,

(c) at least five births to obtain two girls.

52. ***Drawing Cards*** Cards are drawn, without replacement, from an ordinary 52-card deck.

(a) How many must be drawn before the probability of obtaining at least one face card is greater than $\frac{1}{2}$?

(b) How many must be drawn before the probability of obtaining at least one king is greater than $\frac{1}{2}$?

Fair Decisions from Biased Coins *Many everyday decisions, like who will drive to lunch, or who will pay for the coffee, are made by the toss of a (presumably fair) coin and using the criterion "heads, you will; tails, I will." This criterion is not quite fair, however, if the coin is biased (perhaps due to slightly irregular construction or wear). John von Neumann suggested a way to make perfectly fair decisions even with a possibly biased coin. If a coin, biased so that*

$$P(\text{h}) = 0.5200 \quad \text{and} \quad P(\text{t}) = 0.4800,$$

is tossed twice, find each probability. (Give answers to four decimal places.)

53. $P(\text{hh})$ **54.** $P(\text{ht})$

55. $P(\text{th})$ **56.** $P(\text{tt})$

57. Having completed **Exercises 53–56,** can you suggest what von Neumann's scheme may have been?

Programming a Garage Door Opener *Kevin Frye installed a certain brand of automatic garage door opener that utilizes a transmitter control with six independent switches, each one set on or off. The receiver (wired to the door) must be set with the same pattern as the transmitter. (Exercises 58–61 are based on ideas similar to those of the "birthday problem" in the **For Further Thought** feature in this section.)*

58. How many different ways can Kevin set the switches?

59. If one of Kevin's neighbors also has this same brand of opener, and both of them set the switches randomly, what is the probability, to four decimal places, that they are able to open each other's garage doors?

60. If five neighbors with the same type of opener set their switches independently, what is the probability of at least one pair of neighbors using the same settings? (Give your answer to four decimal places.)

61. What is the minimum number of neighbors who must use this brand of opener before the probability of at least one duplication of settings is greater than $\frac{1}{2}$?

62. *Choosing Cards* There are three cards, one that is green on both sides, one that is red on both sides, and one that is green on one side and red on the other. One of the three cards is selected randomly and laid on the table. If it happens that the card on the table has a red side up, what is the probability that it is also red on the other side?

Weather Conditions on Successive Days *In November, the rain in a certain valley tends to fall in storms of several days' duration. The unconditional probability of rain on any given day of the month is 0.500. But the probability of rain on a day that follows a rainy day is 0.800, and the probability of rain on a day following a nonrainy day is 0.300. Find the probability of each event in Exercises 63–66. Give answers to three decimal places.*

63. rain on two randomly selected consecutive days in November

64. rain on three randomly selected consecutive days in November

65. rain on November 1 and 2, but not on November 3

66. rain on the first four days of November, given that October 31 was clear all day

Engine Failures in a Vintage Aircraft *In a certain four-engine vintage aircraft, now quite unreliable, each engine has a 10% chance of failure on any flight, as long as it is carrying its one-fourth share of the load. But if one engine fails, then the chance of failure increases to 20% for each of the other three engines. And if a second engine fails, each of the remaining two has a 30% chance of failure.*

Assuming that no two engines ever fail simultaneously, and that the aircraft can continue flying with as few as two operating engines, find each probability for a given flight of this aircraft. (Give answers to four decimal places.)

67. no engine failures

68. exactly one engine failure (any one of four engines)

69. exactly two engine failures (any two of four engines)

70. a failed flight

One-and-one Free Throw Shooting in Basketball *In basketball, "one-and-one" free throw shooting (commonly called foul shooting) is done as follows: if the player makes the first shot (1 point), he is given a second shot. If he misses the first shot, he is not given a second shot (see the tree diagram).*

Christine Ellington, a basketball player, has a 70% foul shot record. (She makes 70% of her foul shots.) Find the probability that, on a given one-and-one foul shooting opportunity, Christine will score each number of points.

71. no points   **72.** one point

73. two points

74. *Comparing Empirical and Theoretical Probabilities in Dice Rolling* Roll a pair of dice until a sum of seven appears, keeping track of how many rolls it took. Repeat the process a total of 50 times, each time recording the number of rolls it took to get a sum of seven.

   (a) Use your experimental data to compute an empirical probability (to two decimal places) that it would take at least three rolls to get a sum of seven.

   (b) Find the theoretical probability (to two decimal places) that it would take at least three rolls to obtain a sum of seven.

75. Go to the Web site mentioned in the *cosmic impact* margin note in this section and write a report on the threat to humanity of cosmic impacts. Include an explanation of the abbreviation *NEO*.

11.4 BINOMIAL PROBABILITY

Binomial Probability Distribution • Binomial Probability Formula

Binomial Probability Distribution

Suppose the spinner in the margin is spun twice. We are interested in the number of times a 2 is obtained. (Assume that 1, 2, and 3 all are equally likely on a given spin.) We can think of the outcome 2 as a "success," while a 1 or a 3 would be a "failure."

When the outcomes of an experiment are divided into just two categories, success and failure, the associated probabilities are called "binomial" (the prefix *bi* meaning *two*). Repeated performances of such an experiment, where the probability of success remains constant throughout all repetitions, are also known as repeated **Bernoulli trials** (after James Bernoulli). If we use an ordered pair to represent the result of each pair of spins, then the sample space for this experiment is

$$S = \{(1,1), (1,2), (1,3), (2,1), (2,2), (2,3), (3,1), (3,2), (3,3)\}.$$

The nine outcomes in S are all equally likely. (This follows from the numbers 1, 2, and 3 being equally likely on a particular spin.)

If x denotes the number of 2s occurring on each pair of spins, then x is an example of a *random variable*. Although we cannot predict the result of any particular pair of spins, we can find the probabilities of various events from the sample space listing. In S, the number of 2s is 0 in four cases, 1 in four cases, and 2 in one case, as reflected in **Table 8**. Because the table includes all possible values of x, together with their probabilities, it is an example of a *probability distribution*. In this case, we have a **binomial probability distribution.** Notice that the probability column in **Table 8** has a sum of 1, in agreement with property 3 of probability (**Section 11.2**).

In order to develop a general formula for binomial probabilities, we can consider another way to obtain the probability values in **Table 8**. The various spins of the spinner are independent of one another, and on each spin the probability of success (S) is $\frac{1}{3}$ and the probability of failure (F) is $\frac{2}{3}$. We will denote success on the first spin by S_1, failure on the second by F_2, and so on.

Table 8 Probability Distribution for the Number of 2s in Two Spins

x	$P(x)$
0	$\frac{4}{9}$
1	$\frac{4}{9}$
2	$\frac{1}{9}$

Sum = $\frac{9}{9}$ = 1

$$
\begin{aligned}
P(x = 0) &= P(F_1 \text{ and } F_2) \\
&= P(F_1) \cdot P(F_2) \quad &\text{Multiplication rule} \\
&= \frac{2}{3} \cdot \frac{2}{3} \quad &\text{Substitute values.} \\
&= \frac{4}{9} \quad &\text{Multiply.}
\end{aligned}
$$

$$
\begin{aligned}
P(x = 1) &= P[(S_1 \text{ and } F_2) \text{ or } (F_1 \text{ and } S_2)] \quad &\text{2 ways to get } x = 1 \\
&= P(S_1 \text{ and } F_2) + P(F_1 \text{ and } S_2) \quad &\text{Addition rule} \\
&= P(S_1) \cdot P(F_2) + P(F_1) \cdot P(S_2) \quad &\text{Multiplication rule} \\
&= \frac{1}{3} \cdot \frac{2}{3} + \frac{2}{3} \cdot \frac{1}{3} \quad &\text{Substitute values.} \\
&= \frac{2}{9} + \frac{2}{9} \quad &\text{Multiply.} \\
&= \frac{4}{9} \quad &\text{Add.}
\end{aligned}
$$

James Bernoulli (1654–1705) is also known as Jacob or Jacques. He was charmed away from theology by the writings of Leibniz, became his pupil, and later headed the mathematics faculty at the University of Basel. His results in probability are contained in the *Art of Conjecture*, which was published in 1713, after his death, and which also included a reprint of the earlier Huygens paper. Bernoulli also made many contributions to calculus and analytic geometry.

$$P(x = 2) = P(S_1 \text{ and } S_2)$$

$$= P(S_1) \cdot P(S_2) \quad \text{Multiplication rule}$$

$$= \frac{1}{3} \cdot \frac{1}{3} \quad \text{Substitute values.}$$

$$= \frac{1}{9} \quad \text{Multiply.}$$

Notice the following pattern in the above calculations. There is only one way to get $x = 0$ (namely, F_1 and F_2). And there is only one way to get $x = 2$ (namely, S_1 and S_2). But there are two ways to get $x = 1$. One way is S_1 and F_2; the other is F_1 and S_2. There are two ways because the one success required can occur on the first spin or on the second spin. How many ways can exactly one success occur in two repeated trials? This question is equivalent to:

How many size-one subsets are there of the set of two trials?

The answer is $_2C_1 = 2$. (The expression $_2C_1$ denotes "combinations of 2 things taken 1 at a time." Combinations were discussed in **Section 10.3.**) Each of the two ways to get exactly one success has a probability equal to $\frac{1}{3} \cdot \frac{2}{3}$, the probability of success times the probability of failure.

If the same spinner is spun three times rather than two, then x, the number of successes (2s) could have values of 0, 1, 2, or 3. Then the number of ways to get exactly 1 success is $_3C_1 = 3$. They are: S_1 and F_2 and F_3, F_1 and S_2 and F_3, F_1 and F_2 and S_3. The probability of each of these three ways is $\frac{1}{3} \cdot \frac{2}{3} \cdot \frac{2}{3} = \frac{4}{27}$.

$$P(x = 1) = 3 \cdot \frac{4}{27} = \frac{12}{27} = \frac{4}{9}$$

Figure 11 shows all possibilities for three spins, and **Table 9** gives the associated probability distribution. In the tree diagram, the number of ways of getting two successes in three trials is 3, in agreement with the fact that $_3C_2 = 3$. Also the sum of the $P(x)$ column in **Table 9** is again 1.

Table 9	Probability Distribution for the Number of 2s in Three Spins	
x	$P(x)$
0	$\frac{8}{27}$
1	$\frac{12}{27}$
2	$\frac{6}{27}$
3	$\frac{1}{27}$
	Sum $= \frac{27}{27} = 1$

First spin	Second spin	Third spin	Number of successes	Probability
		S	3	$\frac{1}{3} \cdot \frac{1}{3} \cdot \frac{1}{3} = \frac{1}{27}$
	S	F	2	$\frac{1}{3} \cdot \frac{1}{3} \cdot \frac{2}{3} = \frac{2}{27}$
S		S	2	$\frac{1}{3} \cdot \frac{2}{3} \cdot \frac{1}{3} = \frac{2}{27}$
	F	F	1	$\frac{1}{3} \cdot \frac{2}{3} \cdot \frac{2}{3} = \frac{4}{27}$
	S	S	2	$\frac{2}{3} \cdot \frac{1}{3} \cdot \frac{1}{3} = \frac{2}{27}$
		F	1	$\frac{2}{3} \cdot \frac{1}{3} \cdot \frac{2}{3} = \frac{4}{27}$
F		S	1	$\frac{2}{3} \cdot \frac{2}{3} \cdot \frac{1}{3} = \frac{4}{27}$
	F	F	0	$\frac{2}{3} \cdot \frac{2}{3} \cdot \frac{2}{3} = \frac{8}{27}$

Tree diagram for three spins

Figure 11

PROBLEM-SOLVING HINT One of the problem-solving strategies from **Chapter 1** was "Look for a pattern." Having constructed complete probability distributions for binomial experiments with 2 and 3 repeated trials (and probability of success $\frac{1}{3}$), we can now generalize the observed pattern to any binomial experiment, as shown next.

Binomial Probability Formula

Define the following quantities.

$$n = \text{the number of repeated trials}$$
$$p = \text{the probability of success on any given trial}$$
$$q = 1 - p = \text{the probability of failure on any given trial}$$
$$x = \text{the number of successes that occur}$$

Note that p remains fixed throughout all n trials. This means that all trials are independent of one another. The random variable x (number of successes) can have any integer value from 0 through n. In general, x successes can be assigned among n repeated trials in $_nC_x$ different ways, since this is the number of different subsets of x positions among a set of n positions. Also, regardless of which x of the trials result in successes, there will always be x successes and $n - x$ failures, so we multiply x factors of p and $n - x$ factors of q together.

Binomial Probability Formula

When n independent repeated trials occur, where

$$p = \text{probability of success} \quad \text{and} \quad q = \text{probability of failure}$$

with p and q (where $q = 1 - p$) remaining constant throughout all n trials, the probability of exactly x successes is calculated as follows.

$$P(x) = {_nC_x}\,p^x q^{n-x} = \frac{n!}{x!(n-x)!}p^x q^{n-x}$$

Binomial probabilities for particular values of n, p, and x can be found directly using tables, statistical software, and some handheld calculators. In the following examples, we use the formula derived above.

From the DISTR menu

binompdf(5,.5,3)
                    .3125
Ans▶Frac
                    $\frac{5}{16}$

The TI-83/84 Plus calculator will find the probability discussed in **Example 1**.

▌▌ EXAMPLE 1 Finding Probability in Coin Tossing

Find the probability of obtaining exactly three heads in five tosses of a fair coin.

SOLUTION

Let heads be "success." Then this is a binomial experiment with $n = 5, p = \frac{1}{2}, q = \frac{1}{2}$, and $x = 3$.

$$P(3) = {_5C_3}\left(\frac{1}{2}\right)^3\left(\frac{1}{2}\right)^2 = 10 \cdot \frac{1}{8} \cdot \frac{1}{4} = \frac{5}{16} \quad \text{Binomial probability formula} \quad ▇▇▇$$

▌▌ EXAMPLE 2 Finding Probability in Dice Rolling

Find the probability of obtaining exactly two 5s in six rolls of a fair die.

SOLUTION

Let 5 be "success." Then $n = 6, p = \frac{1}{6}, q = \frac{5}{6}$, and $x = 2$.

$$P(2) = {_6C_2}\left(\frac{1}{6}\right)^2\left(\frac{5}{6}\right)^4 = 15 \cdot \frac{1}{36} \cdot \frac{625}{1296} = \frac{3125}{15{,}552} \approx 0.201 \quad ▇▇▇$$

binompdf(6,1/6,2)
                    .200938786

This screen supports the answer in **Example 2**.

In the case of repeated independent trials, when an event involves more than one specific number of successes, we can employ the binomial probability formula along with the complement or addition rules.

▮▮ **EXAMPLE 3**   Finding Probability of Female Children

A couple plans to have 5 children. Find the probability they will have more than 3 girls. (Assume girl and boy babies are equally likely.)

SOLUTION

Let a girl be "success." Then $n = 5$, $p = q = \frac{1}{2}$, and $x > 3$.

$$\begin{aligned}
P(x > 3) &= P(x = 4 \text{ or } 5) & \text{More than 3 means 4 or 5.} \\
&= P(4) + P(5) & \text{Addition rule} \\
&= {}_5C_4\left(\frac{1}{2}\right)^4\left(\frac{1}{2}\right)^1 + {}_5C_5\left(\frac{1}{2}\right)^5\left(\frac{1}{2}\right)^0 & \text{Binomial probability formula} \\
&= 5 \cdot \frac{1}{16} \cdot \frac{1}{2} + 1 \cdot \frac{1}{32} \cdot 1 & \text{Simplify.} \\
&= \frac{5}{32} + \frac{1}{32} = \frac{6}{32} = \frac{3}{16} = 0.1875
\end{aligned}$$

This screen supports the answer in
Example 3.

▮▮ **EXAMPLE 4**   Finding Probability of Hits in Baseball

Andrew Crowley, a baseball player, has a well-established career batting average of .300. In a brief series with a rival team, Andrew will bat 10 times. Find the probability that he will get more than two hits in the series.

SOLUTION

This "experiment" involves $n = 10$ repeated Bernoulli trials, with probability of success (a hit) given by $p = 0.3$ (which implies $q = 1 - 0.3 = 0.7$). Since, in this case, "more than 2" means

"3 or 4 or 5 or 6 or 7 or 8 or 9 or 10"   (eight different possibilities),

it will be less work to apply the complement rule.

$$\begin{aligned}
P(x > 2) &= 1 - P(x \le 2) & \text{Complement rule} \\
&= 1 - P(x = 0 \text{ or } 1 \text{ or } 2) & \text{Only three different possibilities} \\
&= 1 - [P(0) + P(1) + P(2)] & \text{Addition rule} \\
&= 1 - [{}_{10}C_0(0.3)^0(0.7)^{10} & \text{Binomial probability formula} \\
&\quad + {}_{10}C_1(0.3)^1(0.7)^9 + {}_{10}C_2(0.3)^2(0.7)^8] \\
&\approx 1 - [0.0282 + 0.1211 + 0.2335] & \text{Simplify.} \\
&= 1 - 0.3828 \\
&= 0.6172
\end{aligned}$$

> **Scrolled Equation**
> 1−(binompdf(10,.3,0)+bin▸
>   ◂ompdf(10,.3,1)+binompdf▸
>   ◂(10,.3,2))
>   .6172172136

This screen supports the answer in
Example 4.

11.4 EXERCISES

For Exercises 1–24, give all numerical answers as common fractions reduced to lowest terms. For Exercises 25–54, give all numerical answers to three decimal places.

Coin Tossing *If three fair coins are tossed, find the probability of each number of heads.*

1. 0   **2.** 1   **3.** 2

4. 3   **5.** 1 or 2   **6.** at least 1

7. no more than 1   **8.** fewer than 3

9. *Gender in Sequences of Babies* Assuming boy and girl babies are equally likely, find the probability that a family with three children will have exactly two boys.

10. **Relating Pascal's Triangle to Coin Tossing** Pascal's triangle was shown in **Table 5** of **Section 10.4.** Explain how the probabilities in **Exercises 1–4** here relate to row 3 of the "triangle." (Recall that we referred to the topmost row of the triangle as "row number 0" and to the leftmost entry of each row as "entry number 0.")

11. Generalize the pattern in **Exercise 10** to complete the following statement. If n fair coins are tossed, the probability of exactly x heads is the fraction whose numerator is entry number _____ of row number _____ in Pascal's triangle, and whose denominator is the sum of the entries in row number _____.

Binomial Probability Applied to Tossing Coins Use the pattern noted in **Exercises 10 and 11** to find the probabilities of each number of heads when seven fair coins are tossed.

12. 0	**13.** 1	**14.** 2	**15.** 3
16. 4	**17.** 5	**18.** 6	**19.** 7

Binomial Probability Applied to Rolling Dice A fair die is rolled three times. A 4 is considered "success," while all other outcomes are "failures." Find the probability of each number of successes.

20. 0	**21.** 1	**22.** 2	**23.** 3

24. **Exercises 10 and 11** established a way of using Pascal's triangle rather than the binomial probability formula to find probabilities of different numbers of successes in coin-tossing experiments. Explain why the same process would not work for **Exercises 20–23.**

For n repeated independent trials, with constant probability of success p for all trials, find the probability of exactly x successes in each of Exercises 25–28.

25. $n = 5$, $p = \frac{1}{3}$, $x = 4$

26. $n = 10$, $p = 0.7$, $x = 5$

27. $n = 20$, $p = \frac{1}{8}$, $x = 2$

28. $n = 30$, $p = 0.6$, $x = 22$

*For Exercises 29–31, refer to **Example 4.***

29. **Batting Averages in Baseball** Does Andrew's probability of a hit really remain constant at exactly 0.300 through all ten times at bat? Explain your reasoning.

30. **Batting Averages in Baseball** If Andrew's batting average is exactly .300 going into the series, and that value is based on exactly 1200 career hits out of 4000 previous times at bat, what is the greatest his average could possibly be (to three decimal places) when he goes up to bat the tenth time of the series? What is the least his average could possibly be when he goes up to bat the tenth time of the series?

31. Do you think the use of the binomial probability formula was justified in **Example 4,** even though p is not strictly constant? Explain your reasoning.

Random Selection of Answers on a Multiple-choice Test Beth Dahlke is taking a ten-question multiple-choice test for which each question has three answer choices, only one of which is correct. Beth decides on answers by rolling a fair die and marking the first answer choice if the die shows 1 or 2, the second if it shows 3 or 4, and the third if it shows 5 or 6. Find the probability of each event in Exercises 32–35.

32. exactly four correct answers

33. exactly seven correct answers

34. fewer than three correct answers

35. at least seven correct answers

Side Effects of Prescription Drugs It is known that a certain prescription drug produces undesirable side effects in 35% of all patients who use it. Among a random sample of eight patients using the drug, find the probability of each event.

36. None have undesirable side effects.

37. Exactly one has undesirable side effects.

38. Exactly two have undesirable side effects.

39. More than two have undesirable side effects.

Likelihood of Capable Students Attending College In a certain state, it has been shown that only 60% of the high school graduates who are capable of college work actually enroll in colleges. Find the probability that, among nine capable high school graduates in this state, each number will enroll in college.

40. exactly 4	**41.** from 4 through 6
42. all 9	**43.** at least 3

44. **Student Ownership of Personal Computers** At a large midwestern university, 90% of all students have their own personal computers. If five students at that university are selected at random, find the probability that exactly three of them have their own computers.

45. *Frost Survival Among Orange Trees* If it is known that 65% of all orange trees will survive a hard frost, then what is the probability that at least half of a group of six trees will survive such a frost?

46. *Rate of Favorable Media Coverage of an Incumbent President* During a presidential campaign, 64% of the political columns in a certain group of major newspapers were favorable to the incumbent president. If a sample of fifteen of these columns is selected at random, what is the probability that exactly ten of them will be favorable?

Selecting Balls From a Bag A bag contains only white balls and black balls. Let p be the probability that a ball selected at random is black. Each time a ball is selected, it is placed back in the bag before the next ball is selected. Four balls are selected at random.

47. What is the probability that two of the four balls are black and two are white? (*Mathematics Teacher* calendar problem) (*Hint:* Use the binomial probability formula to express the probability in terms of p.)

48. Evaluate the probability of **Exercise 47** in case the bag actually contains 15 black balls and 25 white balls. Give your answer to four decimal places.

Taking a Random Walk Abby Gartland is parked at a mile marker on an east-west country road. She decides to toss a fair coin 10 times, each time driving 1 mile east if it lands heads up and 1 mile west if it lands tails up. The term "random walk" applies to this process, even though Abby drives rather than walks. It is a simplified model of Brownian motion, mentioned on **page 580.** (See also **Exercises 9–12** in the **Extension** at the end of this chapter.)

In each of Exercises 49–56, find the probability that Abby's "walk" will end as described.

49. 10 miles east of the start

50. 6 miles east of the start

51. 6 miles west of the start

52. 5 miles west of the start

53. 2 miles east of the start

54. at least 2 miles east of the start

55. at least 2 miles from the start

56. exactly at the start

11.5 EXPECTED VALUE

Expected Value • Games and Gambling • Investments • Business and Insurance

Expected Value

The probability distribution in **Table 10**, from **Example 6** of **Section 11.2,** shows the probabilities assigned by Amy to the various lengths of time her homework may take on a given night. If Amy's friend Tara asks her how many hours her studies will take, what would be her best guess? Six different time values are possible, with some more likely than others. One thing Amy could do is calculate a "weighted average" by multiplying each possible time value by its probability and then adding the six products.

$$1(0.05) + 2(0.10) + 3(0.20) + 4(0.40) + 5(0.10) + 6(0.15)$$

$$= 0.05 + 0.20 + 0.60 + 1.60 + 0.50 + 0.90 = 3.85$$

Thus 3.85 hours is the **expected value** (or the **mathematical expectation**) of the quantity of time to be spent. Since the original time values in the table were rounded to the nearest hour, the expected value also should be rounded, to 4 hours.

Table 10

x	P(x)
1	0.05
2	0.10
3	0.20
4	0.40
5	0.10
6	0.15

Expected Value

If a random variable x can have any of the values $x_1, x_2, x_3, \ldots, x_n$, and the corresponding probabilities of these values occurring are $P(x_1), P(x_2), P(x_3), \ldots, P(x_n)$, then the **expected value of x** is calculated as follows.

$$E(x) = x_1 \cdot P(x_1) + x_2 \cdot P(x_2) + x_3 \cdot P(x_3) + \cdots + x_n \cdot P(x_n)$$

EXAMPLE 1   Finding the Expected Number of Boys

Find the expected number of boys for a three-child family (that is, the expected value of the number of boys). Assume girls and boys are equally likely.

SOLUTION

The sample space for this experiment is

$$S = \{ggg, ggb, gbg, bgg, gbb, bgb, bbg, bbb\}.$$

The probability distribution is shown in **Table 11**, along with the products and their sum, which gives the expected value.

Table 11

Number of Boys x	Probability $P(x)$	Product $x \cdot P(x)$
0	$\frac{1}{8}$	0
1	$\frac{3}{8}$	$\frac{3}{8}$
2	$\frac{3}{8}$	$\frac{6}{8}$
3	$\frac{1}{8}$	$\frac{3}{8}$

Expected value: $E(x) = \frac{12}{8} = \frac{3}{2}$

The expected number of boys is $\frac{3}{2}$, or 1.5. This result seems reasonable. Since boys and girls are equally likely, "half" the children are expected to be boys.   ███

The expected value for the number of boys in the family could never actually occur. It is only a kind of long run average of the various values that *could* occur. (For more information on "averages," see **Section 12.2.**) If we record the number of boys in many different three-child families, then by the law of large numbers, as the number of observed families increases, the observed average number of boys should approach the expected value.

Games and Gambling

EXAMPLE 2   Finding Expected Winnings

A player pays $3 to play the following game: He tosses three fair coins and receives back "payoffs" of $1 if he tosses no heads, $2 for one head, $3 for two heads, and $4 for three heads. Find the player's expected net winnings for this game.

SOLUTION

Display the information as in **Table 12** on the next page. (Notice that, for each possible event, "net winnings" are "gross winnings" (payoff) minus cost to play.) Probabilities are derived from the sample space.

$$S = \{ttt, htt, tht, tth, hht, hth, thh, hhh\}$$

The expected net loss of 50 cents is a long-run average only. On any particular play of this game, the player would lose $2 or lose $1 or break even or win $1. Over a long series of plays, say 100, there would be some wins and some losses, but the total net result would likely be around a $100 \cdot (\$0.50) = \$50$ *loss*.

Solution to the Chapter Opener Problem One way to look at the problem, given that the car is *not* behind Door 3, is that Doors 1 and 2 are now equally likely to contain the car. Thus, switching doors will neither help nor hurt your chances of winning the car.

However, there is another way to look at the problem. When you picked Door 1, the probability was $\frac{1}{3}$ that it contained the car. Being shown the goat behind Door 3 doesn't really give you any new information; after all, you knew that there was a goat behind at least one of the other doors. So seeing the goat behind Door 3 does nothing to change your assessment of the probability that Door 1 has the car. It remains $\frac{1}{3}$. But because Door 3 has been ruled out, the probability that Door 2 has the car is now $\frac{2}{3}$. Thus, you should switch.

Analysis of this problem depends on the psychology of the host. If we suppose that the host must *always* show you a losing door and then give you an option to switch, then you should switch. This was not specifically stated in the problem as posed above but was pointed out by many mathematicians who became involved in the discussion.

(The authors wish to thank David Berman of the University of New Orleans for his assistance with this explanation.)

For a convincing simulation of the Monty Hall problem, see http://www.grand-illusions.com/simulator/montysim.htm

Table 12

Number of Heads	Payoff	Net Winnings x	Probability $P(x)$	Product $x \cdot P(x)$
0	$1	−$2	$\frac{1}{8}$	−$$\frac{2}{8}$
1	2	−1	$\frac{3}{8}$	−$\frac{3}{8}$
2	3	0	$\frac{3}{8}$	0
3	4	1	$\frac{1}{8}$	$\frac{1}{8}$

Expected value: $E(x) = -\$\frac{1}{2} = -\$0.50$

▮▮▮

A game in which the expected net winnings are zero is called a **fair game.** The game in **Example 2** has negative expected net winnings, so it is unfair against the player. A game with positive expected net winnings is unfair in favor of the player.

▮▮ **EXAMPLE 3** Finding the Fair Cost to Play a Game

The $3 cost to play the game of **Example 2** makes the game unfair against the player (since the player's expected net winnings are negative). What cost would make this a fair game?

SOLUTION

We already computed, in **Example 2,** that the $3 cost to play resulted in an expected net loss of $0.50. Therefore we can conclude that the $3 cost was 50 cents too high. A fair cost to play the game would then be $3 − $0.50 = $2.50. ▮▮▮

The result in **Example 3** can be verified. Disregard the cost to play and find the expected *gross* winnings (by summing the products of payoff times probability).

$$E(\text{gross winnings}) = \$1 \cdot \frac{1}{8} + \$2 \cdot \frac{3}{8} + \$3 \cdot \frac{3}{8} + \$4 \cdot \frac{1}{8} = \frac{\$20}{8} = \$2.50$$

Expected gross winnings (payoff) are $2.50, so this amount is a fair cost to play.

▮▮ **EXAMPLE 4** Finding the Fair Cost to Play a Game

In a certain state lottery, a player chooses three digits, in a specific order. (Leading digits may be 0, so numbers such as 028 and 003 are legitimate entries.) The lottery operators randomly select a three-digit sequence, and any player matching their selection receives a payoff of $600. What is a fair cost to play this game?

SOLUTION

In this case, no cost has been proposed, so we have no choice but to compute expected *gross* winnings. The probability of selecting all three digits correctly is $\frac{1}{10} \cdot \frac{1}{10} \cdot \frac{1}{10} = \frac{1}{1000}$, and the probability of not selecting all three correctly is $1 - \frac{1}{1000} = \frac{999}{1000}$. The expected gross winnings are

$$E(\text{gross winnings}) = \$600 \cdot \frac{1}{1000} + \$0 \cdot \frac{999}{1000} = \$0.60.$$

Thus the fair cost to play this game is 60 cents. (In fact, the lottery charges $1 to play, so players should expect to lose 40 cents per play *on the average.*) ▮▮▮

Roulette ("little wheel") was invented in France in the seventeenth or early eighteenth century. It has been a featured game of chance in the gambling casino of Monte Carlo.

The disk is divided into red and black alternating compartments, numbered 1 to 36 (but not in that order). There is a compartment also for 0 (and for 00 in the United States). In roulette, the wheel is set in motion, and an ivory ball is thrown into the bowl opposite to the direction of the wheel. When the wheel stops, the ball comes to rest in one of the compartments—the number and color determine who wins.

The players bet against the banker (person in charge of the pool of money) by placing money or equivalent chips in spaces on the roulette table corresponding to the wheel's colors or numbers. Bets can be made on one number or several, on odd or even, on red or black, or on combinations. The banker pays off according to the odds against the particular bet(s). For example, the classic payoff for a winning single number is $36 for each $1 bet.

State lotteries must be unfair against players because they are designed to help fund benefits (such as the state's school system) as well as to cover administrative costs and certain other expenses. Among people's reasons for playing may be a willingness to support such causes, but most people undoubtedly play for the chance to "beat the odds" and be one of the few net winners.

Gaming casinos are major business enterprises, by no means designed to break even; the games they offer are always unfair in favor of the house. The bias does not need to be great, however, since even relatively small average losses per player multiplied by large numbers of players can result in huge profits for the house.

▌▌ **EXAMPLE 5**   Finding Expected Winnings in Roulette

One simple type of *roulette* is played with an ivory ball and a wheel set in motion. The wheel contains thirty-eight compartments. Eighteen of the compartments are black, eighteen are red, one is labeled "zero," and one is labeled "double zero." (These last two are neither black nor red.) In this case, assume the player places $1 on either red or black. If the player picks the correct color of the compartment in which the ball finally lands, the payoff is $2; otherwise the payoff is zero. Find the expected net winnings.

SOLUTION

By the expected value formula, expected net winnings are

$$E(\text{net winnings}) = (\$1)\frac{18}{38} + (-\$1)\frac{20}{38} = -\$\frac{1}{19}.$$

The expected net *loss* here is $\$\frac{1}{19}$, or about 5.3¢, per play.   ▌▌▌

Investments

▌▌ **EXAMPLE 6**   Finding Expected Investment Profits

Nick Jovanovich has $5000 to invest and will commit the whole amount, for six months, to one of three technology stocks. A number of uncertainties could affect the prices of these stocks, but Nick is confident, based on his research, that one of only several possible profit scenarios will prove true of each one at the end of the six-month period. His complete analysis is shown in **Table 13**. (For example, stock *ABC* could lose $400, gain $800, or gain $1500.)

Table 13

Company *ABC*		Company *RST*		Company *XYZ*	
Profit or Loss x	Probability $P(x)$	Profit or Loss x	Probability $P(x)$	Profit or Loss x	Probability $P(x)$
−$400	0.2	$500	0.8	$0	0.4
800	0.5	1000	0.2	700	0.3
1500	0.3			1200	0.1
				2000	0.2

Find the expected profit (or loss) for each of the three stocks and select Nick's optimum choice based on these calculations. (The solution is on the next page.)

The first **Silver Dollar Slot Machine** was fashioned in 1929 by the Fey Manufacturing Company, San Francisco, inventors of the 3-reel, automatic payout machine (1895).

SOLUTION

Apply the expected value formula.

ABC: $-\$400 \cdot (0.2) + \$800 \cdot (0.5) + \$1500 \cdot (0.3) = \$770$

RST: $\$500 \cdot (0.8) + \$1000 \cdot (0.2) = \$600$

XYZ: $\$0 \cdot (0.4) + \$700 \cdot (0.3) + \$1200 \cdot (0.1) + \$2000 \cdot (0.2) = \$730$

The largest expected profit is $770. By this analysis, Nick should invest the money in stock ABC. ■■■

Of course, by investing in stock ABC, Nick may in fact *lose* $400 over the six months. The "expected" return of $770 is only a long-run average over many identical situations. Since this particular investment situation may never occur again, you may argue that using expected values is not the best approach for Nick to use.

An optimist would ignore most possibilities and focus on the *best* that each investment could do, while a pessimist would focus on the *worst* possibility for each investment.

■ **EXAMPLE 7** Choosing Stock Investments

Decide which stock of **Example 6** Nick would pick in each case.

(a) He is an optimist.   **(b)** He is a pessimist.

SOLUTION

(a) Disregarding the probabilities, he would focus on the best case for each stock. Since ABC could return as much as $1500, RST as much as $1000, and XYZ as much as $2000, the optimum is $2000. He would buy stock XYZ (the best of the three *best* cases).

(b) In this situation, he would focus on the worst possible cases. Since ABC might return as little as $-\$400$ (a $400 loss), RST as little as $500, and XYZ as little as $0, he would buy stock RST (the best of the three *worst* cases). ■■■

Business and Insurance

■ **EXAMPLE 8** Finding Expected Lumber Revenue

Mike Crenshaw, a lumber wholesaler, is considering the purchase of a (railroad) carload of varied dimensional lumber. Mike calculates that the probabilities of reselling the load for $10,000, $9000, or $8000 are 0.22, 0.33, and 0.45, respectively. In order to ensure an *expected* profit of at least $3000, how much can Mike afford to pay for the load?

SOLUTION

The expected revenue (or income) from resales can be found in **Table 14**.

Table 14	Expected Lumber Revenue	
Income x	**Probability** $P(x)$	**Product** $x \cdot P(x)$
$10,000	0.22	$2200
9000	0.33	2970
8000	0.45	3600
	Expected revenue:	$8770

In general, we have the relationship

$$\text{profit} = \text{revenue} - \text{cost}.$$

Therefore, in terms of expectations,

$$\text{expected profit} = \text{expected revenue} - \text{cost}.$$

So $3000 = $8770 − cost, or equivalently, cost = $8770 − $3000 = $5770. Mike can pay up to $5770 and still maintain an expected profit of at least $3000. ▪▪▪

▌▌ **EXAMPLE 9** Analyzing an Insurance Decision

Jeff Marsalis, a farmer, will realize a profit of $150,000 on his wheat crop, unless there is rain before harvest, in which case he will realize only $40,000. The long-term weather forecast assigns rain a probability of 0.16. (The probability of no rain is 1 − 0.16 = 0.84.) An insurance company offers crop insurance of $150,000 against rain for a premium of $20,000. Should Jeff buy the insurance?

SOLUTION

In order to make a wise decision, Jeff computes his expected profit under both options: to insure and not to insure. The complete calculations are summarized in the two "expectation" **Tables 15 and 16**.

For example, if insurance is purchased and it rains, Jeff's net profit is

$$\begin{bmatrix} \text{Insurance} \\ \text{proceeds} \end{bmatrix} + \begin{bmatrix} \text{Reduced} \\ \text{crop profit} \end{bmatrix} - \begin{bmatrix} \text{Insurance} \\ \text{premium} \end{bmatrix} \quad \text{Net profit}$$

$$\$150,000 \ + \ \ \$40,000 \ \ - \ \ \$20,000 \ = \ \$170,000.$$

Table 15 Expectation when Insuring

	Net Profit x	Probability $P(x)$	Product $x \cdot P(x)$
Rain	$170,000	0.16	$27,200
No rain	130,000	0.84	109,200
		Expected profit:	$136,400

Table 16 Expectation when Not Insuring

	Net Profit x	Probability $P(x)$	Product $x \cdot P(x)$
Rain	$40,000	0.16	$6400
No rain	150,000	0.84	126,000
		Expected profit:	$132,400

By comparing expected profits (136,400 > 132,400), we conclude that Jeff is better off buying the insurance. ▪▪▪

For Further Thought

Expected Value of Games of Chance

Slot machines are a popular game for those who want to lose their money with very little mental effort. We cannot calculate an expected value applicable to all slot machines since payoffs vary from machine to machine. But we can calculate the "typical expected value."

A player operates a slot machine by pulling a handle after inserting a coin or coins. Reels inside the machine then rotate, and come to rest in some random order. Assume that three reels show the pictures listed in **Table 17**. For example, of the 20 pictures on the first reel, 2 are cherries, 5 are oranges, 5 are plums, 2 are bells, 2 are melons, 3 are bars, and 1 is the number 7.

A picture of cherries on the first reel, but not on the second, leads to a payoff of 3 coins (*net* winnings: 2 coins); a picture of cherries on the first two reels, but not the third, leads to a payoff of 5 coins (*net* winnings: 4 coins). These and all other winning combinations are listed in **Table 18**.

Since, according to **Table 17**, there are 2 ways of getting cherries on the first reel, 15 ways of *not* getting cherries on the second reel, and 20 ways of getting anything on the third reel, we have a total of $2 \cdot 15 \cdot 20 = 600$ ways of getting a net payoff of 2. Since there are 20 pictures per reel, there are a total of $20 \cdot 20 \cdot 20 = 8000$ possible outcomes. Hence, the probability of receiving a net payoff of 2 coins is 600/8000.

This Cleveland Indians fan hit four 7s in a row on a progressive nickel slot machine at the Sands Casino in Las Vegas in 1988.

Table 17	Pictures on Reels		
	Reels		
Pictures	**1**	**2**	**3**
Cherries	2	5	4
Oranges	5	4	5
Plums	5	3	3
Bells	2	4	4
Melons	2	1	2
Bars	3	2	1
7s	1	1	1
Totals	20	20	20

Table 18	Calculating Expected Loss on a Three-Reel Slot Machine				
Winning Combinations	**Number of Ways**	**Probability**	**Number of Coins Received**	**Net Winnings (in coins)**	**Probability Times Net Winnings**
1 cherry (on first reel)	$2 \cdot 15 \cdot 20 = 600$	600/8000	3	2	1200/8000
2 cherries (on first two reels)	$2 \cdot 5 \cdot 16 = 160$	160/8000	5	4	640/8000
3 cherries	$2 \cdot 5 \cdot 4 = 40$	40/8000	10	9	360/8000
3 oranges	$5 \cdot 4 \cdot 5 = 100$	100/8000	10	9	900/8000
3 plums	$5 \cdot 3 \cdot 3 = 45$	45/8000	14	13	585/8000
3 bells	$\_ \cdot \_ \cdot \_ = \_\_$	___/8000	18	___	___/8000
3 melons (jackpot)	$\_ \cdot \_ \cdot \_ = \_\_$	___/8000	100	___	___/8000
3 bars (jackpot)	$\_ \cdot \_ \cdot \_ = \_\_$	___/8000	200	___	___/8000
3 7s (jackpot)	$\_ \cdot \_ \cdot \_ = \_\_$	___/8000	500	___	___/8000
Totals	___				6318/8000

Table 18 takes into account all *winning* outcomes, with the necessary products for finding expectation added in the last column. However, since a *nonwinning* outcome can occur in

$$8000 - 988 = 7012 \text{ ways (with winnings of } -1 \text{ coin),}$$

the product $(-1) \cdot 7012/8000$ must also be included. Hence, the expected value of this particular slot machine is

$$\frac{6318}{8000} + (-1) \cdot \frac{7012}{8000} \approx -0.087 \text{ coin.}$$

On a machine costing one dollar per play, the expected *loss* (per play) is about

$$(0.087)(1 \text{ dollar}) = 8.7 \text{ cents.}$$

Actual slot machines vary in expected loss per dollar of play. But author Hornsby was able to beat a Las Vegas slot machine in 1988. (See the photo on **page 618**.)

Table 19 comes from an article by Andrew Sterrett in *The Mathematics Teacher* (March 1967), in which he discusses rules for various games of chance and calculates their expected values. He uses expected values to find expected times it would take to lose $1000 if you played continually at the rate of $1 per play and one play per minute.

For Group or Individual Investigation

1. Explain why the entries of the "Net Winnings" column of **Table 18** are all one fewer than the corresponding entries of the "Number of Coins Received" column.

2. Find the 29 missing values in **Table 18**. (Refer to **Table 17** for the values in the "Number of Ways" column.)

3. In order to make your money last as long as possible in a casino, which game should you play?

Table 19 Expected Time to Lose $1000

Game	Expected Value	Days	Hours	Minutes
Roulette (with one 0)	−$0.027	25	16	40
Roulette (with 0 and 00)	−$0.053	13	4	40
Chuck-a-luck	−$0.079	8	19	46
Keno (one number)	−$0.200	3	11	20
Numbers	−$0.300	2	7	33
Football pool (4 winners)	−$0.375	1	20	27
Football pool (10 winners)	−$0.658	1	1	19

11.5 EXERCISES

1. Explain in words what is meant by "expected value of a random variable."

2. Explain what a couple means by the statement, "We expect to have 1.5 sons."

3. *Tossing Coins* Five fair coins are tossed. Find the expected number of heads.

4. *Drawing Cards* Two cards are drawn, with replacement, from a standard 52-card deck. Find the expected number of diamonds.

Expected Winnings in a Die-rolling Game For Exercises 5 and 6, a game consists of rolling a single fair die and pays off as follows: $3 for a 6, $2 for a 5, $1 for a 4, and no payoff otherwise.

5. Find the expected winnings for this game.

6. What is a fair price to pay to play this game?

Expected Winnings in a Die-rolling Game For Exercises 7 and 8, consider a game consisting of rolling a single fair die, with payoffs as follows. If an even number of spots turns up, you receive as many dollars as there are spots up. But if an odd number of spots turns up, you must pay as many dollars as there are spots up.

7. Find the expected net winnings of this game.

8. Is this game fair, or unfair against the player, or unfair in favor of the player?

9. *Expected Winnings in a Coin-tossing Game* A certain game involves tossing 3 fair coins, and it pays 10¢ for 3 heads, 5¢ for 2 heads, and 3¢ for 1 head. Is 5¢ a fair price to pay to play this game? (That is, does the 5¢ cost to play make the game fair?)

10. *Expected Winnings in Roulette* In a form of roulette slightly different from that in **Example 5,** a more generous management supplies a wheel having only thirty-seven compartments, with eighteen red, eighteen black, and one zero. Find the expected net winnings if you bet on red in this game.

11. *Expected Number of Absences in a Math Class* In a certain mathematics class, the probabilities have been empirically determined for various numbers of absentees on any given day. These values are shown in the table below. Find the expected number of absentees on a given day. (Give the answer to two decimal places.)

Number absent	0	1	2	3	4
Probability	0.18	0.26	0.29	0.23	0.04

12. *Expected Profit of an Insurance Company* An insurance company will insure a $200,000 home for its total value for an annual premium of $650. If the company spends $25 per year to service such a policy, the probability of total loss for such a home in a given year is 0.002, and you assume that either total loss or no loss will occur, what is the company's expected annual gain (or profit) on each such policy?

Profits from a College Foundation Raffle A college foundation raises funds by selling raffle tickets for a new car worth $36,000.

13. If 600 tickets are sold for $120 each, determine

  (a) the expected *net* winnings of a person buying one of the tickets,

  (b) the total profit for the foundation, assuming they had to purchase the car,

  (c) the total profit for the foundation, assuming the car was donated.

14. For the raffle described in **Exercise 13,** if 720 tickets are sold for $120 each, determine

  (a) the expected *net* winnings of a person buying one of the tickets,

  (b) the total profit for the foundation, assuming they had to purchase the car,

  (c) the total profit for the foundation, assuming the car was donated.

Winnings and Profits of a Raffle Five thousand raffle tickets are sold. One first prize of $1000, two second prizes of $500 each, and three third prizes of $100 each will be awarded, with all winners selected randomly.

15. If you purchased one ticket, what are your expected gross winnings?

16. If you purchased ten tickets, what are your expected gross winnings?

17. If the tickets were sold for $1 each, how much profit goes to the raffle sponsor?

18. *Expected Sales at a Theater Snack Bar* A children's theater found in a random survey that 58 customers bought one snack bar item, 49 bought two items, 31 bought three items, 4 bought four items, and 8 avoided the snack bar altogether. Use this information to find the expected number of snack bar items per customer. (Round your answer to the nearest tenth.)

19. *Expected Number of Children to Attend an Amusement Park* An amusement park, considering adding some new attractions, conducted a study over several typical days and found that, of 10,000 families entering the park, 1020 brought just one child (defined as younger than age twelve), 3370 brought two children, 3510 brought three children, 1340 brought four children, 510 brought five children, 80 brought six children, and 170 brought no children at all. Find the expected number of children per family attending this park. (Round your answer to the nearest tenth.)

20. *Expected Sums of Randomly Selected Numbers* Four cards are numbered 1 through 4. Two of these cards are chosen randomly (without replacement), and the numbers on them are added. Find the expected value of this sum.

21. *Prospects for Electronics Jobs in a City* In a certain California city, projections for the next year are that there is a 20% chance that electronics jobs will increase by 200, a 50% chance that they will increase by 300, and a 30% chance that they will decrease by 800. What is the expected change in the number of electronics jobs in that city in the next year?

22. *Expected Winnings in Keno* In one version of the game *keno*, the house has a pot containing 80 balls, numbered 1 through 80. A player buys a ticket for $1 and marks one number on it (from 1 to 80). The house then selects 20 of the 80 numbers at random. If the number selected by the player is among the 20 selected by the management, the player is paid $3.20. Find the expected net winnings for this game.

23. Refer to **Examples 6 and 7.** Considering the three different approaches (expected values, optimist, and pessimist), which one seems most reasonable to you, and why?

Contractor Decisions Based on Expected Profits Lori Hales, a commercial building contractor, will commit her company to one of three projects depending on her analysis of potential profits or losses as shown here.

Project A		Project B		Project C	
Profit or Loss x	Probability $P(x)$	Profit or Loss x	Probability $P(x)$	Profit or Loss x	Probability $P(x)$
$60,000	0.10	$0	0.20	$40,000	0.65
180,000	0.60	210,000	0.35	340,000	0.35
250,000	0.30	290,000	0.45		

Determine which project Lori should choose according to each approach.

24. expected values

25. the optimist viewpoint

26. the pessimist viewpoint

Expected Winnings in a Game Show A game show contestant is offered the option of receiving a computer system worth $2300 or accepting a chance to win either a luxury vacation worth $5000 or a boat worth $8000. If the second option is chosen the contestant's probabilities of winning the vacation or the boat are 0.20 and 0.15, respectively.

27. If the contestant were to turn down the computer system and go for one of the other prizes, what would be the expected winnings?

28. Purely in terms of monetary value, what is the contestant's wiser choice?

Evaluating an Insurance Purchase David Glenn, the promoter of an outdoor concert, expects a gate profit of $100,000, *unless it rains, which would reduce the gate profit to $30,000. The probability of rain is 0.20. For a premium of $25,000 David can purchase insurance coverage that would pay him $100,000 in case of rain.*

Use this information for Exercises 29–32.

29. Find the expected net profit when the insurance is purchased.

30. Find the expected net profit when the insurance is not purchased.

31. Based on expected values, which is David's wiser choice in this situation?

32. If you were the promoter, would you base your decision on expected values? Explain your reasoning.

Expected Values in Book Sales Jessica Lasda, an educational publisher representative, presently has five accounts, and her manager is considering assigning her three more accounts. The new accounts would bring potential volume to her business, and some of her present accounts have potential for growth as well. See the following table and continue on the next page.

1	2	3	4	5	6
Account Number	Existing Volume	Potential Additional Volume	Probability of Getting Additional Volume	Expected Value of Additional Volume	Existing Volume plus Expected Value of Additional Volume
1	$10,000	$10,000	0.40	$4000	$14,000
2	30,000	0	—	—	30,000
3	25,000	15,000	0.20	3000	
4	35,000	0	—	—	
5	15,000	5,000	0.30		
6	0	30,000	0.10		
7	0	25,000	0.70		
8	0	45,000	0.60		

Use the previous table to work Exercises 33–37.

33. Compute the four missing expected values in column 5.

34. Compute the six missing amounts in column 6.

35. What is Jessica's total "expected" additional volume?

36. If Jessica achieved her expected additional volume in all accounts, what would be the total volume of all her accounts?

37. If Jessica achieved her expected additional volume in all accounts, by what percentage (to the nearest tenth of a percent) would she increase her total volume?

38. *Expected Winnings in Keno* Recall that in the game keno of **Exercise 22,** the house randomly selects 20 numbers from the counting numbers 1–80. In the variation called 6-spot keno, the player pays 60¢ for his ticket and marks 6 numbers of his choice. If the 20 numbers selected by the house contain at least 3 of those chosen by the player, he gets a payoff according to this scheme.

3 of the player's numbers among the 20	$0.35
4 of the player's numbers among the 20	2.00
5 of the player's numbers among the 20	60.00
6 of the player's numbers among the 20	1250.00

Find the player's expected net winnings in this game. [*Hint:* The four probabilities required here can be found using combinations (**Section 10.3**), the fundamental counting principle (**Section 10.2**), and the theoretical probability formula (**Section 11.1**).]

EXTENSION Estimating Probabilities by Simulation

Simulating Genetic Traits • Simulating Human Births

Simulating Genetic Traits An important area within probability theory is the process called **simulation.** It is possible to study a complicated, or unclear, phenomenon by *simulating,* or imitating, it with a simpler phenomenon involving the same basic probabilities.

For example, recall from **Section 11.1** Mendel's discovery that when two Rr pea plants (red-flowered but carrying both red and white genes) are crossed, the offspring will have red flowers if an R gene is received from either parent or from both. This is because red is dominant and white is recessive. **Table 3**, reproduced here in the margin, shows that three of the four equally likely possibilities result in red-flowered offspring.

Now suppose we want to estimate the probability that three offspring in a row will have red flowers. It is much easier (and quicker) to toss coins than to cross pea plants. And the equally likely outcomes, heads and tails, can be used to simulate the transfer of the equally likely genes, R and r. If we toss two coins, say a nickel and a penny, then we can interpret the results as follows.

		Second Parent	
		R	**r**
First Parent	**R**	RR	Rr
	r	rR	rr

hh $\Rightarrow$ RR $\Rightarrow$ red gene from first parent and red gene from second parent $\Rightarrow$ red flowers

ht $\Rightarrow$ Rr $\Rightarrow$ red gene from first parent and white gene from second parent $\Rightarrow$ red flowers

th $\Rightarrow$ rR $\Rightarrow$ white gene from first parent and red gene from second parent $\Rightarrow$ red flowers

tt $\Rightarrow$ rr $\Rightarrow$ white gene from first parent and white gene from second parent $\Rightarrow$ white flowers

Simulation methods, also called **"Monte Carlo" methods,** require huge numbers of random digits, so computers are used to produce them. A computer, however, cannot toss coins. It must use an algorithmic process, programmed into the computer, which is called a **random number generator.** It is very difficult to avoid all nonrandom patterns in the results, so the digits produced are called "pseudorandom" numbers. They must pass a battery of tests of randomness before being "approved for use."

Computer scientists and physicists have been encountering unexpected difficulties with even the most sophisticated random number generators. Therefore, they must be carefully checked along with each new simulation application proposed.

Although nothing is certain for a few tosses, the law of large numbers indicates that larger and larger numbers of tosses should become better and better indicators of general trends in the genetic process.

▮▮ **EXAMPLE 1** Simulating Genetic Processes

Toss two coins 50 times and use the results to approximate the probability that the crossing of Rr pea plants will produce three successive red-flowered offspring.

SOLUTION

We actually tossed two coins 50 times and got the following sequence.

> th, hh, th, tt, th, hh, ht, th, ht, th, hh, hh, tt, th, hh,
> ht, ht, ht, ht, th, hh, hh, hh, tt, ht, tt, hh, ht, ht, hh, tt,
> tt, tt, th, tt, tt, hh, ht, ht, ht, hh, tt, th, hh, tt, hh, ht,
> tt, tt, tt

By the color interpretation described on the previous page, this gives the following sequence of flower colors in the offspring.

> Only "both tails" gives white.

> red–red–red–white–red–red–red–red–red–red–red–red–white–
> red–red–red–red–red–red–red–red–red–red–white–red–white–
> red–red–red–red–white–white–white–red–white–white–red–red–
> red–red–red–white–red–red–white–red–red–white–white–white

We now have an experimental list of 48 sets of three successive plants, the 1st, 2nd, and 3rd entries, then the 2nd, 3rd, and 4th entries, and so on. Do you see why there are 48 in all?

Now we just count up the number of these sets of three that are "red-red-red." Since there are 20 of those, our empirical probability of three successive red offspring, obtained through simulation, is $\frac{20}{48} = \frac{5}{12}$, or about 0.417. By applying the multiplication rule of probability (with all outcomes independent of one another), we find that the theoretical value is $\left(\frac{3}{4}\right)^3 = \frac{27}{64}$, or about 0.422, so our approximation obtained by simulation is very close. ▮▮▮

Simulating Human Births   In human births boys and girls are (essentially) equally likely. Therefore, an individual birth can be simulated by tossing a fair coin, letting a head correspond to a girl and a tail to a boy.

▮▮ **EXAMPLE 2** Simulating Births with Coin Tossing

A sequence of 40 actual coin tosses produced the results below.

> bbggb, gbbbg, gbgbb, bggbg, bbbbg, gbbgg, gbbgg, bgbbg

(For every head we have written g, for girl. For every tail, b, for boy.)

(a) How many pairs of two successive births are represented by the sequence?

(b) How many of those pairs consist of both boys?

(c) Find the empirical probability, based on this simulation, that two successive births both will be boys. Give your answer to three decimal places.

SOLUTION

(a) Beginning with the 1st–2nd pair and ending with the 39th–40th pair, there are 39 pairs.

(b) Observing the sequence of boys and girls, we count 11 pairs of two consecutive boys.

(c) Utilizing parts (a) and (b), we have $\frac{11}{39} \approx 0.282$. ▮▮▮

Pilots, astronauts, race car drivers, and others train in **simulators.** Some of these devices, which may be viewed as very technical, high-cost versions of video games, imitate conditions to be encountered later in the "real world." A simulator session allows estimation of the likelihood, or probability, of different responses that the learner would display under actual conditions. Repeated sessions help the learner to develop more successful responses before actual equipment and lives are put at risk.

Table 20
→51592
77876
36500
40571
04822
→53033
92080
01587
36006
63698
→17297
22841
→91979
96480
74949
76896
47588
45521
02472
55184
40177
84861
86937
20931
22454
→73219
→55707
48007
→65191
06772
94928
→15709
39922
96365
14655
65587
76905
12369
54219
89329
90060
06975
05050
69774
→78351
11464
84086
→51497
12307
68009

Another way to simulate births, and other phenomena, is with random numbers. The spinner in **Figure 12** can be used to obtain a table of random digits, like in **Table 20**. The 250 random digits generated have been grouped conveniently so that we can easily follow down a column or across a row to carry out a simulation.

Figure 12

▋▋ **EXAMPLE 3** Simulating Births with Random Numbers

A couple plans to have five children. Use random number simulation to estimate the probability they will have more than three boys.

SOLUTION

Let each sequence of five digits, as they appear in **Table 20,** represent a family with five children, and (arbitrarily) associate odd digits with boys, even digits with girls. (Recall that 0 is even.) Verify that, of the fifty families simulated, only the ten marked with arrows have more than 3 boys (4 boys or 5 boys). Therefore, the estimated (empirical) probability is

$$P(\text{more than 3 boys}) = \frac{10}{50} = 0.20.$$ ▋▋▋

The theoretical value for the probability in **Example 3** above would be the same as that obtained in **Example 3** of **Section 11.4.** It was 0.1875. Our estimate above was fairly close. In light of the law of large numbers, a larger sampling of random digits (more than 50 simulated families) would likely yield a closer approximation.

▋▋ **EXAMPLE 4** Simulating Card Drawing with Random Numbers

Use random number simulation to estimate the probability that two cards drawn from a standard deck with replacement both will be of the same suit.

SOLUTION

Use this correspondence: 0 and 1 mean clubs, 2 and 3 mean diamonds, 4 and 5 mean hearts, 6 and 7 mean spades, 8 and 9 are disregarded. Now refer to **Table 20**. If we (arbitrarily) use the first digit of each five-digit group, omitting 8s and 9s, we obtain the sequence

5–7–3–4–0–5–0–3–6–1–2–7–7–4–4–0–5–4–2–2–

7–5–4–6–0–1–3–1–6–7–1–5–0–0–6–7–1–5–1–6.

First digits of all groups

This 40-digit sequence of digits yields the sequence of suits shown next.

5 gives hearts, 7 gives spades, 3 gives diamonds, and so on.

hearts–spades–diamonds–hearts–clubs–hearts–clubs–diamonds–spades–
clubs–diamonds–spades–spades–hearts–hearts–clubs–hearts–hearts–
diamonds–diamonds–spades–hearts–hearts–spades–clubs–clubs–
diamonds–clubs–spades–spades–clubs–hearts–clubs–clubs–spades–
spades–clubs–hearts–clubs–spades

Verify that, of the 39 successive pairs of suits (hearts–spades, spades–diamonds, diamonds–hearts, etc.), 9 of them are pairs of the same suit. This makes the estimated probability $\frac{9}{39} \approx 0.23$. (For comparison, the theoretical value is 0.25.) ▋▋▋

EXTENSION EXERCISES

1. **Simulating Pea Plant Reproduction with Coin Tossing** Explain why, in **Example 1,** fifty tosses of the coins produced only 48 sets of three successive offspring.

2. **Simulating Pea Plant Reproduction with Coin Tossing** Use the sequence of flower colors of **Example 1** to approximate the probability that *four* successive offspring all will have red flowers.

3. **Comparing the Likelihoods of Girl and Boy Births** Should the probability of two successive girl births be any different from that of two successive boy births?

4. **Finding Empirical Probability** Simulate 40 births by tossing coins yourself, and obtain an empirical probability for two successive girls.

5. **Simulating Boy and Girl Children with Random Numbers** Use **Table 20** to simulate fifty families with three children. Let 0–4 correspond to boys and 5–9 to girls, and use the middle three digits of the 5-digit groupings (159, 787, 650, and so on). Estimate the probability of exactly two boys in a family of three children. Compare with the theoretical probability, which is $\frac{3}{8} = 0.375$.

Simulating One-and-One Foul Shooting with Random Numbers
*In **Exercises 71–73** of **Section 11.3**, Christine, who had a 70% foul-shooting record, had probabilities of scoring 0, 1, or 2 points of 0.30, 0.21, and 0.49, respectively.*

*Use **Table 20** (with digits 0–6 representing hit and 7–9 representing miss) to simulate 50 one-and-one shooting opportunities for Christine. Begin at the top left (5, 7, 3, etc., to the bottom), then move to the second column (1, 7, 6, etc.), going until 50 one-and-one opportunities are obtained. (Some "opportunities" involve one shot and one random digit, while others involve two shots and two random digits.) Keep a tally of the numbers of times 0, 1, and 2 points are scored.*

Number of Points	**Tally**
0	
1	
2	

From the tally, find the empirical probability (to two decimal places) of each event.

6. no points   **7.** 1 point   **8.** 2 points

Determining the Path of a Random Walk Using a Die and a Coin
Exercises 49–56 of Section 11.4 illustrated a simple version of the idea of a "random walk." Atomic particles released in nuclear fission also move in a random fashion. During World War II, John von Neumann and Stanislaw Ulam used simulation with random numbers to study particle motion in nuclear reactions. Von Neumann coined the name "Monte Carlo" for the methods used.

The figure suggests a model for random motion in two dimensions. Assume that a particle moves in a series of 1-unit "jumps," each one in a random direction, any one of 12 equally likely possibilities. One way to choose directions is to roll a fair die and toss a fair coin. The die determines one of the directions 1–6, coupled with heads on the coin. Tails on the coin reverses the direction of the die, so that the die coupled with tails gives directions 7–12. So 3h (meaning 3 with the die and heads with the coin) gives direction 3; 3t gives direction 9 (opposite to 3); and so on.

9. Simulate the motion described above with 10 rolls of a die (and tosses of a coin). Draw the 10-jump path you get. Make your drawing accurate enough so you can estimate (by measuring) how far from its starting point the particle ends up.

10. Repeat the experiment of **Exercise 9** four more times. Measure distance from start to finish for each of the 5 "random trips." Add these 5 distances and divide the sum by 5, to arrive at an "expected net distance" for such a trip.

For Exercises 11 and 12, consider another two-dimensional random walk governed by the following conditions.

- *Start out from a given street corner, and travel one block north. At each intersection:*
- *Turn left with probability $\frac{1}{6}$.*
- *Go straight with probability $\frac{2}{6} (= \frac{1}{3})$.*
- *Turn right with probability $\frac{3}{6} (= \frac{1}{2})$.*

  (Never turn around.)

11. **A Random Walk Using a Fair Die** Explain how a fair die could be used to simulate this random walk.

12. **A Random Walk Using a Random Number Table** Use **Table 20** to simulate this random walk. For every 1 encountered in the table, turn left and proceed for another block. For every 2 or 3, go straight and proceed for another block. For every 4, 5, or 6, turn right and proceed for another block. Disregard all other digits, that is, 0s, 7s, 8s, and 9s. (Do you see how this scheme satisfies the probabilities given before **Exercise 11**?) This time begin at the upper right corner of the table, running down the column 2, 6, 0, and so on, to the bottom. When this column of digits is used up, stop the "walk." Describe, in terms of distance and direction, where you have ended up relative to your starting point.

COLLABORATIVE INVESTIGATION

Finding Empirical Values of π

The information in this investigation was obtained from Burton's History of Mathematics: An Introduction, Third Edition, by David M. Burton, published by Wm. C. Brown, 1995, page 440.

The following problem was posed by Georges Louis Leclerc, Comte de Buffon (1707–1788) in his *Histoire Naturelle* in 1777. A large plane area is ruled with equidistant parallel lines, the distance between two consecutive lines of the series being *a*. A thin needle of length

$$\ell < a$$

is tossed randomly onto the plane. What is the probability that the needle will intersect one of these lines?

The answer to this problem is found using integral calculus, and the probability *p* is shown to be $p = \frac{2\ell}{\pi a}$. Solving for π gives us the formula

$$\pi = \frac{2\ell}{pa}, \qquad \textbf{(1)}$$

which can be used to approximate the value of π experimentally. This was first observed by Pierre Simon de Laplace, and such an experiment was carried out by Johann Wolf, a professor of astronomy at Bern, in about 1850. In this investigation, we will perform a similar experiment.

See http://webspace.ship.edu/deensley/mathdl/stats/Buffon.html for a dynamic illustration of this Buffon Needle Problem.

Topics for Discussion

Divide the class into groups of 3 or 4 students each. Each group will need the materials listed in the next column.

1. a sheet of paper with a series of parallel lines evenly spaced across it

2. a thin needle, or needlelike object, with a length less than the distance between adjacent parallel lines on the paper

Each group should carry out these steps:

1. Measure and record the distance between lines (*a*) and the length of the needle (ℓ), using the same units for both.

2. Assign one member to drop the needle onto the paper, another to determine whether the needle "hits" a line or not, and another to keep a tally of hits and misses.

3. Discuss ways to minimize bias so that the position and orientation of the dropped needle will be as random as possible.

4. Drop the needle 100 times, and record the number of hits.

5. Calculate the probability $p = $ (number of hits)/100. Is this probability value theoretical or empirical?

6. Enter the calculated value of *p* and the measured values of *a* and ℓ into formula (1) to obtain a value of π. Round this value to four decimal places.

Now come back together as a class and record the various values obtained for π. Discuss the following questions.

1. The correct value of π, to four decimal places, is 3.1416. Which value of π, reported by the various groups, is most accurate? How far off is it?

2. Was it necessary to drop the needle 100 times, or could more or fewer tosses have been used?

3. Wolf tossed his needle 5000 times and it hit a line 2532 times, leading to an experimental value of π equal to 3.1596. How far off was Wolf's value?

4. How could the experiment be modified to produce "better" values for π?

5. Why could different groups use different ℓ to *a* ratios and still all obtain legitimate approximations for π?

6. Does the simulation method investigated here seem like a reasonable way to approximate π? Why, or why not?

CHAPTER 11 TEST

1. Explain the difference between *empirical* and *theoretical* probabilities.

2. State the *law of large numbers,* and use coin tossing to illustrate it.

Drawing Cards *A single card is chosen at random from a standard 52-card deck. Find the odds against its being each of the following.*

3. a heart

4. a red queen

5. a king or a black face card

Genetics of Cystic Fibrosis *The chart represents genetic transmission of cystic fibrosis. C denotes a normal gene while c denotes a cystic fibrosis gene. (Normal is dominant.) Both parents in this case are Cc, which means that they inherited one of each gene, and are, therefore, carriers but do not have the disease.*

		Second Parent	
		C	c
First Parent	C		Cc
	c		

6. Complete the chart, showing all four equally likely gene arrangements.

7. Find the probability that a child of these parents will also be a carrier without the disease.

8. What are the odds that a child of these parents actually will have cystic fibrosis?

Days Off for Pizza Parlor Workers *The manager of a pizza parlor (which operates seven days a week) allows each of three employees to select one day off next week. Assuming the selection is done randomly and independently, find the probability of each event.*

9. All three select different days.

10. All three select the same day, given that all three select a day beginning with the same letter.

11. Exactly two of them select the same day.

Building Numbers from Sets of Digits *Two numbers are randomly selected without replacement from the set {1, 2, 3, 4, 5}. Find the probability of each event.*

12. Both numbers are even.

13. Both numbers are prime.

14. The sum of the two numbers is odd.

15. The product of the two numbers is odd.

Selecting Committees *A three-member committee is selected randomly from a group consisting of three men and two women.*

16. Let x denote the number of men on the committee, and complete the probability distribution table.

x	$P(x)$
0	0
1	
2	
3	

17. Find the probability that the committee members are not all men.

18. Find the expected number of men on the committee.

Rolling Dice *A pair of dice are rolled. Find the following.*

19. the probability of "doubles" (the same number on both dice)

20. the odds in favor of a sum greater than 2

21. the odds against a sum of "7 or 11"

22. the probability of a sum that is even and less than 5

Making Par in Golf *Ted Krischak has a 0.78 chance of making par on each hole of golf that he plays. Today he plans to play just three holes. Find the probability of each event. Round answers to three decimal places.*

23. He makes par on all three holes.

24. He makes par on exactly two of the three holes.

25. He makes par on at least one of the three holes.

26. He makes par on the first and third holes but not on the second.

Drawing Cards *Two cards are drawn, without replacement, from a standard 52-card deck. Find the probability of each event.*

27. Both cards are red.

28. Both cards are the same color.

29. The second card is a queen, given that the first card is an ace

30. The first card is a face card and the second is black.

PERSONAL FINANCIAL MANAGEMENT

13

The second season of *The Andy Griffith Show* provided an episode that beautifully illustrated an application of the mathematics of finance. In "Mayberry Goes Bankrupt," Sheriff Taylor was reluctantly forced to evict kindly old gentleman Frank Myers from his home due to nonpayment of taxes. But Frank then produced a bond purchased for $100 in 1861 and paying 8.5% interest compounded annually. It had been stored away for 100 years. When the town banker told the Mayor he could not pay Frank, Andy explained why this was so.

> *Well, Mayor ... according to the computation machines down at the bank ... and they're good machines ... we ... owe Frank Myers $349,119.27. (To which Frank responds: I'll take it in cash.)*

By applying the formula for *compound interest* found in **Section 13.1,** you will find that the figure quoted is correct to the penny.

13.1 THE TIME VALUE OF MONEY

Interest • Simple Interest • Future Value and Present Value • Compound Interest
• Effective Annual Yield • Inflation

Interest

To determine the value of money, we consider not only the amount (number of dollars) but also the particular point in time that the value is to be determined. If we borrow an amount of money today, we will repay a larger amount later. This increase in value is known as **interest.** The money *gains value over time.*

The amount of a loan or a deposit is called the **principal.** The interest is usually computed as a percent of the principal. This percent is called the **rate of interest** (or the **interest rate,** or simply the **rate**). The rate of interest is always assumed to be an annual rate unless otherwise stated.

Interest calculated only on principal is called **simple interest.** Interest calculated on principal plus any previously earned interest is called **compound interest.**

Simple Interest

Simple interest is calculated according to the following formula.

Simple Interest

If P = principal, r = annual interest rate, and t = time (in years), then the **simple interest** I is calculated as follows.

$$I = Prt$$

▌▌ **EXAMPLE 1** Finding Simple Interest

Find the simple interest paid to borrow $5350 for 5 months at 6%.

SOLUTION

$$I = Prt \qquad \text{Simple interest formula}$$

$$= \$5350(0.06)\left(\frac{5}{12}\right) \qquad \boxed{\text{5 months is } \tfrac{5}{12} \text{ of a year.}}$$
$$\phantom{= \$5350(0.06)\left(\frac{5}{12}\right)} \quad P = \$5350, r = 6\% = 0.06$$

$$= \$133.75 \qquad \text{Calculate.} \qquad \blacksquare\blacksquare\blacksquare$$

> 5350*.06*(5/12)
> $\qquad\qquad$ 133.75
>
> This is the computation required to solve **Example 1.**

Future Value and Present Value

In **Example 1,** at the end of 5 months the borrower would have to repay.

Principal $\qquad$ Interest

$$\$5350 \quad + \quad \$133.75 = \$5483.75.$$

The total amount repaid is sometimes called the **maturity value** (or simply the **value**) of the loan. We will generally refer to it as the **future value,** or **future amount,** since when a loan is being set up, repayment will be occurring in the future. We use A to denote future amount (or value). The original principal, denoted P, can also be thought of as **present value.**

Future value depends on principal (present value) and interest as follows.

$$A = P + I = P + Prt = P(1 + rt)$$

Future Value for Simple Interest

If a principal P is borrowed at simple interest for t years at an annual interest rate of r, then the **future value** of the loan, denoted A, is calculated as follows.

$$A = P(1 + rt)$$

■■ EXAMPLE 2   Finding Future Value for Simple Interest

James Albertone took out a simple interest loan for $210 to purchase textbooks and school supplies. If the annual interest rate is 6% and he must repay the loan after 8 months, find the future value (the maturity value) of the loan.

SOLUTION

$$A = P(1 + rt) \qquad \text{Future value formula}$$
$$= \$210\left[1 + 0.06\left(\frac{8}{12}\right)\right] \qquad P = \$210, r = 6\% = 0.06, t = \frac{8}{12}$$
$$= \$218.40 \qquad \text{Calculate.}$$

At the end of 8 months, James will need to repay $218.40.   ■■■

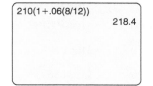

210(1+.06(8/12))
                218.4

This is the computation required to solve
Example 2.

Sometimes the future value is known, and we need to compute the present value. For this purpose, we solve the future value formula for P.

$$A = P(1 + rt) \qquad \text{Future value formula for simple interest}$$

$$P = \frac{A}{1 + rt} \qquad \text{Solve the formula for } P.$$

■■ EXAMPLE 3   Finding Present Value for Simple Interest

Suppose that James (**Example 2**) is granted an 8-month *deferral* of the $210 payment rather than a loan. That is, instead of incurring interest for 8 months, he will have to pay just the $210 at the end of that period. If he has extra money right now, and if he can earn 2% simple interest on savings, what lump sum must he deposit now so that its value will be $210 after 8 months?

SOLUTION

$$P = \frac{A}{1 + rt} \qquad \text{Future value formula solved for } P$$

$$P = \frac{\$210}{1 + (0.02)\left(\frac{8}{12}\right)} = \$207.24 \qquad \text{Substitute known values and simplify.}$$

210/(1+.02(8/12))
                207.24

This is the computation required to solve
Example 3.

A deposit of $207.24 now, growing at 2% simple interest, will grow to $210 over an 8-month period.   ■■■

Compound Interest

Interest paid on principal plus interest is called *compound interest*. After a certain period, the interest earned so far is *credited* (added) to the account, and the sum (principal plus interest) then earns interest during the next period.

To borrow from the title of the Clint Eastwood classic *The Good, the Bad, and the Ugly*, the 1994 movie *Blank Check* includes a scene that qualifies as **ugly mathematics.** Twelve-year-old Preston Waters receives a check for $11.00 and uses his computer to determine how long it will take for this amount to grow to $1,000,000 at 3.45% annual interest.

While there is no information on the number of compounding periods, the answer given in the movie is incorrect for any number. The computer determines that it would take 342,506 years. Even with interest compounded just once a year, the time would "only" be 337 years.

▌▌ EXAMPLE 4 Comparing Simple and Compound Interest

Compare simple and compound interest for a $1000 deposit at 4% interest for 5 years.

SOLUTION

$$A = P(1 + rt) \qquad \text{Future value formula}$$

$$= \$1000(1 + 0.04 \cdot 5) \qquad P = \$1000, r = 4\% = 0.04, t = 5$$

$$= \$1200 \qquad \text{Calculate.}$$

After 5 years, $1000 grows to $1200 subject to 4% simple interest.

The result of compounding (annually) for 5 years is shown in **Table 1.**

Table 1	A $1000 Deposit at 4% Interest Compounded Annually		
Year	Beginning Balance	Interest Earned $I = Prt$	Ending Balance
1	$1000.00	$1000.00(0.04)(1) = $40.00	$1040.00
2	$1040.00	$1040.00(0.04)(1) = $41.60	$1081.60
3	$1081.60	$1081.60(0.04)(1) = $43.26	$1124.86
4	$1124.86	$1124.86(0.04)(1) = $44.99	$1169.85
5	$1169.85	$1169.85(0.04)(1) = $46.79	$1216.64

Under annual compounding for 5 years, $1000 grows to $1216.64, which is $16.64 more than under simple interest.   ■■■

Based on the compounding pattern of **Example 4,** we now develop a future value formula for compound interest. In practice, earned interest can be credited to an account at time intervals other than 1 year (usually more often). For example, it can be done semiannually, quarterly, monthly, or daily. This time interval is called the **compounding period** (or simply the **period**). Start with the following definitions:

P = original principal deposited, $\qquad r$ = annual interest rate,

m = number of periods per year, $\qquad n$ = total number of periods.

During each individual compounding period, interest is earned according to the simple interest formula, and as interest is added, the beginning principal increases from one period to the next. During the first period, the interest earned is given by

$$\text{Interest} = P(r)\left(\frac{1}{m}\right) \qquad \begin{array}{l}\text{Interest} = (\text{Principal})(\text{rate})(\text{time}),\\ \text{one period} = \frac{1}{m}\ \text{year}\end{array}$$

$$= P\left(\frac{r}{m}\right). \qquad \text{Rewrite } (r)(\tfrac{1}{m}) \text{ as } (\tfrac{r}{m}).$$

At the end of the first period, the account then contains

$$\overset{\text{Beginning amount}}{\underset{\downarrow}{}} \quad \overset{\text{Interest}}{\underset{\downarrow}{}}$$

$$\text{Ending amount} = P + P\left(\frac{r}{m}\right)$$

$$= P\left(1 + \frac{r}{m}\right). \qquad \text{Factor } P \text{ from both terms.}$$

Now during the second period, the interest earned is given by

$$\text{Interest} = \left[P\left(1 + \frac{r}{m}\right)\right](r)\left(\frac{1}{m}\right) \qquad \text{Interest} = [\text{Principal}]\,(\text{rate})\,(\text{time})$$

$$= P\left(1 + \frac{r}{m}\right)\left(\frac{r}{m}\right),$$

so that the account ends the second period containing

$$\text{Ending amount} = \overset{\text{Beginning amount}}{P\left(1 + \frac{r}{m}\right)} + \overset{\text{Interest}}{P\left(1 + \frac{r}{m}\right)\left(\frac{r}{m}\right)}$$

$$= P\left(1 + \frac{r}{m}\right)\left[1 + \frac{r}{m}\right] \qquad \text{Factor } P\left(1 + \frac{r}{m}\right) \text{ from both terms.}$$

$$= P\left(1 + \frac{r}{m}\right)^2. \qquad a \cdot a = a^2$$

Consider one more period, namely, the third. The interest earned is

$$\text{Interest} = \left[P\left(1 + \frac{r}{m}\right)^2\right](r)\left(\frac{1}{m}\right) \qquad \text{Interest} = [\text{Principal}]\,(\text{rate})\,(\text{time})$$

$$= P\left(1 + \frac{r}{m}\right)^2\left(\frac{r}{m}\right),$$

so the account ends the third period containing

$$\text{Ending amount} = \overset{\text{Beginning amount}}{P\left(1 + \frac{r}{m}\right)^2} + \overset{\text{Interest}}{P\left(1 + \frac{r}{m}\right)^2\left(\frac{r}{m}\right)}$$

$$= P\left(1 + \frac{r}{m}\right)^2\left[1 + \frac{r}{m}\right] \qquad \text{Factor } P\left(1 + \frac{r}{m}\right)^2 \text{ from both terms.}$$

$$= P\left(1 + \frac{r}{m}\right)^3. \qquad a^2 \cdot a = a^3$$

Table 2 summarizes the preceding results.

Table 2   Compound Amount

Period Number	Beginning Amount	Interest Earned During Period	Ending Amount
1	P	$P\left(\frac{r}{m}\right)$	$P\left(1 + \frac{r}{m}\right)$
2	$P\left(1 + \frac{r}{m}\right)$	$P\left(1 + \frac{r}{m}\right)\left(\frac{r}{m}\right)$	$P\left(1 + \frac{r}{m}\right)^2$
3	$P\left(1 + \frac{r}{m}\right)^2$	$P\left(1 + \frac{r}{m}\right)^2\left(\frac{r}{m}\right)$	$P\left(1 + \frac{r}{m}\right)^3$
⋮	⋮	⋮	⋮
n	$P\left(1 + \frac{r}{m}\right)^{n-1}$	$P\left(1 + \frac{r}{m}\right)^{n-1}\left(\frac{r}{m}\right)$	$P\left(1 + \frac{r}{m}\right)^n$

King Hammurabi tried to hold interest rates at 20 percent for both silver and gold, but moneylenders ignored his decrees.

The lower right entry of **Table 2** provides the following formula.

The quantity

$$\left(1 + \frac{r}{m}\right)^n$$

can be evaluated using a key such as $\boxed{y^x}$ on a scientific calculator or $\boxed{\wedge}$ on a graphing calculator.

Future Value for Compound Interest

If P dollars are deposited at an annual interest rate of r, compounded m times per year, and the money is left on deposit for a total of n periods, then the **future value, A** (the final amount on deposit), is calculated as follows.

$$A = P\left(1 + \frac{r}{m}\right)^n$$

▮▮ EXAMPLE 5   Finding Future Value for Compound Interest

Find the future value (final amount on deposit) and the amount of interest earned for the following deposits.

(a) $12,450 at 3% compounded quarterly for 5 years

(b) $3419 at 4.1% compounded monthly for 30 months

SOLUTION

(a) Here $P = \$12{,}450$, $r = 3\% = 0.03$, and $m = 4$. Over 5 years,

$$n = 5m = (5)(4) = 20.$$

We use the future value formula and a calculator.

$$A = \$12{,}450\left(1 + \frac{0.03}{4}\right)^{20} = \$14{,}456.74$$

Now we subtract to find the interest earned.

Future value   Present value
↓   ↓

$$\text{Interest earned} = \$14{,}456.74 - \$12{,}450$$

$$= \$2006.74$$

```
N=20
I%=3
PV=⁻12450
PMT=0
→   FV=14456.74257
P/Y=4
C/Y=4
PMT: END  BEGIN
```

The financial functions of the TI-83/84 Plus calculator allow the user to solve for a missing quantity regarding the time value of money. The arrow indicates the display that supports the future value answer in **Example 5(a).**

(b) Here $P = \$3419$, $r = 4.1\% = 0.041$, $m = 12$, and $n = 30$.

$$A = \$3419\left(1 + \frac{0.041}{12}\right)^{30} = \$3787.38$$

Future value   Present value
↓   ↓

$$\text{Interest earned} = \$3787.38 - \$3419$$

$$= \$368.38$$ ▮▮▮

Compound interest problems sometimes require that we solve the formula for P to compute the present value when the future value is known.

$$A = P\left(1 + \frac{r}{m}\right)^n \qquad \text{Future value for compound interest}$$

$$P = \frac{A}{\left(1 + \frac{r}{m}\right)^n} \qquad \text{Solve the formula for } P.$$

The 1957 movie *The Pajama Game* was inspired by the Broadway musical of the same name. It was recently revived on Broadway and starred Harry Connick, Jr. The female lead in the movie, "Babe" Williams, was played by Doris Day. She and her coworkers at the Sleeptite Pajama Factory were attempting to get a $7\frac{1}{2}$ cent per hour raise.

The musical number **"Seven and a Half Cents"** features three computations, determining how much this seemingly small raise will earn in three time periods. Based on pencil and paper calculations, the lyrics state that in 5 years, the raise will amount to $852.74, in 10 years $1705.48, and in 20 years $3411.96. Assuming that the figure for 5 years is correct, is the one for 10 years also correct? Now, how about the one for 20 years? Oops!

▌▌ **EXAMPLE 6** Finding Present Value for Compound Interest

Lisa Ashley will need $27,000 in 5 years to help pay for her college education. What lump sum, deposited today at 4% compounded quarterly, will produce the necessary amount?

SOLUTION

This question requires that we find the present value P based on the following.

Future value:	$A = \$27,000$
Annual rate:	$r = 4\% = 0.04$
Periods per year:	$m = 4$
Total number of periods:	$n = (5)(4) = 20$

$$P = \frac{A}{\left(1 + \frac{r}{m}\right)^n} \quad \text{Future value formula solved for } P$$

$$P = \frac{\$27,000}{\left(1 + \frac{0.04}{4}\right)^{20}} \quad \text{Substitute known values.}$$

$$P = \$22,127.70 \quad \text{Calculate.}$$

Assuming interest of 4% compounded quarterly can be maintained, $27,000 can be attained 5 years in the future by depositing $22,127.70 today.   ▌▌▌

The next example uses logarithms. See the discussion of logarithms in **Section 8.6** (or your calculator manual).

▌▌ **EXAMPLE 7** Finding the Time Required to Double a Principal Deposit

In a savings account paying 3% interest, compounded daily, when will the amount in the account be twice the original principal?

SOLUTION

The future value must equal two times the present value.

$$2P = P\left(1 + \frac{r}{m}\right)^n \quad \text{Substitute } 2P \text{ for } A \text{ in the future value formula.}$$

$$2 = \left(1 + \frac{r}{m}\right)^n \quad \text{Divide both sides by } P.$$

$$2 = \left(1 + \frac{0.03}{365}\right)^n \quad \text{Substitute values of } r \text{ and } m.$$

$$\log 2 = \log\left(1 + \frac{0.03}{365}\right)^n \quad \text{Take the logarithm of both sides.}$$

$$\log 2 = n \log\left(1 + \frac{0.03}{365}\right) \quad \text{Use the power property of logarithms.}$$

$$n = \frac{\log 2}{\log\left(1 + \frac{0.03}{365}\right)} \quad \text{Solve for } n.$$

$$n = 8434 \quad \text{Round to the nearest whole number.}$$

Because n denotes the number of periods, which is days in this case, the required amount of time is 8434 days, or 23 years, 39 days (ignoring leap years).   ▌▌▌

The power of compound interest is being put to use in the town of Union City, Michigan. Eli Hooker, chairman of the local Bicentennial Committee in 1976, saw that there was not enough money to put on a proper celebration that year. So, in order to help his town prepare for the tricentennial, in 2076, he collected twenty-five dollars apiece from 42 patriotic residents and deposited the money in a local bank. Compounded at seven percent, that money would grow to a million dollars by 2076.

Unfortunately, the million dollars won't be worth as much then as we might think. If the community decides to hire people to parade around in historical costumes, it might have paid them $4 per hour in 1976. The going wage in 2076, assuming 7% annual inflation for a hundred years, would be well over $3000 per hour.

Example 8 shows the importance of starting early to maximize the long-term advantage of compounding.

▮▮ **EXAMPLE 8** Comparing Retirement Plans

Compare the results at age 65 for the following two retirement plans. Both plans earn 8% annual interest throughout the account building period.

Plan A: Gina Fox begins saving at age 20, deposits $2000 on every birthday from age 21 to age 30 (10 deposits, or $20,000 total), and thereafter makes no additional contributions.

Plan B: Peter Harris waits until age 30 to start saving, makes deposits of $2000 on every birthday from age 31 to age 65 (35 deposits, or $70,000 total).

SOLUTION

Table 3 shows how both accounts build over the years. $20,000, deposited earlier, produces $83,744 more than $70,000, deposited later.

Table 3		
Age	**Plan A**	**Plan B**
20	0	0
25	11,733	0
30	28,973	0
35	42,571	11,733
40	62,551	28,973
45	91,908	54,304
50	135,042	91,524
55	198,422	146,212
60	291,547	226,566
65	428,378	344,634

▮▮▮

In **Example 8,** the *early* deposits of Plan A outperformed the *greater number* of deposits of Plan B because the interest rate was high enough to result in a Plan A balance at age 30 that Plan B could never overtake, despite additional Plan B deposits from then on. If the interest rate had been 6% rather than 8%, Plan B would have overtaken Plan A (at age 57) and at age 65 would have come out ahead by $20,253 (to the nearest dollar).

Effective Annual Yield

Banks, credit unions, and others often advertise two rates: first, the actual annualized interest rate, or **nominal rate** (the "named" or "stated" rate), and second, the equivalent rate that would produce the same final amount, or future value, at the end of 1 year if the interest being paid were simple rather than compound. This is called the "effective rate," or more commonly the **effective annual yield.** (It may be denoted **APY** for **"annual percentage yield."**) Because the interest is normally compounded multiple times per year, the yield will usually be somewhat higher than the nominal rate.

▌▌ **EXAMPLE 9** Finding Effective Annual Yield

What is the effective annual yield of an account paying a nominal rate of 2.50%, compounded quarterly?

SOLUTION

From the given data, $r = 0.025$ and $m = 4$. Suppose we deposited $P = \$1$ and left it for 1 year ($n = 4$). Then the compound future value formula gives

$$A = 1 \cdot \left(1 + \frac{0.025}{4}\right)^4 \approx 1.0252.$$

The initial deposit of $1, after 1 year, has grown to $1.0252.

Interest earned $= 1.0252 - 1$ Interest = future value − present value

$= 0.0252,$ or   2.52%

A nominal rate of 2.50% results in an effective annual yield of 2.52%. ▮▮▮

►Eff(2.50,4)
               2.523535309

Financial calculators are programmed to compute effective interest rate. Compare to the result in **Example 9.**

Generalizing the procedure of **Example 9** gives the following formula.

Effective Annual Yield

A nominal interest rate of r, compounded m times per year, is equivalent to the following **effective annual yield.**

$$Y = \left(1 + \frac{r}{m}\right)^m - 1$$

When shopping for loans or savings opportunities, a borrower should seek the least yield available, while a depositor should look for the greatest.

▌▌ **EXAMPLE 10** Comparing Savings Rates

Christine Ellington wants to deposit $2800 into a savings account and has narrowed her choices to the three institutions represented here. Which is the best choice?

Institution	Rate on Deposits of $1000 to $5000
Friendly Credit Union	2.08% annual rate, compounded monthly
Premier Savings	2.09% annual yield
Neighborhood Bank	2.05% compounded daily

SOLUTION

Compare the effective annual yields for the three institutions.

Friendly: $Y = \left(1 + \dfrac{0.0208}{12}\right)^{12} - 1 = 0.0210 = 2.10\%$

Premier: $Y = 2.09\%$

Neighborhood: $Y = \left(1 + \dfrac{0.0205}{365}\right)^{365} - 1 = 0.0207 = 2.07\%$

The best of the three yields, 2.10%, is offered by Friendly Credit Union. ▮▮▮

Table 4	Consumer Price Index (CPI-U)*	
Year	Average CPI-U	Percent Change in CPI-U
1979	72.6	11.3
1980	82.4	13.5
1981	90.9	10.3
1982	96.5	6.2
1983	99.6	3.2
1984	103.9	4.3
1985	107.6	3.6
1986	109.6	1.9
1987	113.6	3.6
1988	118.3	4.1
1989	124.0	4.8
1990	130.7	5.4
1991	136.2	4.2
1992	140.3	3.0
1993	144.5	3.0
1994	148.2	2.6
1995	152.4	2.8
1996	156.9	3.0
1997	160.5	2.3
1998	163.0	1.6
1999	166.6	2.2
2000	172.2	3.4
2001	177.1	2.8
2002	179.9	1.6
2003	184.0	2.3
2004	188.9	2.7
2005	195.3	3.4
2006	201.6	3.2
2007	207.3	2.8
2008	215.3	3.8
2009	214.5	−0.4

Source: Bureau of Labor Statistics.

*The period 1982 to 1984: 100

Inflation

Interest reflects how money *gains value over time* when it is borrowed or lent. On the other hand, in terms of the equivalent number of goods or services that a given amount of money will buy, money normally *loses value over time*. This results in a periodic increase in the cost of living, which is called **price inflation.**

In the United States, the Bureau of Labor Statistics publishes **consumer price index (CPI)** figures, which reflect the prices of certain items purchased by large numbers of people. The items include such things as food, housing, automobiles, fuel, and clothing. Items such as yachts or expensive jewelry are not included.

Current data are published regularly at www.bls.gov/cpi. **Table 4** gives values of the primary index representing "all urban consumers" (the CPI-U). The value shown for a given year is actually the average (arithmetic mean) of the twelve monthly figures for that year. The table shows, for example, that the average CPI-U for 2007 (207.3) was 2.8% greater than the average value for 2006 (201.6).

Deflation is a *decrease* in price levels from one year to the next. A brief period of minor deflation, along with a general economic slowdown, usually is called a **recession.** (For example, in **Table 4**, note the 2009 rate of −0.4.)

Unlike account values under interest compounding, which make sudden jumps at just certain points in time (such as quarterly, monthly, or daily), price levels tend to fluctuate gradually over time. Thus, it is appropriate, for inflationary estimates, to use the formula for continuous compounding (introduced in **Section 8.6.**)

Future Value for Continuous Compounding

If an initial deposit of P dollars earns continuously compounded interest at an annual rate r for a period of t years, then the **future value, A,** is calculated as follows.

$$A = Pe^{rt}$$

■■ **EXAMPLE 11** Predicting Inflated Salary Levels

Suppose you earn a salary of $34,000 per year. About what salary would you need 20 years from now to maintain your purchasing power in case the inflation rate were to persist at each of the following levels?

(a) 2% (approximately the 1999 level)

(b) 13% (approximately the 1980 level)

SOLUTION

(a) In this case we can use the continuous compounding future value formula with $P = \$34{,}000$, $r = 0.02$, and $t = 20$, and the $\boxed{e^x}$ key on a calculator.

$$A = Pe^{rt} = (\$34{,}000)e^{(0.02)(20)} = \$50{,}722.04$$

The required salary 20 years from now would be about $51,000.

(b) For this level of inflation, we would have the following.

$$A = Pe^{rt} = (\$34{,}000)e^{(0.13)(20)} = \$457{,}767.09$$

The required salary 20 years from now would be about $458,000. ■■■

To compare equivalent general price levels in any 2 years, we can use the proportion at the top of the next page. (A proportion is a statement that says that two ratios are equal. See **Section 7.3.**)

$34000e^{(.02*20)}$

50722.04

$34000e^{(.13*20)}$

457767.09

These are the computations required to solve the two parts of **Example 11.**

> **Inflation Proportion**
>
> For a given consumer product or service subject to average inflation, prices in two different years are related as follows.
>
> $$\frac{\text{Price in year A}}{\text{Price in year B}} = \frac{\text{CPI in year A}}{\text{CPI in year B}}$$

▌▌ **EXAMPLE 12**   Comparing a Tuition Increase to Average Inflation

Michael Dew's college tuition in 2009 was $9910. His uncle attended the same school in 1990 and paid $4990 in tuition. Compare the school's tuition increase to average inflation over the same period.

SOLUTION

Let x represent what we would expect the tuition to be in 2009 if it had increased at the average rate since 1990.

$$\frac{\text{Price in 2009}}{\text{Price in 1990}} = \frac{\text{CPI in 2009}}{\text{CPI in 1990}} \qquad \text{Inflation proportion}$$

$$\frac{x}{\$4990} = \frac{214.5}{130.7} \qquad \text{Substitute. CPI values are from \textbf{Table 4.}}$$

$$x = \frac{214.5}{130.7} \cdot \$4990 \qquad \text{Solve for } x.$$

$$x \approx \$8189$$

Now compare the actual 2009 tuition, $9910, with the expected figure, $8189.

$$\frac{\$9910}{\$8189} = 1.21 \qquad 1.21 = 100\% + 21\%$$

Over the period from 1990 to 2009, tuition at Michael's college increased approximately 21% more than the average CPI-U rate. ▌▌▌

When working with quantities, such as inflation, where continual fluctuations and inexactness prevail, we often develop rough "rules of thumb" for obtaining quick estimates. One example is the estimation of the **years to double,** which is the number of years it takes for the general level of prices to double for a given annual rate of inflation. We can derive an estimation rule as follows.

$$A = Pe^{rt} \qquad \text{Future value formula}$$

$$2P = Pe^{rt} \qquad \text{Prices are to double.}$$

$$2 = e^{rt} \qquad \text{Divide both sides by } P.$$

$$\ln 2 = rt \qquad \text{Take the natural logarithm of both sides.}$$

$$t = \frac{\ln 2}{r} \qquad \text{Solve for } t.$$

$$t = \frac{100 \ln 2}{100r} \qquad \text{Multiply numerator and denominator by 100.}$$

$$\textbf{years to double} \approx \frac{\textbf{70}}{\textbf{annual inflation rate}} \qquad 100 \ln 2 \approx 70$$

(Because r is the inflation rate as a *decimal,* $100r$ is the inflation rate as a *percent.*)

The result above usually is called the **rule of 70.** The value it produces, if not a whole number, should be rounded *up* to the next whole number of years.

Monetary inflation devalues the currency just as **price inflation** does, but it does so through a direct increase in the money supply within the economy. An example in the United States was the issuance in 2009 and 2010 of massive government debt and massive government spending on "stimulus" programs. Debate persisted among economists as to whether actions of the government and central bank would accomplish their goals. Would economic recovery continue, or would major deflation occur? Most everyone agreed that the long-term result of monetary inflation would be more and more price inflation. Some deny that any real distinction exists, that due to complex interrelated economic forces, monetary and price inflation are essentially the same thing.

```
(100*ln(2))/2.3
            30.13683394
70/2.3
            30.43478261
```

Because 100 ln 2 ≈ 70, the two results shown here are approximately equal. See **Example 13** and the preceding discussion.

■■ **EXAMPLE 13** Estimating Years to Double by the Rule of 70

Estimate the years to double for an annual inflation rate of 2.3%.

SOLUTION

$$\text{Years to double} \approx \frac{70}{2.3} \approx 30.43 \quad \text{Rule of 70}$$

With a sustained inflation rate of 2.3%, prices would double in about 31 years. ■■■

13.1 EXERCISES

In the following exercises, assume whenever appropriate that, unless otherwise known, there are 12 months per year, 30 days per month, and 365 days per year.

Find the simple interest owed for each loan.

1. $800 at 6% for 1 year

2. $3000 at 5% for 1 year

3. $920 at 7% for 9 months

4. $5400 at 7% for 4 months

5. $2675 at 7.3% for $2\frac{1}{2}$ years

6. $2620 at 4.82% for 22 months

Find the future value of each deposit if the account pays **(a)** *simple interest, and* **(b)** *interest compounded annually.*

7. $700 at 3% for 6 years

8. $2000 at 4% for 5 years

9. $2500 at 2% for 3 years

10. $3000 at 5% for 4 years

Solve each interest-related problem.

11. *Simple Interest on a Late Property Tax Payment* Andrew Draa was late on his property tax payment to the county. He owed $7500 and paid the tax 4 months late. The county charges a penalty of 5% simple interest. Find the amount of the penalty.

12. *Simple Interest on a Loan for Work Uniforms* Austin Caperton bought a new supply of delivery uniforms. He paid $922 for the uniforms and agreed to pay for them in 5 months at 6% simple interest. Find the amount of interest that he will owe.

13. *Simple Interest on a Small Business Loan* Kelly Kunert opened a security service on March 1. To pay for office furniture and guard dogs, Kelly borrowed $12,800 at the bank and agreed to pay the loan back in 10 months at 7% simple interest. Find the *total amount* required to repay the loan.

14. *Simple Interest on a Tax Overpayment* Paul Lewis is owed $530 by the Internal Revenue Service for overpayment of last year's taxes. The IRS will repay the amount at 4% simple interest. Find the *total amount* Paul will receive if the interest is paid for 8 months.

Find the missing final amount (future value) and/or interest earned.

	Principal	Rate	Compounded	Time	Final Amount	Compound Interest
15.	$ 975	4%	quarterly	4 years	$1143.26	_____
16.	$1150	7%	semiannually	6 years	$1737.73	_____
17.	$ 480	6%	semiannually	9 years	_____	$337.17
18.	$2370	5%	quarterly	5 years	_____	_____
19.	$7500	$3\frac{1}{2}$ %	annually	25 years	_____	_____
20.	$3450	2.4%	semiannually	10 years	_____	_____

For each deposit, find the future value (that is, the final amount on deposit) when compounding occurs (a) *annually,* (b) *semiannually, and* (c) *quarterly.*

	Principal	Rate	Time
21.	$2000	4%	3 years
22.	$5000	2%	7 years
23.	$18,000	1%	5 years
24.	$10,000	3%	9 years

Occasionally a savings account may actually pay interest compounded continuously. For each deposit, find the interest earned if interest is compounded (a) *semiannually,* (b) *quarterly,* (c) *monthly,* (d) *daily, and* (e) *continuously.*

	Principal	Rate	Time
25.	$850	1.6%	4 years
26.	$1550	2.8%	33 months (Assume 1003 days in parts (d) and (e).)

27. Describe the effect of interest being compounded more and more often. In particular, how good is continuous compounding?

Solve each interest-related problem.

28. *Finding the Amount Borrowed in a Simple Interest Loan* Jay Jenkins takes out a 7% simple interest loan today that will be repaid 15 months from now with a payoff amount of $815.63. What amount is Jay borrowing?

29. *Finding the Amount Borrowed in a Simple Interest Loan* What is the maximum amount Ginger Logan can borrow today if it must be repaid in 4 months with simple interest at 8% and she knows that at that time she will be able to repay no more than $1500?

30. In the development of the future value formula for compound interest in the text, at least four specific problem-solving strategies were employed. Identify (name) as many of them as you can and describe their use in this case.

Find the present value for each future amount.

31. $1000 (6% compounded annually for 5 years)

32. $14,000 (4% compounded quarterly for 3 years)

33. $9860 (8% compounded semiannually for 10 years)

34. $15,080 (5% compounded monthly for 4 years)

Finding the Present Value of a Compound Interest Retirement Account Robyn Martin wants to establish an account that will supplement her retirement income beginning 30 years from now. For each interest rate find the lump sum she must deposit today so that $500,000 will be available at time of retirement.

35. 5% compounded quarterly

36. 6% compounded quarterly

37. 5% compounded daily

38. 6% compounded daily

Finding the Effective Annual Yield in a Savings Account Suppose a savings and loan pays a nominal rate of 2% on savings deposits. Find the effective annual yield if interest is compounded as stated in Exercises 39–45. (Give answers to the nearest thousandth of a percent.)

39. annually

40. semiannually

41. quarterly

42. monthly

43. daily

44. 1000 times per year

45. 10,000 times per year

46. Judging from **Exercises 39–45,** what do you suppose is the effective annual yield if a nominal rate of 2% is compounded continuously? Explain your reasoning.

Comparing Savings Rates and Yields The table shows the two best savings rates available on a certain online listing on May 25, 2010. Use this information in Exercises 47 and 48.

	Rate	Yield
Sallie Mae	1.390%	1.400%
Capital One Direct Banking	1.340%	1.349%

47. If you deposit $30,000 with Sallie Mae, how much would you have in 1 year?

48. How often does compounding occur in the Capital One account: daily, monthly, quarterly, or semiannually?

Solve each problem.

49. *Finding Years to Double* How long would it take to double your money in an account paying 4% compounded quarterly? (Answer in years plus days, ignoring leap years.)

50. *Comparing Principal and Interest Amounts* After what time period would the interest earned equal the original principal in an account paying 2% compounded daily? (Answer in years plus days, ignoring leap years.)

51. Solve the effective annual yield formula for r to obtain a general formula for nominal rate in terms of yield and the number of compounding periods per year.

52. *Finding the Nominal Rate of a Savings Account* Ridgeway Savings compounds interest monthly, and the effective annual yield is 1.95%. What is the nominal rate?

53. *Comparing Bank Savings Rates* Bank A pays a nominal rate of 3.800% compounded daily on deposits. Bank B produces the same annual yield as the first but compounds interest only quarterly and pays no interest on funds deposited for less than an entire quarter.

   (a) What nominal rate does Bank B pay (to the nearest thousandth of a percent)?

   (b) Which bank should Nancy Dennis choose if she has $2000 to deposit for 10 months? How much more interest will she earn than in the other bank?

   (c) Which bank should Dara Lanier choose for a deposit of $6000 for one year? How much interest will be earned?

Estimating the Years to Double by the Rule of 70 Use the rule of 70 *to estimate the years to double for each annual inflation rate.*

54. 1% **55.** 2%

56. 8% **57.** 9%

Estimating the Inflation Rate by the Rule of 70 Use the rule of 70 *to estimate the annual inflation rate (to the nearest tenth of a percent) that would cause the general level of prices to double in each time period.*

58. 5 years **59.** 7 years

60. 16 years **61.** 22 years

62. Derive a rule for estimating the "years to triple," that is, the number of years it would take for the general levels of prices to triple for a given annual inflation rate.

Estimating Future Prices for Constant Annual Inflation The year 2010 prices of several items are given below. Find the estimated future prices required to fill the blanks in the chart. (Give a number of significant figures consistent with the 2010 price figures provided.)

Item	2010 Price	2015 Price 2% Inflation	2025 Price 2% Inflation	2015 Price 10% Inflation	2025 Price 10% Inflation
63. Fast food meal	$ 5.89	_____	_____	_____	_____
64. House	$265,000	_____	_____	_____	_____
65. Small car	$ 18,500	_____	_____	_____	_____
66. Gallon of gasoline	$ 2.65	_____	_____	_____	_____

Estimating Future Prices for Variable Annual Inflation As seen in **Table 4**, inflation rates do not often stay constant over a period of years. Assume that prices for the items below increased at the average annual rates shown in **Table 4**. Use the inflation proportion to find the missing prices in the last column of the chart. Round to the nearest dollar.

Item	Price	Year Purchased	Price in 2009
67. Evening dress	$ 175	2000	_____
68. Desk	$ 450	2002	_____
69. Lawn tractor	$1099	1996	_____
70. Designer puppy	$ 250	1998	_____

Solve each interest-related problem.

71. *Finding the Present Value of a Future Equipment Purchase* Human gene sequencing is a major research area of biotechnology. PE Biosystems leased 300 of its sequencing machines to a sibling company, Celera. If Celera was able to earn 7% compounded quarterly on invested money, what lump sum did they need to invest in order to purchase those machines 18 months later at a price of $300,000 each? (*Source: Forbes,* February 21, 2000, p. 102.)

72. *Finding the Present Value of a Future Real Estate Purchase* A California couple are selling their small dairy farm to a developer, but they wish to defer receipt of the money until 2 years from now, when they will be in a lower tax bracket. Find the lump sum that the developer can deposit today, at 5% compounded quarterly, so that enough will be available to pay the couple $1,450,000 in 2 years.

13.2 CONSUMER CREDIT

Types of Consumer Credit • Installment Loans • Revolving Loans

Types of Consumer Credit

Consumer credit refers to borrowing money to finance purchases of cars, furniture, appliances, jewelry, electronics, and many other things. Technically, **real estate mortgages,** loans to finance home purchases, are also consumer credit, but they usually involve much larger amounts and longer repayment periods.

In this section we discuss two common types of consumer credit. The first type, **installment loans,** or **closed-end** credit, involves borrowing a set amount up front and paying a series of equal installments (payments) until the loan is paid off. Furniture, appliances, and cars commonly are financed through closed-end credit.

With the second type of consumer credit, **revolving loans,** or **open-end** credit, there is no fixed number of installments—the consumer continues paying until no balance is owed. With revolving loans, additional credit often is extended before the initial amount is paid off. Examples of open-end credit include most department store charge accounts and bank charge cards such as MasterCard and VISA.

Installment Loans

Installment loans, set up under closed-end credit, often are based on **add-on interest.** This means that interest is calculated by the simple interest formula $I = Prt$, and we simply "add on" this amount of interest to the principal borrowed to arrive at the total debt (or amount to be repaid).

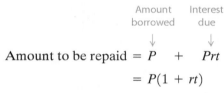

$$\text{Amount to be repaid} = P + Prt$$
$$= P(1 + rt)$$

The total debt is then equally divided among the payments (usually monthly) to be made over the t years.

Credit card debt among students has raised increasing concern in recent years among lawmakers, college officials, and consumer advocacy groups. As a result, hundreds of colleges have banned card marketers from campus, and new federal law brought significant new regulations effective in 2010.

A 2010 study by Sallie Mae (a college financing company) pegged average undergraduate credit card debt at $3,173. The National Center for Education Statistics reported that average total debt among graduating seniors (including credit cards and private and federal loans) was $27,803. (*Source:* www.thelantern.com, Ohio State University student newspaper)

▮▮ **EXAMPLE 1** Repaying an Add-On Loan

Mary Kaye Leonard buys $5400 worth of furniture and appliances for her first apartment. She pays $1100 down and agrees to pay the balance at a 7% add-on rate for 2 years. Find

(a) the total amount to be repaid,

(b) the monthly payment, and

(c) the total cost of the purchases, including finance charges.

SOLUTION

(a)   Amount to be financed = $5400 − $1100
                              = $4300

Amount to be repaid = $P(1 + rt)$ Future value formula
                    = $4300(1 + 0.07 · 2)   Substitute known values.
                    = $4902   Calculate.

(b) Monthly payment $= \dfrac{\$4902}{24}$ ← Amount to be repaid
                                        ← Number of payments

$= \$204.25$

Down payment   Loan repayment
              ↓   ↓
(c) Total cost of purchases $= \$1100 \quad + \quad \$4902$

$= \$6002$

Mary Kaye will end up paying $6002, which is 11.1% more than the price tag total. ▮▮▮

Notice that the repayment amount in **Example 1,** $P(1 + rt)$, was the same as the final amount A in a savings account paying a simple interest rate r for t years. (See **Section 13.1.**) But in the case of savings, the bank keeps all of your money for the entire time period. In **Example 1,** Mary Kaye did not keep the full principal amount for the full time period. She repaid it in 24 monthly installments. The 7% add-on rate turns out to be equivalent to a much higher "true annual interest" rate.

Revolving Loans

With a typical department store account, or bank card, a credit limit is established initially and the consumer can make many purchases during a month (up to the credit limit). The required monthly payment can vary from a set minimum (which may depend on the account balance) up to the full balance.

For purchases made in a store or other retail location, the customer may authorize adding the purchase price to his or her charge account by signing on a paper "charge slip," or perhaps on an electronic signature pad. Authorization also can be given by telephone or over the Internet for mail orders and other expenditures.

At the end of each billing period (normally once a month), the customer receives an **itemized billing,** a statement listing purchases and cash advances, the total balance owed, the minimum payment required, and perhaps other account information. Any charges beyond cash advanced and cash prices of items purchased are called **finance charges.** Finance charges may include interest, an annual fee, credit insurance coverage, a time payment differential, or carrying charges.

Most revolving credit plans calculate finance charges by the **average daily balance method.** The average daily balance is the *weighted mean* (see **Section 12.2**) of the various amounts of credit utilized for different parts of the billing period, with the weighting factors being the number of days that each credit amount applied.

| **EXAMPLE 2** | Using the Average Daily Balance Method for Credit Card Charges |

The activity in Jessica Lasda's MasterCard account for one billing period is shown below. If the previous balance (on March 3) was $209.46, and the bank charges 1.3% per month on the average daily balance, find

(a) the average daily balance for the next billing (April 3),

(b) the finance charge to appear on the April 3 billing, and

(c) the account balance on April 3.

March 3	Billing date	
March 12	Payment	$50.00
March 17	Clothes	$28.46
March 20	Mail order	$31.22
April 1	Auto parts	$59.10

SEPTEMBER
30

Learning the following rhyme will help you in problems like the one found in **Example 2.**

Thirty days hath September, April, June, and November. All the rest have thirty-one, Save February which has twenty-eight days clear, And twenty-nine in each leap year.

SOLUTION

(a) First make a table that shows the beginning date of the billing period and the dates of all transactions in the billing period. Along with each of these, compute the running balance on that date.

Date	Running Balance
March 3	$209.46
March 12	$209.46 − $50 = $159.46
March 17	$159.46 + $28.46 = $187.92
March 20	$187.92 + $31.22 = $219.14
April 1	$219.14 + $59.10 = $278.24

Next, tabulate the running balance figures, along with the number of days until the balance changed. Multiply each balance amount by the number of days. The sum of these products gives the "sum of the daily balances."

Date	Running Balance	Number of Days Until Balance Changed	$\left(\dfrac{\text{Running}}{\text{Balance}}\right) \cdot \left(\dfrac{\text{Number}}{\text{of Days}}\right)$
March 3	$209.46	9	$1885.14
March 12	$159.46	5	$ 797.30
March 17	$187.92	3	$ 563.76
March 20	$219.14	12	$2629.68
April 1	$278.24	2	$ 556.48
		Totals: 31	$6432.36

$$\text{Average daily balance} = \frac{\text{Sum of daily balances}}{\text{Days in billing period}} = \frac{\$6432.36}{31} = \$207.50$$

Jessica will pay a finance charge based on the average daily balance of $207.50.

(b) The finance charge for the April 3 billing will be

$$1.3\% \text{ of } \$207.50 = 0.013 \cdot \$207.50 \quad \text{\small 1.3\% = 1.3 × 0.01 = 0.013}$$

$$= \$2.70.$$

(c) The account balance on the April 3 billing will be the latest running balance plus the finance charge.

$$\$278.24 + \$2.70 = \$280.94 \qquad ███$$

Other features of revolving accounts can be at least as important as interest. For example:

1. Is an annual fee charged? If so, how much is it?
2. Is a special "introductory" rate offered? If so, how long will it last?
3. Are there other incentives, such as rebates, credits toward certain purchases, "free" airline miles, or return of interest charges for long-time use?

Credit cards and other revolving loans are relatively expensive credit. The monthly rate of 1.3% in **Example 2** is typical and is equivalent to an annual rate of 15.6%. A single card (like VISA or MasterCard), however, can be a great convenience, as most all merchants accept it and it eliminates the need to carry cash or write checks.

A wise practice, if at all possible, is *not* to carry a balance from month to month, but to pay the entire new balance by the due date each month. Since purchases made during the month are not billed until the next billing date, and the payment due date may be 20 days or more after the billing date, items can often be charged on a card without actually paying for them for nearly two months. To obtain this form of "free credit," resist the temptation to buy more than can be paid for by the next payment date.

13.2 EXERCISES

*Round all monetary answers to the nearest cent unless directed
otherwise. Assume that unless otherwise known, there are 12
months per year, 30 days per month, and 365 days per year*

Financing an Appliance Purchase *Krishna Gil bought appliances costing $3450 at a store charging 8% add-on interest.
She made a $500 down payment and agreed to monthly pay-
ments over two years.*

1. Find the total amount to be financed.

2. Find the total interest to be paid.

3. Find the total amount to be repaid.

4. Find the monthly payment.

5. Find the total cost, for appliances plus interest.

Financing a New Car Purchase *Suppose you want to buy a
new car that costs $16,500. You have no cash—only your old
car, which is worth $3000 as a trade-in.*

6. How much do you need to finance to buy the new car?

7. The dealer says the interest rate is 9% add-on for 3 years.
   Find the total interest.

8. Find the total amount to be repaid.

9. Find the monthly payment.

10. Find your total cost, for the new car plus interest.

*In Exercises 11–16, use the add-on method of calculating
interest to find the total interest and the monthly payment.*

	Amount of Loan	Length of Loan	Interest Rate
11.	$4500	3 years	9%
12.	$2700	2 years	8%
13.	$ 750	18 months	7.4%
14.	$2450	30 months	9.2%
15.	$ 535	16 months	11.1%
16.	$ 798	29 months	10.3%

Work each problem.

17. **Finding the Monthly Payment for an Add-On Interest Furni-
    ture Loan** The Giordanos buy $8500 worth of furniture
    for their new home. They pay $3000 down. The store
    charges 10% add-on interest. The Giordanos will pay
    off the furniture in 30 monthly payments ($2\frac{1}{2}$ years).
    Find the monthly payment.

18. **Finding the Monthly Payment for an Add-On Interest Auto
    Loan** Find the monthly payment required to pay off an
    auto loan of $9780 over 3 years if the add-on interest
    rate is 9.3%.

19. **Finding the Monthly Payment for an Add-On Interest Home
    Electronics Loan** The total purchase price of a new home
    entertainment system is $14,240. If the down payment is
    $2900 and the balance is to be financed over 48 months
    at 10% add-on interest, what is the monthly payment?

20. **Finding the Monthly Payment for an Add-On Interest Loan**
    What are the monthly payments Donna De Simone
    pays on a loan of $1680 for a period of 10 months if 9%
    add-on interest is charged?

21. **Finding the Amount Borrowed in an Add-On Interest Car
    Loan** Joshua Eurich has misplaced the sales contract for
    his car and cannot remember the amount he originally
    financed. He does know that the add-on interest rate
    was 9.8% and the loan required a total of 48 monthly
    payments of $314.65 each. How much did Joshua bor-
    row (to the nearest dollar)?

22. **Finding an Add-On Interest Rate** Susan Dratch is making
    monthly payments of $207.31 to pay off a $3\frac{1}{2}$ year loan
    for $6400. What is her add-on interest rate (to the near-
    est tenth of a percent)?

23. **Finding the Term of an Add-On Interest Loan** How long (in
    years) will it take Michael Garbin to pay off an $8000
    loan with monthly payments of $172.44 if the add-on
    interest rate is 9.2%?

24. **Finding the Number of Payments of an Add-On Interest Loan**
    How many monthly payments must Jawann make on a
    $10,000 loan if he pays $417.92 a month and the add-on
    interest rate is 10.15%?

Finding Finance Charges *Find the finance charge for each
charge account. Assume interest is calculated on the average
daily balance of the account.*

	Average Daily Balance	Monthly Interest Rate
25.	$ 249.94	1.4%
26.	$ 350.75	1.5%
27.	$ 419.95	1.38%
28.	$ 450.21	1.26%
29.	$1073.40	1.425%
30.	$1320.42	1.375%

Finding Finance Charges and Account Balances Using the Average Daily Balance Method *For each credit card account, assume one month between billing dates (with the appropriate number of days) and interest of 1.3% per month on the average daily balance. Find* **(a)** *the average daily balance,* **(b)** *the monthly finance charge, and* **(c)** *the account balance for the next billing.*

31. Previous balance: $728.36

May 9	Billing date	
May 17	Payment	$200
May 30	Dinner	$ 46.11
June 3	Theater tickets	$ 64.50

32. Previous balance: $514.79

January 27	Billing date	
February 9	Candy	$11.08
February 13	Returns	$26.54
February 20	Payment	$59
February 25	Repairs	$71.19

33. Previous balance: $462.42

June 11	Billing date	
June 15	Returns	$106.45
June 20	Jewelry	$115.73
June 24	Car rental	$ 74.19
July 3	Payment	$115
July 6	Flowers	$ 68.49

34. Previous balance: $983.25

August 17	Billing date	
August 21	Mail order	$ 14.92
August 23	Returns	$ 25.41
August 27	Beverages	$ 31.82
August 31	Payment	$108
September 9	Returns	$ 71.14
September 11	Concert tickets	$110
September 14	Cash advance	$100

Finding Finance Charges *Assume no purchases or returns are made in Exercises 35 and 36.*

35. At the beginning of a 31-day billing period, Sandra Lazzaro has an unpaid balance of $720 on her credit card. Three days before the end of the billing period, she pays $600. Find her finance charge at 1.4% per month using the average daily balance method.

36. Anthony Marsella's VISA bill dated April 14 shows an unpaid balance of $1070. Five days before May 14, the end of the billing period, Anthony makes a payment of $900. Find his finance charge at 1.32% per month using the average daily balance method.

Analyzing a "90 Days Same as Cash" Offer *One version of the "90 Days Same as Cash" promotion was offered by a "major purchase card," which established an account charging 1.3167% interest per month on the account balance. Interest charges are added to the balance each month, becoming part of the balance on which interest is computed the next month.*

If you pay off the original purchase charge within 3 months, all interest charges are cancelled. Otherwise you are liable for all the interest. Suppose you purchase $2900 worth of carpeting under this plan.

37. Find the interest charge added to the account balance at the end of

(a) the first month,

(b) the second month,

(c) the third month.

38. Suppose you pay off the account 1 day late (3 months plus 1 day). What total interest amount must you pay? (Do not include interest for the one extra day.)

39. Treating the 3 months as $\frac{1}{4}$ year, find the equivalent simple interest rate for this purchase (to the nearest tenth of a percent).

Various Charges of a Bank Card Account *Beth Johnson's bank card account charges 1.1% per month on the average daily balance as well as the following special fees:*

Cash advance fee:	2% (*not less than* $2 *nor more than* $10)
Late payment fee:	$15
Over-the-credit-limit fee:	$5

In the month of June, Beth's average daily balance was $1846. She was on vacation during the month and did not get her account payment in on time, which resulted in a late payment and resulted in charges accumulating to a sum above her credit limit. She also used her card for six $100 cash advances while on vacation. Find the following based on account transactions in that month.

40. interest charges to the account

41. special fees charged to the account

Write out your response to each of the following.

42. Is it possible to use a bank credit card for your purchases without paying anything for credit? If so, explain how.

43. Obtain applications or descriptive brochures for several different bank card programs, compare their features (including those in fine print), and explain which deal would be best for you, and why.

44. Research and explain the difference, if any, between a "credit" card and a "debit" card.

45. Many charge card offers include the option of purchasing credit insurance coverage, which would make your monthly payments if you became disabled and could not work and/or would pay off the account balance if you died. Find out the details on at least one such offer, and discuss why you would or would not accept it.

46. Make a list of "special incentives" offered by bank cards you are familiar with, and briefly describe the pros and cons of each one.

47. One bank offered a card with a "low introductory rate" of 5.9%, good through the end of the year. And furthermore, you could receive back a percentage (up to 100%!) of all interest you pay, as shown in the table.

Use your card for:	2 years	5 years	10 years	15 years	20 years
Get back:	10%	25%	50%	75%	100%

(As soon as you take a refund, the time clock starts over.) Because you can eventually claim all your interest payments back, is this card a good deal? Explain.

48. Recall a car-buying experience you have had, or visit a new-car dealer and interview a salesperson. Describe the procedure involved in purchasing a car on credit.

Comparing Bank Card Accounts Dorothy Laymon is considering two bank card offers that are the same in all respects except for the following:

> *Bank A charges no annual fee and charges monthly interest of 1.18% on the unpaid balance.*
>
> *Bank B charges a $30 annual fee and monthly interest of 1.01% on the unpaid balance.*

From her records, Dorothy has found that the unpaid balance she tends to carry from month to month is quite consistent and averages $900.

49. Estimate her total yearly cost to use the card if she chooses the card from
  (a) Bank A
  (b) Bank B.

50. Which card is her better choice?

13.3 TRUTH IN LENDING

Annual Percentage Rate (APR) • Unearned Interest

Annual Percentage Rate (APR)

The Consumer Credit Protection Act, which was passed in 1968, has commonly been known as the **Truth in Lending Act.** In this section we discuss two major issues addressed in the law:

1. How can we tell the true annual interest rate a lender is charging?

2. How much of the finance charge are we entitled to save if we decide to pay off a loan sooner than originally scheduled?

Question 1 above arose because lenders were computing and describing the interest they charged in several different ways. For example, how does 1.5% per month at Sears compare to 9% per year add-on interest at a furniture store? Truth in Lending standardized the so-called true annual interest rate, or **annual percentage rate,** commonly denoted **APR.** All sellers (car dealers, stores, banks, insurance agents, credit card companies, and the like) must disclose the APR when asked, and the written contract must state the APR in all cases. This enables a borrower to more easily compare the true costs of different loans.

Theoretically, a borrower should not need to calculate APR, but it is possible to verify the value stated by the lender. Since the formulas for finding APR are quite involved, it is easiest to use a table provided by the Federal Reserve Bank. We show an abbreviated version in **Table 5** on the next page. It identifies APR values to the nearest half percent from 8.0% to 14.0%, for loans requiring *monthly* payments and extending over the most common lengths for consumer loans from 6 to 60 months.

Table 5 relates the following three quantities.

APR = true annual interest rate (shown across the top)

n = total number of scheduled monthly payments (shown down the left side)

h = finance charge per $100 of amount financed (shown in the body of the table)

Table 5 **Annual Percentage Rate (APR) for Monthly Payment Loans**

Number of Monthly Payments (*n*)	Annual Percentage Rate (APR)												
	8.0%	8.5%	9.0%	9.5%	10.0%	10.5%	11.0%	11.5%	12.0%	12.5%	13.0%	13.5%	14.0%
	(Finance charge per $100 of amount financed) (*h*)												
6	$2.35	$2.49	$2.64	$2.79	$2.94	$3.08	$3.23	$3.38	$3.53	$3.68	$3.83	$3.97	$4.12
12	4.39	4.66	4.94	5.22	5.50	5.78	6.06	6.34	6.62	6.90	7.18	7.46	7.74
18	6.45	6.86	7.28	7.69	8.10	8.52	8.93	9.35	9.77	10.19	10.61	11.03	11.45
24	8.55	9.09	9.64	10.19	10.75	11.30	11.86	12.42	12.98	13.54	14.10	14.66	15.23
30	10.66	11.35	12.04	12.74	13.43	14.13	14.83	15.54	16.24	16.95	17.66	18.38	19.10
36	12.81	13.64	14.48	15.32	16.16	17.01	17.86	18.71	19.57	20.43	21.30	22.17	23.04
48	17.18	18.31	19.45	20.59	21.74	22.90	24.06	25.23	26.40	27.58	28.77	29.97	31.17
60	21.66	23.10	24.55	26.01	27.48	28.96	30.45	31.96	33.47	34.99	36.52	38.06	39.61

▐▐ **EXAMPLE 1** Finding the APR for an Add-On Loan

Recall that Mary Kaye (in **Example 1** of **Section 13.2**) paid $1100 down on a $5400 purchase and agreed to pay the balance at a 7% add-on rate for 2 years. Find the APR for her loan.

SOLUTION

As shown previously, the total amount financed was

$$\underset{\substack{\text{Purchase}\\\text{price}\\\downarrow}}{\$5400} - \underset{\substack{\text{Down}\\\text{payment}\\\downarrow}}{\$1100} = \$4300.$$

The finance charge (interest) was

$$I = Prt = \$4300 \cdot 0.07 \cdot 2 = \$602.$$

Next find the finance charge per $100 of the amount financed. To do this, divide the finance charge by the amount financed, then multiply by $100.

$$\left(\begin{array}{c}\text{Finance charge per}\\ \text{\$100 financed}\end{array}\right) = \frac{\text{Finance charge}}{\text{Amount financed}} \cdot \$100$$

$$= \frac{\$602}{\$4300} \cdot \$100, \quad \text{or} \quad \$14$$

This amount, $14, represents *h*, the finance charge per $100 of the amount financed. Because the loan was to be paid over 24 months, look down to the "24 monthly payments" row of **Table 5** (*n* = 24). Then look across the table for the *h*-value closest to $14.00, which is $14.10. From that point, read up the column to find the APR, 13.0% (to the nearest half percent). In this case, a 7% add-on rate is equivalent to an APR of 13.0%. ▐▐▐

```
5400−1100
                    4300
4300*.07*2
                    602
(602/4300)*100
                    14
```

These are the computations required in the solution of **Example 1.**

▮▮ **EXAMPLE 2** Finding the APR for a Car Loan

After a down payment on her new car, Yvette Freeman still owed $7454. She agreed to repay the balance in 48 monthly payments of $185 each. What is the APR on her loan?

SOLUTION

First find the finance charge.

Total payments   Amount financed
↓   ↓
$$\text{Finance charge} = 48 \cdot \$185 - \$7454$$
$$= \$1426 \quad \boxed{\text{Multiply first. Then subtract.}}$$

Now find the finance charge per $100 financed as in **Example 1.**

$$\left(\begin{array}{c} \text{Finance charge per} \\ \$100 \text{ financed} \end{array} \right) = \frac{\text{Finance charge}}{\text{Amount financed}} \cdot \$100$$

$$= \frac{\$1426}{\$7454} \cdot \$100, \quad \text{or} \quad \$19.13$$

```
48*185−7454
              1426.00
(1426/7454)*100
               19.13
```

These are the computations required in the solution of **Example 2.**

Find the "48 payments" row of **Table 5**, read across to find the number closest to 19.13, which is 19.45. From there read up to find the APR, which is 9.0%. ▮▮▮

Unearned Interest

Question 2 at the beginning of the section arises when a borrower decides to pay off an installment loan earlier than originally scheduled. In such a case, it turns out that the lender has not loaned as much money for as long as planned and so he has not really "earned" the full finance charge originally disclosed.

   If a loan is paid off early, the amount by which the original finance charge is reduced is called the **unearned interest.** We will discuss two common methods of calculating unearned interest, the **actuarial method** and the **rule of 78.** The Truth in Lending Act requires that the method for calculating this refund (or reduction) of finance charge be disclosed at the time the loan is initiated. Whichever method is used, the borrower may not, in fact, save all the unearned interest, since the lender is entitled to impose an **early payment penalty** to recover certain costs. A lender's intention to impose such a penalty in case of early payment also must be disclosed at initiation of the loan.

Rights and responsibilities apply to all credit accounts, and the consumer should read all disclosures provided by the lender. *The Fair Credit Billing Act* and *The Fair Credit Reporting Act* regulate, among other things, procedures for billing and for disputing bills, and for providing and disputing personal information on consumers.

   If you have ever applied for a charge account, a personal loan, insurance, or a job, then information about where you work and live, how you pay your bills, and whether you've been sued, arrested, or have filed for bankruptcy appears in the files of Consumer Reporting Agencies (CRAs), which sell that information to creditors, employers, insurers, and other businesses.

   For more detailed information on these and many other consumer issues, you may want to consult the Web site www.consumeraction.gov.

Unearned Interest—Actuarial Method

For an installment loan requiring *monthly* payments, which is paid off earlier than originally scheduled, let

R = regular monthly payment,

k = remaining number of scheduled payments (*after* current payment), and

h = finance charge per $100, corresponding to a loan with the same APR and k monthly payments.

Then the **unearned interest, u,** is calculated as follows.

$$u = kR\left(\frac{h}{\$100 + h} \right)$$

Once the unearned interest u is calculated (by any method), the amount required to pay off the loan early is easily found. It consists of the present regular payment due, plus k additional future payments, minus the unearned interest.

Payoff Amount

An installment loan requiring regular monthly payments R can be paid off early, along with the current payment. If the original loan had k additional payments scheduled (after the current payment), and the unearned interest is u, then, disregarding any possible prepayment penalty, the **payoff amount** is calculated as follows.

$$\text{Payoff amount} = (k + 1)R - u$$

▮▮ EXAMPLE 3 Finding the Early Payoff Amount by the Actuarial Method

Yvette Freeman got an unexpected pay raise and wanted to pay off her car loan of **Example 2** at the end of 3 years rather than paying for 4 years as originally agreed.

(a) Find the unearned interest (the amount she will save by retiring the loan early).

(b) Find the "payoff amount" (the amount required to pay off the loan at the end of 3 years).

SOLUTION

(a) From **Example 2,** recall that $R = \$185$ and APR $= 9.0\%$. The current payment is payment number 36, so $k = 48 - 36 = 12$. Use **Table 5**, with 12 payments and APR 9.0%, to obtain $h = \$4.94$. Then use the actuarial method formula.

$$u = 12 \cdot \$185\left(\frac{\$4.94}{\$100 + \$4.94}\right) = \$104.51$$

By this method, Yvette will save $104.51 in interest by retiring the loan early.

(b) The payoff amount is found by using the appropriate formula.

$$\text{Payoff amount} = (12 + 1)\$185 - \$104.51 = \$2300.49$$

The required payoff amount at the end of 3 years is $2300.49. ▮▮▮

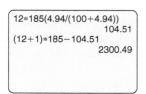

These are the computations required in the solution of **Example 3.**

The actuarial method, because it is based on the APR value, probably is the better method. However, some lenders still use the second method, the **rule of 78.**

Unearned Interest—Rule of 78

For a closed-end loan requiring *monthly* payments, which is paid off earlier than originally scheduled, let

   F = original finance charge,

   n = number of payments originally scheduled, and

   k = remaining number of scheduled payments (*after* current payment).

Then the **unearned interest, u,** is calculated as follows.

$$u = \frac{k(k + 1)}{n(n + 1)} \cdot F$$

▋▋ **EXAMPLE 4** Finding the Early Payoff Amount by the Rule of 78

Again assume that the loan in **Example 2** is paid off at the time of the thirty-sixth monthly payment. This time however, instead of the actuarial method, use the rule of 78 to find

(a) the unearned interest,   and   **(b)** the payoff amount.

SOLUTION

(a) From **Example 2,** the original finance charge is $F = \$1426$. Also, $n = 48$ and $k = 12$.

$$u = \frac{12(12 + 1)}{48(48 + 1)} \cdot \$1426 = \$94.58 \quad \text{Rule of 78}$$

By the rule of 78, Yvette will save $94.58 in interest, which is $9.93 *less* than her savings by the actuarial method.

(b)   Payoff amount $= (12 + 1)\$185 - \$94.58 = \$2310.42$

The payoff amount is $2310.42, which is $9.93 *more* than the payoff amount calculated by the actuarial method in **Example 3.**   ▋▋▋

(12*(12+1))/(48(48+1))*1426
                        94.58
(12+1)*185−94.58
                      2310.42

These are the computations required in the solution of **Example 4.**

When the rule of 78 was first introduced into financial law (by the Indiana legislature in 1935), loans were ordinarily written for 1 year or less, interest rates were relatively low, and loan amounts were less than they tend to be today. For these reasons the rule of 78 was acceptably accurate then. Today, however, with very accurate tables and/or calculators readily available, the rule of 78 is used much less often than previously.

Suppose we want to compute unearned interest accurately (so we don't trust the rule of 78), but the APR value, or the number of scheduled payments, or the number of remaining payments (or at least one of the three) is not included in **Table 5.** Then what? Actually, in the actuarial method, we can evaluate h (the finance charge per $100 financed) using the same formula that was used to generate **Table 5.**

> **Finance Charge per $100 Financed**
>
> If an installment loan requires n equal monthly payments and APR denotes the true annual interest rate for the loan (as a decimal), then h, the **finance charge per $100 financed,** is calculated as follows.
>
> $$h = \frac{n \cdot \frac{\text{APR}}{12} \cdot \$100}{1 - \left(1 + \frac{\text{APR}}{12}\right)^{-n}} - \$100$$

▋▋ **EXAMPLE 5** Finding Unearned Interest and Early Payoff Amount

Mark Foss borrowed $4000 to pay for music equipment for his band. His loan contract states an APR of 9.8% and stipulates 28 monthly payments of $160.39 each. Mark decides to pay the loan in full at the time of his nineteenth scheduled payment. Find

(a) the unearned interest,   and   **(b)** the payoff amount.

(9*(.098/12)*100)/(1−(1+▸
  ◂.098/12)⁻⁹)−100
                          4.13
9*160.39*4.13/(100+4.13)
                         57.25

These are the computations required in the solution of **Example 5(a)**.

SOLUTION

(a) First find h from the finance charge formula just given.

Remember to use the remaining number of payments, $28 - 19 = 9$, as the value of n.

$$h = \frac{9\left(\frac{0.098}{12}\right)(\$100)}{1 - \left(1 + \frac{0.098}{12}\right)^{-9}} - \$100 = \$4.13$$

Next use the actuarial formula for unearned interest.

Regular monthly payment: $R = \$160.39$

Remaining number of payments: $k = 28 - 19 = 9$

Finance charge per \$100: $h = \$4.13$

$$u = 9 \cdot \$160.39 \cdot \frac{\$4.13}{\$100 + \$4.13} = \$57.25$$

The amount of interest Mark will save is \$57.25.

(b)   Payoff amount $= (9 + 1)(\$160.39) - \$57.25 = \$1546.65.$

To pay off the loan at the time of his nineteenth scheduled payment, Mark must pay \$1546.65.   ▌▌▌

13.3 EXERCISES

Round all monetary answers to the nearest cent unless otherwise directed.

Finding True Annual Interest Rate *Find the APR (true annual interest rate), to the nearest half percent, for each loan.*

	Amount Financed	Finance Charge	Number of Monthly Payments
1.	\$1000	\$75	12
2.	\$1700	\$202	24
3.	\$6600	\$750	30
4.	\$5900	\$1150	48

Finding the Monthly Payment *Find the monthly payment for each loan.*

	Purchase Price	Down Payment	Finance Charge	Number of Monthly Payments
5.	\$3000	\$500	\$250	24
6.	\$4280	\$450	\$700	36
7.	\$3950	\$300	\$800	48
8.	\$8400	\$2500	\$1300	60

Finding True Annual Interest Rate *Find the APR (true annual interest rate), to the nearest half percent, for each loan.*

	Purchase Price	Down Payment	Add-on Interest Rate	Number of Payments
9.	\$4190	\$390	6%	12
10.	\$3250	\$750	7%	36
11.	\$7480	\$2200	5%	18
12.	\$12,800	\$4500	6%	48

Unearned Interest by the Actuarial Method *Each loan was paid in full before its due date.* **(a)** *Obtain the value of h from* **Table 5**. *Then* **(b)** *use the actuarial method to find the amount of unearned interest, and* **(c)** *find the payoff amount.*

	Regular Monthly Payment	APR	Remaining Number of Scheduled Payments After Payoff
13.	\$346.70	11.0%	18
14.	\$783.50	8.5%	12
15.	\$595.80	9.5%	6
16.	\$314.50	10.0%	24

Finding Finance Charge and True Annual Interest Rate *For each loan, find* **(a)** *the finance charge, and* **(b)** *the APR.*

17. John Lanza financed a $1990 computer with 24 monthly payments of $91.50 each.

18. Jessica Luther bought a horse trailer for $5090. She paid $1240 down and paid the remainder at $152.70 per month for $2\frac{1}{2}$ years.

19. Brandon Hight still owed $2000 on his new garden tractor after the down payment. He agreed to pay monthly payments for 18 months at 6% add-on interest.

20. Alfred Juarez paid off a $15,000 car loan over 3 years with monthly payments of $487.54 each.

Comparing the Actuarial Method and the Rule of 78 for Unearned Interest *Each loan was paid off early. Find the unearned interest by* **(a)** *the actuarial method, and* **(b)** *the rule of 78.*

	Amount Financed	Regular Monthly Payments	Total Number of Payments Scheduled	Remaining Number of Scheduled Payments After Payoff
21.	$3310	$201.85	18	6
22.	$10,230	$277.00	48	12
23.	$29,850	$641.58	60	12
24.	$16,730	$539.82	36	18

Unearned Interest by the Actuarial Method *Each loan was paid in full before its due date.* **(a)** *Obtain the value of h from the appropriate formula. Then* **(b)** *use the actuarial method to find the amount of unearned interest, and* **(c)** *find the payoff amount.*

	Regular Monthly Payment	APR	Remaining Number of Scheduled Payments After Payoff
25.	$212	8.6%	4
26.	$575	9.33%	8

Comparing Loan Choices *Laura Kennedy needs to borrow $5000 to pay for NBA season tickets for her family. She can borrow the amount from a finance company (at 6.5% add-on interest for 3 years) or from the credit union (36 monthly payments of $164.50 each). Use this information for Exercises 27–30.*

27. Find the APR (to the nearest half percent) for each loan and decide which one is Laura's better choice.

28. Laura takes the credit union loan. At the time of her thirtieth payment she pays it off. If the credit union uses the rule of 78 for computing unearned interest, how much will she save by paying in full now?

29. What would Laura save in interest if she paid in full at the time of the thirtieth payment and the credit union used the actuarial method for computing unearned interest?

30. Under the conditions of **Exercise 29,** what amount must Laura come up with to pay off her loan?

31. Describe why, in **Example 1,** the APR and the add-on rate differ. Which one is more legitimate? Why?

Approximating the APR of an Add-On Rate *To convert an add-on interest rate to its corresponding APR, some people recommend using the formula*

$$APR = \frac{2n}{n+1} \cdot r,$$

where r is add-on rate and n is total number of payments.

32. Apply the given formula to calculate the APR (to the nearest half percent) for the loan of **Example 1** ($r = 0.07, n = 24$).

33. Compare your APR value in **Exercise 32** to the value in **Example 1.** What do you conclude?

The Rule of 78 with Prepayment Penalty *A certain retailer's credit contract designates the rule of 78 for computing unearned interest and imposes a "prepayment penalty." In case of any payoff earlier than the due date, they will charge an additional 10% of the original finance charge. Find the least value of k (remaining payments after payoff) that would result in any net savings in each case.*

34. 24 payments originally scheduled

35. 36 payments originally scheduled

36. 48 payments originally scheduled

The actuarial method of computing unearned interest assumes that, throughout the life of the loan, the borrower is paying interest at the rate given by APR for money actually being used by the borrower. When contemplating complete payoff along with the current payment, think of k future payments as applying to a separate loan with the same APR and h being the finance charge per $100 of that loan. Refer to the following formula.

$$u = kR\left(\frac{h}{\$100 + h}\right)$$

37. Describe in words the quantity represented by

$$\frac{h}{\$100 + h}.$$

38. Describe in words the quantity represented by *kR*.

39. Explain why the product of the two quantities above represents unearned interest.

Write out your response to each exercise.

40. Why might a lender be justified in imposing a prepayment penalty?

41. Discuss reasons that a borrower may want to pay off a loan early.

42. Find out what federal agency you can contact if you have questions about compliance with the Truth in Lending Act. (Any bank, or retailer's credit department, should be able to help you with this, or you could try a Web search.)

43. Study the table at the right, which pertains to a 12-month loan. The column-3 entries are designed so that they are in the same ratios as the column-2 entries but will add up to 1 because their denominators are all equal to

$$1 + 2 + 3 + 4 + 5 + \ldots + 12 = \frac{12 \cdot 13}{2} = 78.$$

(This is the origin of the term "rule of 78.")

Month	Fraction of Loan Principal Used by Borrower	Fraction of Finance Charge Owed
1	12/12	12/78
2	11/12	11/78
3	10/12	10/78
4	9/12	9/78
5	8/12	8/78
6	7/12	7/78
7	6/12	6/78
8	5/12	5/78
9	4/12	4/78
10	3/12	3/78
11	2/12	2/78
12	1/12	1/78
		78/78 = 1

Suppose the loan is paid in full after eight months. Use the table to determine the unearned fraction of the total finance charge.

44. Find the fraction of unearned interest of **Exercise 43** by using the rule of 78 formula.

13.4 THE COSTS AND ADVANTAGES OF HOME OWNERSHIP

Fixed-Rate Mortgages • Adjustable-Rate Mortgages • Closing Costs • Taxes, Insurance, and Maintenance

Fixed-Rate Mortgages

Heating a house is another cost that may get you involved with banks and interest rates after you finally get a roof over your head. The roof you see above does more than keep off the rain. It holds solar panels, part of the solar heating system in the building.

For many decades, home ownership has been considered a centerpiece of the "American dream." For most people, a home represents the largest purchase of their lifetime, and it is certainly worth careful consideration.

A loan for a substantial amount, extending over a lengthy time interval (typically up to 30 years), for the purpose of buying a home or other property or real estate, and for which the property is pledged as security for the loan, is called a **mortgage.** (In some areas, a mortgage may also be called a **deed of trust** or a **security deed.**) The time until final payoff is called the **term** of the mortgage. The portion of the purchase price of the home that the buyer pays initially is called the **down payment.** The **principal amount of the mortgage** (the amount borrowed) is found by subtracting the down payment from the purchase price.

With a **fixed-rate mortgage,** the interest rate will remain constant throughout the term, and the initial principal balance, together with interest due on the loan, is repaid to the lender through regular (constant) periodic (we assume monthly) payments. This is called **amortizing** the loan. The regular monthly payment needed to amortize a loan depends on the amount financed, the term of the loan, and the interest rate, according to the formula on the next page.

The **regular monthly payment** required to repay a loan of P dollars, together with interest at an annual rate r, over a term of t years, is calculated as follows.

$$R = \frac{P\left(\frac{r}{12}\right)}{1 - \left(\frac{12}{12 + r}\right)^{12t}}$$

▌▌ **EXAMPLE 1** Using a Formula to Find a Monthly Mortgage Payment

Find the monthly payment necessary to amortize a $75,000 mortgage at 5.5% annual interest for 15 years.

SOLUTION

$$R = \frac{\$75,000\left(\frac{0.055}{12}\right)}{1 - \left(\frac{12}{12 + 0.055}\right)^{(12)(15)}} = \$612.81$$ ▪▪▪

N=180
I%=5.5
PV=75000
→ ▪PMT=-612.81
FV=0
P/Y=12
C/Y=12
PMT: END BEGIN

The arrow indicates a payment of $612.81, supporting the result of **Example 1**.

With a programmable or financial calculator, you can store the formula above and minimize the work. Another option is to use a tool such as **Table 6**, which gives payment values (per $1000 principal) for typical ranges of mortgage terms and interest rates. The entries in the table are given to five decimal places so that accuracy to the nearest cent can be obtained for most normal mortgage amounts.

Table 6	**Monthly Payments to Repay Principal and Interest on a $1000 Mortgage**					
Annual rate (r)	**Term of Mortgage (Years) (t)**					
	5	**10**	**15**	**20**	**25**	**30**
4.0%	$18.41652	$10.12451	$7.39688	$6.05980	$5.27837	$4.77415
4.5%	18.64302	10.36384	7.64993	6.32649	5.55832	5.06685
5.0%	18.87123	10.60655	7.90794	6.59956	5.84590	5.36822
5.5%	19.10116	10.85263	8.17083	6.87887	6.14087	5.67789
6.0%	19.33280	11.10205	8.43857	7.16431	6.44301	5.99551
6.5%	19.56615	11.35480	8.71107	7.45573	6.75207	6.32068
7.0%	19.80120	11.61085	8.98828	7.75299	7.06779	6.65302
7.5%	20.03795	11.87018	9.27012	8.05593	7.38991	6.99215
8.0%	20.27639	12.13276	9.55652	8.36440	7.71816	7.33765
8.5%	20.51653	12.39857	9.84740	8.67823	8.05227	7.68913
9.0%	20.75836	12.66758	10.14267	8.99726	8.39196	8.04623
9.5%	21.00186	12.93976	10.44225	9.32131	8.73697	8.40854
10.0%	21.24704	13.21507	10.74605	9.65022	9.08701	8.77572
10.5%	21.49390	13.49350	11.05399	9.98380	9.44182	9.14739
11.0%	21.74242	13.77500	11.36597	10.32188	9.80113	9.52323
11.5%	21.99261	14.05954	11.68190	10.66430	10.16469	9.90291
12.0%	22.24445	14.34709	12.00168	11.01086	10.53224	10.28613

EXAMPLE 2   Using a Table to Find a Monthly Mortgage Payment

Find the monthly payment necessary to amortize a $98,000 at 6.5% for 25 years.

SOLUTION

In **Table 6**, read down to the 6.5% row and across to the column for 25 years, to find the entry 6.75207. As this is the monthly payment amount needed to amortize a loan of $1000, and our loan is for $98,000, our required monthly payment is

$$98 \cdot \$6.75207 = \$661.70.$$ ▮▮▮

So that the borrower pays interest only on the money actually owed in a month, interest on real-estate loans is computed on the decreasing balance of the loan. Each equal monthly payment is first applied toward interest for the previous month. The remainder of the payment is then applied toward reduction of the principal amount owed.

Payments in the early years of a real-estate loan are mostly interest (typically 80% or more); only a small amount goes toward reducing the principal. The amount of interest decreases each month, so that larger and larger amounts of the payment will apply to the principal. During the last years of the loan, most of the monthly payment is applied toward the principal. (See **Table 8** on **page 716.**)

Once the regular monthly payment has been determined, as in **Examples 1 and 2,** an **amortization schedule** (or **repayment schedule**) can be generated. It will show the allotment of payments for interest and principal, and the principal balance, for one or more months during the life of the loan. Tables showing these breakdowns are available from lenders or can be produced on a computer spreadsheet. The following steps demonstrate how the computations work.

Step 1   Interest for the month $= \left(\begin{array}{c} \text{Old balance} \\ \text{of principal} \end{array} \right) \left(\begin{array}{c} \text{Annual} \\ \text{interest rate} \end{array} \right) \left(\frac{1}{12} \text{year} \right)$

Step 2   Payment on principal $= \left(\begin{array}{c} \text{Monthly} \\ \text{payment} \end{array} \right) - \left(\begin{array}{c} \text{Interest for} \\ \text{the month} \end{array} \right)$

Step 3   New balance of principal $= \left(\begin{array}{c} \text{Old balance} \\ \text{of principal} \end{array} \right) - \left(\begin{array}{c} \text{Payment on} \\ \text{principal} \end{array} \right)$

This sequence of steps is done for the end of each month. The new balance obtained in Step 3 becomes the Step 1 old balance for the next month.

EXAMPLE 3   Preparing an Amortization Schedule

The Petersons have a $60,000 mortgage with a term of 30 years and a 4.5% interest rate. Prepare an amortization schedule for the first 2 months of their mortgage.

SOLUTION

First get the monthly payment. We use **Table 6**. (You could also use the formula.)

Mortgage amount in $1000s ↓   Intersection of 4.5% row with 30-year column in **Table 6** ↓

$$R = 60 \quad \cdot \quad \$5.06685 = \$304.01$$

Now apply Steps 1–3.

Step 1   Interest for the month $= \$60,000(0.045)\left(\frac{1}{12} \right) = \$225$

Step 2   Payment on principal $= \$304.01 - \$225 = \$79.01$

Step 3   New balance of principal $= \$60,000 - \$79.01 = \$59,920.99$

N=300.00
I%=6.50
PV=98000.00
→ ▪PMT=⁻661.70
FV=0.00
P/Y=12.00
C/Y=12.00
PMT: END BEGIN

Under the conditions of **Example 2,** the monthly payment is $661.70. Compare with the table method.

The book, *You Can Do the Math*, by Ron Lipsman of the University of Maryland, is a practical resource for most aspects of **personal financial management.** The associated Web site, www.math.umd.edu/~rll/cgi-bin/finance.html, provides "calculators," with which you can easily input your own values to get the results of many different financial computations.

Starting with an old balance of $59,920.99, repeat the steps for the second month.

Step 1 Interest for the month = $59,920.99(0.045)$\left(\frac{1}{12}\right)$ = $224.70

Step 2 Payment on principal = $304.01 − $224.70 = $79.31

Step 3 New balance of principal = $59,920.99 − $79.31 = $59,841.68

These calculations are summarized in **Table 7**.

Table 7   **Amortization Schedule**

Payment Number	Interest Payment	Principal Payment	Balance of Principal
			$60,000.00
1	$225.00	$79.01	$59,920.99
2	$224.70	$79.31	$59,841.68

▮▮▮

Prevailing mortgage interest rates have varied considerably over the years. **Table 8** shows portions of the amortization schedule for the Petersons' loan of **Example 3** and shows what the corresponding values would have been had their interest rate been 14.5%. (Rates that high have not been seen for many years.) Notice how much interest is involved in this home mortgage. At the (low) 4.5% rate, $49,444.03 in interest was paid along with the $60,000 principal. At a rate of 14.5%, the interest alone would total the huge sum of $204,504.88, which is about 3.4 times greater than the mortgage principal.

Table 8   **Amortization Schedules for a $60,000, 30-Year Mortgage**

4.5% Interest Monthly Payment: $304.01				14.5% Interest Monthly Payment: $734.73			
Payment Number	Interest Payment	Principal Payment	Balance of Principal	Payment Number	Interest Payment	Principal Payment	Balance of Principal
Initially →			60,000.00	Initially →			60,000.00
1	225.00	79.01	59,920.99	1	725.00	9.73	59,990.27
2	224.70	79.31	59,841.68	2	724.88	9.85	59,980.42
3	224.41	79.60	59,762.08	3	724.76	9.97	59,970.45
12	221.68	82.33	59,032.06	12	723.63	11.11	59,875.11
60	205.47	98.54	54,694.75	60	714.96	19.77	59,149.53
175	152.47	151.54	40,506.65	175	656.05	78.69	54,214.82
176	151.90	152.11	40,354.54	176	655.10	79.64	54,135.18
236	113.60	190.41	30,102.65	236	571.02	163.72	47,092.76
237	112.88	191.13	29,911.52	237	569.04	165.70	46,927.07
240	110.73	193.28	29,333.83	240	562.96	171.78	46,417.87
303	59.33	244.68	15,575.66	303	368.65	366.09	30,142.47
304	58.41	245.60	15,330.05	304	364.22	370.51	29,771.96
359	2.27	301.74	302.88	359	17.44	717.29	725.96
360	1.14	302.88	0.00	360	8.77	725.96	0.00
Totals:	49,444.03	60,000.00		**Totals:**	204,504.88	60,000.00	

Adjustable-Rate Mortgages

The lending industry uses many variations on the basic fixed-rate mortgage. An **adjustable-rate mortgage (ARM),** also known as a **variable-rate mortgage (VRM),** generally starts out with a lower rate than similar fixed-rate loans, but the rate changes periodically, reflecting changes in prevailing rates.

Quantities Governing Adjustable-rate Mortgages (ARMS)

- **Adjustment period**—Time interval between rate adjustments (typically 1, 3, or 5 years)
- **Index**—Standard fluctuating average that is the basis for the new, adjusted rate (typically the 1-, 3-, or 5-year U.S. Treasury security rate, or a national or regional "cost of funds" index)
- **Margin**—Additional amount added to the index by the lender (typically a few percentage points)
- **Discount**—Amount by which the *initial* rate may be less than the sum of the index and the margin (typically arranged between the seller and the lender)
- **Interest rate cap**—Limits on (interest) rate increases
- **Periodic cap**—Limit on rate increase per adjustment period (typically about 1% per 6 months or 2% per year)
- **Overall cap**—Limit on rate increases over the life of the loan (typically about 5% total)
- **Payment cap**—Limit on how much the payment can increase at each adjustment
- **Negative amortization**—An increasing loan principal (perhaps caused by a payment cap preventing the payment from covering a higher interest rate)
- **Convertibility feature**—A contractual ability to convert to a fixed-rate mortgage (usually at certain designated points in time)
- **Prepayment penalty**—Charges imposed by the lender if payments are made early

---

▎▎ **EXAMPLE 4**   Comparing ARM Payments Before and After a Rate Adjustment

We pay $20,000 down on a $180,000 house and take out a 1-year ARM for a 30-year term. The lender uses the 1-year Treasury index (at 4%) and a 2% margin.

(a) Find the monthly payment for the first year.

(b) Suppose that after a year the 1-year Treasury index has increased to 5.1%. Find the monthly payment for the second year.

SOLUTION

(a)
Cost of house   Down payment
   ↓   ↓
Mortgage amount = $180,000 − $20,000 = $160,000

The first-year interest rate will be

ARM interest rate = Index rate + Margin = 4% + 2% = 6%.

Now from **Table 6** (using 6% over 30 years) we obtain 5.99551.

First-year monthly payment = 160 · $5.99551 = $959.28

(b) During the first year, a small amount of the mortgage principal has been paid, so in effect we will now have a new "mortgage amount." (Also, the term will now be 1 year less than the original term.) The amortization schedule for the first year (not shown here) yields a loan balance, after the twelfth monthly payment, of $158,035.19.

For the second year,

$$\text{ARM interest rate} = \text{Index rate} + \text{Margin} = 5.1\% + 2\% = 7.1\%.$$

Because 7.1% is not included in **Table 6**, we use the regular monthly payment formula with the new mortgage balance and 29 years for the remaining term.

$$\text{Second-year monthly payment} = \frac{P\left(\frac{r}{12}\right)}{1 - \left(\frac{12}{12 + r}\right)^{12t}} \qquad \text{\small Regular payment formula}$$

$$= \frac{\$158,035.19\left(\frac{0.071}{12}\right)}{1 - \left(\frac{12}{12 + 0.071}\right)^{(12)(29)}} \qquad \text{\small Substitute known values.}$$

$$= \$1072.74$$

The first ARM interest rate adjustment has caused the second-year monthly payment to rise to $1072.74, which is an increase of $113.46 over the initial monthly payment. ▮▮▮

A "seller buydown" occurs when the seller (a new-home builder, for example) pays the lender an amount in order to discount the buyer's loan. This reduces the initial rate and monthly payments, but it may be combined with higher initial fees or even an increase in the price of the house.

▮▮ **EXAMPLE 5** Discounting a Mortgage Rate

In **Example 4,** suppose that a seller buydown discounts our initial (first-year) rate by 1.5%. Find the first-year and second-year monthly payments.

SOLUTION

The 4% index rate is discounted to 2.5%. Adding the 2% margin yields a net first-year rate of 4.5% (rather than the 6% of **Example 4**), so the **Table 6** entry is 5.06685.

$$\text{First-year monthly payment} = 160(\$5.06685) = \$810.70$$

The amortization schedule shows a balance at the end of the first year of $157,418.79. The discount now expires, and the index has increased to 5.1%, so for the second year,

$$\text{ARM interest rate} = \text{Index rate} + \text{Margin} = 5.1\% + 2\% = 7.1\%.$$

(This is just as in **Example 4.**) Using the monthly payment formula, with $r = 7.1\%$ and $t = 29$,

$$\text{Second-year monthly payment} = \frac{\$157,418.79\left(\frac{0.071}{12}\right)}{1 - \left(\frac{12}{12 + 0.071}\right)^{(12)(29)}} \qquad \text{\small Substitute values in the monthly payment formula.}$$

$$= \$1068.55.$$

The initial monthly payment of $810.70 looks considerably better than the $959.28 of **Example 4,** but at the start of year two, monthly payments jump by $257.85. ▮▮▮

Making sure an ARM has adequate rate and payment caps will help avoid "payment shock." It is also wise to have convertibility and no prepayment penalty.

Closing Costs

Apart from principal and interest payments, buying a home involves a variety of one-time expenses called **closing costs,** or **settlement charges,** which are imposed when the loan is finalized (at "closing"). A buyer is entitled to a "good faith estimate" of these costs from the lender and, if desired, may shop for alternative providers of settlement services. Typical closing costs are illustrated in the following example.

▌▌ EXAMPLE 6 Computing Total Closing Costs

For a $58,000 mortgage, the borrower was charged the following closing costs.

Loan origination fee (1% of mortgage amount)	$____
Broker loan fee	1455
Lender document and underwriting fees	375
Lender tax and wire fees	205
Fee to title company	200
Title insurance fee	302
Title reconveyance fee	65
Document recording fees	35

Compute the total closing costs for this mortgage.

SOLUTION

"Loan origination fees" are commonly referred to as **points**. Each "point" amounts to 1% of the mortgage amount. By imposing points, the lender can effectively raise the interest rate without raising monthly payments (because points are normally paid at closing rather than over the life of the loan). In this case, "one point" translates to $580. Adding this to the other amounts listed gives total closing costs of $3217. ▌▌▌

As there is considerable potential for abuse in the area of closing costs, Truth in Lending regulations require the lender to provide clarifying information, including the APR for the loan. The APR, the cost of the loan as a yearly rate, will probably be higher than the stated interest rate since it must reflect all points and other fees paid directly for credit as well as the actual interest.

Taxes, Insurance, and Maintenance

The primary financial considerations for most new homeowners are the following.

1. Accumulating the down payment
2. Having sufficient cash and income to qualify for the loan
3. Making the mortgage payments

Three additional ongoing expenses are

taxes, insurance, and maintenance,

all of which should be anticipated realistically. They can be significant.

Property taxes are collected by a county or other local government. Depending on location and the home value, they can range up to several thousand dollars annually. An advantage is that property taxes and mortgage interest are income tax deductible. Therefore, money expended for those items will decrease income taxes. This is one way that the government, through the tax code, encourages home ownership.

▮▮ **EXAMPLE 7** Taking Taxes into Account in Home Ownership

Darryl Graves is in a 30% combined state and federal income tax bracket. He has calculated that he can afford a net average monthly expenditure of $1400 for a home. Can he afford the home of his dreams, which would require a 20-year, $205,000 fixed-rate mortgage at 6% plus $1920 in annual property taxes?

SOLUTION

Let's "do the math."

Mortgage amount in $1000s → | Value from **Table 6** →

$$\text{Regular monthly mortgage payment} = 205 \cdot \$7.16431$$
$$\approx \$1469$$

$$\text{Monthly property taxes} = \frac{\$1920 \leftarrow \text{Annual taxes}}{12 \leftarrow \text{Months per year}}$$
$$= \$160$$

Mortgage payment ↓ Property taxes ↓

$$\text{Total monthly expense} = \$1469 + \$160$$
$$= \$1629$$

Because $1629 > $1400, it seems that Darryl cannot afford this home. But wait—remember that mortgage interest and property taxes are both income tax deductible. Let's consider further.

$$\text{Monthly interest} = \$205{,}000\,(0.06)\left(\frac{1}{12}\right) \quad \text{Interest} = Prt$$
$$= \$1025$$

Of the $1469 mortgage payment, $1025 would be interest (initially).

Mortgage interest ↓ Property tax ↓

$$\text{Monthly deductible expenses} = \$1025 + \$160$$
$$= \$1185$$

Deductible expense ↓ Tax bracket ↓

$$\text{Monthly income tax savings} = \$1185 \cdot 30\%$$
$$\approx \$356$$

Gross cost ↓ Tax savings ↓

$$\text{Net monthly cost of home} = \$1629 - \$356$$
$$= \$1273$$

By considering the effect of taxes, we see that the net monthly cost, $1273, is indeed within Darryl's $1400 affordability limit. ▮▮▮

Homeowner's insurance usually covers losses due to fire, storm damage, and other casualties. Some types, such as earthquake or hurricane coverage, could be unavailable or very expensive, depending on location. Also, all homes require **maintenance,** but these costs can vary greatly, depending mainly on the size, construction type, age, and condition of the home. These expenses are necessary in order to protect the home investment. They are not generally tax deductible.

Government-backed mortgages, including FHA (Federal Housing Administration) and VA (Veterans Administration) loans, carry a government guarantee to protect the lender in case the borrower fails to repay the loan. Those who do not qualify for these loans, and obtain a conventional loan instead, usually are required to buy private mortgage insurance (PMI) as part of the loan package.

This feature can be a surprise to first-time home purchasers. It was introduced to protect lenders but indirectly protects the buyers, who may lose a bundle if some catastrophe makes it impossible to make the payments.

Over the second half of the twentieth century the amount of credit life insurance in force (for the purpose of covering consumer debt) increased by over 500 times, while group life insurance increased by only about 200 times, ordinary life insurance increased by about 60 times, and industrial life insurance actually decreased. (*Source:* American Council of Life Insurance.)

▮▮ **EXAMPLE 8** Including Insurance and Maintenance in Home Costs

In moving ahead with his home purchase, Darryl (**Example 7**) estimates that homeowner's insurance will be about $550 per year, and that maintenance will be about $650 per year. Will these additional expenses mean that he cannot afford the home?

SOLUTION

These items carry no tax advantage (they are not deductible), so the added monthly expense is simply

$$\text{Monthly insurance and maintenance expense} = \frac{\$550 + \$650}{12} = \$100.$$

With insurance and maintenance included, we obtain

$$\text{Adjusted monthly expense} = \$1273 + \$100 = \$1373,$$

which is still less than $1400. Darryl can still afford the purchase.   ▮▮▮

Payments for property taxes and homeowner's insurance are commonly made from a **reserve account** (also called an **escrow,** or **impound, account**) maintained by the mortgage lender. The borrower must pay enough each month, along with amortization costs, so that the reserve account will be sufficient to make the payments when they come due. (In some cases, the homeowner pays taxes directly to the taxing authority and insurance premiums directly to an insurance company, totally separate from mortgage payments to the lender.)

Examples 7 and 8 raise some reasonable questions.

1. Is it wise to buy a house close to your spending limit, in light of future uncertainties?

2. What about the fact that the interest portion of mortgage payments, and therefore the tax savings, will decrease over time?

3. Won't taxes, insurance, and maintenance costs likely increase over time, making it more difficult to keep up the payments?

Some possible responses follow.

1. Darryl may have built in sufficient leeway when he decided on his $1400 per month allowance.

2. **(a)** Look again at **Table 8** to see how slowly the interest portion drops.

   (b) Most people find that their income over time increases faster than expenses for a home that carries a fixed-rate mortgage. (A variable-rate mortgage is more risky and should have its initial rate locked in for as long as possible.)

   (c) Prevailing interest rates rise and fall over time. While rising rates will not affect a fixed-rate mortgage, falling rates may offer the opportunity to reduce mortgage expenses by refinancing. (See the margin note on refinancing for guidelines.)

3. Here again, increases in income will probably keep pace. While most things, including personal income, tend to follow inflation, the fixed-rate mortgage insures that mortgage amortization, a major item, will stay constant.

Round all monetary answers to the nearest cent unless directed otherwise.

Monthly Payment on a Fixed-Rate Mortgage *Find the monthly payment needed to amortize principal and interest for each fixed-rate mortgage. You can use either the regular monthly payment formula or* **Table 6**, *as appropriate.*

	Loan Amount	Interest Rate	Term			Loan Amount	Interest Rate	Term
1.	$70,000	10.0%	20 years	**5.**		$227,750	12.5%	25 years
2.	$50,000	11.0%	15 years	**6.**		$95,450	15.5%	5 years
3.	$57,300	8.7%	25 years	**7.**		$132,500	7.6%	22 years
4.	$85,000	7.9%	30 years	**8.**		$205,000	5.5%	10 years

Amortization of a Fixed-Rate Mortgage *Complete the first one or two months (as required) of each amortization schedule for a fixed-rate mortgage.*

9. Mortgage: $58,500
Interest rate: 10.0%
Term of loan: 30 years

Amortization Schedule

Payment Number	Total Payment	Interest Payment	Principal Payment	Balance of Principal
1	(a) _____	(b) _____	(c) _____	(d) _____

10. Mortgage: $87,000
Interest rate: 8.5%
Term of loan: 20 years

Amortization Schedule

Payment Number	Total Payment	Interest Payment	Principal Payment	Balance of Principal
1	(a) _____	(b) _____	(c) _____	(d) _____

11. Mortgage: $143,200
Interest rate: 6.5%
Term of loan: 15 years

Amortization Schedule

Payment Number	Total Payment	Interest Payment	Principal Payment	Balance of Principal
1	(a) _____	(b) _____	(c) _____	(d) _____
2	(e) _____	(f) _____	(g) _____	(h) _____

12. Mortgage: $124,750
Interest rate: 9%
Term of loan: 25 years

Amortization Schedule

Payment Number	Total Payment	Interest Payment	Principal Payment	Balance of Principal
1	(a) _____	(b) _____	(c) _____	(d) _____
2	(e) _____	(f) _____	(g) _____	(h) _____

13. Mortgage: $113,650
Interest rate: 8.2%
Term of loan: 10 years

Amortization Schedule

Payment Number	Total Payment	Interest Payment	Principal Payment	Balance of Principal
1	(a) _____	(b) _____	(c) _____	(d) _____
2	(e) _____	(f) _____	(g) _____	(h) _____

14. Mortgage: $150,000

Interest rate: 6.25%

Term of loan: 16 years

Amortization Schedule

Payment Number	Total Payment	Interest Payment	Principal Payment	Balance of Principal
1	(a) _____	(b) _____	(c) _____	(d) _____
2	(e) _____	(f) _____	(g) _____	(h) _____

Finding Monthly Mortgage Payments *Find the total monthly payment, including taxes and insurance.*

	Mortgage	Interest Rate	Term of Loan	Annual Taxes	Annual Insurance
15.	$ 62,300	7%	20 years	$610	$220
16.	$ 51,800	10%	25 years	$570	$145
17.	$ 89,560	6.5%	10 years	$915	$409
18.	$ 72,890	5.5%	15 years	$1850	$545
19.	$115,400	8.8%	20 years	$1295.16	$444.22
20.	$128,100	11.3%	30 years	$1476.53	$565.77

Comparing Total Principal and Interest on a Mortgage *Suppose $140,000 is owed on a house. The monthly payment for principal and interest at 8.5% for 30 years is* $140 \cdot \$7.68913 = \$1076.48.$

21. How many monthly payments will be made over the 30-year period?

22. What is the total amount that will be paid for principal and interest?

23. The total interest charged is the total amount paid minus the amount financed. What is the total interest?

24. Which is more—the amount financed or the total interest paid? By how much?

Long-Term Effect of Interest Rates *You may remember seeing home mortgage interest rates fluctuate widely in a period of not too many years. The following exercises show the effect of changing rates. Refer to **Table 8**, which compared the amortization of a $60,000, 30-year mortgage for rates of 4.5% and 14.5%. Give values of each of the following for **(a)** a 4.5% rate, and **(b)** a 14.5% rate.*

25. monthly payments

26. percentage of first monthly payment that is principal

27. balance of principal after 1 year

28. balance of principal after 20 years

29. the first monthly payment that includes more toward principal than toward interest

30. amount of interest included in final monthly payment of mortgage

The Effect of the Term on Total Amount Paid *Suppose a $60,000 mortgage is to be amortized at 7.5% interest. Find the total amount of interest that would be paid for each term.*

31. 10 years   **32.** 20 years   **33.** 30 years   **34.** 40 years

The Effect of Adjustable Rates on the Monthly Payment *For each adjustable-rate mortgage, find **(a)** the initial monthly payment, **(b)** the monthly payment for the second adjustment period, and **(c)** the change in monthly payment at the first adjustment.*

	Beginning Balance	Term	Initial Index Rate	Margin	Adjustment Period	Adjusted Index Rate	Adjusted Balance
35.	$75,000	20 years	6.5%	2.5%	1 year	8.0%	$73,595.52
36.	$44,500	30 years	7.2%	2.75%	3 years	6.6%	$43,669.14

(The "adjusted balance" is the principal balance at the time of the first rate adjustment. Assume no caps apply.)

The Effect of Rate Caps on Adjustable-Rate Mortgages James Kinchen has a 1-year ARM for $50,000 over a 20-year term. The margin is 2% and the index rate starts out at 7.5% and increases to 10.0% at the first adjustment. The balance of principal at the end of the first year is $49,119.48. The ARM includes a periodic rate cap of 2% per adjustment period. (Use this information for Exercises 37–40.)

37. Find **(a)** the interest owed and **(b)** the monthly payment due for the first month of the first year.

38. Find **(a)** the interest owed and **(b)** the monthly payment due for the first month of the second year.

39. What is the monthly payment adjustment at the end of the first year?

40. If the index rate has dropped slightly at the end of the second year, will the third-year monthly payments necessarily drop? Why or why not?

Closing Costs of a Mortgage For Exercises 41–44, refer to the following list of closing costs for the purchase of a $175,000 house requiring a 20% down payment, and find each requested amount.

Title insurance premium	$240
Document recording fee	30
Loan fee (two points)	___
Appraisal fee	225
Prorated property taxes	685
Prorated fire insurance premium	295

41. the mortgage amount

42. the loan fee

43. the total closing costs

44. the total amount of cash required of the buyer at closing (including down payment)

Consider the scenario of **Example 7.** *Recalling that mortgage interest is income tax deductible, find (to the nearest dollar) the additional initial net monthly savings resulting from each strategy. (In each case, only the designated item changes. All other features remain the same.)*

45. Change the mortgage term from 20 years to 30 years.

46. Change the mortgage from fixed at 6% to an ARM with an initial rate of 5%.

For each of Exercises 47–50, find all of the following quantities for a $200,000 fixed-rate mortgage. (Give answers to the nearest dollar.)

(a) *Monthly mortgage payment (principal and interest)*

(b) *Monthly house payment (including property taxes and insurance)*

(c) *Initial monthly interest*

(d) *Income tax deductible portion of initial house payment*

(e) *Net initial monthly cost for the home (considering tax savings)*

Term of Mortgage	Interest Rate	Annual Property Tax	Annual Insurance	Owner's Income Tax Bracket
47. 15 years	5.5%	$960	$480	20%
48. 20 years	6.0%	$840	$420	25%
49. 10 years	6.5%	$1092	$540	30%
50. 30 years	7.5%	$1260	$600	40%

On the basis of material in this section, or your own research, give brief written responses to each problem.

51. Give other ways Darryl (**Examples 7 and 8**) could possibly decrease the initial net monthly payments for his home.

52. Suppose your ARM allows conversion to a fixed-rate loan at each of the first five adjustment dates. Describe circumstances under which you would want to convert.

53. Describe each type of mortgage.

Graduated payment

Balloon payment

Interest-only

Option ARM ("neg-am")

54. Should a home buyer always pay the smallest down payment that will be accepted? Explain.

55. Should a borrower always choose the shortest term available in order to minimize the total interest expense? Explain.

56. Under what conditions would an ARM probably be a better choice than a fixed-rate mortgage?

57. Why are second-year monthly payments (slightly) less in **Example 5** than in **Example 4** even though the term, 29 years, and the interest rate, 7.1%, are the same in both cases?

58. Do you think that the discount in **Example 5** actually makes the overall cost of the mortgage less? Explain.

59. Discuss the term "payment shock" mentioned at the end of **Example 5.**

60. Find out what is meant by each term and describe some of the features of each.

FHA-backed mortgage

VA-backed mortgage

Conventional mortgage

13.5 FINANCIAL INVESTMENTS

Stocks • Bonds • Mutual Funds • Evaluating Investment Returns • Building a Nest Egg

Stocks

In a general sense, an *investment* is a way of putting resources to work so that (hopefully) they will grow. Our main emphasis here will be on the basic mathematical aspects of a restricted class of financial investments, namely, *stocks, bonds,* and *mutual funds.*

Buying stock in a corporation makes you a part owner of the corporation. You then share in any profits the company makes, and your share of profits is called a **dividend.** If the company prospers (or if increasing numbers of investors believe it will prosper in the future), your stock will be attractive to others, so that you may, if you wish, sell your shares at a profit. The profit you make by selling for more than you paid is called a **capital gain.** A negative gain, or **capital loss,** results if you sell for less than you paid. By **return on investment,** we mean the net difference between what you receive (including your sale price and any dividends received) and what you paid (your purchase price plus any other expenses of buying and selling the stock).

▐▐ **EXAMPLE 1** Finding the Return on a Stock Ownership

Lauren Hileman bought 100 shares of stock in Company A on January 15, 2010, paying $30 per share. On January 15, 2011, she received a dividend of $0.50 per share, and the stock price had risen to $30.85 per share. (Ignore any costs other than the purchase price.) Find the following.

(a) Lauren's total cost for the stock

(b) The total dividend amount

(c) Lauren's capital gain if she sold the stock on January 15, 2011

(d) Lauren's total return on her one year of ownership of this stock

(e) The percentage return

SOLUTION

(a) Cost = ($30 per share) · (100 shares) = $3000

She paid $3000 total.

(b) Dividend = ($0.50 per share) · (100 shares) = $50

The dividend amount was $50.

$$\underset{\downarrow}{\text{Change in price per share}} \qquad \underset{\downarrow}{\text{Number of shares}}$$

(c) Capital gain = ($30.85 − $30.00) · 100 = $0.85 · 100 = $85

The capital gain was $85.

$$\underset{\downarrow}{\text{Dividend}} \quad \underset{\downarrow}{\text{Capital gain}}$$

(d) Total return = $50 + $85 = $135

Total return on the investment was $135.

(e) Percentage return = $\dfrac{\text{Total return}}{\text{Total cost}} \cdot 100\% = \dfrac{\$135}{\$3000} \cdot 100\% = 4.5\%$

The percentage return on the investment was 4.5%.

▐▐▐

The **NASDAQ (National Association of Securities Dealers Advanced Quotations),** unlike the NYSE and other exchanges that actually carry out trading at specific locations, is an electronic network of brokerages established in 1971 to facilitate the trading of over-the-counter (unlisted) stocks. Most of the high-tech company stocks, which grew very rapidly as a group in the 1980s and especially the 1990s (and many of which declined as rapidly in 2000–2002), are (or were) listed on the Nasdaq market.

The price of a share of stock is determined by the law of supply and demand at institutions called **stock exchanges.** In the United States, the oldest and largest exchange is the New York Stock Exchange (NYSE), established in 1792 and located on Wall Street in New York City. Members of the public buy their stock through stockbrokers, people who have access to the exchange. Stockbrokers do business in offices throughout the country. They charge a fee for buying or selling stock.

Current prices and other information about particular stocks are published daily in many newspapers and on various Web sites, where information may be updated every few minutes. **Table 9** below shows examples of trading on the NYSE, on June 4, 2010. The exchange opens at 9:30 A.M. and closes at 4:00 P.M., Eastern time.

Observe the column headings and the numbers for the first company listed, Allstate, with market symbol ALL. The first four numbers show that the first sale of Allstate shares after 9:30 A.M. was for $29.62 per share, the highest sale during the trading day was for $29.77, the lowest was for $28.86, and the last sale before 4:00 P.M. was for $28.94 per share.

Moving across to the right, the next two numbers show that the closing price for the day was $1.23 lower than that of the previous day, that is 4.08% lower. The volume number indicates that 5,383,700 shares (to the nearest 100 shares) of Allstate stock were sold that day.

The next two numbers show that, over the last year, the greatest and least prices paid for ALL were $35.51 and $22.82, respectively. The following two numbers show that Allstate's current dividend is 80 cents per share and that represents a current yield of 2.76% (of the current stock closing price for the day).

PE is the **price-to-earnings ratio,** the current price per share divided by the earnings per share over the past 12 months. For ALL, this ratio was 12.58. Finally, the year-to-date percent change means that Allstate's price per share is now $3.66 less than it was at the start of this calendar year.

Table 9 Selected Stock Quotes (June 4, 2010)

Company	Symbol	Open	Daily Hi	Daily Lo	Close	Net Change	% Change	Volume (100s)	52-wk HI	52-wk LO	Div	% Yield	PE	YTD % Change
Allstate	ALL	29.62	29.77	28.86	28.94	−1.23	−4.08	53837	35.51	22.82	0.80	2.76	12.58	−3.66
Bank of America	BAC	15.50	15.73	15.25	15.35	−0.46	−2.91	1479077	19.86	11.20	0.04	0.26	...	1.93
CarMax	KMX	21.72	21.87	20.75	20.93	−1.46	−6.52	25150	26.50	21.10	...	...	16.74	−13.69
Caterpillar, Inc.	CAT	59.49	60.20	57.36	57.76	−3.35	−5.48	102585	72.83	30.01	1.68	2.91	29.62	1.35
Chevron	CVX	72.15	72.71	70.80	71.28	−2.63	−3.56	180765	83.41	60.88	2.88	4.04	10.82	−7.42
Deere	DE	58.37	59.33	56.50	56.88	−2.79	−4.68	51837	63.68	34.90	1.20	2.11	24.73	5.16
Duke Energy	DUK	15.87	15.88	15.58	15.61	−0.44	−2.74	99430	17.94	13.91	0.96	6.15	17.54	−9.30
FedEx	FDX	82.21	82.62	78.84	79.37	−4.61	−5.49	38621	97.75	49.76	0.44	0.55	...	−4.89
General Mills	GIS	74.28	74.28	73.04	73.30	−1.44	−1.93	33270	75.14	51.37	1.96	2.67	14.84	3.52
Harley-Davidson	HOG	28.33	28.35	27.16	27.35	−1.88	−6.43	58195	36.13	14.99	0.40	1.46	...	8.53
Kimberly-Clark	KMB	60.73	60.83	59.98	60.18	−1.10	−1.80	62518	67.03	50.42	2.64	4.39	13.52	−5.54
Pearson ADS	PSO	13.80	13.83	13.52	13.57	−0.52	−3.69	990	16.37	9.29	0.56	4.13	15.96	−5.50
Sara Lee	SLE	14.42	14.50	14.20	14.24	−0.38	−2.60	152351	15.06	8.72	0.44	3.09	20.06	16.91
Walt Disney	DIS	34.06	34.35	33.44	33.69	−1.02	−2.94	217056	37.98	22.05	0.35	1.04	17.64	4.47
Yum!Brands	YUM	41.36	41.60	40.70	40.86	−1.06	−2.53	47957	44.00	32.24	0.84	2.06	18.08	16.84

▮▮ **EXAMPLE 2** Reading the Stock Table
_____

Use the stock table (**Table 9**) to find the required amounts below.

(a) The highest price for the last 52 weeks for FedEx (FDX)

(b) The dividend for Kimberly-Clark (KMB)

SOLUTION

(a) Find the correct line from the stock table for FedEx.

The highest price for FedEx for the last 52 weeks was $97.75.

(b) The div value of 2.64 means that KMB paid a dividend of $2.64 per share.   ▮▮▮

▮▮ **EXAMPLE 3** Finding the Cost of a Stock Purchase
_____

Find the cost for 100 shares of Deere (DE) stock, purchased at the closing price for the day.

SOLUTION

From **Table 9**, the closing price for the day for Deere was $56.88 per share.

$$\underset{\underset{\text{share}}{\text{Price per}}}{\downarrow} \qquad \underset{\underset{\text{shares}}{\text{Number of}}}{\downarrow}$$

$$\text{Total cost} = \$56.88 \ \cdot \ 100 = \$5688.00$$

One hundred shares of this stock would cost $5688.00, plus any broker's fees.   ▮▮▮

Most stock purchases and sales are done through a broker, who has representatives at the exchange to execute a buy or sell order. The broker will charge a **commission** (the broker's fee) for executing an order. Before 1974, commission rates were set by stock exchange rules and were uniform from broker to broker. Since then, however, rates are competitive and vary considerably among brokers.

Full-service brokers, who offer research, professional opinions on buying and selling individual issues, and various other services, tend to charge the highest commissions on transactions they execute. Many **discount brokers,** on the other hand, merely buy and sell stock for their clients, offering little in the way of additional services.

During the 1990s, when it often seemed that almost any reasonable choice of stock would pay off for almost any investor, a number of online companies appeared, offering much cheaper transactions than were available through conventional brokers. Subsequently, most conventional brokerage firms, as well as the major discount brokerages, introduced their own automated (online) services. Investors today should compare a number of options before deciding which brokerage can best provide the stock investment services they need.

Commissions normally are a percentage of the value of a purchase or sale (called the **principal**). Some firms charge additional amounts in certain cases. For example, rates may depend on whether the order is for a **round lot** of shares (a multiple of 100) or an **odd lot** (any portions of an order for fewer than 100 shares). On the odd-lot portion, you may be charged an **odd-lot differential** (say, 10¢ per share). Also, it is possible to place a **limit order,** where the broker is instructed to execute a buy or sell if and when a stock reaches a predesignated price. An extra fee may be added to the commision on a limit order. One prominent discount brokerage does not charge these special fees but uses a tiered commission structure depending on the principal amount of the purchase or sale and distinguishes between **broker-assisted** and **automated** trades, as shown on the next page.

Typical Discount Commission Structure	
Broker-Assisted Trade	
Principal Amount	**Commission**
Up to $2499.99	$35 + 1.7% of principal
$2500.00–$6249.99	$65 + 0.66% of principal
$6250.00–$19,999.99	$76 + 0.34% of principal
$20,000.00–$49,999.99	$100 + 0.22% of principal
$50,000.00–$499,999.99	$155 + 0.11% of principal
$500,000.00 or more	$255 + 0.09% of principal
Automated Trade	
Number of Shares	**Commission**
Up to 1000	$29.95
More than 1000	$0.03 per share

Also, the Securities and Exchange Commission (SEC), a federal agency that regulates stock markets, supports its own activities by charging the exchanges, based on volume of transactions. Typically this charge is passed on to investors, through brokers, in the form of an **SEC fee,** assessed on stock sales only (not purchases). As of June 2010, this fee was 1.69¢ per $1000 of principal (rounded *up* to the next cent). For example, to find the fee for a sale of $1600, first divide $1600 by $1000, then multiply by 1.69¢.

$$\text{SEC fee} = \frac{\$1600}{\$1000} \cdot \$0.0169 = \$0.02704, \quad \text{which is rounded up to } \$0.03.$$

1.69¢ = $0.0169

▊▊ EXAMPLE 4 Finding Total Cost for a Broker-Assisted Stock Purchase

Find the total cost (including expenses) to Merideth Kolaski, who executes a broker-assisted purchase of 325 shares of Duke Energy stock at the average price of the day on June 4, 2010. Use the typical discount commission structure outlined above.

SOLUTION

Daily high   Daily low

$$\text{Average price} = \frac{\$15.88 + \$15.58}{2} \quad \text{arithmetic mean}$$

$$= \$15.73$$

Price per share   Number of shares

$$\text{Basic cost} = \$15.73 \cdot 325$$

$$= \$5112.25$$

Because this principal amount falls in the second tier of the commission structure, the broker's commission is $65 plus 0.66% of this amount.

$$\text{Broker's commission} = \$65 + 0.0066 \cdot \$5112.25 \quad \text{Multiply first, then add.}$$

$$= \$65 + \$33.74$$

$$= \$98.74$$

Basic cost   Commission

$$\text{Total cost} = \$5112.25 + 98.74$$

$$= \$5210.99$$

The total cost to Merideth for this purchase is $5210.99. ▊▊▊

▮▮ **EXAMPLE 5** Finding Proceeds for an Automated Stock Sale

Find the amount received by David Hertzenberg, when executing an automated sale of 500 shares of General Mills stock at the high price of the day on June 4, 2010.

SOLUTION

From **Table 9**, the basic price of the stock sold is

$$(\$74.28 \text{ per share}) \cdot (500 \text{ shares}) = \$37,140.00.$$

Because fewer than 1000 shares are sold, the commission is $29.95. Find the SEC fee as described before **Example 4.**

$$\frac{\$37,140.00}{\$1000} \cdot \$0.0169 = \$0.627666$$

Round up to obtain an SEC fee of $0.63. Then

Basic price   Commission   SEC fee
↓   ↓   ↓

$$\text{Amount received} = \$37,140.00 - \$29.95 - \$0.63$$
$$= \$37,109.42.$$

David received $37,109.42. ▮▮▮

Bonds

Rather than contributing your capital (money) to a company, you may prefer merely to *lend* money to the company, receiving an agreed-upon rate of interest for the use of your money. In this case you would buy a bond from the company rather than purchase stock. The bond (loan) is issued with a stated term (life span), after which the bond "matures" and the principal (or **face value**) is paid back to you. Over the term, the company pays you a fixed rate of interest, which depends upon prevailing interest rates at the time of issue (and to some extent on the company's credit rating), rather than on the underlying value of the company.

A corporate bondholder has no stake in company profits but is (quite) certain to receive timely interest payments. If a company is unable to pay both bond interest and stock dividends, the bondholders must be paid first.

▮▮ **EXAMPLE 6** Finding the Return on a Bond Investment

Jerry Higgins invests $10,000 in a 5-year corporate bond paying 6% annual interest, paid semiannually. Find the total return on this investment, assuming Jerry holds the bond to maturity (for the entire 5 years). Ignore any broker's fees.

SOLUTION

By the simple interest formula (see **Section 13.1**),

$$I = Prt = \$10,000(0.06)(5) = \$3000.$$

Notice that this amount, $3000, is the *total* return, over the 5-year period, not the annual return. Also, the fact that interest is paid twice per year (3% of the face value each time) has no bearing here since compounding does not occur. ▮▮▮

Historically the overall rate of return over most time periods has been greater for stocks than for bonds. This fact (along with the general appeal of ownership) has led some investors to avoid bonds altogether. On the other hand, there are fewer uncertainties involved with bonds, and a bond investor's capital is subject to less risk. These facts can make bonds more attractive than stocks, especially for retired investors who depend on a steady stream of income from their investments. Many investors, however, seek to build a balanced portfolio that includes both stocks and bonds.

Mutual Funds

A **mutual fund** is a pool of money collected by an investment company from many individuals and/or institutions and invested in many stocks, bonds, or money market instruments. By the late 1990s approximately $5 trillion was invested in more than 7000 separate mutual funds. By 2000 over 50 million U.S. households held mutual funds, and the largest category of these holdings was within retirement accounts.

The **Wall Street reform bill of 2010** put forth "the most sweeping set of changes to the financial regulatory system since the 1930s." Prompted by the failure of a number of large financial and other companies and a steep international recession beginning in 2007, the bill created a new Consumer Financial Protection Bureau within the Federal Reserve, headed by a presidentially-appointed "independent" regulator, and with authority to write new rules to (theoretically) protect consumers from unfair or abusive practices in mortgages and credit cards. In fact, the bill creates vast bureaucratic control over virtually all financial areas discussed in this chapter.

Decade earlier, in 1999, Congressional repeal of many earlier legal and regulatory barriers had allowed large financial conglomerates to offer one-stop shopping for services in the areas of insurance, banking, and investments.

It took over a year for the Democrat-controlled Congress to bring the 2010 bill to a vote. According to the watchdog group Public Citizen, over that period the financial industry spent nearly $600 million to hire some 1,000 lobbyists to promote their interests.

Debate raged about whether the bill was really to help consumers or to control business (or perhaps a combination of the two). It was predicted that it would take about a year for the rules to be established and the impact to be felt.

(*Source: www.CNNMoney.com*)

Mutual Funds Versus Individual Stocks and Bonds

Advantages of Mutual Funds

1. *Simplicity*
   Let someone else do the work.

2. *Diversification*
   Being part of a large pool makes it easier to own interests in many different stocks, which decreases vulnerability to large losses in one particular stock or one particular sector of the economy.

3. *Access to New Issues*
   Initial public offerings (IPOs) can sometimes be very profitable. Whereas individual investors find it difficult to get in on these, the large overall assets of a mutual fund give its managers much more access.

4. *Economies of Scale*
   Large stock purchases usually incur smaller expenses per dollar invested.

5. *Professional Management*
   Professional managers may have the expertise to pick stocks and time purchases to achieve better the stated objectives of the fund.

6. *Indexing*
   With minimal management, an index fund can maintain a portfolio that mimics a popular index (such as the S&P 500). This makes it easy for individual fund investors to achieve returns at least close to those of the index.

Disadvantages of Mutual Funds

1. *Impact of One-Time Charges and Recurring Fees*
   Sales charges, management fees, "12b-1" fees (used to pay sales representatives), and fund expenses can mount and can be difficult to identify. And paying management fees does not guarantee getting *quality* management.

2. *Hidden Cost of Brokerage*
   Recurring fees and expenses are added to give the *expense ratio* of a fund. But commissions paid by the fund for stock purchases and sales are in addition to the expense ratio. (Since 1995, funds have been required to disclose their average commission costs in their annual reports.)

3. *Some Hidden Risks of Fund Ownership*
   (a) In the event of a market crash, getting out of the fund may mean accepting securities rather than cash, and these may be difficult to redeem for a fair price.

   (b) Managers may stray from the stated strategies of the fund.

   (c) Since tax liability is passed on to fund investors and depends on purchases and sales made by fund managers, investors may be unable to avoid inheriting unwanted tax basis.

Source: Forbes Guide to the Markets, John Wiley & Sons, Inc.

An abundance of information about **mutual funds** is available on the Internet. For example, the Investment Company Institute (ICI), the national association of the American investment company industry, provides material at the site www.ici.org/.

Because a mutual fund owns many different stocks, each share of the fund owns a fractional interest in each of those companies. In an "open-end" fund (by far the most common type), new shares are created and issued to buyers while the fund company absorbs the shares of sellers. Each day, the value of a share in the fund (called the ***net asset value,*** or ***NAV***) is determined as follows.

Net Asset Value of a Mutual Fund

If A = Total fund assets, L = Total fund liabilities, and N = Number of shares outstanding, then the **net asset value** is calculated as follows.

$$NAV = \frac{A - L}{N}$$

▌▌ **EXAMPLE 7** Finding the Number of Shares in a Mutual Fund Purchase

Suppose, on a given day, a mutual fund has $500 million worth of stock, $500,000 in cash (not invested), and $300,000 in other assets. Total liabilities amount to $4 million, and there are 25 million shares outstanding. If Elaine Jefferson invests $50,000 in this fund, how many shares will she obtain?

SOLUTION

$$A = \$500,000,000 + \$500,000 + \$300,000$$
$$= \$500,800,000$$
$$L = \$4,000,000$$
$$N = 25,000,000$$

$NAV = \dfrac{A - L}{N}$ ⟶ Formula

$\quad = \dfrac{\$500,800,000 - \$4,000,000}{25,000,000}$ ⟶ Substitute values of A, L, and N.

$\quad = \$19.872$ ⟶ Calculate.

Because $\frac{\$50,000}{\$19.872} \approx 2516$, Elaine's $50,000 investment will purchase (to the nearest whole number) 2516 shares.   ▮▮▮

Evaluating Investment Returns

Regardless of the type of investment you have or are considering (stocks, bonds, mutual funds, or others), it is important to be able to accurately evaluate and compare returns (profits or losses). Even though past performance is never a guarantee of future returns, it is crucial information. A wealth of information on stock and bond markets and mutual funds is available in many publications (for example, the *Wall Street Journal, Investor's Business Daily,* and *Barron's Weekly*) and on numerous Internet sources (for example, www.nasdaq.com).

The most important measure of performance of an investment is the **annual rate of return.** This is not *necessarily* the same as percentage return, as calculated in **Example 1,** because annual rate of return depends on the time period involved. Some commonly reported periods are daily, seven-day, monthly, month-to-date, quarterly, quarter-to-date, annual, year-to-date, 2-year, 3-year, 5-year, 10-year, 20-year, and "since inception" (since the fund or other investment vehicle was begun).

Examples 8 and 9 illustrate some of the many complications that arise when one tries to evaluate and compare different investments.

▮▮ **EXAMPLE 8** Analyzing a Stock's Annual Rate of Return

Theo Lieber owns 50 shares of stock. His brokerage statement for the end of August showed that the stock closed that month at a price of $40 (per share) and the statement for the end of September showed a closing price of $40.12. For purposes of illustration, disregard any possible dividends, and assume that the money gained in a given month has no opportunity to earn additional returns. (Those earnings cannot be "reinvested.") Find the following.

(a) The value of these shares at the end of August

(b) Theo's monthly return on this stock

(c) The monthly percentage return

(d) The annual rate of return

SOLUTION

(a)

Price per share   Number of shares

$$\text{Value} = \overset{\downarrow}{\$40} \cdot \overset{\downarrow}{50} = \$2000$$

(b)

Change in price per share   Number of shares

$$\text{Return} = (\$40.12 - \$40) \cdot \overset{\downarrow}{50}$$
$$= \$6$$

(c)

$$\text{Percentage return} = \frac{\text{Total return}}{\text{Total value}} \cdot 100\%$$
$$= \frac{\$6}{\$2000} \cdot 100\%$$
$$= 0.3\%$$

(d) Because monthly returns do not earn more returns, we use an "arithmetic" return here. Simply add 0.3% twelve times (or multiply 0.3% by 12), to obtain 3.6%. The annual rate of return is 3.6%. ▮▮▮

▮▮ **EXAMPLE 9** Analyzing a Mutual Fund's Annual Rate of Return

Kathryn Lutterschmidt owns 80 shares of a mutual fund with a net asset value of $10 on October 1. Assume that the only return that the fund earns is dividends of 0.4% per month, which are automatically reinvested. Find the following.

(a) The value of Kathryn's holdings in this fund on October 1

(b) The monthly return   **(c)** The annual rate of return

SOLUTION

(a) Value = NAV · number of shares = $10 · 80 = $800

(b) Monthly return = 0.4% of $800 = $3.20

(c) In this case, monthly returns get reinvested. Compounding occurs. Therefore, we use a "geometric" return rather than arithmetic. To make this calculation, first find the "return relative," which is 1 plus the monthly rate of return:

$$1 + 0.4\% = 1 + 0.004 = 1.004.$$

Then multiply this return relative 12 times (raise it to the 12th power) to get an annual return relative: $1.004^{12} \approx 1.049$. Finally, subtract 1 and multiply by 100 to convert back to a percentage rate. The annual rate of return is 4.9%. ▮▮▮

A geometric return such as the one just found in **Example 9** often is called the "effective annual yield." (Notice that an arithmetic return calculation would have ignored the reinvestment compounding and would have understated the effective annual rate of return by 0.1%, because $12(0.4\%) = 4.8\%$.)

Building a Nest Egg

The most important function of investing, for most people, is to build an account for some future use, probably for retirement living. In **Example 8** of **Section 13.1,** we compared two retirement programs, Plan A and Plan B, to emphasize the importance of starting a retirement investment program early in life. The performance of investments over time is generally governed by formulas based on the summation of geometric sequences, which is discussed in the **Extension** on investment fraud following this section. The formulas given here will be used without showing their derivations.

There are two major barriers to building a retirement nest egg (or college tuition fund, or legacy to leave to heirs or to charity, or whatever the goal is for accumulating wealth). These barriers are *inflation* and (*income*) *taxes*.

Table 4 (**page 696**) shows the actual historical inflation rates over 30 years (1979–2009). This reflects an average of about 4.0% per year. If we had invested for retirement over that time span, the inflation proportion (see **page 697**) indicates that we would have ended up in 2009 paying about $\frac{214.5}{72.6} = 3.0$ times as much for goods and services as when we started, in 1979.

This inflationary effect, if unanticipated, could make a sizable dent in retirement living, but there is a fairly painless way to make provision for it. Recall that the CPI reflects the (usually) rising trend in pricing, and that salaries and wages more or less follow along. Periodically (maybe once a year), we can simply increase contributions by enough to keep pace with inflation.

The formula below allows us to compute the future values of an account where regular deposits are systematically adjusted for inflation. If the inflation rate is i, then the amount R is deposited at the end of year 1, $R(1 + i)$ is deposited at the end of year 2, and so on, with the deposit at the end of the year n, in general, being $R(1 + i)^{n-1}$.

Future Value of an Inflation-Adjusted Retirement Account

Assume annual deposits into a retirement account, adjusted for inflation. If

i = annual rate of inflation,

R = initial deposit (at the end of year 1),

r = annual rate of return on money in the account,

and n = number of years deposits are made,

then the value V of the account at the end of n years is calculated as follows.

$$V = R\left[\frac{(1 + r)^n - (1 + i)^n}{r - i}\right]$$

▮▮ **EXAMPLE 10** Adjusting a Retirement Account for Inflation

In **Example 8** of **Section 13.1,** Gina executed Plan A, depositing $2000 on each birthday from age 21 to age 30, then stopped depositing, and at age 65 had $428,378. Peter, with Plan B, waited until age 31 to make the first $2000 deposit, then deposited $2000 every year to age 65 and came out with only $344,634.

Compute the final account value, at age 65, for Peter's Plan B, assuming that the 35 annual deposits had been adjusted for a 4% annual inflation rate.

Putting off paying taxes for as long as possible, though often urged by financial advisors, is not always the best plan. The **Roth IRA**, available since 1998, is funded with taxed dollars, but all funds, both principal and earnings, are withdrawn later tax-free. For a young person, with many years to "grow" the investment, the prospect of avoiding taxes on that growth is attractive, especially if withdrawals will be made when the account holder is in a higher tax bracket than when contributions were made. Advantages also include less restriction on who qualifies, no forced withdrawals, and no restrictions on when withdrawals can be made.

SOLUTION

Use the "inflation-adjusted" formula given in the box with $R = \$2000$, $r = 0.08$, $i = 0.04$, and $n = 35$. The final account value is

$$V = \$2000\left[\frac{(1 + 0.08)^{35} - (1 + 0.04)^{35}}{0.08 - 0.04}\right] \approx \$541{,}963.$$

With inflation adjustment, Plan B, by age 65, accumulates the amount $541,963. ▌▌▌

The second barrier to building wealth—taxes—is not so easily dealt with. You will find that the more you invest and the more you earn, the higher the percentage that our progressive tax system will claim of your earnings. Probably your most effective tool in softening (though not overcoming) this effect is to take full advantage of tax-deferred accounts, such as a TSA (Tax-Sheltered Annuity, or 403(b) Plan); an IRA (Individual Retirement Account, or 401(k) plan), especially if your employer will contribute matching funds; or, if self-employed, a SEP (Simplified Employee Pension) or a Keogh plan.

With most tax-deferred retirement accounts, the accumulated money is all taxed when it is withdrawn (presumably during retirement years). Therefore, it may seem that tax deferral is not an advantage but simply puts off when the tax is paid, assuming your tax rate remains the same. To demonstrate the decided advantage of deferral, we will compare the two situations using the following formulas. For a fair comparison, we look at both account values *after all taxes have been paid*.

Tax-Deferred Versus Taxable Retirement Accounts

In both cases,

$R =$ amount withheld annually from current salary to build the retirement account,

$n =$ number of years contributions are made,

$r =$ annual rate of return on money in the account,

$t =$ marginal tax rate of account holder,

$V =$ final value of the account, **following all accumulations and payment of all taxes.**

Tax-Deferred Account

The entire amount R is contributed each year, all contributions, plus earnings, earn a return over the n years, at which time tax is paid on all money in the account. The final account value is calculated as follows.

$$V = \frac{(1 - t)R[(1 + r)^n - 1]}{r}$$

Taxable Account

Each amount R withheld from salary is taxed up front, decreasing the amount of the annual deposit to $(1 - t)R$. Furthermore, annual earnings are also taxed at the end of each year. But at the end of the accumulation period, no more tax will be due. The final account value is calculated as follows.

$$V = \frac{R[(1 + r(1 - t))^n - 1]}{r}$$

▮▮ **EXAMPLE 11** Comparing Tax-Deferred and Taxable Retirement Accounts

Tara Culliney and Steve Day, both in a 20% marginal tax bracket, will each contribute $2000 annually for 20 years to retirement accounts that return 5% annually. Tara chooses a tax-deferred account, while Steve chooses a taxable account. Compare their final account values at the end of the accumulation period, after payment of all taxes.

SOLUTION

We have $R = \$2000$, $n = 20$, $r = 0.05$, and $t = 0.20 = 0.2$.

Tara: $V = \dfrac{(1 - 0.2)\$2000[(1 + 0.05)^{20} - 1]}{0.05}$ Substitute values in the "tax-deferred" formula.

$\approx \$52{,}906.$

Steve: $V = \dfrac{\$2000[(1 + 0.05(1 - 0.2))^{20} - 1]}{0.05}$ Substitute values in the "taxable" formula.

$\approx \$47{,}645.$

By deferring taxes, Tara ends up with $5261, or about 11%, more.   ▮▮▮

Greater contributions, a longer accumulation period, a higher rate of return, and a higher tax bracket all will accentuate the positive effect of tax deferral.

▮▮ **EXAMPLE 12** Comparing Tax-Deferred and Taxable Retirement Accounts

Repeat **Example 11,** but this time let $R = \$5000$, $n = 40$, $r = 0.10$, and $t = 0.40 = 0.4$.

SOLUTION

Tara: $V = \dfrac{(1 - 0.4)\,\$5000\,[(1 + 0.10)^{40} - 1]}{0.10}$ Substitute values in the "tax-deferred" formula.

$\approx \$1{,}327{,}778.$

Steve: $V = \dfrac{\$5000[(1 + 0.10\,(1 - 0.4))^{40} - 1]}{0.10}$ Substitute values in the "taxable" formula.

$\approx \$464{,}286.$

With these higher parameters, Tara's advantage is dramatic: $863,492, or about 186%, more.   ▮▮▮

Tax-deferred is not the same as "tax-free," which makes the result of **Example 12** less impressive than it may seem. This type of retirement income is taxed at the time it is withdrawn. People who sell tax-deferred plans stress that you will probably be in a lower tax bracket after retirement because of reduced income. But many find this is not so, especially compared to early career income, and especially if your retirement account investments have done very well, which could make your required withdrawals quite large. Besides, who can tell what general tax rates will be 30 years from now?

For Further Thought

Summary of Investments

The summary of various types of investments in **Table 10,** on the next page, is based on average cases and is intended only as a general comparison of investment opportunities. There are numerous exceptions to the characteristics shown. For example, though the table shows no selling fees for mutual funds, this is really true only for the so-called no-load funds. The "loaded" funds do charge "early redemption fees" or other kinds of sales charges. That is not to say that a no-load fund is necessarily better. For example, the absence of sales fees may be offset by higher "management fees."

These various costs, as well as other important factors, will be clearly specified in a fund's prospectus and should be studied carefully before a purchase decision is made. Some expertise is not entirely

(continued)

For Further Thought (*cont.*)

unnecessary for mutual fund investing, just less so than with certain other options, like direct stock purchases, raw land, or collectibles.

To use the table, read across the columns to find the general characteristics of the investment. "Liquidity" refers to the ability to get cash from the investment quickly.

For Group or Individual Investigation

List (a) some investment types you would recommend considering and (b) some you would recommend avoiding for a friend whose main investment objective is as follows.

1. Avoid losing money.
2. Avoid losing purchasing power.
3. Avoid having to learn about investments.
4. Avoid having to work on investments.
5. Be sure to realize a gain.
6. Be able to "cash in" at any time.
7. Get as high a return as possible.
8. Be able to "cash in" without paying fees.
9. Realize quick profits.
10. Realize growth over the long term.

Table 10 Summary of Investments

Investment	Protection of Principal	Protection Against Inflation	Rate of Return (%)	Certainty of Return	Selling Fees	Liquidity	Long-Term Growth	Requires Work from Investor	Expert Knowledge Required
Cash	excellent	none	0			excellent	no	no	no
Ordinary life insurance	good	poor	2–4	excellent	high	excellent	no	no	no
Savings bonds	excellent	poor	3–5	excellent	none	excellent	no	no	no
Bank savings	excellent	poor	2–4	excellent	none	excellent	no	no	no
Credit union	excellent	poor	3–4	excellent	none	excellent	no	no	no
Corporation bonds	good	poor	5–7	excellent	low	good	no	some	some
Tax-free municipal bonds	excellent	poor	2–5	excellent	medium	good	no	no	some
Corporation stock	good	good	3–12	good	medium	good	yes	some	some
Preferred stock	good	poor	4–8	excellent	medium	good	no	some	some
Mutual funds	good	good	3–12	good	none	good	yes	no	no
Your own home	good	good	4–10	good	medium	poor	yes	yes	no
Mortgages on the homes of others	fair	poor	5–8	fair	high	poor	no	yes	some
Raw land	fair	good	?	fair	medium	poor	yes	no	yes
Rental properties	good	good	4–8	fair	medium	poor	yes	yes	some
Stamps, coins, antiques	fair	good	0–10	fair	high	poor	yes	yes	yes
Your own business	fair	good	0–20	poor	high	poor	yes	yes	yes

13.5 EXERCISES

Refer to the stock table (**Table 9** *on* **page 726)** *for Exercises 1–36.*

Reading Stock Charts *Find each of the following.*

1. closing price for CarMax (KMX)

2. sales for the day for FedEx (FDX)

3. change from the previous day for Harley-Davidson (HOG)

4. closing price for Sara Lee (SLE)

5. 52-week high for Pearson ADS (PSO)

6. 52-week low for Walt Disney (DIS)

7. dividend for Allstate (ALL)

8. opening price for Bank of America (BAC)

9. sales for the day for General Mills (GIS)

10. percent change from the previous day for Caterpillar Inc. (CAT)

11. year-to-date percentage change for CarMax (KMX)

12. year-to-date percentage change for Yum!Brands (YUM)

13. price-to-earnings ratio for Caterpillar Inc. (CAT)

14. percentage yield for Chevron (CVX)

Finding Stock Costs *Find the basic cost (ignoring any broker fees) for each stock purchase, at the day's closing price.*

15. 600 shares of Chevron (CVX)

16. 100 shares of Sara Lee (SLE)

17. 500 shares of FedEx (FDX)

18. 800 shares of Allstate (ALL)

Finding Stock Costs *Find the cost, at the day's closing price, for each stock purchase. Include typical discount broker commissions as described in the text.*

	Stock Symbol	Number of Shares	Transaction Type
19.	PSO	60	broker-assisted
20.	GIS	70	broker-assisted
21.	BAC	355	automated
22.	CAT	585	automated
23.	HOG	2500	broker-assisted
24.	DUK	1500	automated
25.	YUM	2400	automated
26.	DIS	20,000	broker-assisted

Finding Receipts for Stock Sales *Find the amount received by the sellers of each stock (at the day's closing prices). Deduct sales expenses as described in the text.*

	Stock Symbol	Number of Shares	Transaction Type
27.	ALL	400	broker-assisted
28.	KMX	600	broker-assisted
29.	CVX	500	automated
30.	DE	700	automated
31.	FDX	1350	automated
32.	KMB	2740	automated
33.	SLE	1480	broker-assisted
34.	PSO	1270	broker-assisted

Finding Net Results of Combined Transactions *For each combined transaction (executed at the closing price of the day), find the net amount paid out or taken in. Assume typical expenses as outlined in the text.*

35. Paul Burke bought 100 shares of Walt Disney and sold 20 shares of General Mills, both broker-assisted trades.

36. Rebecca Leidy bought 800 shares of Bank of America and sold 300 shares of Chevron, both automated trades.

Costs and Returns of Stock Investments *For each of the following stock investments, find* **(a)** *the total purchase price,* **(b)** *the total dividend amount,* **(c)** *the capital gain or loss,* **(d)** *the total return, and* **(e)** *the percentage return.*

	Number of Shares	Purchase Price per Share	Dividend per Share	Sale Price per Share
37.	40	$20.00	$2.00	$44.00
38.	20	$25.00	$1.00	$22.00
39.	100	$12.50	$1.08	$10.15
40.	200	$ 8.80	$1.12	$11.30

Total Return on Bond Investments *Find the total return earned by each bond in Exercises 41–44.*

	Face Value	Annual Interest Rate	Term to Maturity
41.	$ 1000	5.5%	5 years
42.	$ 5000	6.4%	10 years
43.	$10,000	7.11%	3 months
44.	$50,000	4.88%	6 months

Net Asset Value of a Mutual Fund *For each investment, find* **(a)** *the net asset value, and* **(b)** *the number of shares purchased.*

	Amount Invested	Total Fund Assets	Total Fund Liabilities	Total Shares Outstanding
45.	$ 3500	$875 million	$ 36 million	80 million
46.	$ 1800	$643 million	$102 million	50 million
47.	$25,470	$2.31 billion	$135 million	263 million
48.	$83,250	$1.48 billion	$ 84 million	112 million

Finding Monthly and Annual Investment Returns *For each investment, assume that there is no opportunity for reinvestment of returns. In each case find* **(a)** *the monthly return,* **(b)** *the annual return, and* **(c)** *the annual percentage return.*

	Amount Invested	Monthly Percentage Return
49.	$ 645	1.3%
50.	$ 895	0.9%
51.	$2498	2.3%
52.	$4983	1.8%

Effective Annual Rate of Return of Mutual Fund Investments *Assume that each mutual fund investment earns monthly returns that are reinvested and subsequently earn at the same rate. In each case find* **(a)** *the beginning value of the investment,* **(b)** *the first monthly return, and* **(c)** *the effective annual yield.*

	Beginning NAV	Number of Shares Purchased	Monthly Percentage Return
53.	$ 9.63	125	1.5%
54.	$12.40	185	2.3%
55.	$11.94	350	1.83%
56.	$18.54	548	2.22%

Finding Commissions *For each of the following trades, determine the missing amounts in columns* **(a)**, **(b)**, *and* **(c)**.

	Number of Shares	Price per Share	(a) Principal Amount	(b) Broker-assisted Commission	(c) Automated Commission
57.	10	$1.00	_____	_____	_____
58.	10	$100.00	_____	_____	_____
59.	400	$1.00	_____	_____	_____
60.	400	$100.00	_____	_____	_____
61.	4000	$1.00	_____	_____	_____
62.	4000	$100.00	_____	_____	_____

63. Referring to **Exercises 57–62,** fill in the blanks in the following statement.

A broker-assisted purchase is cheaper than an automated purchase only when a relatively _____ number of shares are purchased for a relatively _____ price per share.
(large/small)   (high/low)

Inflation-Adjusted Retirement Accounts *Find the future value (to the nearest dollar) of each inflation-adjusted retirement account. Deposits are made at the end of each year.*

	Annual Inflation Rate	Initial Deposit	Annual Rate of Return	Number of Years
64.	2%	$1000	6%	20
65.	3%	$2000	5%	25
66.	4%	$2500	7%	30
67.	1%	$5000	6.5%	40

The Effect of Tax Deferral on Retirement Accounts *Find the final value, after all taxes are paid, for each account if* **(a)** *taxes are deferred, or* **(b)** *taxes are not deferred. In both cases, deposits are made at the end of each year.*

	Marginal Tax Rate	Regular Deferred Contribution	Annual Rate of Return	Number of Years
68.	10%	$500	7%	15
69.	15%	$1000	5%	30
70.	28%	$3000	10%	25
71.	35%	$1500	6%	10

72. *Monthly Deposits Adjusted for Inflation* In an inflation-adjusted retirement account, let i denote annual inflation, let r denote annual return, and let n denote number of years, as in the text, but suppose deposits are made monthly rather than yearly with initial deposit R.

(a) What expression represents the amount that would be deposited at the end of the second month?

(b) Modify the future value formula for an inflation-adjusted account to accommodate the more frequent deposits.

(c) Find (to the nearest dollar) the future value for monthly deposits of $100 (initially) for 20 years if $i = 0.03$ and $r = 0.06$.

73. *Finding an Unknown Rate* Given the compound interest formula

$$A = P\left(1 + \frac{r}{m}\right)^n,$$

do the following.

(a) Solve the formula for r.

(b) Find the annual rate r if $50 grows to $85.49 in 10 years with interest compounded quarterly. Give r to the nearest tenth of a percent.

74. *Comparing Continuous with Annual Compounding* It was suggested in the text that inflation is more accurately reflected by the continuous compounding formula than by periodic compounding. Compute the ratio

$$\frac{Pe^{rt}}{P(1 + r)^n} = \frac{e^{rt}}{(1 + r)^n}$$

to find how much (to the nearest tenth of a percent) continuous compounding exceeds annual compounding. Use a rate of 3% over a period of 30 years.

Spreading Mutual Fund Investments Among Asset Classes *Mutual funds (as well as other kinds of investments) normally are categorized into one of several "asset classes," according to the kinds of stocks or other securities they hold. Small capitalization funds are most aggressive, while cash is most conservative.*

Asset Classes
a. Aggressive Growth (small cap)
b. Growth
c. Growth & Income
d. Income
e. Cash

Many investors, often with the help of an advisor, try to construct their portfolios in accordance with their stages of life. Basically, the idea is that a younger person can afford to be more aggressive (and assume more risk) while an older investor should be more conservative (assuming less risk). The investment diagrams here show typical percentage ranges that might be recommended by an investment advisor.

In Exercises 75–78, divide the given investor's money into the five categories so as to position them right at the middle of the recommended ranges.

75. Candace Cooney, in her early investing years, with $20,000 to invest

a	5–9%	**Early Investing Years**
b	38–48%	Relatively few holdings
c	26–36%	Long-term investing outlook
d	9–19%	
e	3–7%	

76. Stephen Jennings, in his good earning years, with $250,000 to invest

a	4–8%	**Good Earning Years**
b	24–34%	Ten or more years to retirement
c	31–41%	Long-term investing outlook
d	19–29%	
e	3–7%	Low investment income needs

77. Kevin Clarke, in his high income/saving years, with $400,000 to invest

a	0–4%	**High Income/**
b	23–33%	**Saving Years**
		Less than 10 years
c	31–41%	to retirement
		Fewer financial
d	24–34%	responsibilities
e	3–7%	

78. Lauren Ellis, retired, with $845,000 to invest

a	0–4%	**Retirement Years**
b	10–20%	Reduced earning power
c	39–49%	High investment
		income needs
d	29–39%	
e	3–7%	

The Effect of Taxes on Investment Returns   *Income from municipal bonds generally is exempt from federal, and sometimes state, income tax. For an investor with a marginal combined state and federal tax rate of 35%, a taxable return of 6% would yield only 3.9% (65% of 6%). So at that tax rate, a tax-exempt return of 3.9% is equivalent to a taxable return of 6%. Find the tax-exempt rate of return that is equivalent to the given taxable rate of return for each investor.*

Investor	Marginal Combined Tax Rate	Taxable Rate of Return
79. Patrick Campbell	25%	5%
80. Jaclyn Autrey	30%	7%
81. Brandi Bankston	35%	8%
82. Chris Barker	40%	10%

Write responses to Exercises 83–90. Some research may be required.

83. Describe "dollar-cost averaging," and relate it to advantage number 1 of mutual funds as listed in the text.

84. From **Table 9** in the text, would you say that June 4, 2010, was a "good day" on Wall Street or a "bad day"?

85. Log onto www.napfa.org to research financial planners. Then report on what you would look for in a planner.

86. A great deal of research has been done in attempts to understand and predict trends in the stock market. Discuss the term *financial engineering*. Within this area of study, what is a *rocket scientist* (or *quant*)?

87. Regarding mutual funds, discuss the difference between a *front-end load* and a *contingent deferred sales charge*.

88. What is meant by *growth stock* and *income stock*?

89. With respect to investing in corporate America, describe the difference between being an owner and being a lender.

90. Comment on the graph shown here.

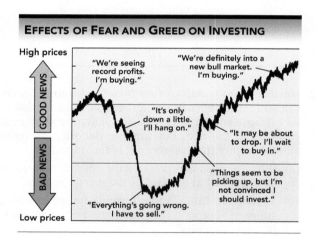

EXTENSION Ponzi Schemes and Other Investment Frauds*

Geometric Sequences • Pyramid Schemes • Ponzi Schemes

Geometric Sequences In a **geometric sequence** (first seen in **Chapter 1**), each term after the first is generated by multiplying the previous term by the **common ratio,** a number remaining constant throughout the sequence. For example, a geometric sequence with first term 3 and common ratio 2 starts out as follows:

$$3, 6, 12, 24, 48, 96, \ldots.$$

Sources: www.usatoday.com, www.moneymorning.com, www.nytimes.com, www.wikipedia.org

In general, if the first term is denoted a, the common ratio is denoted r, and there are n terms altogether, then the complete sequence is

$$a, ar, ar^2, ar^3, \ldots, ar^{n-1}.$$

(Verify by inductive reasoning that the nth term really is ar^{n-1}.)

The sum of all n terms of the geometric sequence above can be written

$$S = a + ar + ar^2 + \cdots + ar^{n-2} + ar^{n-1}.$$

Multiply both sides of this equation by r:

$$Sr = ar + ar^2 + ar^3 + \cdots + ar^{n-1} + ar^n.$$

Now position these two equations, one below the other, and subtract as follows.

$$
\begin{aligned}
S &= a & + \, ar & & + \, ar^2 & & + \cdots + ar^{n-2} & & + \, ar^{n-1} \\
Sr &= ar & + \, ar^2 & & + \, ar^3 & & + \cdots + ar^{n-1} & & + \, ar^n \\
\hline
S - Sr &= (a - ar) + (ar - ar^2) + (ar^2 - ar^3) + \cdots + (ar^{n-2} - ar^{n-1}) + (ar^{n-1} - ar^n)
\end{aligned}
$$

Now we can rearrange and regroup the terms on the right to obtain the following.

$$S - Sr = a + (ar - ar) + (ar^2 - ar^2) + \cdots + (ar^{n-1} - ar^{n-1}) - ar^n$$
$$= a + 0 + 0 + \cdots + 0 - ar^n$$

Notice that all terms on the right, except a and $-ar^n$, were arranged in pairs to cancel out. So we get the following.

$$S - Sr = a - ar^n$$
$$S(1 - r) = a(1 - r^n) \quad \text{Factor both sides.}$$
$$S = \frac{a(1 - r^n)}{1 - r} \quad \text{Solve for the sum } S.$$

The Sum of a Geometric Sequence

If a geometric sequence has first term a and common ratio r, and has n terms altogether, then the sum of all n terms is calculated as follows.

$$S = \frac{a(1 - r^n)}{1 - r}$$

The ability to recognize a geometric sequence and to sum its terms is very helpful in many applications, including detecting investment fraud.

Pyramid Schemes Most everyone has been invited, through email or otherwise, to pass on some message to two (or more) other people. Sometimes it is an innocent "chain letter." But if it involves sending money to someone, it is likely a **pyramid scheme.**

▮▮ **EXAMPLE 1** Analyzing Payoffs in a Pyramid Scheme

You receive a letter with a list of three names, along with the following instructions.

1. Send $1 to the top name on the list.

2. Remove that name and move the other two names up on the list.

3. Add your own name at the bottom of the list.

4. Send the same letter, with the new list, to two other people.

Suppose you decide to participate (become a member), both of your two recruits also participate, all of their four recruits participate, and all of their eight recruits participate. We call this the "each one recruits two" model. (It is also known, classically, as the 8-ball model.) You and the next three levels of participation are illustrated in **Figure 1**.

Level	Participation Chart	Number of Members
1		1
2		2
3		4
4		8

Participation chart for an 8-ball pyramid scheme

Figure 1

(a) With you and all your downstream recruits, how many members are there?

(b) How much money will you receive?

(c) What is your profit?

SOLUTION

(a) $1 + 2 + 4 + 8 = 15$

(b) You receive \$1 from each level-4 member, for a total of \$8.

Income Cost
  ↓   ↓

(c) Profit $= \$8 - \$1 = \$7$ (minus two envelopes and two postage stamps) ▌▌▌

Observe, from **Figure 1** of **Example 1,** that, beginning with one member at level 1, the number of members in a given level is double the number of members in the previous level.

▌▌ **EXAMPLE 2** Finding the Number of Members in a Pyramid Scheme

For each of the following numbers of levels, find the total number of members, from level 1 up to and including the given level. Use inductive reasoning in part (c).

(a) 4   **(b)** 7   **(c)** N

SOLUTION

(a) $1 + 2 + 4 + 8 = 15$ (or, $2^4 - 1$)

(b) $1 + 2 + 4 + 8 + 16 + 32 + 64 = 127$ (or, $2^7 - 1$)

(c) Assuming the pattern observed in parts (a) and (b) holds, the total number of members from level 1 through level N, inclusive, would be

$$2^N - 1.$$ ▌▌▌

The expression, $2^N - 1$, of **Example 2(c)** was derived inductively, but can also be deduced using the formula for the sum of a geometric sequence given earlier.

EXAMPLE 3 Deducing the Number of Members in a Pyramid Scheme

Use deductive reasoning to *prove* that $2^N - 1$ is the total number of members in an "each one recruits two" pyramid with N levels.

SOLUTION

The number of members in the N levels are 1, 2, 4, 8, . . . , and 2^{N-1}. Their sum is the sum of a geometric sequence with

first term $a = 1$, common ratio $r = 2$, number of terms $n = N$.

So the sum is found as follows.

$$S = \frac{a(1 - r^n)}{1 - r} \qquad \text{Sum formula}$$

$$= \frac{1(1 - 2^N)}{1 - 2} \qquad \text{Substitute } a = 1, r = 2, n = N.$$

$$= \frac{2^N - 1}{2 - 1} \qquad \text{Multiply numerator and denominator by } -1.$$

$$= 2^N - 1 \qquad \text{Simplify.} \qquad\qquad ▮▮▮$$

Table 11 summarizes the various values involved as the pyramid builds downward.

Table 11 The Numbers in an "Each One Recruits Two" Pyramid Scheme

Level Number n	Number of Members in Level n	Total Number of Members in all Levels Up To and Including Level n
1	$1 = 2^{1-1}$	$1 = 2^1 - 1$
2	$2 = 2^{2-1}$	$1 + 2 = 3 = 2^2 - 1$
3	$4 = 2^{3-1}$	$1 + 2 + 4 = 7 = 2^3 - 1$
4	$8 = 2^{4-1}$	$1 + 2 + 4 + 8 = 15 = 2^4 - 1$
5	$16 = 2^{5-1}$	$1 + 2 + 4 + 8 + 16 = 31 = 2^5 - 1$
.	.	.
.	.	.
.	.	.
N	2^{N-1}	$1 + 2 + 4 + 8 + 16 + \ldots + 2^{N-1} = 2^N - 1$

The pyramid must keep building downward indefinitely if all the members are to receive their profit. But a pyramid with, say, 20 levels requires

$$2^{20} - 1 = 1{,}048{,}575 \text{ members.}$$

And just 33 levels would involve

$$2^{33} - 1 = 8{,}589{,}934{,}591 \text{ members,}$$

which exceeds the population of the world. Therefore, every pyramid scheme must eventually fail, and most likely long before achieving 33 levels. And when it fails, the members in the last three levels will not get paid. This means that if failure occurs after N levels, then the number of members who lose their money is

$$2^{N-1} + 2^{N-2} + 2^{N-3}.$$

The fact that a **pyramid scheme** profits relatively few at the expense of many, most of whom don't really understand how it works, is part of why these schemes are illegal in the United States (and many other countries). If participants are provided goods or services comparable in value to their "entry fee," then the combination of promotion (recruiting) and selling (goods or services) can become (technically) a legal multi-level marketing (MLM) plan. But there is a fine line between legitimate business and fraud. The legal distinction rests on whether the recruitment exists to promote the product or the product exists to promote the recruitment.

We can now express the fraction of all participants who will lose money as follows.

$$\text{Fraction who lose} = \frac{2^{N-1} + 2^{N-2} + 2^{N-3}}{2^N - 1} \quad \begin{matrix} \leftarrow \text{ Number who lose} \\ \leftarrow \text{ Number who participate} \end{matrix}$$

$$= \frac{2^{N-3}(2^2 + 2 + 1)}{2^N - 1} \quad \text{Factor } 2^{N-3} \text{ from numerator.}$$

$$= \frac{2^{N-3}(7)}{2^N - 1} \quad \text{Add.}$$

Now deleting the -1 from the denominator makes the denominator (slightly) greater, hence the overall fraction lesser. So we can state the following.

$$\text{Fraction who lose} > \frac{2^{N-3}(7)}{2^N}$$

$$= \frac{7}{2^{N-(N-3)}} \quad \text{Apply rule of exponents.}$$

$$= \frac{7}{2^3} \quad \text{Simplify exponent.}$$

$$= \frac{7}{8} \quad \text{Simplify.}$$

No matter how many levels succeed, everyone in the last three levels loses, and these are more than $\frac{7}{8}$ of all participants.

Ponzi Schemes Pyramid schemes are relatively straightforward, though promoters tend to avoid the use of terms like "pyramid" and "scheme." **Ponzi schemes,** on the other hand, come in many varieties and usually involve financial instruments (like "derivatives") and terms (like "alternative asset classes") that can confuse even experienced investors. These scams always pretend to offer real investment returns of one kind or another, but in fact an investor's "returns" come only from his own money or from the deposits of later investors.

The name comes from the years following World War I, when an Italian immigrant, Charles Ponzi, realized that non-uniform international currency exchange rates and other factors made it possible, theoretically, to profit by buying postal reply coupons in Italy and exchanging them for U.S. stamps. There was a money-making potential in this, but over time, Ponzi solicited and received far more deposits ("investments") than could be placed in that market. His operation, mostly in the New England area, drew in more and more participants as he returned profits to early investors out of the deposits of later investors.

Charles Ponzi, like many other scheme operators who followed him, possessed personal attributes, including charm and salesmanship, that allowed him to accummulate much more than what was required just to pay out the profits demanded. As he seemed to be making good on his promises, most investors left both principal and profit to increase in the plan. On some days, he had thousands of zealous investors lined up to give him their money.

It is important, for the success of a Ponzi scheme, that the illusion of successful investment returns be maintained early on to build confidence and attract an ever-growing number of investors. And it helps if the true details of the operation are obscure and difficult or impossible to actually verify.

| EXAMPLE 4 | Finding the Minimum Number of Investors Needed to Support a Ponzi Scheme |

Ponzi promised investors a 50% profit within 45 days or a 100% profit within 90 days. Assuming that he started the year with one investor, who put in $1000, and that all investors always withdrew their 90-day profit and left their principal with Ponzi, how many investors would he need within a year?

SOLUTION

Consider the absolute minimum number of investors required at the end of each quarter (although this certainly was not Ponzi's objective).

- After one quarter (90 days) the single investor's $1000 could be paid back to him as his quarterly profit. So at that point no new investors are necessary.

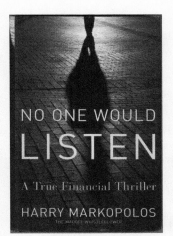

The 2010 book *No One Would Listen,* by Harry Markopolos, describes the longest running and largest Ponzi scheme ever revealed, as well as the futile efforts made by Markopolos, over a decade, to convince governmental regulators to take action against its operator, Bernard Madoff. (See **Exercises 23–25.**) Extensive resources, for the general reader and for classroom use, are available at www.noonewouldlisten.com.

- At the end of the second quarter, the investor wants another $1000 profit, and no money is available without an additional investor. So one investor must be added. His deposit can be used to pay the original investor.

- At the end of the third quarter, there are two investors, and no money. Two additional investors must be recruited to pay profits to the two previous investors.

- At the end of the fourth quarter (one year), four investors expect quarterly profit, so four new investors must be recruited.

Just to pay out profits, Ponzi would need to double his number of investors at the end of each quarter starting with the second. By the end of the year, 1 has doubled to 2, 2 to 4, and 4 to 8. He must end the year with 8 investors. Nothing is left for Ponzi. And if anyone wanted their principal back, he would be in trouble. ▮▮▮

▮▮ EXAMPLE 5 | Analyzing Cash Flow in a Ponzi Scheme

Suppose that investors are promised 100% profit per quarter. At the beginning of each quarter (90 days), 1000 investors contribute $1000 each, and all monies stay in until the end of the year. There are then four categories of investors.

1. those who have been in for 4 quarters

2. those who have been in for 3 quarters

3. those who have been in for 2 quarters

4. those who have been in for 1 quarter

At the end of the year, 10% of those in each category take out their profits, but leave their principal. What amount does that leave with the operator?

SOLUTION

The amount taken in during the year is 4000 · $1000 = $4,000,000. At the end of the year, the supposed profits would be: $4000 for each category 1 investor, $3000 for each category 2 investor, $2000 for each category 3 investor, and $1000 for each category 4 investor. Ten percent of each category take out their profits, and 10% of 1000 is 100, so the payout would then be

Category 1   Category 2   Category 3   Category 4
↓   ↓   ↓   ↓

$$100 \cdot \$4000 + 100 \cdot \$3000 + 100 \cdot \$2000 + 100 \cdot \$1000 = \$1,000,000.$$

The amount the operator retains is

$$\$4,000,000 - \$1,000,000 = \$3,000,000.$$ ▮▮▮

EXTENSION EXERCISES

Analyzing an "Each One Recruits Three" Pyramid Scheme For Exercises 1–11, consider a pyramid scheme just like in Example 1, except that "each one recruits three," rather than two. (Work these all, in order.)

1. Draw a chart like in **Example 1** showing the first four levels.

2. How many members are in each of the following levels?

    (a) 1   **(b)** 2   **(c)** 3   **(d)** 4

3. If the chart is extended, in general how many members are in level N?

4. If you are the top person in the chart, and each person's entry fee is $1, how much money will you receive?

5. What will your profit be?

6. What is the total number of members, from level 1 through each of the following levels, inclusive?

    (a) 1   **(b)** 2

    (c) 3   **(d)** 4

    (e) 5   **(f)** 6

7. Fill in the blanks in the following statements. The total number of members in levels 1 through N, inclusive, is $1 + 3 + 9 + \ldots +$ _____. This is the sum of a _____ sequence with $a =$ ____, $r =$ ____, and $n =$ ____. So the total number of members is _____.

8. If the pyramid fails after level N, how many members will lose?

9. Suppose the scheme runs through level 6 and then fails. How many members lose?

10. Under the conditions of **Exercise 9,** what fraction of the members lose?

11. In an "each one recruits two" pyramid scheme, it was shown that more than $\frac{7}{8}$ of all members will lose. Use a similar analysis to characterize the fraction who will lose in an "each one recruits three" scheme.

12. Suppose you enter an "each one recruits two" pyramid scheme (at level 1), paying your $1 entry fee. If x denotes the number of level-4 recruits that eventually send you $1, then x is a random variable that can take on any of the values 0, 1, 2, 3, 4, 5, 6, 7, or 8. If the probability that any given person invited to join actually will join is $\frac{1}{2}$, then, using binomial probabilities gives the following probability distribution for x.

x	$P(x)$
0	0.34361
1	0.39270
2	0.19635
3	0.05610
4	0.01002
5	0.00114
6	0.00008
7	0.00000
8	0.00000

Find each of the following.

(a) the sum of these probability values

(b) your expected income

13. In **Exercise 12,** what is your expected profit?

14. If you were initiating a pyramid scheme, what would be the advantages and disadvantages of "each one recruits three" rather than two?

15. In a pyramid scheme, even if you and your three levels of recruits are embedded in a much larger chart, with multiple levels above you and many more below you, it is still only your four levels that affect your cost and income. Explain why this is so.

16. In an "each one recruits two" pyramid scheme, more than $\frac{7}{8}$ of all members will lose. What is the *greatest* fraction that could lose, and how could it happen?

17. Discuss places you have encountered "chain letters" or pyramid schemes with promises of money rewards for entering.

18. A number of other types of frauds have surfaced over the years. (Someone always has a new angle.) Research and write a report on "matrix schemes."

Finding the Required Number of Investors in a Ponzi Scheme Refer to **Example 4** for Exercises 19 and 20.

19. How many investors would be required by the end of two years with the same promised return of 100% per 90 days?

20. If the year began with 1000 investors, how many would be required at the end of each time period?

(a) one year   (b) two years   (c) three years

Exploring Cash Flow in a Ponzi Scheme Refer to **Example 5** for Exercises 21 and 22.

21. Suppose that at the end of the year, those 10% of investors actually invest another $1000 rather than taking out profit. Now what amount stays with the operator going into the second year?

22. Explain what factors may have convinced investors to put in more money and not take out profit.

Bernie Made Off with Billions. *As of mid 2010, the largest Ponzi scheme in history was operated by Bernard Madoff, a New York financier and former chairman of the NASDAQ Stock Market. When he was arrested in December of 2008, Mr. Madoff had swindled investors, including charities, foundations, large hedge funds, and funds of funds, as well as individuals, out of some $21 billion. He claimed to be trading in Standard & Poor's 500 Index options, but no one could tell what his fund actually held because he sold out of each option before reporting became mandatory.*

23. Assume that Charles Ponzi bilked his investors out of $4 million in 1920. If inflation averaged 3% from 1920 to 2008, compare the magnitudes of the Ponzi and Madoff scams in comparable dollars.

24. Speculate as to whether Bernard Madoff set out to swindle his investors in the beginning.

25. Considering the serious economic downturn in 2008, why do you think the Madoff scheme, and many others also, were discovered around the same time.

26. Research online or elsewhere to find out about other notable Ponzi schemes over the years. Can you identify any common traits among the operators?

COLLABORATIVE INVESTIGATION

To Buy or to Rent?

Divide your class into groups of at least four students each. Every group is to first read the following.

> Ian and Tami, a young couple with a child, live in a rented apartment. After taxes, Ian earns $38,180 per year and Tami's part-time job brings in $7000 per year. In the foreseeable future, their earnings probably will just keep pace with inflation. They are presently operating on the following monthly budget.
>
> | | |
> |---|---|
> | Rent | $1050 |
> | Food | 600 |
> | Day care | 525 |
> | Clothing | 420 |
> | Utilities | 120 |
> | Entertainment | 300 |
> | Savings | 450 |
> | Other | 300 |
>
> They have accumulated $36,000 in savings.
>
> Having found a house they would like to buy, which is priced at $162,500, they have consulted several lenders and have discovered that, at best, purchasing the house would involve costs as shown here.
>
> | | |
> |---|---|
> | Down payment required (20%) | _____ |
> | Closing costs (required at closing): | |
> | Loan fee (1 point) | _____ |
> | Appraisal fee | 300 |
> | Title insurance premium | 375 |
> | Document and recording fees | 70 |
> | Prorated property taxes | 650 |
> | Prorated fire insurance premium | 270 |
> | Other | 230 |
>
> Total immediate costs: _____
>
> Ongoing monthly ownership costs would be as follows.
>
> | | |
> |---|---|
> | Fixed-rate 30-year mortgage at 7.5% | _____ |
> | Taxes ($1350 annually) | _____ |
> | Fire insurance ($540 annually) | _____ |
>
> In order to own their own home, Ian and Tami are willing to cut their clothing and entertainment expenditures by 30% each and could decrease their savings allotments by 20%. (Some savings still will be necessary to provide for additional furnishings they would need and for expenses of an expanding family in the future.) They also figure that the new house and yard would require $130 monthly for maintenance and that utilities will be twice what they have been in the apartment. Other than that, their present budget allotments would remain the same.

Now divide your group into two "subgroups." The first subgroup is to answer these questions:

1. What amount would the home purchase cost Ian and Tami in immediate expenditures?

2. Do they have enough cash on hand?

The second subgroup is to answer these questions:

3. What amount would the house cost Ian and Tami on an ongoing monthly basis?

4. What amount will their monthly budget allow toward this cost?

5. Can they meet the monthly expenses of owning the house?

Within your group, decide whether Ian and Tami can afford to purchase the house. Select a representative to report your findings to the class.

Compare the evaluations of the various groups, and try to resolve any discrepancies.

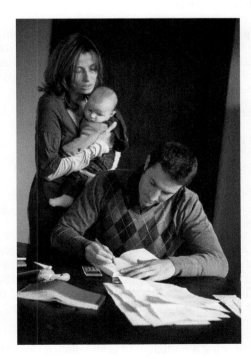

CHAPTER 13 TEST

Find all monetary answers to the nearest cent. Use tables and formulas from the chapter as necessary.

Finding the Future Value of a Deposit *Find the future value of each deposit.*

1. $100 for 5 years at 6% simple interest

2. $50 for 2 years at 8% compounded quarterly

Solve each problem.

3. **Effective Annual Yield of an Account** Find the effective annual yield to the nearest hundredth of a percent for an account paying 3% compounded monthly.

4. **Years to Double by the Rule of 70** Use the rule of 70 to estimate the years to double at an inflation rate of 5%.

5. **Finding the Present Value of a Deposit** What amount deposited today in an account paying 4% compounded semiannually would grow to $100,000 in 10 years?

6. **Finding Bank Card Interest by the Average Daily Balance Method** Caroline DiJullio's MasterCard statement shows an average daily balance of $680. Find the interest due if the rate is 1.6% per month.

Analyzing a Consumer Loan *Jason Hoffa buys a turquoise necklace for his wife on their anniversary. He pays $4000 for the necklace with $1000 down. The dealer charges add-on interest of 7.5% per year. Jason agrees to make payments for 24 months. Use this information for Exercises 7–10.*

7. Find the total amount of interest he will pay.

8. Find the monthly payment.

9. Find the APR value (to the nearest half percent).

10. Find the unearned interest if he repays the loan in full with six payments remaining. Use the most accurate method available.

11. **True Annual Interest Rate in Consumer Financing** Newark Hardware wants to include financing terms in their advertising. If the price of a floor waxer is $150 and the finance charge with no down payment is $5 over a 6-month period (six equal monthly payments), find the true annual interest rate (APR).

12. Explain what a mutual fund is and discuss several of its advantages and disadvantages.

Finding the Monthly Payment on a Home Mortgage *Find the monthly payment required for each home loan.*

13. The mortgage is for $150,000 at a fixed rate of 7% for 20 years. Amortize principal and interest only, disregarding taxes, insurance, and other costs.

14. The purchase price of the home is $218,000. The down payment is 20%. Interest is at 8.5% fixed for a term of 30 years. Annual taxes are $1500 and annual insurance is $750.

Solve each problem.

15. **Cost of Points in a Home Loan** If the lender in **Exercise 14** charges two *points,* how much does that add to the cost of the loan?

16. Explain in general what *closing costs* are. Are they different from *settlement charges*?

17. **Adjusting the Rate in an Adjustable-Rate Mortgage** To buy your home you obtain a 1-year ARM with 2.25% margin and a 2% periodic rate cap. The index starts at 7.85% but has increased to 10.05% by the first adjustment date. What interest rate will you pay during the second year?

18. **Reading Stock Charts** According to the stock table (**Table 9** on **page 726**), how many shares of Sara Lee were traded on June 4, 2010?

Finding the Return on a Stock Investment *Laurie Campbell bought 1000 shares of stock at $12.75 per share. She received a dividend of $1.38 per share shortly after the purchase and another dividend of $1.02 per share one year later. Eighteen months after buying the stock she sold the 1000 shares for $10.36 per share.*

19. Find Laurie's total return on this stock.

20. Find her percentage return. Is this the *annual rate of return* on this stock transaction? Why or why not?

21. **The Final Value of a Retirement Account** $1800 is deposited at the end of each year in a tax-deferred retirement account. The account earns a 6% annual return, the account owner's marginal tax rate is 25%, and taxes are paid at the end of 30 years. Find the final value of the account.

22. What is meant by saying that a retirement account is "adjusted for inflation"?

GRAPH THEORY

Edward James Olmos as Jaime Escalante in Stand and Deliver   *What is his Bacon number? See* **page 802.**

The popular game *The Six Degrees of Kevin Bacon* was developed by three Albright College friends a number of years ago. The object of the game is to link actor Kevin Bacon to another actor or actress using movies, with six or fewer titles in the link. Thanks to the International Movie Data Base (www.imdb.com), this goal can be reached almost instantaneously. The minimum number of links necessary is called the *Bacon number* for the other performer. For example, Mae West has a Bacon number of three, as she can be linked to Kevin Bacon in three steps as follows:

- *Mae West was in Myra Breckinridge (1970) with Calvin Lockhart.*
- *Calvin Lockhart was in Wild at Heart (1990) with Sherilyn Fenn.*
- *Sherilyn Fenn was in Cavedweller (2004) with Kevin Bacon.*

The linking process used in *The Six Degrees of Kevin Bacon* can be applied to other situations (Web pages, for example) and can be modeled using concepts from *graph theory*.

791

Graph theory has many real-world applications, with particularly important ones related to the Internet and telecommunications. (*Sources:* www.imdb.com, www.oracleofbacon.org.)

15.1 BASIC CONCEPTS

Graphs • Walks, Paths, and Circuits • Complete Graphs and Subgraphs • Graph Coloring

Graphs

Suppose a preschool teacher has ten children in her class: Andy, Claire, Dave, Erin, Glen, Katy, Joe, Mike, Sam, and Tim. The teacher wants to analyze the social interactions among these children. She observes with whom the children play during recess over a 2-week period and records her observations.

Child	Played with
Andy	no one
Claire	Dave, Erin, Glen, Katy, Sam
Dave	Claire, Erin, Glen, Katy
Erin	Claire, Dave, Katy
Glen	Claire, Dave, Sam
Katy	Claire, Dave, Erin
Joe	Mike, Tim
Mike	Joe
Sam	Claire, Glen
Tim	Joe

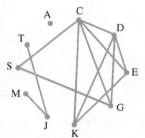

The **World Wide Web** is sometimes studied as a very large graph. The vertices are Web pages, with the edges links between pages. This graph is unimaginably large. It is very hard to even get a good estimate of how many vertices this graph has. In 2005 it was estimated that there were about 11.5 billion Web pages. By 2008 Google software engineers announced in a blog that they had found one trillion distinct URLs on the Web.

Despite these enormous numbers, because of the way the Web is connected, one can get from any randomly chosen Web page to any other using hyperlinks in an average of about 19 clicks. Even if the Web becomes 10 to 100 times larger, this would still be possible in only 20 or 21 clicks. Because of this, search engines such as Google can find keywords very quickly. (*Sources:* http://jmm.aaa.net.au/articles/15080.htm; Antonio Gulli Universit di Pisa, Informatica; Alessio Signorini, University of Iowa, Computer Science; R. Albert, H. Jeong, and A.-L. Barabsi, *Nature* 401, 130–131, 1999.)

It is not easy to see patterns in the children's friendships from this list. Instead, the information may be shown in a diagram, as in **Figure 1**, where each letter is the first letter of a child's name. Such a diagram is called a *graph.** Each dot is called a **vertex** (plural **vertices**) of the graph. The lines between vertices are called **edges.**

In **Figure 1**, each vertex represents one of the preschool children, and the edges show the relationship "play with each other." An edge must always begin and end at a vertex. We may have a vertex with no edges joined to it, such as A in **Figure 1**.

Figure 1

Graph

A **graph** is a collection of vertices (at least one) and edges. Each edge goes from a vertex to a vertex.

---

*Here *graph* will mean finite graph. A finite graph is a graph with finitely many edges and vertices.

Why are they called graphs? The name was first used by chemist **A. Crum Brown.** He made a major breakthrough in chemistry in 1864 by inventing the now familiar diagrams to show different molecules with the same chemical composition. For example, both molecules illustrated above have chemical formula C_4H_{10}. Brown called his sketches **graphic formulae.** Mathematicians got involved in helping to classify all possible structures with a particular chemical composition and adopted the term "graph."

The graph in **Figure 1** has ten vertices and twelve edges. The only vertices of the graph are the dots. There is *no* vertex where edges TJ and SG intersect, since the intersection point does not represent one of the children. The positions of the vertices and the lengths of the edges have no significance. Also, the edges do not have to be drawn as straight lines. ***Only the relation between the vertices has significance, indicated by the presence or absence of an edge between them.***

Why not draw two edges for each friendship pair? For example, why not draw one edge showing that Tim plays with Joe and another edge showing that Joe plays with Tim? Since Tim and Joe play with each other, the extra edge would show no additional information. Graphs in which there is no more than one edge between any two vertices and in which no edge goes from a vertex to the same vertex are called **simple graphs.** See **Figure 2.**

These are simple graphs.　　These are not simple graphs.

Figure 2

In this chapter, the word* graph *means simple graph, unless indicated otherwise. (The meaning of "simple" here is different from its meaning in the phrase "simple curves" discussed with geometry in **Chapter 9.**)

From the graph in **Figure 1**, we can determine the size of a child's friendship circle by counting the number of edges coming from that child's vertex. There are five edges coming from the vertex labeled C, indicating that Claire plays with five different children. The number of edges joined to a vertex is called the **degree of the vertex.** In **Figure 1**, the degree of vertex C is 5, the degree of vertex M is 1, and the degree of vertex A is 0, as no edges are joined to A. (Here, the use of *degree* has nothing to do with its use in geometry in measuring the size of an angle.)

While **Figure 1** clarifies the friendship patterns of the preschoolers, the graph can be drawn in a different, more informative way as in **Figure 3.** The graph still has edges between the same pairs of vertices. We think of **Figure 3** as one graph, even though it has three pieces, since it represents a single situation. By drawing the graph in this way, we make the friendship patterns more apparent. Although the graph in **Figure 3** looks different from that in **Figure 1**, it shows the same relationships between the vertices. The two graphs are said to be *isomorphic.*

Figure 3

Isomorphic Graphs

Two graphs are **isomorphic** if there is a one-to-one matching between vertices of the two graphs with the property that whenever there is an edge between two vertices of either one of the graphs, there is an edge between the corresponding vertices of the other graph.

The word **isomorphism** comes from the Greek words *isos*, meaning "same," and *morphe*, meaning "form." Other words that come from the Greek root *isos* include

isobars: lines drawn on a map connecting places with the same barometric pressure;

isosceles: a triangle with two legs (*scelos*) of equal length; and

isomers: chemical compounds with the same chemical composition but different chemical structures.

A useful way to think about isomorphic graphs is to imagine a graph drawn with computer software that allows you to drag vertices without detaching any of the edges from their vertices. Any graph we can obtain by simply dragging vertices in this way will be isomorphic to the original graph.

Replacing a graph with an isomorphic graph sometimes can convey more about the relationships being examined. For example, it is clear from **Figure 3** on the previous page that there are no friendship links between the group consisting of Joe, Tim, and Mike, and the other children. We say that the graph is *disconnected*.

Connected and Disconnected Graphs

A graph is **connected** if we can move from each vertex of the graph to every other vertex of the graph *along edges of the graph*. If not, the graph is **disconnected.** The connected pieces of a graph are called the **components** of the graph.

Figure 3 shows clearly that the friendship relationships among the children in the preschool class have three components. Although the graph in **Figure 1** also is disconnected and includes three components, the way in which the graph is drawn does not make this as clear.

Using the graph in **Figure 3** to analyze the relationships in her class, the teacher might feel concerned that Tim, Mike, and Joe do not interact with the other children. Certainly she would feel concerned about Andy's isolation. She might observe that Claire seems to get along well with other children and encourage interaction between Claire and Tim, Mike, and Joe, and she might make a special attempt to encourage the children to include Andy in their games. Showing the friendship relationships as in **Figure 3** made it much easier to analyze them.

PROBLEM-SOLVING HINT   Using different colors for different components can help determine how many components a graph has. We choose a color, begin at any vertex, and color all edges and vertices that we can get to from our starting vertex along edges of the graph. If the whole graph is not colored, we then choose a different color and an uncolored vertex, and repeat the process, continuing until the whole graph is colored.

██ **EXAMPLE 1**   Determining Number of Components

Is the graph in **Figure 4** connected or disconnected? How many components does the graph have?

Figure 4   Figure 5

SOLUTION

Coloring the graph helps to solve the problem. The graph with color (**Figure 5**) shows three connected components. The original graph is disconnected.   ███

James Joseph Sylvester (1814–1897) was the first mathematician to use the word *graph* for these diagrams in the context of mathematics. Sylvester spent most of his life in Britain, but had an important influence on American mathematics from 1876 to 1884 as a professor at the newly founded Johns Hopkins University in Baltimore, Maryland. As a young man he worked as an actuary and lawyer in London, tutoring math on the side. One of his students was Florence Nightingale. His only published book, *The Laws of Verse*, was about poetry.

▐▐ **EXAMPLE 2** Deciding Whether Graphs Are Isomorphic

Are the two graphs in **Figure 6** isomorphic? Justify your answer.

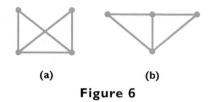

(a)   (b)

Figure 6

SOLUTION

These graphs are isomorphic. To show this, we label corresponding vertices with the same letters and color-code the matching edges in graphs (a) and (b) of **Figure 7**.

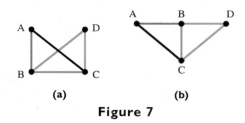

(a)   (b)

Figure 7   ▐▐▐

▐▐ **EXAMPLE 3** Deciding Whether Graphs Are Isomorphic

Are the two graphs in **Figure 8** isomorphic?

(a)   (b)

Figure 8

SOLUTION

These graphs are not isomorphic. If we imagine graph (a) drawn with our special computer software, we can see that no matter how we drag the vertices we can not get this graph to look exactly like graph (b). For example, graph (b) has vertex X of degree 3 joined to vertex Y of degree one. Neither of the vertices of degree 3 in graph (a) is joined to a vertex of degree one.   ▐▐▐

▐▐ **EXAMPLE 4** Summing Degrees

For each graph in **Figure 9**, determine the number of edges and the sum of the degrees of the vertices. (Note that graph (b) is not a simple graph.)

(a)   (b)

Figure 9

SOLUTION

Start by writing the degree of each vertex next to the vertex, as in **Figure 10**.

(a)   (b)

Figure 10

For graph (a):
Number of edges = 7
Sum of degrees of vertices
= 2 + 3 + 2 + 3 + 4 = 14

For graph (b):
Number of edges = 6
Sum of degrees of vertices
= 2 + 3 + 4 + 3 = 12   ■■■

For each graph in **Example 4,** the sum of the degrees of the vertices is twice the number of edges. This is true for all graphs. Check that it is true for graphs in previous examples.

Sum of the Degrees Theorem

In any graph, the sum of the degrees of the vertices equals twice the number of edges.

To understand why this theorem is true, we think of any graph and imagine cutting each edge at its midpoint (without adding any vertices to the graph, however). Now we have precisely twice as many half edges as we had edges in our original graph. For each vertex, we count the number of half edges joined to the vertex. This is, of course, the degree of the vertex. We add these answers to determine the sum of the degrees of the vertices. We know that the number of half edges is twice the number of edges in our original graph. So, the sum of the degrees of the vertices in the graph is twice the number of edges in the graph.

Networks are at the forefront of research in biology. Biologists have made enormous strides in understanding the structure of molecules in living organisms. It is now important to understand how these molecules interact with each other. This can be viewed as a network, or graph.

For example, current research aims to identify how proteins in cells interact with other proteins. Insights into such networks may help explain the growth of cancerous tumors. This may lead to better treatments for cancer. It was discovered that as graphs, these biological networks are surprisingly similar to the graphs representing the World Wide Web.

EXAMPLE 5 Using the Sum of the Degrees Theorem

A graph has precisely six vertices, each of degree 3. How many edges does this graph have?

SOLUTION

The sum of the degrees of the vertices of the graph is

$$3 + 3 + 3 + 3 + 3 + 3 = 18.$$

By the theorem above, this number is twice the number of edges, so the number of edges in the graph is

$$\frac{18}{2}, \quad \text{or} \quad 9.$$ ■■■

A **call graph** has telephone numbers as vertices, while edges represent a call placed from one number to another. A call graph for one company for just one day contained nearly 54 million vertices and 170 million edges. It had 3.7 million components. One of these was a giant component containing nearly 80% of the vertices.

EXAMPLE 6 Planning a Tour

Suppose we decide to explore the upper Midwest next summer. We plan to travel by Greyhound bus and would like to visit Grand Forks, Fargo, Bemidji, St. Cloud, Duluth, Minneapolis, Escanaba, and Green Bay. A check of the Greyhound website shows direct bus links between destinations as indicated.

City	Direct bus links with
Grand Forks	Bemidji, Fargo
Fargo	Grand Forks, St. Cloud, Minneapolis
Bemidji	Grand Forks, St. Cloud
St. Cloud	Bemidji, Fargo, Minneapolis
Duluth	Escanaba, Minneapolis
Minneapolis	Fargo, St. Cloud, Duluth, Green Bay
Escanaba	Duluth, Green Bay
Green Bay	Escanaba, Minneapolis

Draw a graph with vertices representing the destinations and edges representing the relation "there is a direct bus link." Is this a connected graph? Explain.

SOLUTION

Begin with eight vertices representing the eight destinations as in **Figure 11**. Use the bus link information to fill in the edges of the graph.

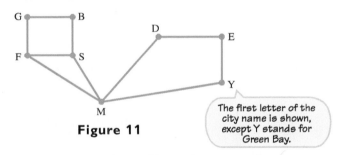

Figure 11

The first letter of the city name is shown, except Y stands for Green Bay.

Figure 11 is a connected graph. It shows that we can travel by bus from any of our chosen destinations to any other. ■■■

Walks, Paths, and Circuits

Example 6 suggests several important ideas. For example, what trips could we take among the eight destinations, using only direct bus links? If we do not mind riding the same bus route more than once, we could take the following route.

$$M \rightarrow S \rightarrow F \rightarrow S \rightarrow B$$

Note that we used the St. Cloud to Fargo link twice. We could not take the $M \rightarrow D \rightarrow S$ route, however, since there is no direct bus link from Duluth to St. Cloud. Each possible route on the graph is called a *walk*.

Maps of subway systems in large cities usually do not faithfully represent the positions of stations, nor the distances between them. They are essentially graphs with vertices representing stations and edges showing subway links.

> ### Walk
>
> A **walk** in a graph is a sequence of vertices, each linked to the next vertex by a specified edge of the graph.

This diagram shows a **Venn diagram** relationship among walks, paths, and circuits.

We can think of a walk as a route we can trace with a pencil without lifting the pencil from the graph.

$$M \to S \to F \to S \to B \quad \text{and} \quad F \to M \to D \to E \quad \text{Walks}$$

$$M \to D \to S \quad \text{Not a walk (There is no edge between D and S in \textbf{Figure 11}.)}$$

Suppose that the travel time for our trip is restricted, and we do not want to use any bus link more than once. A *path* is a special kind of walk.

Path

A **path** in a graph is a walk that uses no edge more than once.*

$$M \to S \to F \to M, \quad F \to M \to D \to E, \quad M \to S \to F \to M \to D \quad \text{Paths}$$

Trace these paths with a finger on the graph in **Figure 11**. Note that a path may use a *vertex* more than once.

$$B \to S \to F \to M \to S \to B \quad \text{Not a path (It uses edge BS more than once.)}$$

$$M \to D \to S \quad \text{Not a path (It is not even a walk.)}$$

Perhaps we want to begin and end our tour in the same city (and still not use any bus route more than once). A path such as this is known as a *circuit*. Two circuits we could take follow.

$$M \to S \to F \to M, \quad M \to S \to F \to M \to D \to E \to Y \to M \quad \text{Circuits}$$

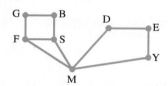

Figure 11 (repeated)

Circuit

A **circuit** in a graph is a path that begins and ends at the same vertex.

Notice that a circuit is a kind of path and, therefore, is also a kind of walk.

▋▋ **EXAMPLE 7**   Classifying Walks

Using the graph in **Figure 12**, classify each sequence as a walk, a path, or a circuit.

(a) $E \to C \to D \to E$ **(b)** $A \to C \to D \to E \to B \to A$

(c) $B \to D \to E \to B \to C$ **(d)** $A \to B \to C \to D \to B \to A$

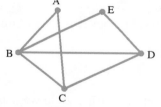

Figure 12

SOLUTION

	Walk	Path	Circuit
(a)	No (no edge E to C)	No[†]	No[†]
(b)	Yes	Yes	Yes
(c)	Yes	Yes	No
(d)	Yes	No (edge AB is used twice)	No[††]

[†] If a sequence of vertices is not a walk, it cannot possibly be either a path or a circuit.
[††] If a sequence of vertices is not a path, it cannot possibly be a circuit, since a circuit is defined as a special kind of path. ▋▋▋

---

*Some books call this a *trail* and use the term *path* for a walk that visits no vertex more than once.

When planning our trip, it would be useful to know the length of time the bus ride takes. We write the time for each bus ride on the graph, as shown in **Figure 13**.

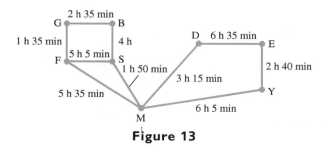

Figure 13

A graph with numbers on the edges as in **Figure 13** is known as a **weighted graph.** The numbers on the edges are called **weights.**

> **PROBLEM-SOLVING HINT** Drawing a sketch is a useful problem-solving strategy. **Example 8** illustrates how drawing a sketch can simplify a problem that at first seems complicated.

▐▐ EXAMPLE 8 Analyzing a Round-Robin Tournament

In a round-robin tournament, every contestant plays every other contestant. The winner is the contestant who wins the most games. Suppose six tennis players compete in a round-robin tournament. How many matches will be played?

SOLUTION

Draw a graph with six vertices to represent the six players. Then, as in **Figure 14**, draw an edge for each match between a pair of contestants. We can count the edges to find out how many matches must be played. Or, we can reason as follows: There are 6 vertices each of degree 5, so the sum of the degrees of the vertices in this graph is 6 · 5, or 30. We know that the sum of the degrees is twice the number of edges. Therefore, there are 15 edges in this graph and, thus, 15 matches in the tournament. ▐▐▐

Figure 14

Complete Graphs and Subgraphs

The graph for **Example 8** in **Figure 14** is an example of a *complete graph.*

(a)

> **Complete Graph**
>
> A **complete graph** is a graph in which there is exactly one edge going from each vertex to each other vertex in the graph.

▐▐ EXAMPLE 9 Deciding Whether a Graph Is Complete

Decide whether each of the graphs in **Figure 15** is complete. If a graph is not complete, explain why it is not.

SOLUTION

Graph (a) is not complete. There is no edge from vertex A to vertex D. Graph (b) is complete. (Check that there is an edge from each of the ten vertices to each of the other nine vertices in the graph.) ▐▐▐

(b)
Figure 15

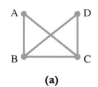

Mazes have always fascinated people. Mazes are found on coins from ancient Knossos (Greece), in the sand drawings at Nazca in Peru, on Roman pavements, on the floors of renaissance cathedrals in Europe, and, of course, as hedge mazes in gardens. Graphs can be used to clarify the structure of mazes.

EXAMPLE 10 Finding a Complete Graph

Find a complete graph with four vertices in the preschoolers' friendship pattern depicted in **Figure 3**, repeated here.

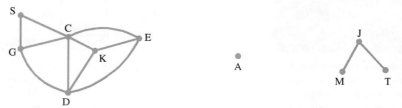

Figure 3 (repeated)

SOLUTION

Figure 16 shows a portion of the friendship graph from **Figure 3**. This is a complete graph with four vertices. ▋▋▋

Figure 16 includes some complete graphs with three vertices. In general, a graph consisting of some of the vertices of the original graph and some of the original edges between those vertices is called a **subgraph.** Vertices or edges not included in the original graph cannot be in the subgraph. (Notice the similarity to the idea of subset, discussed earlier in the text.)

A subgraph may include anywhere from one to all the vertices of the original graph and anywhere from none to all the edges of the original graph. Notice that a subgraph is a graph, and recall that in a graph every edge goes from a vertex to a vertex. Therefore, no edge can be included in a subgraph without the vertices at both of its ends also being included.

- The subgraph shown in **Figure 16** is a complete graph, but a subgraph does not have to be complete. For example, the graphs in **Figures 17(a) and (b)** are both subgraphs of the graph in **Figure 3**.

- The graph in **Figure 17(b)** is a subgraph even though it has no edges. (However, we could not form a subgraph by taking edges without vertices. In a graph every edge goes from a vertex to a vertex.)

- The graph in **Figure 17(c)** is *not* a subgraph of the graph in **Figure 3**, since there was no edge between M and T in the original graph.

Graph Coloring

Tabatha works at the college learning center, and one of her tasks is to schedule study groups for the courses listed at the left below. Study groups for different courses must be scheduled at different times if there are students taking both courses. The column on the right shows, for each course, which of the other courses have students in common with it. For example, the first row shows that each of the courses statistics, chemistry, history, and physics has one or more students also taking algebra.

Figure 16

(a)

(b)

(c)

Figure 17

Course	Other courses taken by students in this course
Algebra	Statistics, Chemistry, History, Physics
History	Statistics, Chemistry, Biology, Algebra
Chemistry	Physics, Biology, Writing, Algebra, History
Biology	Physics, Statistics, Writing, History, Chemistry
Physics	Statistics, Algebra, Chemistry, Biology
Statistics	Writing, Algebra, History, Biology, Physics
Writing	Chemistry, Biology, Statistics

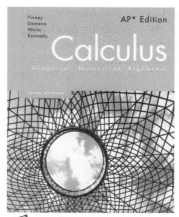

Stand and Deliver (1998) stars **James Edward Olmos** as Jaime Escalante, an inner-city high school mathematics teacher who inspires his students and defies all odds in successfully preparing them for the Advanced Placement calculus exam. Olmos is shown in the chapter opener photo.

The concept of Bacon number is described in the chapter opener. Olmos' Bacon number is two. Can you justify this result? (The answer is on **page 802**.)

Tabatha's task is to figure out the least number of time slots needed for the seven study groups and to decide which (if any) can be scheduled at the same time. We can draw a graph, with a vertex for each course and an edge between two vertices, *if there are students taking both courses*. See **Figure 18**.

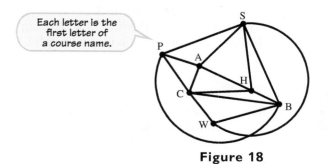

Figure 18

If there is an edge between two vertices, the corresponding courses have students in common, and the study groups must *not* meet at the same time. To show this we use a different color for each time slot for study groups. We will color the vertices with the different colors to show when the study groups could be scheduled.

To make sure that study groups are at different times if the courses have students in common, we must make sure that any two vertices joined by an edge have different colors. To ensure the least number of time slots, we use as few colors as possible. In **Figure 19**, we show one possible coloring of the vertices using three colors. We cannot color the graph as required with fewer than three colors.

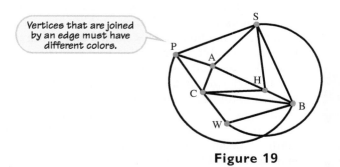

Figure 19

Tabatha can schedule the required study groups in no fewer than 3 time slots. She can schedule statistics and chemistry at one time, physics, history, and writing at a second time, and biology and algebra at a third time.

The method we used is called a *coloring** for the graph.

Coloring and Chromatic Number

A **coloring** for a graph is an assignment of a color to each vertex in such a way that vertices joined by an edge have different colors. The **chromatic number** of a graph is the least number of colors needed to make a coloring.

Using this terminology, Tabatha had to determine the chromatic number for the graph in **Figure 18**. The chromatic number was 3, which equaled the least number of time slots needed for the study groups.

---

*This is sometimes called a *vertex* coloring for the graph.

Have you ever had bad reception on your cell phone? This often occurs because signals are being sent at roughly the same frequency to too many cell phones located close together. Graph coloring can be used to help analyze this problem. However, with over 4 billion cell-phone subscribers in the world (United Nations International Telecommunications Union estimate in 2008) and a fairly narrow frequency range available for cell-phone transmission, many believe that governments should make more frequencies available for cell phone usage.

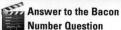
Answer to the Bacon Number Question

Olmos was not in a movie with Bacon, so Olmos' Bacon number must be greater than one.

- Edward James Olmos was in *My Family* (1995) with Bibi Besch.
- Bibi Besch was in *Tremors* (1990) with Kevin Bacon.

Thus, Olmos has a Bacon number of two.

The idea of using vertex coloring to solve problems like this is straightforward. Determining the chromatic number for a graph with many vertices or producing a coloring using the least possible number of colors can be difficult. No one has yet found an efficient method for finding the exact chromatic number for arbitrarily large graphs. (The term *efficient algorithm* has a specific, technical meaning for computer scientists. See **Section 15.3.**)

While the following method for coloring a graph may not give a coloring with the least number of colors, it may be helpful.

Coloring a Graph

Step 1 Choose a vertex with greatest degree, and color it. Use the same color to color as many vertices as you can without coloring two vertices the same color if they are joined by an edge.

Step 2 Choose a new color, and repeat what you did in Step 1 for vertices not already colored.

Step 3 Repeat Step 1 until all vertices are colored.

Graph coloring is used to solve many practical problems. It is useful in management science for solving scheduling problems, such as the study groups example above. Graph coloring is also related to allocating transmission frequencies to TV and radio stations and cell phone companies.

The coloring of graphs has an interesting history involving maps. Maps need to be colored so that territories with common boundaries have different colors. How many colors are needed? For map makers, four colors have always sufficed. In about 1850, mathematicians started pondering this. For over a hundred years, they were neither able to prove that four colors are always enough, nor find a map that needed more than four colors. This was called the **four-color problem.**

In 1976 two mathematicians, Kenneth Appel and Wolfgang Haken, provided a proof that four colors are always enough. This proof created a controversy in mathematics, as it relied on computer calculations so lengthy (fifty 24-hour days of computer time) that no person could check the entire proof. Because of this, some mathematicians still feel that the four-color theorem has not yet been proved, and many keep looking for a shorter proof.

The postmark shown above was used by the Urbana, IL, post office to commemorate the proof of the four-color theorem.

15.1 EXERCISES

For Exercises 1–6, determine how many vertices and how many edges each graph has.

1. **2.**

3. **4.**

5. **6.**

For each graph indicated, find the degree of each vertex in the graph. Then add the degrees to get the sum of the degrees of the vertices of the graph. What relationship do you notice between the sum of degrees and the number of edges?

7. Exercise 1   **8.** Exercise 2

9. Exercise 3   **10.** Exercise 4

In Exercises 11–16, determine whether the two graphs are isomorphic. If so, label corresponding vertices of the two graphs with the same letters and color-code corresponding edges, as in **Example 2.** (Note that there is more than one correct answer for many of these exercises.)

11.

(a)   (b)

12.

(a)   (b)

13.

(a)   (b)

14.

(a)   (b)

15.

(a)   (b)

16.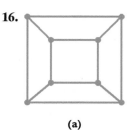

(a)   (b)

In Exercises 17–22, determine whether the graph is connected or disconnected. Then determine how many components the graph has.

17.

18.

19.

20.

21.   **22.**

In Exercises 23–26, use the theorem that relates the sum of degrees to the number of edges to determine the number of edges in the graph (without drawing the graph).

23. A graph with 5 vertices, each of degree 4

24. A graph with 7 vertices, each of degree 4

25. A graph with 5 vertices, three of degree 1, one of degree 2, and one of degree 3

26. A graph with 8 vertices, two of degree 1, three of degree 2, one of degree 3, one of degree 5, and one of degree 6

In Exercises 27–29, refer to the following graph.

27. Which are walks in the graph? If not, why not?

(a) A → B → C

(b) B → A → D

(c) E → F → A → E

(d) B → D → F → B → D

(e) D → E

(f) C → B → C → B

28. Which are paths in the graph? If not, why not?

(a) B → D → E → F

(b) D → F → B → D

(c) B → D → F → B → D

(d) D → E → F → G → F → D

(e) B → C → D → B → A

(f) A → B → E → F → A

29. Which are circuits in the graph? If not, why not?

(a) A → B → C → D → E → F

(b) A → B → D → E → F → A

(c) C → F → E → D → C

(d) G → F → D → E → F

(e) F → D → F → E → D → F

In Exercises 30 and 31, refer to the following graph.

30. Which are walks in the graph? If not, why not?

(a) F → G → J → H → F

(b) D → F

(c) B → A → D → F → H

(d) B → A → D → E → D → F → H

(e) I → G → J

(f) I → G → J → I

31. Which are paths in the graph? If not, why not?

(a) A → B → C

(b) J → G → I → G → F

(c) D → E → I → G → F

(d) C → A

(e) C → A → D → E

(f) C → A → D → E → D → A → B

In Exercises 32–37, refer to the following graph. In each case, determine whether the sequence of vertices is (i) a walk, (ii) a path, (iii) a circuit in the graph.

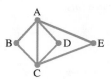

32. A → B → C → D → E

33. A → B → C

34. A → B → C → D → A

35. A → B → A → C → D → A

36. A → B → C → A → D → C → E → A

37. C → A → B → C → D → A → E

In Exercises 38–43, determine whether the graph is a complete graph. If not, explain why it is not complete.

38.

39.

40.

41.

42.

43.

Solve each problem.

44. Chess Competition Students from two schools compete in chess. Each school has a team of four students. Each student must play one game against each student on the opposing team. Draw a graph with vertices representing the students, and edges representing the chess games. How many games must be played in the competition?

45. Chess Competition A chess master plays seven simultaneous games with seven other players. Draw a graph with vertices representing the players and edges representing the chess games. How many games are being played?

46. ***Dancing Partners*** At a party there were four males and five females. During the party each male danced with each female (and no female pair or male pair danced together). Draw a graph with vertices representing the people at the party and edges showing the relationship "danced with." How many edges are there in the graph?

47. ***Number of Handshakes*** There are six members on a hockey team (including the goalie). At the end of a hockey game, each member of the team shakes hands with each member of the opposing team. How many handshakes occur?

48. ***Number of Handshakes*** There are seven people at a business meeting. One of these shakes hands with four people, four shake hands with two people, and two shake hands with three people. How many handshakes occur? (*Hint:* Use the theorem that the sum of the degrees of the vertices in a graph is twice the number of edges.)

49. ***Spread of a Rumor*** A lawyer is preparing his argument in a libel case. He has evidence that a libelous rumor about his client was discussed in various telephone conversations among eight people. Two of the people involved had four telephone conversations in which the rumor was discussed, one person had three, four had two, and one had one such telephone conversation. How many telephone conversations were there in which the rumor was discussed among the eight people?

50. ***Vertices and Edges of a Cube*** Draw a graph with vertices representing the vertices (the corners) of a cube and edges representing the edges of the cube. In your graph, find a circuit that visits four different vertices. What figure does your circuit form on the actual cube?

51. ***Vertices and Edges of a Tetrahedron*** Draw a graph with vertices representing the vertices (or corners) of a tetrahedron and edges representing the edges of the tetrahedron. In the graph, identify a circuit that visits three different vertices. What figure does the circuit form on the actual tetrahedron?

52. ***Students in the Same Class*** Mary, Erin, Sue, Jane, Katy, and Brenda are friends at college. Mary, Erin, Sue, and Jane are in the same math class. Sue, Jane, and Katy take the same English composition class.

  (a) Draw a graph with vertices representing the six students and edges representing the relation "take a common class."

  (b) Is the graph connected or disconnected? How many components does the graph have?

  (c) In the graph, identify a subgraph that is a complete graph with four vertices.

  (d) In the graph, identify three different subgraphs that are complete graphs with three vertices. (There are several correct answers.)

53. Here is another theorem about graphs: ***In any graph, the number of vertices with odd degree must be even.*** Explain why this theorem is true. (*Hint:* Use the theorem about the relationship between the number of edges and the sum of degrees.)

54. Draw two nonisomorphic (simple) graphs with 6 vertices, with each vertex having degree 3.

55. Explain why the graphs in **Exercise 54** are not isomorphic.

56. ***Analyzing a Cube with a Graph*** Draw a graph whose vertices represent the *faces* of a cube and in which an edge between two vertices shows that the corresponding faces of the actual cube share a common boundary. What is the degree of each vertex in the graph? What does the degree of any vertex in the graph tell about the actual cube?

57. Graphs may be used to clarify the structure of mazes. Vertices represent entrances and points in the maze where there is a dead end or a choice of two or more edges by which to proceed. For example, the 1690 design for the hedge maze at Hampton Court in England and a corresponding graph are shown below.

  Write a paper on mazes. Use graphs to analyze the structures of the mazes. Perhaps focus on a particular kind of maze, such as mazes in gardens, mazes in art and architecture, or mazes in ancient cultures.

58. Graphs may be used to clarify the rhyme schemes in poetry. Vertices represent words at the end of a line, edges are drawn, and a path is used to indicate the rhyme scheme. For example, here is the first stanza of *Ode to Autumn* by John Keats, with the rhyme scheme analyzed using a graph:

Season of mists and mellow fruitfulness,	A
Close bosom-friend of the maturing sun;	B
Conspiring with him how to load and bless	A
With fruit the vines that round the thatch-eves run;	B
To bend with apples the moss'd cottage-trees	C
And fill all fruit with ripeness to the core;	D
To swell the gourd, and plump the hazel shells	E
With a sweet kernel; to set budding more,	D
And still more, later flowers for the bees,	C
Until they think that warm days will never cease,	C
For Summer has o'er brimm'd their clammy cells.	E

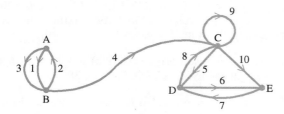

Write a paper on rhyme schemes in poetry, using graphs to illustrate. Focus either on a particular poet or on a particular type of poem.

In Exercises 59 through 64, color the graph using as few colors as possible. Determine the chromatic number of the graph. (Hint: The chromatic number is fixed, but there may be more than one correct coloring.)

59.   **60.**

61.   **62.**

63.

64.

65. Color each graph using as few colors as possible. Use this to determine the chromatic number of the graph. (Graphs like these are called **cycles.**)

(a)   **(b)**

(c)   **(d)**

(e) Use the results from parts (a)–(d) to make a prediction about the chromatic number of a cycle. (*Hint:* Consider two cases.)

66. Sketch a complete graph with the specified number of vertices, color the graph with as few colors as possible, and use this to determine the chromatic number of the graph.

(a) 3 vertices

(b) 4 vertices

(c) 5 vertices

(d) Write a general principle by completing this statement: A complete graph with *n* vertices has chromatic number ____ .

(e) Why is the statement in part (d) true?

(f) Generalize further by completing this statement: If a graph has a *subgraph* that is a complete graph with *n* vertices, then the chromatic number of the graph must be at least ____ .

In Exercises 67–70, color the vertices using as few colors as possible. Then state the chromatic number of the graph. (Hint: It might help to first identify the largest subgraph that is a complete graph.)

67.   **68.**

69.   **70.**

71. Scheduling Meeting Times Campus Life must schedule weekly meeting times for the six organizations listed below in such a way that organizations with members in common meet at different times. Use graph coloring to determine the least number of different meeting times and to decide which organizations should meet at the same time.

Organization	Members also belong to
Choir	Caribbean Club, Dance Club, Theater, Service Club
Caribbean Club	Dance Club, Service Club, Choir
Service Club	Forensics, Choir, Theater, Caribbean Club
Forensics	Dance Club, Service Club
Theater	Choir, Service Club
Dance Club	Choir, Caribbean Club, Forensics

72. Assigning Frequencies to Transmitters Interference can occur between radio stations. To avoid this, transmitters that are less than 60 miles apart must be assigned different broadcast frequencies. The transmitters for 7 radio stations are labeled A through G. The information below shows, for each transmitter, which of the others are within 60 miles. Use graph coloring to determine the least number of different broadcast frequencies that must be assigned to the 7 transmitters. Include a plan for which transmitters could broadcast on the same frequency to use this least number of frequencies.

Transmitter	Transmitters within 60 miles of this
A	B, E, F
B	A, C, E, F, G
C	B, D, G
D	C, F, G
E	A, B, F
F	A, B, D, E, G
G	B, C, D, F

73. Inviting Colleagues to a Gathering Tiffany wants to invite her work colleagues to her home. However, several of her colleagues do not get along with each other, as summarized in the list at the top of the next column. Tiffany plans to organize several gatherings, so that colleagues who do not get along are not there at the same time. Use graph coloring to determine the least number of gatherings needed to achieve this, and decide which colleagues should be invited each time.

- Joe does not get along with Brad and Phil.
- Caitlin does not get along with Lindsay and Brad.
- Lindsay does not get along with Phil.
- Mary does not get along with Lindsay.
- Eva gets along with everyone.

Graph Coloring *In Exercises 74–76, the graph shows the vertices and edges of the figure specified. Color the vertices of each figure in such a way that vertices with an edge between them have different colors. Use graph coloring to find a way to do this, and specify the least number of colors needed.*

74. Cube

75. Octahedron

76. Dodecahedron

Graph Coloring *In Exercises 77 and 78, draw a vertex for each region shown in the map. Draw an edge between two vertices if the two regions have a common boundary. (Do not draw an edge if the regions meet at just one point.) Then find a coloring for the graph, using as few colors as possible.*

77.

78.

79. *Map Coloring* The map shows areas of upstate New York. Use graph coloring to determine the least number of colors that can be used to color the map so that areas with common boundaries have different colors.

80. *Map Coloring* The map at the top of the next column shows countries of Southern Africa. Use graph coloring to determine the least number of colors that can be used to color the map so that countries with common boundaries have different colors.

Map Drawing *In Exercises 81–83, draw a map with the specified number of countries that can be colored using the stated number of colors, and no fewer. (Countries may not consist of disconnected pieces.) If it is not possible to draw such a map, say why not.*

81. 6 countries, 3 colors

82. 6 countries, 4 colors

83. 6 countries, 5 colors

84. Write a short paper on the history of the four-color problem. Include discussion of the proof by Appel and Haken.

15.2 EULER CIRCUITS

Königsberg Bridge Problem • Fleury's Algorithm

Königsberg Bridge Problem

In the early 1700s, the city of Königsberg was the capital of East Prussia. (Königsberg is now called Kaliningrad and is in Russia.) The river Pregel ran through the city in two branches with an island between the branches. **Figure 20** shows the city as it looked in the early 1700s.

Figure 20

Leonhard Euler (1707–1783) was a devoted father and grandfather. He had thirteen children and frequently worked on mathematics with children playing around him. He lost the sight in his right eye at age 31, a couple of years after writing the Königsberg bridge paper. He became completely blind at age 58, but produced more than half his mathematical work after that. Euler wrote nearly a thousand books and papers.

There were seven bridges joining various parts of the city. **Figure 21** on the next page shows a map of the river and bridges in the city. According to Leonhard Euler (pronounced "oiler"), the following problem was well known in his time (around 1730):

Is it possible for a citizen of Königsberg to take a stroll through the city, crossing each bridge exactly once, and beginning and ending at the same place?

A university was founded in Königsberg in 1544. It was established as a Lutheran center of learning. Its most famous professor was the philosopher **Immanual Kant,** who was born in Königsberg in 1724. The university was completely destroyed during World War II.

Try to find such a route on the map in **Figure 21**. (Do not cross the river anywhere except at the bridges shown on the map.)

Figure 21

We can simplify the problem by drawing the map as a graph. See **Figure 22**. The graph focuses on the relations between the vertices. This is the relation "there is a bridge." In this graph we have *two* edges between vertices A and C and between vertices A and D. Thus, this graph is not a simple graph. We have labeled the edges with lowercase letters. Now try to find a route as required in the puzzle.

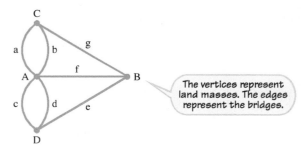

The vertices represent land masses. The edges represent the bridges.

Figure 22

The Königsberg bridge problem requires more than a path and more than a circuit. (Recall that a path is a walk that uses no edge more than once, and a circuit is a path that begins and ends at the same vertex.) The problem requires a circuit that uses *every* edge, *exactly* once. This is called an *Euler circuit.*

Euler Path and Euler Circuit

An **Euler path** in a graph is a path that uses every edge of the graph exactly once. An **Euler circuit** in a graph is a circuit that uses every edge of the graph exactly once.

▌▌ **EXAMPLE 1** Recognizing Euler Circuits

Consider the graph in **Figure 23**.

(a) Is $A \rightarrow B \rightarrow C \rightarrow D \rightarrow E \rightarrow F \rightarrow A$ an Euler circuit for this graph? Justify your answer.

(b) Does the graph have an Euler circuit?

SOLUTION

(a) $A \rightarrow B \rightarrow C \rightarrow D \rightarrow E \rightarrow F \rightarrow A$ is a circuit, but not an Euler circuit, since it does not use every edge of the graph. For example, the edge BD is not used in this circuit.

Figure 23

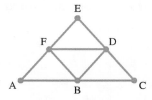

Figure 23 (repeated)

(b) In the graph in **Figure 23**, the circuit

$$A \rightarrow B \rightarrow C \rightarrow D \rightarrow E \rightarrow F \rightarrow D \rightarrow B \rightarrow F \rightarrow A$$

is an Euler circuit. Trace this path on the graph to check that it does use every edge of the graph exactly once. ■■■

Returning to the Königsberg bridge problem, it seemed that no route of the type required could be found. Why was this so? Euler published a paper in 1736 that explained why it is impossible to find a walk of the required kind, and he provided a simple way for deciding whether a given graph has an Euler circuit. Euler did not use the terms *graph* and *circuit*, but his paper was, in fact, the first paper on graph theory. In modern terms, Euler proved the first part of the theorem below. Part 2 was not proved until 1873.

> **Euler's Theorem**
>
> Suppose we have a connected graph.
>
> **1.** If the graph has an Euler circuit, then each vertex of the graph has even degree.
> **2.** If each vertex of the graph has even degree, then the graph has an Euler circuit.

What does Euler's theorem predict about the connected graph in **Figure 23**? The degrees of the vertices are as follows.

A: 2   B: 4   C: 2   D: 4   E: 2   F: 4

Each vertex has even degree, so it follows from part 2 of the theorem that the graph has an Euler circuit. (We already knew this, since we found an Euler circuit for this graph in **Example 1.**)

What does Euler's theorem suggest about the Königsberg bridge problem? Note that the degree of vertex C in **Figure 22** is 3, which is an odd number, and the graph is connected. So, by part 1 of the theorem, the graph cannot have an Euler circuit. (In fact, the graph has many vertices with odd degree, but the presence of *any* vertex of odd degree indicates that the graph does not have an Euler circuit.)

Why is Euler's theorem true? Consider the first part of the theorem:

If a connected graph has an Euler circuit, then each vertex has even degree.

Suppose we have a connected graph with an Euler circuit in the graph. Suppose the circuit begins and ends at a vertex A. Imagine traveling along the Euler circuit, from A all the way back to A, putting an arrow on each edge in our direction of travel. (Of course, we travel along each edge exactly once.)

Now consider any vertex B in the graph. It has edges joined to it, each with an arrow. Some of the arrows point toward B, some point away from B. The number of arrows pointing toward B is the same as the number of arrows pointing away from B, for every time we visit B, we come in on one unused edge and leave via a different unused edge. In other words, we can pair off the edges joined to B, with each pair having one arrow pointing toward B and one arrow pointing away from B. Thus, the total number of edges joined to B must be an even number, and, therefore, the degree of B is even. A similar argument shows that our starting vertex, A, also has even degree.

The following is from Euler's paper on the **Königsberg bridge problem:** "I was told that while some denied the possibility of doing this and others were in doubt, no one maintained that it was actually possible. On the basis of the above, I formulated the following very general problem for myself: Given any configuration of the river and the branches into which it may divide, as well as any number of bridges, to determine whether or not it is possible to cross each bridge exactly once." (*Source:* Newman, James R. (ed.), "The Königsberg Bridges," *Scientific American,* July 1953, in *Readings from Scientific American: Mathematics in the Modern World,* 1968.)

By 1875 a new bridge had been built in Königsberg, joining the land areas we labeled C and D in **Figure 21**. It was now possible for a citizen of Königsberg to take a walk that used each bridge exactly once, provided he or she started at A and ended at B, or vice versa.

The second part of Euler's theorem states the following:

*If each vertex of a connected graph has even degree,
then the graph has an Euler circuit.*

To show that this is true, we will provide a recipe (Fleury's algorithm) for finding an Euler circuit in any such graph. First, however, we consider more examples of how Euler's theorem can be applied.

EXAMPLE 2 Using Euler's Theorem

Decide which of the graphs in **Figure 24** has an Euler circuit. Justify your answers.

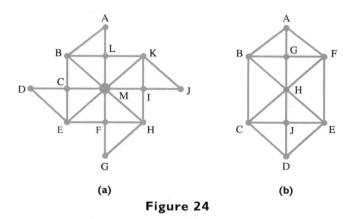

(a)   (b)

Figure 24

SOLUTION

(a) The graph in **Figure 24(a)** is connected. If we write the degree next to each vertex on the graph, as in **Figure 25**, we see that each vertex has even degree. Since the graph is connected, and each vertex has even degree, it follows from Euler's theorem that the graph has an Euler circuit.

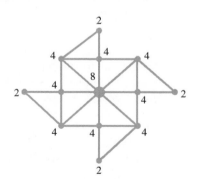

Figure 25

(b) In **Figure 24(b)**, check the degrees of the vertices. Note that vertex A has degree three, an odd degree. We need look no further. It follows from Euler's theorem that this connected graph does not have an Euler circuit. (All the other vertices in this graph except for D have even degree. However, if just one vertex has odd degree, then the graph does not have an Euler circuit.) ■■■

PROBLEM-SOLVING HINT When solving a challenging problem, it is useful to ask whether the problem is related to another problem that you already know how to solve. **Example 3** on the next page illustrates this strategy.

▮▮ **EXAMPLE 3** Tracing Patterns

**Beginning and ending at the same place, is it possible to trace the pattern shown in
Figure 26 below without lifting the pencil off the page and without tracing over any
part of the pattern (except isolated points) more than once?**

SOLUTION

The pattern in **Figure 26** is not a graph. (It has no vertices.) But what we are being
asked to do is very much like being asked to find an Euler circuit. So we imagine
that there are vertices at points where lines or curves of the pattern meet, obtaining
the graph in **Figure 27**.

Figure 26   **Figure 27**

Now we can use Euler's theorem to decide whether we can trace the pattern.
Vertex A has odd degree. Thus, by Euler's theorem, this graph does not have an
Euler circuit. It follows that we cannot trace the original pattern in the manner
required.   ▮▮▮

The tracing problem in **Example 3** illustrates a practical problem that occurs
when designing robotic arms to trace patterns. Automated machines that engrave
identification tags for pets require such a mechanical arm.

Fleury's Algorithm

Fleury's algorithm can be used to find an Euler circuit in any connected graph in which
each vertex has even degree. An algorithm is like a recipe—follow the steps and we
achieve what we need. Before introducing Fleury's algorithm, we need a definition.

> **Cut Edge**
>
> A **cut edge** in a graph is an edge whose removal disconnects a component of
> the graph.

We call such an edge a cut edge, since removing the edge *cuts* a connected piece
of a graph into two pieces.*

▮▮ **EXAMPLE 4** Identifying Cut Edges

Identify the cut edges in the graph in **Figure 28**.

Figure 28

The word **algorithm** comes from the
name of the Persian mathematician,
**Abu Ja'far Muhammad ibn Musa
Al-Khowârizmî,** who lived from about
A.D. 780 to A.D. 850. One of the books he
wrote was on the Hindu-Arabic system
of numerals (the system we use today),
and calculations using them. The Latin
translation of this book was called
Algoritmi de numero Indorum, meaning
"Al-Khowârizmî on the Hindu Art of
Reckoning."

---

*Some mathematicians use "bridge" instead of "cut edge" to describe such an edge.

SOLUTION

This graph has only one component, so we must look for edges whose removal would disconnect the graph.

DE is a cut edge. If we removed this edge, we would disconnect the graph into two components, obtaining the graph of **Figure 29(a)**. HG is also a cut edge. Its removal would disconnect the graph as shown in **Figure 29(b)**.

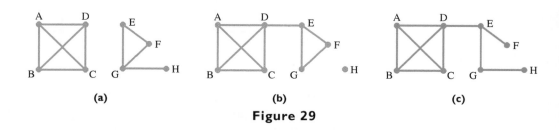

(a)   (b)   (c)

Figure 29

None of the other edges is a cut edge. We could remove any *one* of the other edges and still have a connected graph (that is, we would still have a path from each vertex of the graph to each other vertex). For example, if we remove edge GF, we end up with a graph that still is connected, as shown in **Figure 29(c)**.   ▮▮▮

Recall that Fleury's algorithm is for finding an Euler circuit in a connected graph in which each vertex has even degree.

Fleury's Algorithm

Step 1   Start at any vertex. Go along any edge from this vertex to another vertex. *Remove this edge from the graph.*

Step 2   You are now on a vertex of the revised graph. Choose any edge from this vertex, subject to only one condition: do not use a cut edge (*of the revised graph*) unless you have no other option. Go along your chosen edge. *Remove this edge from the graph.*

Step 3   Repeat Step 2 until you have used all the edges and returned to the vertex at which you started.

▮▮ **EXAMPLE 5** Using Fleury's Algorithm

Find an Euler circuit for the graph in **Figure 30**.

Figure 30

SOLUTION

First we must check that this graph does indeed have an Euler circuit. Check that the graph is connected and that each vertex has even degree.

The **Tshokwe people of northeastern Angola** have a tradition involving continuous patterns in sand. The tracings are called *sona* and they have ritual significance. They are used as mnemonics for stories about the gods and ancestors. Elders trace the drawings while telling the stories. The sona shown here is called *skin of a leopard*. The men draw the grid of dots first, as an aid to recalling the sona. *Source:* Gerdes, Paul. *Geometry from Africa – Mathematical and Educational Explorations.* Mathematical Association of America, 1999, p. 171.

We can start at any vertex. We choose C. We could go from C to B or from C to D. We go to D, removing the edge CD. (We show it scratched out, but we must think of this edge as gone.) Our path begins: C → D. The revised graph is shown in **Figure 31**.

Figure 31

Note that none of the edges DE, DF, or DG is a cut edge for our current graph, so we can choose to go along any one of these. We go from D to G, removing edge DG. So far, our path is C → D → G. (Be sure to keep a record of this path.) **Figure 32** shows the revised graph.

Figure 32

The remaining edges at G are GE, GF, and GH. Note, however, that GH is a cut edge for our revised graph, and we have other options. Thus, according to Fleury's algorithm, *we must not use GH at this stage.* (If we used GH now, we would never be able to get back to use the edges GF, GE, and so on.) We go from G to F. Our path is C → D → G → F, and we show our revised graph in **Figure 33**.

Figure 33

Now we have only one edge from F, namely, FD. This is a cut edge of the revised graph, but *since we have no other option* we may use this edge. Our path is C → D → G → F → D, and our revised graph is shown in **Figure 34**.

Figure 34

We have only one edge left at D, namely DE. It is a cut edge of the remaining graph, but since we have no other option, we may use it.

It is now clear how to complete the Euler circuit. (Be sure to return to the starting vertex.) The complete Euler circuit is:

$$C \rightarrow D \rightarrow G \rightarrow F \rightarrow D \rightarrow E \rightarrow G \rightarrow H \rightarrow B \rightarrow C.$$ ▮▮▮

If we start with a connected graph with all vertices having even degree, then Fleury's algorithm will always produce an Euler circuit for the graph. ***Note that a graph that has an Euler circuit always has more than one Euler circuit.***

Even for a large graph, a computer can successfully apply Fleury's algorithm. This is not the case for all algorithms. (See **For Further Thought** on The Speed of Algorithms on **page 827**.)

Euler circuits have many practical applications. Consider planning a route for mail delivery. **Figure 35** shows a map of a rural district. In rural areas, mailboxes are placed along the same side of a road, so the mail delivery vehicle needs to travel along the road in one direction only. Suppose the roads off the main road in **Figure 35** show a mail delivery region.

Figure 35

It would be ideal if the mail carrier could find an Euler circuit covering the delivery route. If such a circuit existed, it would minimize the distance traveled for the delivery. A glance at the map (thinking of road intersections as vertices) reveals that there is no Euler circuit for this route.

As the next best thing, the delivery vehicle should retrace its path as little as possible. For simplicity, we assume that the time to travel any of the stretches of road when not delivering mail is roughly the same. In **Figure 36**, we added dotted edges to indicate stretches of road to be covered twice. For this delivery route, it is easy to see that we effectively inserted as few edges as possible to obtain a graph that has an Euler circuit.

Figure 36

Now we can use Fleury's algorithm to find an Euler circuit on the graph in **Figure 36**, and this will give the most efficient route for mail delivery.

There are additional complications for mechanical brooms for **street sweeping.**

1. The mechanical brooms have to travel along each curb, in the direction of traffic flow (and some streets are one-way).

2. It takes time to switch the brooms from one side of the vehicle to the other.

3. Sweeping has to be coordinated with city parking so that there are no parked cars when sweeping is to be done.

For a simple delivery area such as this, it is not hard to choose an efficient route intuitively. For route planning in large cities, however, the techniques of this section offer significant savings on services such as mail delivery, mechanized street sweeping, snowplowing, and electric meter checking. In the 1980s a computerized system for planning street sweeping in Washington, D.C., resulted in a 20% savings. In large cities the street sweeping budget is tens of millions of dollars, so savings of 20% easily justify the initial cost of setting up a computerized system.

The study of Euler circuits began in the eighteenth century with a little mathematical puzzle, but the ideas developed provide efficient management techniques for our complex modern cities.

15.2 EXERCISES

In Exercises 1–3, a graph is shown and some sequences of vertices are specified. Determine which of these sequences show Euler circuits. If not, explain why not.

1.

(a) $A \to B \to C \to D \to A \to B \to C \to D \to A$

(b) $C \to B \to A \to D \to C$

(c) $A \to C \to D \to B \to A$

(d) $A \to B \to C \to D$

2.

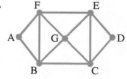

(a) $A \to B \to C \to D \to E \to F \to A$

(b) $F \to B \to D \to B$

(c) $A \to B \to C \to D \to E \to$
$F \to B \to D \to F \to A$

(d) $A \to B \to F \to D \to B \to C \to D \to$
$E \to F \to A$

3.

(a) $A \to B \to C \to D \to E \to F \to A$

(b) $A \to B \to C \to D \to E \to G \to C \to E \to$
$F \to G \to B \to F \to A$

(c) $A \to B \to C \to D \to E \to C \to G \to E \to$
$F \to G \to E \to F \to A$

(d) $A \to B \to G \to E \to D \to C \to G \to F \to$
$B \to C \to E \to F \to A$

In Exercises 4–8, use Euler's theorem to decide whether the graph has an Euler circuit. (Do not actually find an Euler circuit.) Justify each answer briefly.

4.

5.

6.

7.

8.

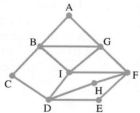

In Exercises 9 and 10, use Euler's theorem to determine whether it is possible to begin and end at the same place, trace the pattern without lifting your pencil, and trace over no line in the pattern more than once.

9.

10.

In Exercises 11–15, use Euler's theorem to determine whether the graph has an Euler circuit, justifying each answer. Then determine whether the graph has a circuit that visits each vertex exactly once, except that it returns to its starting vertex. If so, write down the circuit. (There may be more than one correct answer.)

11.

12.

13.

14.

15.

In Exercises 16–19, different floor tilings are shown. The material applied between tiles is called grout. For which of these floor tilings could the grout be applied beginning and ending at the same place, without going over any joint twice, and without lifting the tool? Justify each answer.

16.

17.

18.

19.

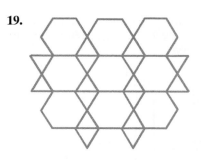

In Exercises 20–22, identify all cut edges in the graph. If there are none, say so.

20.

21.

22.

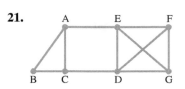

In Exercises 23–25, a graph is shown for which a student has been asked to find an Euler circuit starting at A. The student's revisions of the graph after the first few steps of Fleury's algorithm are shown, and in each case the student is now at B. For each graph, determine all edges that Fleury's algorithm permits the student to use for the next step.

23.

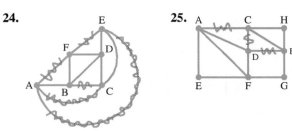

24.

25.

In Exercises 26–28, use Fleury's algorithm to find an Euler circuit for the graph, beginning and ending at A. (There are many different correct answers.)

26.

27.

28.

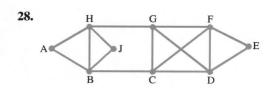

In Exercises 29–31, use Euler's theorem to determine whether the graph has an Euler circuit. If not, explain why not. If the graph does have an Euler circuit, use Fleury's algorithm to find an Euler circuit for the graph. (There are many different correct answers.)

29.

30.

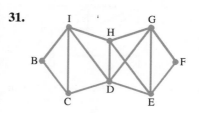

31.

32. *Garden Design* The graph below shows the layout of the paths in a botanical garden. The edges represent the paths. Has the garden been designed in such a way that it is possible for a visitor to find a route that begins and ends at the entrance to the garden (represented by the vertex A) and that goes along each path exactly once? If so, use Fleury's algorithm to find such a route.

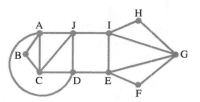

33. *Parking Pattern* The map shows the roads on which parking is permitted at a national monument. This is a pay and display facility. A security guard has the task of periodically checking that all parked vehicles have a valid parking ticket displayed. He is based at the central complex, labeled A. Is there a route that he can take to walk along each of the roads exactly once, beginning and ending at A? If so, use Fleury's algorithm to find such a route.

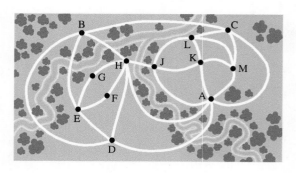

Building Floor Plans *In Exercises 34–36, the floor plan of a building is shown. For which of these is it possible to start outside, walk through each door exactly once, and end up back outside? Justify each answer. (Hint: Think of the rooms and "outside" as the vertices of a graph, and the doors as the edges of the graph.)*

34.

35.

36.

Exercises 37–44 are based on the following theorem:

1. ***If a graph has an Euler path that begins and ends at different vertices, then these two vertices are the only vertices with odd degree. (All the rest have even degree.)***

2. ***If exactly two vertices in a connected graph have odd degree, then the graph has an Euler path beginning at one of these vertices and ending at the other.***

In Exercises 37–40, determine whether the graph has an Euler path that begins and ends at different vertices. Justify your answer. If the graph has such a path, say at which vertices the path must begin and end.

37.

38.

39.

40.

Building Floor Plans *In Exercises 41–43, refer to the floor plan indicated, and determine whether it is possible to start in one of the rooms of the building, walk through each door exactly once, and end up in a different room from the one you started in. Justify each answer.*

41. Refer to the floor plan shown in **Exercise 34.**

42. Refer to the floor plan shown in **Exercise 35.**

43. Refer to the floor plan shown in **Exercise 36.**

44. *New York City Bridges*   The accompanying schematic map shows a portion of the New York City area, including tunnels and bridges.

(a) Is it possible to take a drive around the New York City area using each tunnel and bridge exactly once, beginning and ending in the same place?

(b) Is it possible to take a drive around the New York City area using each tunnel and bridge exactly once, beginning and ending in different places? If so, where must the drive begin and end?

In Exercises 45–47, the graph does not have an Euler circuit. For each graph find a circuit that uses as many edges as possible. (There is more than one correct answer in each case.) How many edges did you use in the circuit?

45.

46.

47.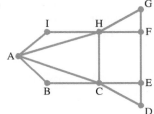

48. There are only five regular polyhedra: the cube, the tetrahedron, the octahedron, the dodecahedron, and the icosahedron. (See **Chapter 9.**) For which of these can you trace your finger along each edge exactly once, beginning and ending at the same vertex? Justify your answer using the ideas developed in this section.

49. Which *complete graphs* have Euler circuits? Justify your answer carefully.

50. Write a paper on the sand tracings of the Bushoong or Tshokwe people.

Hamilton Circuits • Minimum Hamilton Circuits • Brute Force Algorithm
• Nearest Neighbor Algorithm

Hamilton Circuits

In this section we examine *Hamilton circuits* in graphs. The story of Hamilton circuits is a story of very large numbers and of unsolved problems in both mathematics and computer science.

We start with a game, called the Icosian game, invented by Irish mathematician William Hamilton in the mid-nineteenth century. It uses a wooden board marked with the graph shown in **Figure 37**.

Dodecahedron

Hamilton sold the **Icosian game** idea to a games dealer for 25 British pounds. It went on the market in 1859, but it was not a huge success. A later version of the game, *A Voyage Around the World*, consisted of a regular dodecahedron with pegs at each of the 20 vertices. The vertices had names such as Brussels, Delhi, and Zanzibar. The aim was to travel to all vertices along the edges of the dodecahedron, visiting each vertex exactly once. We can show the vertices and edges of a dodecahedron precisely as in **Figure 37**.

The Icosian Game

Figure 37

The game includes 20 pegs numbered 1 through 20. (The word *Icosian* comes from the Greek word for 20.) At each vertex of the graph there is a hole for a peg.

The simplest version of the game is as follows: Put the pegs into the holes in order, following along the edges of the graph, in such a way that peg 20 ends up in a hole that is joined by an edge to the hole of peg 1. Try this now, numbering the vertices in the graph in **Figure 37**, starting at vertex 1.

The Icosian game asks that we find a circuit in the graph, but the circuit need not be an Euler circuit. The circuit must visit each *vertex* exactly once, except for returning to the starting vertex to complete the circuit. (The circuit may or may not travel all edges of the graph.) Circuits such as this are called *Hamilton circuits*.

> **Hamilton Circuit**
>
> A **Hamilton circuit** in a graph is a circuit that visits each vertex exactly once (returning to the starting vertex to complete the circuit).

▌▌ **EXAMPLE 1** Identifying Hamilton Circuits

Which of the following are Hamilton circuits for the graph in **Figure 38**? Justify your answers briefly.

(a) $A \rightarrow B \rightarrow E \rightarrow D \rightarrow C \rightarrow F \rightarrow A$

(b) $A \rightarrow B \rightarrow C \rightarrow D \rightarrow E \rightarrow F \rightarrow C \rightarrow$
$E \rightarrow B \rightarrow F \rightarrow A$

(c) $B \rightarrow C \rightarrow D \rightarrow E \rightarrow F \rightarrow B$

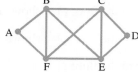

Figure 38

SOLUTION

(a) $A \rightarrow B \rightarrow E \rightarrow D \rightarrow C \rightarrow F \rightarrow A$ is a Hamilton circuit for the graph. It visits each vertex of the graph exactly once, and then returns to the starting vertex. (Trace this circuit on the graph to check it.)

(b) $A \rightarrow B \rightarrow C \rightarrow D \rightarrow E \rightarrow F \rightarrow C \rightarrow E \rightarrow B \rightarrow F \rightarrow A$ is not a Hamilton circuit, since it visits vertex B (and vertices C, E, and F) more than once. (This is, however, an Euler circuit for the graph.)

(c) $B \rightarrow C \rightarrow D \rightarrow E \rightarrow F \rightarrow B$ is not a Hamilton circuit since it does not visit all vertices in the graph. ■ ■ ■

Figure 39

Figure 40

Some graphs, such as the graph in **Figure 39**, do not have a Hamilton circuit. There is no way to visit all the vertices and return to the starting vertex without visiting vertex I more times than allowed.

It can be difficult to determine whether a particular graph has a Hamilton circuit, since there is no theorem that gives necessary and sufficient conditions for a Hamilton circuit to exist. This remains an unsolved problem in Hamilton circuits. (Contrast the simple method provided by Euler's theorem for checking whether a graph has an Euler circuit.)

Fortunately, in many real-world applications of Hamilton circuits we are dealing with complete graphs, and any complete graph with three or more vertices does have a Hamilton circuit. (Recall our discussion of complete graphs in **Section 15.1**.) For example,

$$A \rightarrow B \rightarrow C \rightarrow D \rightarrow E \rightarrow F \rightarrow A$$

is a Hamilton circuit for the complete graph shown in **Figure 40**. We could form a Hamilton circuit for any complete graph with three or more vertices in a similar way.

Hamilton Circuits for Complete Graphs

Any complete graph with three or more vertices has a Hamilton circuit.

The Tutte graph, shown here, has no Hamilton circuit. This graph has a history connected to the four-color problem for map coloring (**Section 15.1**). In 1880 Peter Tate provided a "proof" for the four-color theorem. It was based on the assumption that every connected graph, with all vertices of degree three, and which can be drawn with edges crossing nowhere except at vertices, has a Hamilton circuit. But in 1946, Tutte produced the graph shown here, showing that Tate's basic assumption was wrong, and his proof was, therefore, invalid.

The graph in **Figure 40** has many Hamilton circuits. Try finding some that are different from the one given earlier.

How many Hamilton circuits does a complete graph have? Before we count, we need an agreement about when two sequences of vertices will be considered to be *different* Hamilton circuits. For example, the Hamilton circuits

$$B \rightarrow C \rightarrow D \rightarrow E \rightarrow F \rightarrow A \rightarrow B \quad \text{and} \quad A \rightarrow B \rightarrow C \rightarrow D \rightarrow E \rightarrow F \rightarrow A$$

visit the vertices in essentially the same order in the graph in **Figure 40**, although the sequences start with different vertices. If we mark the circuit on the graph, we can describe it starting at any vertex. For our purposes, it is convenient to consider the two sequences above as representing the same Hamilton circuit.

When Hamilton Circuits Are the Same

Hamilton circuits that differ *only* in their starting points will be considered to be the same circuit.

PROBLEM-SOLVING HINT Tree diagrams are often useful for counting.

We begin by counting the number of Hamilton circuits in a complete graph with four vertices. (See **Figure 41**.) We can use the same starting point for all the circuits we count. We choose A as the starting point. From A we can go to any of the three remaining vertices (B, C, or D). No matter which vertex we choose, we then have two unvisited vertices for our next choice. Then there is only one way to complete the Hamilton circuit. We illustrate this counting procedure in **Figure 42**.

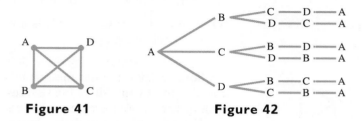

Figure 41   **Figure 42**

The tree diagram in **Figure 42** shows that we have $3 \cdot 2 \cdot 1$ Hamilton circuits in the graph. We write this as 3! (read "3 factorial"). See **Chapter 10**.

Returning to **Figure 40**, we can count the number of Hamilton circuits in the complete graph with 6 vertices. Start at vertex A. From A we can proceed to any of the five remaining vertices. No matter which we choose, we then have four choices for the next vertex along the circuit, three choices for the next, and two for the next. (We could draw a counting tree for this, but it would be rather large.) This means that we have

$$5 \cdot 4 \cdot 3 \cdot 2 \cdot 1 = 5! \quad \text{different Hamilton circuits in all.}$$

Likewise, we would find that a complete graph with 10 vertices has 9! Hamilton circuits. In general, for a complete graph the number of Hamilton circuits in the graph can be obtained by calculating the factorial of the number that is one less than the number of vertices.

Number of Hamilton Circuits in a Complete Graph

A complete graph with n vertices has $(n-1)!$ Hamilton circuits.

As the number of vertices in a complete graph increases, the number of Hamilton circuits for that graph increases very quickly. Previously we considered how quickly exponential functions increase. Factorials increase quickly as well. For example,

$$25! = 15,511,210,043,330,985,984,000,000,$$

or approximately 1.6×10^{25}—more than a trillion trillion.

Minimum Hamilton Circuits

Consider that on a typical day, a UPS van might have to make deliveries to 100 different locations. For simplicity, assume that none are priority deliveries, so they can be made in any order. UPS wants to minimize the time to make these deliveries. Think of the 100 locations and the UPS distribution center as the vertices of a complete graph with 101 vertices.

In principle, the van can go from any of these locations directly to any other, shown by having an edge between each pair of vertices. Suppose we estimate the travel time between each pair of locations (of course, this would depend on distance and traffic conditions along the route). These estimates provide weights on the edges of the graph. The objective is to visit each location exactly once, to begin and end at the same place, and to take as little time as possible.

Traveling Salesman Problems and Archaeology Archaeologists often excavate sites in which there is no clear evidence to show which deposits were made earlier, and which later. Some archaeologists have used minimum Hamilton circuits to solve the problem. For example, if a site consists of a number of burials, they consider a complete graph with vertices representing the various burials, and weights on the edges corresponding roughly to how dissimilar the burials are. A minimum Hamilton circuit in this graph gives the best guess for the order in which the deposits were made.

In graph theory terms, we need a Hamilton circuit for the graph that has *least possible total weight.* The **total weight** of a circuit is the sum of the weights on the edges in the circuit. We call such a circuit a *minimum Hamilton circuit* for the graph.

Minimum Hamilton Circuit

In a weighted graph, a **minimum Hamilton circuit** is a Hamilton circuit with least possible total weight.

A problem whose solution requires us to find a minimum Hamilton circuit for a complete, weighted graph often is called a **traveling salesman problem** (or TSP). (See also the **Chapter 10 Collaborative Investigation.**) Think of the vertices of the complete graph as the cities that a salesperson must visit and the weights on the edges as the cost of traveling directly between the cities. To minimize costs, the salesperson needs a minimum Hamilton circuit for the graph.

Traveling salesman problems are relevant to efficient routing of telephone calls and Internet connections. As another example, to manufacture integrated circuit silicon chips, many lines have to be etched on a silicon wafer. Minimizing production time involves deciding the order in which to etch the lines, a traveling salesman problem. Likewise, to manufacture circuit boards for integrated circuits, laser-drilled holes must be made for connections. Again, the order for drilling the holes is a critical factor in production time.

Brute Force Algorithm

Suppose we are given a complete, weighted graph. How can we find a minimum Hamilton circuit for the graph? One way is to systematically list all the Hamilton circuits in the graph, find the total weight of each, and choose a circuit with least total weight. (In fact, it is sufficient to add up the weights on the edges for just half of the Hamilton circuits, since the total weight of a circuit is the same as the total weight of the circuit that uses the same edges in reverse order.)

The method just described is sometimes called the **brute force algorithm** since we find the solution by checking *all* the Hamilton circuits.

Brute Force Algorithm

Step 1 Choose a starting point.
Step 2 List all the Hamilton circuits with that starting point.
Step 3 Find the total weight of each circuit.
Step 4 Choose a Hamilton circuit with least total weight.

EXAMPLE 2 Using the Brute Force Algorithm

Find a minimum Hamilton circuit for the complete, weighted graph shown in **Figure 43**.

SOLUTION

Choose a starting point, A. List all the Hamilton circuits starting at A. Since this is a complete graph with 4 vertices, there are

$$3! = 3 \cdot 2 \cdot 1 = 6 \text{ circuits.}$$

Thus, we must find 6 Hamilton circuits.

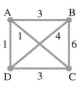

Figure 43

A   3   B

1   3   C

Figure 43 (repeated)

We need a systematic way of writing down all the Hamilton circuits. The counting tree of **Figure 43** provides a guide. We start by finding all the Hamilton circuits that begin A → B, then include those that begin A → C, and finally include those that begin A → D, as shown below. Once all the Hamilton circuits are listed, pair those that visit the vertices in precisely opposite orders. (Circuits in these pairs have the same total weight. This will save some adding.) Finally, determine the sum of the weights in each circuit.

Circuit	Total weight of the circuit
1. A → B → C → D → A	3 + 6 + 3 + 1 = 13
2. A → B → D → C → A	3 + 4 + 3 + 1 = 11 Minimum
3. A → C → B → D → A	1 + 6 + 4 + 1 = 12
4. A → C → D → B → A (opposite of 2)	11
5. A → D → B → C → A (opposite of 3)	12
6. A → D → C → B → A (opposite of 1)	13

We can now see that A → B → D → C → A is a minimum Hamilton circuit for the graph. The weight of this circuit is 11. ▮▮▮

In principle, the brute force algorithm provides a way to find a minimum Hamilton circuit in any complete, weighted graph. In practice, it takes far too long to obtain a complete, weighted graph with 7 vertices. There are 6!, or 720, Hamilton circuits in the graph, and we would have to calculate the total weight for half of these. That means we would have to do 360 separate calculations, in addition to listing the Hamilton circuits.

Most real-world problems involve a great deal more than 7 vertices. Manufacturing a large integrated circuit can involve a graph with almost one million vertices. Likewise, telecommunications companies routinely deal with graphs with millions of vertices. As the number of vertices in the graph increases, the task of finding a minimum Hamilton circuit using the brute force algorithm soon becomes too time-consuming for even our fastest computers. For example, if one of today's supercomputers had started using the brute force algorithm on a 100-vertex traveling salesman problem when the universe was created, it would still be far from done.

In contrast, Fleury's algorithm for finding an Euler circuit in a graph does not take too long for our computers, even for rather large graphs. Algorithms that do not take too much computer time are called **efficient algorithms.** Computer scientists have so far been unable to find an efficient algorithm for the traveling salesman problem, and they suspect that it is simply impossible to create such an algorithm.

The traveling salesman problem is just one of a collection of problems for which there is no known efficient algorithm. Many of these unsolved problems are related in such a way that an efficient algorithm for solving any one of them could be adapted to solve all of them. Probably the most important unsolved problem in computer science is either to find an efficient algorithm for the traveling salesman problem or to explain why no one could create such an algorithm. (We often refer to this as the P = NP problem.)

For the traveling salesman problem, there are some algorithms that do not take too much computer time and that give *reasonably good* solutions *most of the time.* Such algorithms are called **approximate algorithms,** since they give an approximate solution to the problem. We shall consider one such algorithm for the traveling salesman problem. The underlying idea is that from each vertex we proceed to a "nearest" available vertex.

William Rowan Hamilton (1805–1865) spent most of his life in Dublin, Ireland. He was good friends with the poet William Wordsworth, whom he met while touring England and Scotland. Hamilton tried writing poetry, but Wordsworth tactfully suggested that his talents were in mathematics rather than poetry. Catherine Disney was the first great love of his life, but under pressure from her parents, she married another man, much wealthier than Hamilton. Hamilton never seemed to quite get over this.

NP complete is a technical term in computer science describing problems for which all known algorithms take way too much time for large graphs for even the fastest imaginable computers. The traveling salesman problem and determining the chromatic number of a graph are NP complete. The popular puzzle SUDOKU also is in the class of NP complete problems.

Nearest Neighbor Algorithm

> **Nearest Neighbor Algorithm**
>
> ***Step 1*** Choose a starting point for the circuit. Call this vertex A.
>
> ***Step 2*** Check all the edges joined to A, and choose one that has least weight. Proceed along this edge to the next vertex.
>
> ***Step 3*** At each vertex you reach, check the edges from there *to vertices not yet visited*. Choose one with least weight. Proceed along this edge to the next vertex.
>
> ***Step 4*** Repeat Step 3 until you have visited all the vertices.
>
> ***Step 5*** Return to the starting vertex.

▐ EXAMPLE 3 Using the Nearest Neighbor Algorithm

A courier is based at the head office (A) and must deliver documents to four other offices (B, C, D, and E). The estimated time of travel (in minutes) between each of these offices is shown on the graph in **Figure 44**. The courier wants to visit the locations in an order that takes the least time. Use the nearest neighbor algorithm to find an approximate solution to this problem. Calculate the total time required to cover the chosen route.

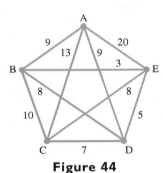

Figure 44   **Figure 45**

SOLUTION

Step 1 Choose a starting point. Let's start at A.

Step 2 Choose an edge with least weight joined to A. Both AB and AD have weight 9, which is less than the weights of the other two edges joined to A. We choose AD* and keep a record of the circuit as we form it.

$$A \xrightarrow{9} D$$

To help ensure that we do not visit a vertex twice, we number the vertices as we visit them and color the edges used, as in **Figure 45**.

Continue to number the vertices as we work through the rest of the solution.

Step 3 Now check edges joined to D, excluding DA (since we have already been to A). DC has weight 7, DB has weight 8, and DE has weight 5. DE has smallest weight, so proceed along DE to E. Our circuit begins this way.

$$A \xrightarrow{9} D \xrightarrow{5} E$$

---

*If using a computer to do this, we would instruct the computer to make a random choice between AB and AD.

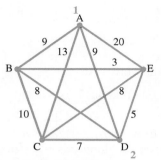

Figure 45 (repeated)

Step 4 Now repeat the process at E. Check all edges from E that go to a vertex not yet visited. EC has weight 8 and EB has weight 3. Proceed along EB to B. Our circuit so far is as follows.

$$A \xrightarrow{9} D \xrightarrow{5} E \xrightarrow{3} B$$

Step 5 We have one vertex not yet visited, C. We go next to C and now have visited all the vertices. We return to our starting point, A. Our Hamilton circuit is

$$A \xrightarrow{9} D \xrightarrow{5} E \xrightarrow{3} B \xrightarrow{10} C \xrightarrow{13} A.$$

Its total weight is $9 + 5 + 3 + 10 + 13 = 40$.

Our advice to the courier would thus be to visit the offices in the order shown in this circuit. This route will take about 40 minutes. ▪▪▪

We might think that we could get a quicker route for the courier just by looking at the graph, rather than following the rules of the algorithm. We would be right. The circuit we found in **Example 3** is not the minimum Hamilton circuit for the graph in **Figure 44**. (See below.) However, the point of an approximate algorithm is that a computer can implement it without taking too much time, and most of the time it will give a reasonably good solution to the problem.

If we had a computer performing the nearest neighbor algorithm for us, we could make a small adjustment that would give better results without taking too much longer. We could repeat the nearest neighbor algorithm for all possible starting points, and then choose from these the Hamilton circuit with least weight. If we do this for the example above, we obtain the results in **Table 1**.

Table 1

Starting Vertex	Circuit Using Nearest Neighbor	Total Weight
A	A → D → E → B → C → A	$9 + 5 + 3 + 10 + 13 = 40$
B	B → E → D → C → A → B	$3 + 5 + 7 + 13 + 9 = 37$
C	C → D → E → B → A → C	$7 + 5 + 3 + 9 + 13 = 37$
D	D → E → B → A → C → D	$5 + 3 + 9 + 13 + 7 = 37$
E	E → B → D → C → A → E	$3 + 8 + 7 + 13 + 20 = 51$

With this information, we would recommend to the courier that he use a circuit with total weight 37, for example the circuit

$$D \rightarrow E \rightarrow B \rightarrow A \rightarrow C \rightarrow D.$$

This does not force him to start his journey at D. If he followed the route

$$A \rightarrow C \rightarrow D \rightarrow E \rightarrow B \rightarrow A,$$

he would be using the same edges as in $D \rightarrow E \rightarrow B \rightarrow A \rightarrow C \rightarrow D$, and his traveling time still would be 37 minutes.

Can we now be sure that we have found the minimum Hamilton circuit for the graph in **Figure 45**? No. This is still an *approximate* solution. If we check the total weights of all possible Hamilton circuits in the graph, we find the Hamilton circuit

$$A \xrightarrow{9} B \xrightarrow{3} E \xrightarrow{8} C \xrightarrow{7} D \xrightarrow{9} A$$

with total weight just 36 minutes. The nearest neighbor algorithm simply will not find this minimum Hamilton circuit for the graph. However, all we expect of an approximate algorithm is that it give a reasonably good solution for the problem in a reasonable amount of time.

Records for Traveling Salesman Problems There is a race on to set records for exact solutions to traveling salesman problems. Computer scientists do this by using parallel processing and more sophisticated algorithms (all still exponential time algorithms—see **For Further Thought** on The Speed of Algorithms). The illustration shows the exact solution to a traveling salesman problem with 3038 vertices on a printed circuit board, obtained in 1993.

Here are some of the other records, showing the year each was set and the number of vertices in the graph.

1980: 318
1987: 666
1994: 7397
1998: 13,509
2001: 15,112
2004: 24,978
2006: 85,900

Source: www.tsp.gatech.edu/index.html

For Further Thought

The Speed of Algorithms

How do computer scientists classify the speed of algorithms? First, they write the number of steps a computer using the algorithm takes to solve a problem as a function of the "size" of the problem. We can think of the size of the problem as the number of vertices in the graph.

Let's suppose that our graph has n vertices. For some algorithms the number of steps is a **polynomial function of n,** for example $n^4 + 2n$. For other algorithms, the number of steps is an **exponential function of n,** for example 2^n. (See **Chapters 7 and 8** for more on polynomial and exponential functions.) As n increases, the number of steps increases much faster for exponential functions than for polynomial functions. Functions that involve factorials increase even faster.

In the table below we show approximate values for functions of the three types for different values of n. (We use scientific notation to make it easier to compare the sizes of the numbers.)

n	n^4	2^n	$n!$
5	6.3×10^2	3.2×10	1.2×10^2
10	1.0×10^4	1.0×10^3	3.6×10^6
15	5.1×10^4	3.3×10^4	1.3×10^{12}
20	1.6×10^5	1.0×10^6	2.4×10^{18}
25	3.9×10^5	3.4×10^7	1.6×10^{25}
30	8.1×10^5	1.1×10^9	2.7×10^{32}
40	2.6×10^6	1.1×10^{12}	8.2×10^{47}
50	6.3×10^6	1.1×10^{15}	3.0×10^{64}

In the first line of the table (where $n = 5$), n^4 gives the largest value. But as n gets larger, 2^n grows much faster than n^4, while $n!$ grows extremely fast. For example, if we double the size of n from 15 to 30, n^4 becomes a little more than 10 times as large, 2^n becomes about

3×10^4 or 30,000 times as large, while $n!$ becomes approximately 2×10^{20} times as large. 10^{20} is more than a billion billion.

Algorithms whose time functions grow no faster than a polynomial function are called **polynomial time algorithms.** These are *efficient* algorithms—they do not take too much computer time.

Algorithms whose time functions grow faster than any polynomial function are called **exponential time algorithms.** These are *not efficient* algorithms. They are by nature too time-consuming for our computers. Our silicon chip computers are getting faster each year, but even this increase in speed hardly puts a dent in the time required for a computer to implement an exponential time algorithm for a very large graph.

Because the brute force algorithm for the traveling salesman problem has a time function involving $n!$, which grows faster than an exponential function of n, this algorithm is an exponential time algorithm.

For Group or Individual Investigation

Use the table to help answer these questions:

1. By approximately what factor does n^4 grow if we double n from 10 to 20?

2. By approximately what factor does 2^n grow if we double n from 10 to 20?

3. By approximately what factor does $n!$ grow if we double n from 10 to 20?

4. Repeat Exercises 1–3 if we double n from 25 to 50.

5. Suppose it would take 2^{30} years using computers at their present speeds to solve a certain problem. (2^{30} is a little over one billion.) If we assume that computers double in speed each year, how long would we have to wait before we could solve the problem in 1 year?

15.3 EXERCISES

In Exercises 1 and 2, a graph is shown, and some paths in the graph are specified. Determine which paths are Hamilton circuits for the graph. If not, say why not.

1.

(a) $A \rightarrow E \rightarrow C \rightarrow D \rightarrow E \rightarrow B \rightarrow A$

(b) $A \rightarrow E \rightarrow C \rightarrow D \rightarrow B \rightarrow A$

(c) $D \rightarrow B \rightarrow E \rightarrow A \rightarrow B$

(d) $E \rightarrow D \rightarrow C \rightarrow B \rightarrow E$

2.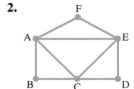

(a) $A \rightarrow B \rightarrow C \rightarrow D \rightarrow E \rightarrow C \rightarrow A \rightarrow E \rightarrow F \rightarrow A$

(b) $A \rightarrow C \rightarrow D \rightarrow E \rightarrow F \rightarrow A$

(c) $F \rightarrow A \rightarrow C \rightarrow E \rightarrow F$

(d) $C \rightarrow D \rightarrow E \rightarrow F \rightarrow A \rightarrow B$

In Exercises 3 and 4, determine whether each sequence of vertices is a circuit, whether it is an Euler circuit, and whether it is a Hamilton circuit. Justify your answers.

3.

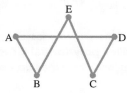

   (a) A → B → C → D → E → A

   (b) B → E → C → D → A → B

   (c) E → B → A → D → A → D → C → E

4.

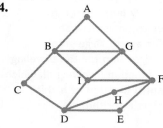

   (a) A → B → C → D → E → F → G → A

   (b) B → I → G → F → E → D → H → F → I → D → C → B → G → A → B

   (c) A → B → C → D → E → F → G → H → I → A

In Exercises 5–10, determine whether the graph has a Hamilton circuit. If so, find one. (There are many different correct answers.)

5.

6.

7.

8.

9.

10.

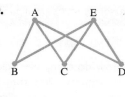

11. Draw a graph that has a Hamilton circuit but no Euler circuit. Specify the Hamilton circuit, and explain why the graph has no Euler circuit. (There are many different correct answers.)

12. Draw a graph that has an Euler circuit but no Hamilton circuit. Specify an Euler circuit in your graph. (There are many different correct answers.)

13. Draw a graph that has both an Euler circuit and a Hamilton circuit. Specify these circuits. (There are many different correct answers.)

14. Decide whether each statement is true or false. If the statement is false, give an example to show that it is false.

   (a) A Hamilton circuit for a graph must visit each vertex in the graph.

   (b) An Euler circuit for a graph must visit each vertex in the graph.

   (c) A Hamilton circuit for a graph must use each edge in the graph.

   (d) An Euler circuit for a graph must use each edge in the graph.

   (e) A circuit cannot be both a Hamilton circuit and an Euler circuit.

   (f) An Euler circuit must visit no vertex more than once, except the vertex where the circuit begins and ends.

In Exercises 15–20, determine whether an Euler circuit, a Hamilton circuit, or neither would solve the problem.

15. *Bandstands at a Festival* The vertices of a graph represent bandstands at a festival and the edges represent paths between the bandstands. A visitor wants to visit each bandstand exactly once, returning to her starting point when she is finished.

16. *Relay Team Running Order* The vertices of a complete graph represent the members of a five-person relay team. The team manager wants a circuit that will show the order in which the team members will run. (He will decide later who will start.)

17. *Paths in a Botanical Garden* The vertices of a graph represent places where paths in a botanical garden cross and the edges represent the paths. A visitor wants to walk along each path in the garden exactly once, returning to his starting point when finished.

18. *Traveling in Western Europe* The vertices of a graph represent the countries on the continent (Western Europe), with edges representing border crossings between the countries. A traveler wants to travel over each border crossing exactly once, returning to the first country visited for his flight home to the United States.

19. *Traveling in Africa* Vertices represent countries in sub-Saharan Africa, with an edge between two vertices if those countries have a common border. A traveler wants to visit each country exactly once, returning to the first country visited for her flight home to the United States.

20. *Reading X-Rays* In using X-rays to analyze the structure of crystals, an X-ray diffractometer measures the intensity of reflected radiation from the crystal in thousands of different positions. Consider the complete graph with vertices representing the positions where measurements must be taken. The researcher must decide the order in which to take these readings, with the diffractometer returning to its starting point when finished.

In Exercises 21–24, use a calculator, if necessary, to find the value.

21. 4!

22. 6!

23. 9!

24. 14!

In Exercises 25–28, determine how many Hamilton circuits there are in a complete graph with this number of vertices. (Leave answers in factorial notation.)

25. 10 vertices

26. 15 vertices

27. 18 vertices

28. 60 vertices

29. List all Hamilton circuits in the graph which start at P.

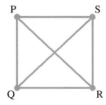

In Exercises 30–36, refer to the following graph. List all Hamilton circuits in the graph that start with the indicated vertices.

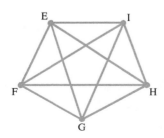

30. Starting E → F → G

31. Starting E → H → I

32. Starting E → I → H

33. Starting E → F

34. Starting E → I

35. Starting E → G

36. Starting at E

37. List all Hamilton circuits in the graph which start at A.

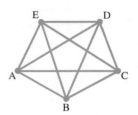

In Exercises 38–41, use the brute force algorithm to find a minimum Hamilton circuit for the graph. In each case determine the total weight of the minimum Hamilton circuit.

38.

39.

40.

41.

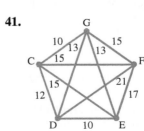

In Exercises 42–44, use the nearest neighbor algorithm starting at each of the indicated vertices to determine an approximate solution to the problem of finding a minimum Hamilton circuit for the graph. In each case, find the total weight of the circuit found.

42.

F — 5 — I, 2, 6, 4, 3, G — 7 — H

(a) Starting at F
(b) Starting at G
(c) Starting at H
(d) Starting at I

43.

E — 7 — D, 2, 5, 6, 8, 6, 3, 1, A, C, 4, 7, B

(a) Starting at A
(b) Starting at C
(c) Starting at D
(d) Starting at E

44.

A — 2.8 — F
1.6 1.7
2.5 1.9 3.2 4.1
1.97 2.3 2.7
B 3 2 E
2.4 1.95
C — 1.8 — D

(a) Starting at A   **(b)** Starting at B
(c) Starting at C   **(d)** Starting at D
(e) Starting at E   **(f)** Starting at F

45. Refer to the accompanying graph. Complete parts (a)–(c) in order.

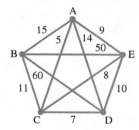

(a) Use the nearest neighbor algorithm starting at each of the vertices in turn to determine an approximate solution to the problem of finding a minimum Hamilton circuit for the graph. In each case, find the total weight of the circuit.

(b) Which of the circuits found in part (a) gives the best solution to the problem of finding a minimum Hamilton circuit for the graph?

(c) Just by looking carefully at the graph, find a Hamilton circuit in the graph that has lower total weight than any of the circuits found in part (a).

46. A graph is called a **complete bipartite graph** if the vertices can be separated into two groups in such a way that there are no edges between vertices in the same group, and there is an edge between each vertex in the first group and each vertex in the second group. An example is shown below.

The notation we use for these graphs is $K_{m,n}$ where m and n are the numbers of vertices in the two groups. For example, the graph shown in this exercise is $K_{4,3}$ (or $K_{3,4}$). Answer the following in order:

(a) Draw $K_{2,2}$, $K_{2,3}$, $K_{2,4}$, $K_{3,3}$, and $K_{4,4}$.

(b) For each of the graphs you have drawn in part (a), find a Hamilton circuit or say that the graph has no Hamilton circuit.

(c) Make a conjecture: What must be true about m and n for $K_{m,n}$ to have a Hamilton circuit?

(d) What must be true about m and n for $K_{m,n}$ to have an Euler circuit? Justify your answer.

In Exercises 47–50, find all Hamilton circuits in the graph which start at A. (Hint: Use counting trees.)

47.

48.

49.

50.

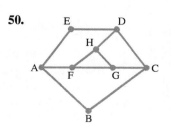

51. Paul A. M. Dirac proved the following theorem in 1952:

Suppose G is a (simple) graph with n vertices, n ≥ 3. If the degree of each vertex is greater than or equal to $\frac{n}{2}$, then the graph has a Hamilton circuit.

Refer to graphs (1)–(5) and answer parts (a)–(e) in order.

(1)

(2)

(3)

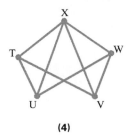

(4)

(5)

(a) Which of the graphs satisfy the condition that the degree of each vertex is greater than or equal to $\frac{n}{2}$?

(b) For which of the graphs can we conclude from **Dirac's theorem** that the graph has a Hamilton circuit?

(c) If a graph does *not* satisfy the condition that the degree of each vertex is greater than or equal to $\frac{n}{2}$, can we be sure that the graph does *not* have a Hamilton circuit? Justify your answer. (*Hint:* Study the accompanying graphs.)

(d) Is Dirac's theorem still true if $n < 3$? Justify your answer.

(e) Use Dirac's theorem to write a convincing argument that any complete graph with 3 or more vertices has a Hamilton circuit.

The graph below shows the Icosian game (described in the text) with the vertices labeled. In Exercises 52–54, find a Hamilton circuit for the graph in the specified version of the game. (We suggest you write numbers on the graph in the order in which you visit the vertices. There are different correct answers for these exercises.)

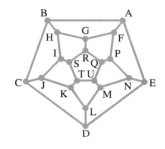

52. The circuit begins at A.

53. The circuit begins A → F.

54. The circuit begins A → B → H.

55. Refer to **Exercise 58** in **Section 15.1** for how one can analyze the rhyme scheme in poetry using graphs. Use this idea to write a paper on sestinas. Be sure to discuss what Hamilton circuits have to do with sestinas.

56. Find out what NP complete problems are, and write a paper on them. Include a careful description of at least one NP complete problem that is different from the traveling salesman problem.

15.4 TREES AND MINIMUM SPANNING TREES

Connected Graphs and Trees • Spanning Trees • Minimum Spanning Trees
• Kruskal's Algorithm • Number of Vertices and Edges

Connected Graphs and Trees

Consider a problem that Peggy has in her garden. She wants to install an underground irrigation system. The system must connect the faucet (F) to outlets at various points in the garden, specifically the rose bed (R), perennial bed (P), daffodil bed (D), annuals bed (A), berry patch (B), vegetable patch (V), cut flower bed (C), and shade bed (S). These are shown as the vertices of the graph in **Figure 46** on the next page.

In graph theory, the botanical words go beyond trees. A **forest** is a graph with all components trees, as shown here. Later in this section you will find the words **root** and **leaf** applied to graphs. The terms **pruning** and **separating** arise in applications of trees to computer analysis of images.

Figure 46

The irrigation system will have pipes connecting these points. For the irrigation system to work well, there should be as few pipes as possible connecting all the outlets.

Think about this problem in terms of a graph with edges representing pipes. Peggy wants water to flow from the faucet (F) to each of the outlets. This means that we need to create a *connected* graph that includes all the vertices in **Figure 46**. We discussed connected graphs in **Section 15.1.** Now that we are familiar with paths, we can give a definition more useful for our purposes here.

> **Connected Graph**
>
> A **connected graph** is one in which there is *at least one path* between each pair of vertices.

To see that this definition agrees with our earlier definition (on **page 794**), observe that if we select any pair of vertices in the connected graph in **Figure 47** (for example, A and C) then there is at least one path between them. (In fact, there are many paths between A and C.) Two examples are

$$A \rightarrow B \rightarrow E \rightarrow C$$

and

$$A \rightarrow F \rightarrow C.$$

Peggy needs a *connected* graph. Also she must use as few pipes as possible to connect all the outlets to the system. This means that the graph *must not contain any circuits.* If the graph had a circuit, we could remove one of the pipes in the circuit, and still have a connected system of pipes.

Figure 48 shows one possible solution to Peggy's problem.

Figure 47

Figure 48

There is a name for graphs that are connected and contain *no circuits.*

Benzene

It seems mathematician **Arthur Cayley** (see **page 835**) invented the term "tree" in graph theory in about 1857 in connection with problems related to counting all trees of certain types. Later he realized the relevancy of his work to nineteenth-century organic chemistry and in the 1870s published a note on this. Of course, not all molecules have treelike structures. Friedrich Kekulé's realization that the structure of benzene is *not* a tree is considered one of the most brilliant breakthroughs in organic chemistry.

> **Tree**
>
> We call a graph a **tree** if the graph is *connected* and contains *no circuits.*

All five of the graphs shown in **Figure 49** are trees.

All are trees.

Figure 49

In contrast, none of the graphs shown in **Figure 50** is a tree. The graph in **Figure 50(a)** is not a tree, because it is not connected. Those in **Figures 50(b) and (c)** are not trees, because each contains at least one circuit.

None are trees.

(a)   (b)   (c)

Figure 50

Unique Path Property of Trees

In a tree there is always **exactly one path** from each vertex in the graph to any other vertex in the graph.

For example, starting with vertices S and B in the tree in **Figure 48**, there is exactly one path from vertex S to vertex B, namely, $S \rightarrow A \rightarrow V \rightarrow B$.

This property follows from the definition of a tree. For as a tree is connected, there is always at least one path between each pair of vertices. Also, if the graph is a tree, there cannot be two different paths between a pair of vertices. If there were, these together would contain a circuit.

It is the unique path property of trees that makes them so important in real-world applications. This also is the reason trees are not a very useful model for telephone networks. Each edge of a tree is a cut edge, so failure along one link would disrupt the service. Telephone companies rely on networks with many circuits to provide alternative routes for calls.

▮▮ EXAMPLE 1 Renovating an Irrigation System

Joe has an old underground irrigation system in his garden, with connections at the faucet (F), outlets A through E in the garden, and existing underground pipes as shown in the graph in **Figure 51**. He wants to renovate this system, keeping only some of the pipes. Water must still be able to flow to each of the original outlets, and the graph of the irrigation system must be a tree. Design an irrigation system that meets Joe's objectives.

SOLUTION

In graph theory terms, we need a *subgraph* of the graph in **Figure 51**. Since water still must be able to flow to each of the original outlets, we need a connected subgraph that *includes all the vertices of the original graph*. Finally, this subgraph must be a *tree*. Thus, we must remove edges (but no vertices) from the graph, without disconnecting the graph, to obtain a subgraph that is a tree. One way to achieve this is shown in **Figure 52**. ▮▮▮

Just how fast are the fastest computers? Computer speeds are sometimes measured in **flops** (floating point operations per second). A speed of one gigaflop means that the computer can perform about one billion (10^9) calculations per second.

A modern desktop computer can perform at a few gigaflops. In 2009, the fastest computer was the Cray Jaguar, which could perform at almost 1800 teraflops. One teraflop is about one trillion (10^{12}) calculations per second. (*Source:* www.top500.org/lists.)

Figure 51

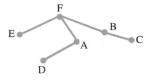

Figure 52

For Further Thought

Binary Coding

The unique path property of a tree can be used to make a code. We illustrate with a **binary code,** that is, one that uses 0s and 1s. (Recall from **Chapter 4** that when we represent numbers in binary form we use only the symbols 0 and 1.)

To set up the code we use a special kind of tree like that shown in the figure below. This tree is a **directed graph** (there are arrows on the edges). The vertex at the top (with no arrows pointing toward it) is called the **root** of the directed tree. The vertices with no arrows pointing away from them are called **leaves** of the directed tree. We label each leaf with a letter we want to encode. The diagram shown encodes only 8 letters, but we could easily draw a bigger tree with more leaves to represent more letters.

We now write a 0 on each branch that goes left and a 1 on each branch that goes right.

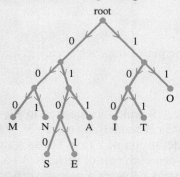

To show how the encoding works, we write the word MAT using the code. Follow the unique path from the root of the tree down to the appropriate leaf, noting in order the labels on the edges.

M is written 000.
A is written 011.
T is written 101.

So MAT is written 000011101.

We can easily translate this code using our tree. Let us see how we could decode 000011101. Referring to the tree, there is only one path from the root to a leaf that can give rise to those first three 0s, and that is the path leading to M. So we can begin to separate the code word into letters: 000–011101. Again following down from the root, the path 011 leads us unambiguously to A. So we have 000–011–101. The path 101 leads unambiguously to T.

The reason we can translate the string of 0s and 1s back to letters without ambiguity is that no letter has a code the same as the first part of the code for a different letter.

For Group Discussion

1. Use the binary encoding tree to write the binary code for each of the following words: ANT, SEAT

2. Use the encoding tree to find the word represented by each of the following codes: 0001111001 0100011101

3. Decode the following messages (commas are inserted to show separation of words).

   (a) 0110011010100, 100001, 1010101001101

   (b) 0101011101, 0001000011010100, 100001, 101100001

   (c) 011, 0000101011001, 1010101011000

   (d) 00001010101101, 0000101, 011101, 1010101011

Spanning Trees

Figure 52 (repeated)

A subgraph of the type shown in **Figure 52** from **Example 1** is called a *spanning tree* for the graph. This kind of subgraph "spans" the graph in the sense that it connects all the vertices of the original graph into a subgraph.

Spanning Tree

A **spanning tree** for a graph is a subgraph that includes every vertex of the original graph, and is a tree.

We can find a spanning tree for any connected graph (think about that) and, if the original graph has at least one circuit, it will have several different spanning trees.

EXAMPLE 2 Finding Spanning Trees

Consider the graph shown in **Figure 53**. Find two different spanning trees for the graph.

Figure 53

To obtain a tree, we must break the two circuits by removing a single edge from each.

SOLUTION

There are several choices for which edges to remove. We could remove edges CD and FH, leaving the subgraph in **Figure 54(a)**. Alternatively, we could remove edges ED and FG, leaving the subgraph in **Figure 54(b)**. There are other correct solutions.

(a)   (b)

Figure 54   ▮▮▮

If two spanning trees use different edges from the original graph, we consider them to be different spanning trees even when they are isomorphic graphs. The subgraphs shown in **Figure 54** are *different* spanning trees, even though they happen to be isomorphic graphs. (Are they isomorphic? To decide, change the labels in graph (a) as follows: Interchange C and E, and interchange G and H. By dragging vertices without detaching edges, we can obtain graphs that look alike.)

Minimum Spanning Trees

Suppose there are six villages in a rural district. At present all the roads in the district are gravel roads. There is not enough funding to pave all the roads, but there is a pressing need to have good paved roads so that emergency vehicles can travel easily between the villages. The vertices in the graph in **Figure 55** represent the villages in the district, and the edges represent the existing gravel roads. Estimated costs for paving the different roads are shown, in millions of dollars. (These estimates take into account distances, as well as features of the terrain.)

Figure 55

Arthur Cayley (1821–1895) was a close friend of James Sylvester. (See **page 795**.) They worked together as lawyers at the courts of Lincolns Inn in London and discussed mathematics with each other during work hours. Cayley considered his work as a lawyer simply a way to support himself so that he could do mathematics. In the fourteen years he worked as a lawyer, he published 250 mathematical papers. At age 42, he took a huge paycut to become a mathematics professor at Cambridge University.

Computer analysis of images is a field of active research, particularly in medicine. (Computer analysis of images refers to having a computer detect relevant features of an image.) Some of this research uses minimum spanning trees. They have been used to identify protein fibers in photographs of cells. The computer detects some points lying on the fibers and then determines a minimum spanning tree to deduce the overall structure of the fiber. Some studies have used minimum spanning trees to analyze cancerous tissue.

Minimum Spanning Trees in Astronomy
The structure of the universe may hold clues about the formation of the universe. The image shows the large-scale structure of the universe in a region comprising approximately 10% of the sky. It shows the distribution of about 2 million galaxies. Galaxies are not uniformly distributed throughout the universe. Instead they seem to be arranged in clusters, which are grouped together into superclusters, which themselves seem to be arranged in vast chains called filaments. As the image shows, there are voids between the filaments. Some astronomers are using spanning trees to help map the filamentary structure of the universe.

The district council wants to pave just enough roads so that emergency vehicles will be able to travel from any village to any other along paved roads, though possibly by a roundabout route. The council would like to achieve this at *lowest possible cost.*

The problem calls for exactly one path from each vertex in the graph to any other, so it requires a spanning tree. This spanning tree should have minimum total weight. (The total weight of a spanning tree is the sum of the weights of the edges in the tree.)

Minimum Spanning Tree

A spanning tree that has minimum total weight is called a **minimum spanning tree** for the graph.

Kruskal's Algorithm

Fortunately for the district planners, there is a good algorithm for finding a minimum spanning tree for any connected, weighted graph. It is called **Kruskal's algorithm.** (The algorithm is an efficient algorithm, since it does not take too much computer time for even very large graphs.)

Kruskal's Algorithm for Finding a Minimum Spanning Tree for Any Connected, Weighted Graph

Choose edges for the spanning tree as follows.

Step 1 First edge: Choose any edge with minimum weight.

Step 2 Next edge: Choose any edge with minimum weight from *those not yet selected.* (At this stage, the subgraph may look disconnected.)

Step 3 Continue to choose edges of minimum weight from those not yet selected, except *do not select any edge that creates a circuit* in the subgraph.

Step 4 Repeat Step 3 until the subgraph connects all vertices of the original graph.

Because Kruskal's algorithm gives a subgraph that is connected, includes all vertices of the original graph, and has no circuits, it certainly provides a spanning tree for the graph. Also, the algorithm always will give us a *minimum* spanning tree for the graph. The explanation for this fact is beyond the scope of this text.

Algorithms such as Kruskal's often are called *greedy* algorithms. Why might this be so?

▌▌ **EXAMPLE 3** Applying Kruskal's Algorithm

Use Kruskal's algorithm to find a minimum spanning tree for the graph in **Figure 55**.

SOLUTION

Note that the graph is connected, so Kruskal's algorithm applies. Choose an edge with minimum weight. ED has the least weight of all the edges, so it is selected first. We color the edge a different color to show that it has been selected. See **Figure 56** on the next page.

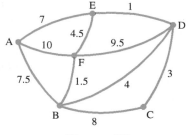

Figure 56   **Figure 57**

Of the remaining edges, BF has the least weight, so it is the second edge chosen, as shown in **Figure 57**. Note that it does not matter that at this stage the subgraph is not connected.

Continuing, we choose CD, then BD, as shown in **Figure 58**. Of the edges remaining, EF has the least weight. However, EF *would create a circuit* in the subgraph. So, ignore EF and note that, of the edges remaining, AE has the least weight. Thus, AE is included in the spanning tree, as shown in **Figure 59**.

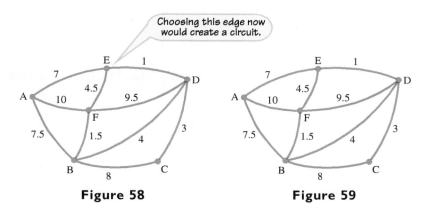

Figure 58   **Figure 59**

We now have a subgraph of the original that connects all vertices of the original graph into a tree. This subgraph is the required minimum spanning tree for the original graph. Its total weight is

$$1 + 1.5 + 3 + 4 + 7 = 16.5.$$

Thus, the district council can achieve its objective at a cost of 16.5 million dollars, by paving only the roads represented by edges in the minimum spanning tree. ■■■

Number of Vertices and Edges

There is an interesting relation between the number of vertices and the number of edges in a tree.

Weather data are complex, involving numerous readings of temperature, pressure, and wind velocity over huge areas, making accurate weather prediction difficult at best. Some current research uses minimum spanning trees to help computers interpret these data. For example, minimum spanning trees are used to identify developing cold fronts.

Number of Vertices and Edges in a Tree

If a graph is a tree, then the number of edges in the graph is one less than the number of vertices.

A tree with n vertices has $n - 1$ edges.

Consider the graphs shown in **Figure 60**. Information about these graphs is shown in **Table 2**. The first three graphs listed are not trees, and there is no uniform relation between the number of edges and the number of vertices for these graphs. In general, graphs may have more or fewer vertices than edges or an equal number of both. In contrast, the last three graphs listed are trees. The number of edges is indeed one less than the number of vertices for these trees.

(a)   (b)   (c)

(d)   (e)   (f)

Figure 60

Table 2			
Graph	**Tree?**	**Number of Vertices**	**Number of Edges**
(a)	No	12	10
(b)	No	7	7
(c)	No	6	9
(d)	Yes	7	6
(e)	Yes	6	5
(f)	Yes	5	4

$6 = 7 - 1$

$5 = 6 - 1$

$4 = 5 - 1$

If we consider only connected graphs, there is a converse for the theorem on the previous page:

For a connected graph, if the number of edges is one less than the number of vertices, then the graph is a tree.

▮▮ **EXAMPLE 4** Using the Vertex/Edge Relation

A chemist has synthesized a new chemical compound. She knows from her analyses that a molecule of the compound contains 54 atoms and that the molecule has a tree-like structure. How many chemical bonds are there in the molecule?

SOLUTION

Think of the atoms in the molecule as the vertices of a tree, and the bonds as edges of the tree. This tree has 54 vertices. Since the number of edges in a tree is one less than the number of vertices, the molecule must have 53 bonds. ▮▮▮

> **PROBLEM-SOLVING HINT** Trial and error is a good problem-solving strategy. Choose an arbitrary proposed solution to the problem and check whether it works. If it does not work, we may gain insight into what to try next.

EXAMPLE 5 Finding a Graph with Specified Properties

Suppose a graph is a tree and has 15 vertices. What is the greatest number of vertices of degree 5 that this graph could have? Draw such a tree.

SOLUTION

Because the graph is a tree with 15 vertices, it must have 14 edges. Recall that the sum of the degrees of the vertices of a graph is twice the number of edges. Thus, the sum of the degrees of the vertices in the tree must be 2 · 14, which is 28.

Now we use trial and error. We want the greatest possible number of vertices with degree 5. Four vertices with degree 5 would contribute 20 to the total degree sum. This would leave 28 − 20 = 8 as the degree sum of the remaining 11 vertices, but this would mean that some of those vertices would have no edges joined to them. The graph would not be connected and would not be a tree.

If we try 3 vertices with degree 5, this would contribute 15 to the total degree sum. It would leave 28 − 15 = 13 as the degree sum for the remaining 12 vertices. We can draw a graph with these specifications, as in **Figure 61**. Thus, the greatest possible number of vertices of degree 5 in a tree with 15 vertices is 3. ███

Figure 61

15.4 EXERCISES

In Exercises 1–7, determine whether the graph is a tree. If not, explain why it is not.

1.

2.

3.

4.

5.

6. a complete graph with 6 vertices

7. a connected graph with all vertices having even degree

In Exercises 8–10, add edges (no vertices) to the graph to change the graph into a tree or explain why this is not possible. (Note: There may be more than one correct answer.)

8.
A   B   C
    E   D
G   H
    F
    I

9.
J   K
        M
    L
        N   O   P

10.
Q——R

S•   •T
       |
       •U

In Exercises 11–13, determine whether the graph described must be a tree.

11. *Spread of a Rumor* A sociologist is investigating the spread of a rumor. He finds that 18 people know of the rumor. One of these people must have started the rumor, and each must have heard the rumor for the first time from one of the others. He draws a graph with vertices representing the 18 people and edges showing from whom each person first heard the rumor.

12. *Internet Search Engine* You are using the Google search engine to search the Web for information on a topic for a paper. You start at the Google page and follow links you find, sometimes going back to a site you've already visited. To keep a record of the sites you visit, you show each site as a vertex of a graph. You draw an edge each time you connect for the *first* time to a *new* site.

13. *Tracking Infectious Disease* A patient has a highly infectious disease. An employee of the Centers for Disease Control is trying to quarantine all people who have had contact over the past week with either the patient or with someone already included in the contact network. The employee draws a graph with vertices representing the patient and all people who have had contact as described. The edges of the graph represent the relation "the two people have had contact."

In Exercises 14–17, determine whether the statement is true *or* false. *If the statement is false, draw an example to show that it is false.*

14. Every graph with no circuits is a tree.

15. Every connected graph in which each edge is a cut edge is a tree.

16. Every graph in which there is a path between each pair of vertices is a tree.

17. Every graph in which each edge is a cut edge is a tree.

In Exercises 18–20, find three different spanning trees for each graph. (There are many different correct answers.)

18.

19.

20.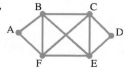

In Exercises 21–23, find all spanning trees for the graph.

21.   **22.**

23.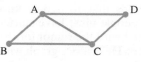

In Exercises 24–26, determine how many spanning trees the graph has.

24.

25.

26.

27. What is a general principle about the number of spanning trees in graphs such as those in **Exercises 24–26**?

28. Complete the parts of this exercise in order.

    (a) Find all the spanning trees of each of the following graphs.

       (i)   **(ii)**   **(iii)**

    (b) For each of the following graphs, determine how many spanning trees the graph has.

       (i)   **(ii)**

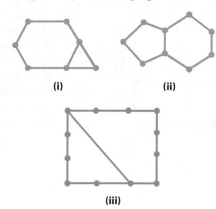

       (iii)

    (c) What is a general principle about the number of spanning trees in graphs of the kind shown in (a) and (b)?

In Exercises 29–32, use Kruskal's algorithm to find a minimum spanning tree for the graph. Find the total weight of this minimum spanning tree.

29.

30.

31.

32.

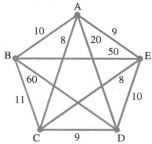

33. *School Building Layout* A school consists of 6 separate buildings, represented by the vertices in the graph.

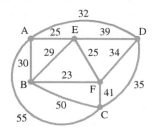

There are paths between some of the buildings as shown. The graph also shows the length in feet of each path. School administrators want to cover some of these paths with roofs so that students will be able to walk between buildings without getting wet when it rains. To minimize cost, they must select paths to be covered such that the total length to be covered is as small as possible. Use Kruskal's algorithm to determine which paths to cover. Also determine the total length of pathways to be covered.

34. *Town Water Distribution* A town council is planning to provide town water to an area that previously relied on private wells. Water will be fed into the area at the point represented by the vertex labeled A in the graph.

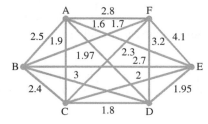

Water must be piped to each of five main distribution points, represented by the vertices labeled B through F in the accompanying graph. Town engineers have estimated the cost of laying the pipes to carry the water between each pair of points in millions of dollars, as indicated in the graph. They must now select which pipes should be laid, so that there is exactly one route for the water to be pumped from A to any one of the five distribution points (possibly via another distribution point), and they want to achieve this at minimum cost. Use Kruskal's algorithm to decide which pipes should be laid. Find the total cost of laying the pipes.

35. How many edges are there in a tree with 34 vertices?

36. How many vertices are there in a tree with 40 edges?

37. How many edges are there in a spanning tree for a complete graph with 63 vertices?

38. A connected graph has 27 vertices and 43 edges. How many edges must be removed to form a spanning tree for the graph?

39. We have said that we can always find at least one spanning tree for a connected graph and usually more than one. Could it happen that different spanning trees for the same graph have different numbers of edges? Justify your answer.

40. Suppose we have a tree with 9 vertices.
   (a) Determine the number of edges in the graph.
   (b) Determine the sum of the degrees of the vertices in the graph.
   (c) Determine the least possible number of vertices of degree 1 in this graph.
   (d) Determine the greatest possible number of vertices of degree 1 in this graph.
   (e) Answer parts (a) through (d) for a tree with n vertices.

41. Suppose we have a tree with 10 vertices.
   (a) Determine the number of edges in the graph.
   (b) Determine the sum of the degrees of the vertices in the graph.
   (c) Determine the least possible number of vertices of degree 4 in this graph.
   (d) Determine the greatest possible number of vertices of degree 4 in this graph.
   (e) Draw a graph to illustrate your answer in part (d).

42. Suppose we have a tree with 17 vertices.
   (a) Determine the number of edges in the graph.
   (b) Determine the sum of the degrees of the vertices in the graph.
   (c) Determine the greatest possible number of vertices of degree 5 in this graph.
   (d) Draw a graph to illustrate your answer in part (c).

43. *Computer Network Layout* A business has 23 employees, each with his or her own desk computer, all working in the same office. The managers want to network the computers. They need to install cables between individual computers so that every computer is linked into the network. Because of the way the office is laid out, it is not convenient to simply connect all the computers in one long line. Determine the least number of cables the managers need to install to achieve their objective.

44. Design of a Garden Maria Jimenez has 12 vegetable and flower beds in her garden and wants to build flagstone paths between the beds so that she can get from each bed along flagstone paths to every other bed. She also wants a path linking her front door to one of the beds. Determine the minimum number of flagstone paths she must build to achieve this.

Exercises 45–47 refer to the following situation: We start with a tree and then draw in extra edges and vertices. For each, say whether it is possible to draw in the number of edges and vertices specified to end up with a connected graph. If it is possible, determine whether the resulting graph must be a tree, may be a tree, or cannot possibly be a tree. Justify each answer briefly.

45. Draw in the same number of vertices as edges.

46. Draw in more vertices than edges.

47. Draw in more edges than vertices.

48. Starting with a tree, is it possible to draw in the same number of vertices as edges and end up with a disconnected graph? If so, give an example. If not, justify briefly.

Exercises 49–51 require the following theorem, proved by Cayley in 1889: A complete graph with n vertices has n^{n-2} spanning trees.

49. How many spanning trees are there for a complete graph with 3 vertices? Draw a complete graph with 3 vertices and find all the spanning trees.

50. How many spanning trees are there for a complete graph with 4 vertices? Draw a complete graph with 4 vertices and find all the spanning trees.

51. How many spanning trees are there for a complete graph with 5 vertices?

52. Find all nonisomorphic trees with 4 vertices. How many are there?

53. Find all nonisomorphic trees with 5 vertices. How many are there?

54. Find all nonisomorphic trees with 6 vertices. How many are there?

55. Find all nonisomorphic trees with 7 vertices. How many are there?

56. In this exercise, we explore why the number of edges in a tree is one less than the number of vertices. Since the statement is clearly true for a tree with only one vertex, we will consider a tree *with more than one vertex.*

Answer parts (a)–(h) in order.

(a) How many components does the tree have?

(b) Why must the tree have at least one edge?

(c) Remove one edge from the tree. How many components does the resulting graph have?

(d) You have not created any new circuits by removing the edge, so each of the components of the resulting graph is a tree. If the remaining graph still has edges, choose any edge and remove it. (You have now removed 2 edges from the original tree.) Altogether, how many components remain?

(e) Repeat the procedure described in (d). If you remove 3 edges from the original tree, how many components remain? If you remove 4 edges from your original tree, how many components remain?

(f) Repeat the procedure in (d) until you have removed all the edges from the tree. If you have to remove n edges to achieve this, determine an expression involving n for the number of components remaining.

(g) What *are* the components that remain when you have removed all the edges from the tree?

(h) What can you conclude about the number of vertices in a tree with n edges?

57. Write a paper on the arrangement of galaxies and the filamentary structure of the universe. Include discussion of how minimum spanning trees are used to analyze this.

58. Write a paper on James Sylvester and Arthur Cayley. Include discussion of their work in graph theory.

EXTENSION   Route Planning

Introduction • Minimizing Deadheading

Introduction   When planning routes for mail delivery, street sweeping, or snowplowing, the roads in the region to be covered usually do not have an Euler circuit. Unavoidably, certain stretches of road must be traveled more than once. This is referred to as **deadheading.** Planners then try to find a route on which the driver will spend as little time as possible deadheading. We now explore how this can be done.

Minimizing Deadheading In **Example 1,** for simplicity we use street grids for which the distance from corner to corner in any direction is the same.

▌▌ **EXAMPLE 1** Finding an Euler Circuit on a Street Grid

The street grid in **Figure 62** has every vertex of odd degree marked with an X. Insert edges coinciding with existing roads to change it to a graph with an Euler circuit.

SOLUTION

A certain amount of trial and error is needed to find the least number of edges that must be inserted to ensure that the street grid graph has an Euler circuit.

If we insert edges as shown in **Figure 63**, we obtain a graph that has an Euler circuit. (Check that all vertices now have even degree.) This solution introduces 11 edges, which turns out to be more deadheading than is necessary.

11 edges

Figure 63

7 edges

Figure 64

This represents the least amount of deadheading.

Figure 62

If we insert edges as shown in **Figure 64**, with just 7 additional edges we obtain a graph with an Euler circuit. This is, in fact, the least number of edges that must be inserted (keeping to the street grid) to change the original street grid graph into a graph that has an Euler circuit. (There are different ways to insert the seven edges.)

▮▮▮

EXTENSION EXERCISES

1. In the graph shown here, we have inserted just six edges in the original street grid from **Example 1.** Why is this not a better solution than the one in **Figure 64**?

For each street grid in Exercises 2–4, insert edges to obtain a street grid that has an Euler circuit. Try to insert as few edges as possible.

2.

3.

4.

COLLABORATIVE INVESTIGATION

Finding the Number of Edges in a Complete Graph

In this investigation we explore two short methods for finding the number of edges in a complete graph with a specified number of vertices. By comparing the methods, we obtain a special sum formula that you encountered in **Chapter 1.**

Divide into groups of 4 or 5 students. Assign to each group member a different complete graph, with 4, 5, 6, or 7 vertices. Each member should sketch his or her complete graph and count the number of edges. Next, make a table showing the number of vertices and the number of edges in complete graphs with 3 through 7 vertices.

For Group Discussion

Is there a pattern in the number of edges for these complete graphs? Guess how many edges there would be in a complete graph with 8 vertices. How many are in a complete graph with 10 vertices?

If there is a pattern in the table, we could find the number of vertices in a complete graph with, for example, 100 vertices. Of course, completing the table all the way up to 100 would take a long time. A short way of determining the number of edges in a complete graph with any specified number of vertices can be used instead. Divide your group into two groups, A and B, and complete the following tasks.

Group A

1. Start by studying the number of edges in a complete graph with eight vertices. Proceed as follows.

   Have someone in the group draw the eight vertices (no edges yet).

   (a) Choose any one of the vertices and draw in all necessary edges *from this vertex.* (Remember, there must be an edge to every other vertex in the graph.) Record the number of edges you drew from this first vertex.   **(a)** ____

   (b) Now choose a different vertex—it is already joined to your first vertex by an edge. Draw in all necessary additional edges *from this vertex.* Record the number of *additional* edges you drew from this vertex.   **(b)** ____

   Continue this process, determining how many *addi-tional* edges you must draw from a third vertex, from a fourth vertex, and so on until the graph is complete. Record the number of additional edges in succession.

   (c) ____   **(d)** ____   **(e)** ____   **(f)** ____   **(g)** ____

   Now add your answers from (a) through (g) to find the total number of edges.

   Total number of edges = ____ + ____ + ____ + ____
   + ____ + ____ + ____ = ____

2. Repeat the procedure just described to find the number of edges in a complete graph with 10 vertices.

3. As in Step 1, write down the numbers you must add to find the number of edges in a complete graph with 100 vertices. (Since there are so many numbers, write only the first three numbers, ellipsis points to indicate the omission, and then the last three numbers.)

   Total number of edges = ____ + ____ + ____ + ⋯
   + ____ + ____ + ____

   To add these numbers by hand (or even with a calculator) would take a long time. Perhaps you remember a formula from a previous chapter?

Group B

1. Start by studying the number of edges in a complete graph with eight vertices. Proceed as follows.

   Have someone draw a graph with 8 vertices. Then answer the following.

   (a) Each vertex in your graph has the same degree. What is it?   **(a)** ____

   (b) Use your answer from (a) to find the sum of the degrees of the vertices in your graph.   **(b)** ____

   (c) Find the number of edges in the complete graph, by using the theorem from **Section 15.1** that relates the sum of degrees to the number of edges in the graph.   **(c)** ____

2. Repeat the procedure described above to find the number of edges in a complete graph with 10 vertices.

3. Repeat the procedure described above to find the number of edges in a complete graph with 100 vertices.

Group B should now rejoin Group A. The members of Group A must explain their method to the whole group. Then the members of Group B must explain their method to the whole group. Use your combined knowledge to answer the following questions.

1. By comparing the work on Step 3 of Group A and Group B, find the sum:

   $$99 + 98 + 97 + \ldots + 3 + 2 + 1 = \underline{\quad}$$

2. Determine the number of edges in a complete graph with 210 vertices.

3. Write a formula for the number of edges in a complete graph with m vertices.

4. Determine the sum of the following numbers. (*Hint:* Regard the sum as the number of edges in a complete graph.)

   $$155 + 154 + 153 + \ldots + 3 + 2 + 1 = \underline{\quad}$$

CHAPTER 15 TEST

In Exercises 1–4, refer to the following graph.

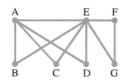

1. Determine how many vertices the graph has.

2. Determine the sum of the degrees of the vertices.

3. Determine how many edges the graph has.

4. Which of the following are paths in the graph? If not, why not?

   (a) $B \to A \to C \to E \to B \to A$

   (b) $A \to B \to E \to A$

   (c) $A \to C \to D \to E$

5. Which of the following are circuits in the graph? If not, why not?

   (a) $A \to B \to E \to D \to A$

   (b) $A \to B \to C \to D \to E \to F \to G \to A$

   (c) $A \to B \to E \to F \to G \to E \to D \to A \to$
      $E \to C \to A$

6. Draw a graph that has 2 components.

7. A graph has 10 vertices, 3 of degree 4, and the rest of degree 2. Use the theorem that relates the sum of degrees to the number of edges to determine the number of edges in the graph (without drawing the graph).

8. Determine whether graphs (a) and (b) are isomorphic. If they are, justify this by labeling corresponding vertices of the two graphs with the same letters and color-coding the corresponding edges.

      (a)   **(b)**

9. *Planning for Dinner* Julia is planning to invite some friends for dinner. She plans to invite John, Adam, Bill, Tina, Nicole, and Rita. John, Nicole, and Tina all know each other. Adam knows John and Tina. Bill also knows Tina, and he knows Rita. Draw a graph with vertices representing the six friends whom Julia plans to invite to dinner and edges representing the relationship "know each other." Is your graph connected or disconnected? Which of the guests knows the greatest number of other guests?

10. *Chess Competition* There are 8 contestants in a chess competition. Each contestant plays one chess game against every other contestant. The winner is the contestant who wins the most games. How many chess games will be played in the competition?

11. Is the accompanying graph a complete graph? Justify your answer.

Color each graph using as few colors as possible. Use the result to determine the chromatic number of the graph.

12.   **13.**

14. *Scheduling Exams* A teacher at a high school must schedule exams for the senior class. Subjects in which there are exams are listed on the left. Several students must take more than one of the exams, as shown on the right. Exams in subjects with students in common must not be scheduled at the same time. Use graph coloring to determine the least number of exam times needed, and to identify exams that can be given at the same times.

Exam	*Students taking this must also take*
History	English, Mathematics, Biology, Geography, Psychology
English	Mathematics, Psychology, History
Mathematics	Chemistry, Biology, History, English
Chemistry	Biology, Mathematics
Biology	Mathematics, Chemistry, History
Psychology	English, History, Geography
Geography	Psychology, History

15. Refer to the graph for **Exercises 1– 4.** Which of the following are Euler circuits for the graph? If not, why not?

   (a) $A \to B \to E \to D \to A$

   (b) $A \to B \to C \to D \to E \to F \to G \to A$

   (c) $A \to B \to E \to F \to G \to E \to D \to A \to$
      $E \to C \to A$

In Exercises 16 and 17, use Euler's theorem to decide whether the graph has an Euler circuit. (Do not actually find an Euler circuit.) Justify your answer briefly.

16.

17.

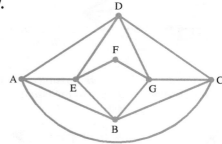

18. *Building Floor Plan* The floor plan of a building is shown. Is it possible to start outside, walk through each door exactly once, and end up back outside? Justify your answer.

19. Use Fleury's algorithm to find an Euler circuit for the accompanying graph, beginning F → B.

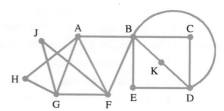

20. Refer to the graph for **Exercises 1–4.** Which of the following are Hamilton circuits for the graph? If not, why not?

(a) A → B → E → D → A

(b) A → B → C → D → E → F → G → A

(c) A → B → E → F → G → E → D → A → E → C → A

21. List all Hamilton circuits in the graph that start F → G. How many are there?

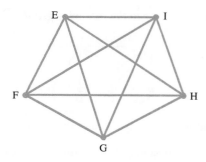

22. Use the brute force algorithm to find a minimum Hamilton circuit for the accompanying graph. Determine the total weight of the minimum Hamilton circuit.

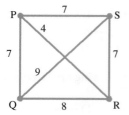

23. Use the nearest neighbor algorithm starting at A to find an approximate solution to the problem of finding a minimum Hamilton circuit for the graph below. Find the total weight of this circuit.

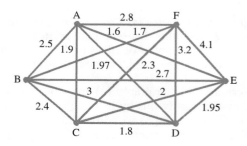

24. How many Hamilton circuits are there in a complete graph with 25 vertices? (Leave your answer as a factorial.)

25. *Rock Band Tour Plan* The agent for a rock band based in Milwaukee is planning a tour for the band. He plans for the band to visit Minneapolis, Santa Barbara, Orlando, Phoenix, and St. Louis. Since the band members want to minimize the time they are away from home, they do not want to go to any of these cities more than once on the tour. Consider the complete graph with vertices representing the 6 cities mentioned. Does the problem of planning the tour require an Euler circuit, a Hamilton circuit, or neither for its solution?

26. Draw three nonisomorphic trees with 7 vertices.

In Exercises 27–29, decide whether the statement is true *or* false.

27. Every tree has a Hamilton circuit.

28. In a tree each edge is a cut edge.

29. Every tree is connected.

30. Find all the different spanning trees for the following graph.

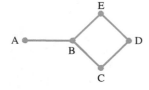

31. Use Kruskal's algorithm to find a minimum spanning tree for the following graph.

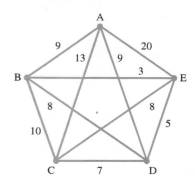

32. Determine the number of edges in a tree with 50 vertices.

APPENDIX: THE METRIC SYSTEM

Joseph Louis Lagrange (1736–1813) was born in Turin, Italy, and became a professor at age 19. In 1776 he came to Berlin at the request of Frederick the Great to take the position Euler left. A decade later Lagrange settled permanently in Paris. Napoleon was among many who admired and honored him.

Lagrange's greatest work was in the theory and application of **calculus.** He carried forward Euler's work of putting calculus on firm algebraic ground in his theory of functions. His *Analytic Mechanics* (1788) applied calculus to the motion of objects.

Lagrange's contributions to algebra had great influence on Galois and, hence, the theory of groups. He also wrote on number theory, proving that every integer is the sum of at most four squares.

The metric system was developed by a committee of the French Academy just after the French Revolution of 1789. The president of the committee was the mathematician Joseph Louis Lagrange. The advantages of the metric system can be seen when compared to our English system. In the English system, one inch is one-twelfth of a foot, while one foot is one-third of a yard. One mile is equivalent to 5280 feet, or 1760 yards. Obviously, there is no consistency in subdivisions.

In the metric system, prefixes are used to indicate multiplications or divisions by powers of ten. For example, the basic unit of length in the metric system is the *meter* (which is a little longer than one yard). To indicate one thousand meters, attach the prefix **"kilo-"** to get **kilo**meter. To indicate one one-hundredth of a meter, use the prefix **"centi-"** to obtain **centi**meter. A complete list of the prefixes of the metric system is shown in **Table 1**, with the most commonly used prefixes appearing in bold type.

Table 1 Metric Prefixes

Prefix	Multiple	Prefix	Multiple
exa	1,000,000,000,000,000,000	deci	0.1
peta	1,000,000,000,000,000	**centi**	0.01
tera	1,000,000,000,000	**milli**	0.001
giga	1,000,000,000	micro	0.000001
mega	1,000,000	nano	0.000000001
kilo	1000	pico	0.000000000001
hecto	100	femto	0.000000000000001
deka	10	atto	0.000000000000000001

Length and Area

Lagrange urged the committee devising the metric system to find some natural measure for length from which weight and volume measures could be derived. It was decided that one **meter (m)** would be the basic unit of length, with a meter being defined as one ten-millionth of the distance from the equator to the North Pole.

To obtain measures longer than one meter, Greek prefixes were added. For measures smaller than a meter, Latin prefixes were used. A meter is a little longer than a yard (about 39.37 inches). A **centimeter (cm)** is one one-hundredth of a meter and is about $\frac{2}{5}$ of an inch. See **Figure 1**.

Figure 1

A Comparison of Distances

Length in Meters	Approximate Related Distances
10^{19}	Distance to the North Star
10^{12}	Distance of Saturn from the sun
10^{11}	Distance of Venus from the sun
10^{9}	Diameter of the sun
10^{8}	Diameter of Jupiter
10^{7}	Diameter of Earth; distance from Washington, D.C. to Tokyo
10^{6}	Distance from Chicago to Wichita, Kansas
10^{5}	Average distance across Lake Michigan
10^{4}	Average width of the Grand Canyon
10^{3}	Length of the Golden Gate Bridge
10^{2}	Length of a football field
10^{1}	Average height of a two-story house
10^{0}	Width of a door
10^{-1}	Width of your hand
10^{-2}	Diameter of a piece of chalk
10^{-3}	Thickness of a dime
10^{-4}	Thickness of a piece of paper
10^{-5}	Diameter of a red blood cell
10^{-7}	Thickness of a soap bubble
10^{-8}	Average distance between molecules of air in a room
10^{-9}	Diameter of a molecule of oil
10^{-14}	Diameter of an atomic nucleus
10^{-15}	Diameter of a proton

Because the metric system is based on decimals and powers of ten, conversions within the system involve multiplying and dividing by powers of ten. For example, to convert 2.5 m to centimeters, multiply 2.5 by 100 (since 100 cm = 1 m) to obtain 250 cm. On the other hand, to convert 18.6 cm to meters, divide by 100 to obtain 0.186 m. Other conversions are made in the same manner, using the meanings of the prefixes. Why is 42 m equal to 42,000 millimeters (mm)?

Long distances usually are measured in kilometers. A **kilometer (km)** is 1000 meters. (According to a popular dictionary, the word *kilometer* may be pronounced with the accent on either the first or the second syllable. Scientists usually stress the second syllable.) A kilometer is equal to about 0.6 mile. **Figure 2** shows the ratio of 1 kilometer to 1 mile.

Conversions from meters to kilometers, and vice versa, are made by multiplying or dividing by 1000 as necessary. For example, 37 kilometers equals 37,000 meters, while 583 meters equals 0.583 km.

The area of a figure can be measured in square metric units. **Figure 3** shows a square that is 1 cm on each side. Thus, it is a **square centimeter (cm²)**. One square meter (m²) is the area of a square with sides one meter long. How many cm² are in one m²?

According to Paul G. Hewitt, in *Conceptual Physics*, 7th edition (HarperCollins):

The distance from the equator to the North Pole was thought at the time to be close to 10,000 kilometers. One ten-millionth of this, the meter, was carefully determined and marked off by means of scratches on a bar of platinum-iridium alloy. This bar is kept at the International Bureau of Weights and Measures in France. The standard meter in France has since been calibrated in terms of the wavelength of light—it is 1,650,763.73 times the wavelength of orange light emitted by the atoms of the gas krypton-86. The meter is now defined as being the length of the path traveled by light in a vacuum during a time interval of 1/299,792,458 of a second.

1 kilometer

1 mile

Observe the ratio.

Figure 2

1 cm

1 cm

Area is 1 cm².

Figure 3

In September 1999, the **Mars *Climate Orbiter*** was lost due to "a failure to use metric units in the coding of a ground software file. . . ." According to Edward Weiler, associate administrator for NASA's Office of Space Science, the metric conversion error that led to the loss "should have been caught five ways to Sunday," but it wasn't. (*Source:* "NASA's Mars Losses Spark Anger and Opportunity" by Leonard David, Washington Contributing Editor to www.space.com.)

Volume, Mass, and Weight

The volume of a three-dimensional figure is measured in cubic units. If, for example, the dimensions are given in centimeters, the volume may be determined by the appropriate formula from geometry, and it will be in **cubic centimeters (cm³)**. See **Figure 4** for a sketch of a box whose volume is one cm³.

Volume is 1 cm³.

Figure 4

In the metric system, one **liter (L)** is the quantity assigned to the volume of a box that is 10 cm on a side. (See **Figure 5**.) A liter is a little more than a quart as seen in **Figure 6**. Notice the advantage of this definition over the equivalent one in the English system—using a ruler marked in centimeters, a volume of 1 liter (symbolized 1 L) can be constructed. On the other hand, given a ruler marked in inches, it would be difficult to construct a volume of 1 quart.

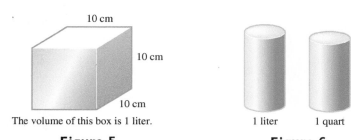

The volume of this box is 1 liter.

Figure 5

1 liter   1 quart

Figure 6

The prefixes mentioned earlier are used throughout the metric system, so one **milliliter (ml)** is one one-thousandth of a liter, one **centiliter (cl)** is one one-hundredth of a liter, one **kiloliter (kl)** is 1000 liters, and so on. Milliliters are used extensively in science and medicine. Many beverages now are sold by milliliters and by liters. For example, 750 ml is a common size for wine bottles, and many soft drinks now are sold in 1- and 2-liter bottles.

Because of the way a liter is defined as the volume of a box 10 cm on a side,

$$1\,L = 10\,cm \times 10\,cm \times 10\,cm = 1000\,cm^3 \quad \text{or} \quad \frac{1}{1000}\,L = 1\,cm^3.$$

Since $\frac{1}{1000}\,L = 1\,ml$, we have the following relationship.

$$1\,ml = 1\,cm^3$$

For example, the volume of a box which is 8 cm by 6 cm by 5 cm may be given as 240 cm³ or as 240 ml.

The box in **Figure 4** is 1 cm by 1 cm by 1 cm. The volume of this box is

$$1\,cm^3, \quad \text{or} \quad 1\,ml.$$

The original scale of **Anders Celsius** had the freezing point of water at 100° and the boiling point at 0°, but biologist Carl von Linne inverted the scale, giving us the familiar Celsius scale of today.

By definition, the mass of the water that fills such a box is **1 gram (g).** A nickel five-cent piece has a mass close to 5 grams, or 5 g. The volume of water used to define a gram is very small, so a gram is a very small mass. For everyday use, a **kilogram (kg),** or one thousand grams, is more practical. A kilogram weighs about 2.2 pounds. A common abbreviation for kilogram is the word **kilo.**

This photo shows that 13 feet, 6 inches is equal to 4.1 meters. Use this information and a proportion to show that one yard is equal to 0.91 meter.

Extremely small masses can be measured with **milligrams (mg)** and **centigrams (cg).** These measures are so small that they, like centiliters and milliliters, are used mainly in science and medicine.

Temperature

In the metric system temperature is measured in **degrees Celsius.** On the Celsius temperature scale, water freezes at 0° and boils at 100°. These two numbers are easier to remember than the corresponding numbers on the Fahrenheit scale, 32° and 212°. The thermometer in **Figure 7** shows some typical temperatures in both Fahrenheit and Celsius.

Figure 7

The formulas given below can be used to convert between Celsius and Fahrenheit temperatures.

Celsius-Fahrenheit Conversion Formulas

To convert a reading from Fahrenheit to Celsius, use $C = \frac{5}{9}(F - 32).$

To convert from Celsius to Fahrenheit, use $F = \frac{9}{5}C + 32.$

Metric Conversions

Due to legislation enacted by Congress, the metric system is used in the United States, and an ultimate goal is for the two systems to be in use, side-by-side, with public acceptance of both systems. Industries that export a great many goods are using the metric system, since this is compatible with most of the countries with which they trade.

Some scientific calculators are programmed to do conversions between the English and metric systems. Approximate conversions can be made with the aid of **Tables 2 and 3** on the next page.

Table 2   Metric to English

To Convert from	To	Multiply by
meters	yards	1.0936
meters	feet	3.2808
meters	inches	39.37
kilometers	miles	0.6214
grams	pounds	0.0022
kilograms	pounds	2.20
liters	quarts	1.0567
liters	gallons	0.2642

Table 3   English to Metric

To Convert from	To	Multiply by
yards	meters	0.9144
feet	meters	0.3048
inches	meters	0.0254
miles	kilometers	1.609
pounds	grams	454
pounds	kilograms	0.454
quarts	liters	0.9464
gallons	liters	3.785

APPENDIX EXERCISES

Perform each conversion by multiplying or dividing by the appropriate power of 10.

1. 8 m to millimeters

2. 14.76 m to centimeters

3. 8500 cm to meters

4. 250 mm to meters

5. 68.9 cm to millimeters

6. 3.25 cm to millimeters

7. 59.8 mm to centimeters

8. 3.542 mm to centimeters

9. 5.3 km to meters

10. 9.24 km to meters

11. 27,500 m to kilometers

12. 14,592 m to kilometers

Use a metric ruler to perform each measurement, first in centimeters, then in millimeters.

13. |———————|

14. |——————————|

15. |———————————————|

16. Based on your measurement of the line segment in **Exercise 13**, one inch is about how many centimeters? How many millimeters?

Perform each conversion by multiplying or dividing by the appropriate power of 10.

17. 6 L to centiliters

18. 4.1 L to milliliters

19. 8.7 L to milliliters

20. 12.5 L to centiliters

21. 925 cl to liters

22. 412 ml to liters

23. 8974 ml to liters

24. 5639 cl to liters

25. 8000 g to kilograms

26. 25,000 g to kilograms

27. 5.2 kg to grams

28. 12.42 kg to grams

29. 4.2 g to milligrams

30. 3.89 g to centigrams

31. 598 mg to grams

32. 7634 cg to grams

Use the formulas given in the text to perform each conversion. Round to the nearest degree.

33. 86°F to Celsius

34. 536°F to Celsius

35. −114°F to Celsius

36. −40°F to Celsius

37. 10°C to Fahrenheit

38. 25°C to Fahrenheit

39. −40°C to Fahrenheit

40. −15°C to Fahrenheit

Solve each problem. Refer to geometry formulas as necessary.

41. *Weight of Nickels*   One nickel weighs 5 g. How many nickels are in 1 kg of nickels?

42. *Salt in Sea Water*   Sea water contains about 3.5 g salt per 1000 ml of water. How many grams of salt would be in one liter of sea water?

43. *Weight of Helium*   Helium weighs about 0.0002 g per milliliter. How much would one liter of helium weigh?

44. *Sugar Solution*   About 1500 g sugar can be dissolved in a liter of warm water. How much sugar could be dissolved in one milliliter of warm water?

45. *Cost of Metal*   Northside Foundry needed seven metal strips, each 67 cm long. Find the total cost of the strips, if they sell for $8.74 per meter.

46. *Cost of Lace*   Uptown Dressmakers bought fifteen pieces of lace, each 384 mm long. The lace sold for $54.20 per meter. Find the cost of the fifteen pieces.

47. *Cost of Marble*   Imported marble for desktops costs $174.20 per square meter. Find the cost of a piece of marble 128 cm by 174 cm.

48. *Cost of Paper*   A special photographic paper sells for $63.79 per square meter. Find the cost to buy 80 pieces of the paper, each 9 cm by 14 cm.

49. *Volume of a Box*   An importer received some special coffee beans in a box measuring 82 cm by 1.1 m by 1.2 m. Give the volume of the box, both in cubic centimeters and cubic meters.

50. *Volume of a Crate*   A fabric center receives bolts of woolen cloth in crates measuring 1.5 m by 74 cm by 97 cm. Find the volume of a crate, both in cubic centimeters and cubic meters.

51. *Medicine Bottles*   A medicine is sold in small bottles holding 800 ml each. How many of these bottles can be filled from a vat holding 160 L of the medicine?

52. *Bottles of Soda Pop*   How many 2-liter bottles of soda pop would be needed for a wedding reception if 80 people are expected, and each drinks 400 ml of soda?

Perform each conversion. Use a calculator and/or the table in the text as necessary.

53. 982 yd to meters

54. 12.2 km to miles

55. 125 mi to kilometers

56. 1000 mi to kilometers

57. 1816 g to pounds

58. 1.42 lb to grams

59. 47.2 lb to grams

60. 7.68 kg to pounds

61. 28.6 L to quarts

62. 59.4 L to quarts

63. 28.2 gal to liters

64. 16 qt to liters

Metric measures are very common in medicine. Since we convert among metric measures by moving the decimal point, errors in locating the decimal point in medical doses are not unknown. Decide whether each dose of medicine seems reasonable *or* unreasonable.

65. Take 2 kg of aspirin three times a day.

66. Take 4 L of liquid Mylanta every evening just before bedtime.

67. Take 25 ml of cough syrup daily.

68. Soak your feet in 6 L of hot water.

69. Inject $\frac{1}{2}$ L of insulin every morning.

70. Apply 40 g of salve to a cut on your finger.

Select the most reasonable choice for each of the following.

71. length of an adult cow
    A. 1 m   **B.** 3 m   **C.** 5 m

72. length of a Lexus
    A. 1 m   **B.** 3 m   **C.** 5 m

73. distance from Seattle to Miami
    A. 500 km   **B.** 5000 km   **C.** 50,000 km

74. length across an average nose
    A. 3 cm   **B.** 30 cm   **C.** 300 cm

75. distance across a page of a book
    A. 1.93 mm   **B.** 19.3 mm   **C.** 193 mm

76. weight of a book
    A. 1 kg   **B.** 10 kg   **C.** 1000 kg

77. weight of a large automobile
    A. 1300 kg   **B.** 130 kg   **C.** 13 kg

78. volume of a 12-ounce bottle of beverage
    A. 35 ml   **B.** 355 ml   **C.** 3550 ml

79. height of a person
    A. 180 cm   **B.** 1800 cm   **C.** 18 cm

80. diameter of the earth
    A. 130 km   **B.** 1300 km   **C.** 13,000 km

81. length of a long freight train
    A. 8 m   **B.** 80 m   **C.** 800 m

82. volume of a grapefruit
    A. 1 L   **B.** 4 L   **C.** 8 L

83. the length of a pair of Levi jeans
    A. 70 cm   **B.** 700 cm   **C.** 7 cm

84. a person's weight
    A. 700 kg   **B.** 7 kg   **C.** 70 kg

85. diagonal measure of a small TV monitor
    A. 5 cm   **B.** 50 cm   **C.** 500 cm

86. width of a standard bedroom door
    A. 1 m   **B.** 3 m   **C.** 5 m

87. thickness of a marking pen
    A. 0.9 mm   **B.** 9 mm   **C.** 90 mm

88. length around the rim of a coffee mug
    A. 300 mm   **B.** 30 mm   **C.** 3000 mm

89. the temperature at the surface of a frozen lake
    A. 0°C   **B.** 10°C   **C.** 32°C

90. the temperature in the middle of Death Valley on a July afternoon
    A. 25°C   **B.** 40°C   **C.** 65°C

91. surface temperature of desert sand on a hot summer day
    A. 30°C   **B.** 60°C   **C.** 90°C

92. temperature of boiling water
    A. 100°C   **B.** 120°C   **C.** 150°C

93. air temperature on a day when you need a sweater
    A. 30°C   **B.** 20°C   **C.** 10°C

94. air temperature on a day when you go swimming
    A. 30°C   **B.** 15°C   **C.** 10°C

95. temperature when baking a cake
    A. 120°C   **B.** 170°C   **C.** 300°C

96. temperature of bath water
    A. 35°C   **B.** 50°C   **C.** 65°C

▌▌▌▌▌▌ ANSWERS TO SELECTED EXERCISES

CHAPTER 1 THE ART OF PROBLEM SOLVING

1.1 Exercises (pages 6–8)

1. deductive **3.** inductive **5.** deductive **7.** deductive
9. inductive **11.** inductive **13.** Answers will vary.
15. 21 **17.** 3072 **19.** 63 **21.** $\frac{11}{12}$ **23.** 216 **25.** 52
27. 5 **29.** One such list is 10, 20, 30, 40, 50, ...
31. $(98{,}765 \times 9) + 3 = 888{,}888$
33. $3367 \times 15 = 50{,}505$
35. $33{,}334 \times 33{,}334 = 1{,}111{,}155{,}556$
37. $3 + 6 + 9 + 12 + 15 = \frac{15(6)}{2}$
39. $5(6) + 5(36) + 5(216) + 5(1296) + 5(7776) = 6(7776 - 1)$
41. $\frac{1}{2} + \frac{1}{4} + \frac{1}{8} + \frac{1}{16} + \frac{1}{32} = 1 - \frac{1}{32}$
43. 20,100 **45.** 320,400 **47.** 15,400 **49.** 2550
51. 1 (These are the numbers of chimes a clock rings, starting with 12 o'clock, if it rings the number of hours on the hour, and 1 chime on the half-hour.)
53. (a) The middle digit is always 9, and the sum of the first and third digits is always 9 (considering 0 as the first digit if the difference has only two digits). **(b)** Answers will vary. **55.** 142,857; 285,714; 428,571; 571,428; 714,285; 857,142. Each result consists of the same six digits, but in a different order. $142{,}857 \times 7 = 999{,}999$

1.2 Exercises (pages 15–18)

1. arithmetic; 56 **3.** geometric; 1215 **5.** neither
7. geometric; 8 **9.** neither **11.** arithmetic; 22
13. 79 **15.** 450 **17.** 4032 **19.** 32,758 **21.** 57; 99
23. $(4321 \times 9) - 1 = 38{,}888$
25. $999{,}999 \times 4 = 3{,}999{,}996$
27. $21^2 - 15^2 = 6^3$ **29.** $5^2 - 4^2 = 5 + 4$
31. $1 + 5 + 9 + 13 = 4 \times 7$ **33.** 45,150 **35.** 228,150
37. 2601 **39.** 250,000 **41.** $S = n(n + 1)$
43. Answers will vary. **45.** *row 1*: 28, 36; *row 2*: 36, 49, 64; *row 3*: 35, 51, 70, 92; *row 4*: 28, 45, 66, 91, 120; *row 5*: 18, 34, 55, 81, 112, 148; *row 6*: 8, 21, 40, 65, 96, 133, 176
47. $8(1) + 1 = 9 = 3^2; 8(3) + 1 = 25 = 5^2; 8(6) + 1 = 49 = 7^2; 8(10) + 1 = 81 = 9^2$
49. The pattern is 1, 0, 1, 0, 1, 0, ...
51.

53. 256 **55.** 117 **57.** 235 **59.** $N_n = \frac{n(7n - 5)}{2}$
61. a square number **63.** a perfect cube **65.** 42
67. 419 **69.** $\frac{101}{2}$ **71.** 2048 **73.** $\frac{1}{2048}$ **75.** $\frac{5}{2048}$

1.3 Exercises (pages 24–29)

1. 32 **3.** 0 (The product of the first and last digits is the two-digit number between them.) **5.** 11 **7.** infinitely many (Any line through the center of the square will do this.) **9.** 48.5 in. **11.** 42 **13.** 6 **15.** If you multiply the two digits in the numbers in the first row, you will get the second row of numbers. The second row of numbers is a pattern of two numbers (8 and 24) repeating. **17.** I put the ring in the box and put my lock on the box. I send you the box. You put your lock on, as well, and send it back to me. I then remove my lock with my key and send the box (with your lock still on) back to you, so you can remove your lock with your key and get the ring. **19.** 59
21. You should choose a sock from the box labeled *red and green socks*. Because it is mislabeled, it contains only red socks or only green socks, determined by the sock you choose. If the sock is green, relabel this box *green socks*. Since the other two boxes were mislabeled, switch the remaining label to the other box and place the label that says *red and green socks* on the unlabeled box. No other choice guarantees a correct relabeling because you can remove only one sock.
23. D **25.** A
27. One example of a solution follows.

29.
9	7	2	14	11	5	4	12	13	3	6	10	15	1	8

(or the same arrangement reading right to left)
31. Here is one solution. **33.** D **35.** $\frac{1}{3}$

37. One possible sequence is shown here. The numbers represent the number of gallons in each bucket in each successive step.

Big	7	4	4	1	1	0	7	5	5
Small	0	3	0	3	0	1	1	3	0

39. 90 **41.** 55 mph **43.** 07 **45.** 437 **47.** 3
49. 21 stamps (5 five-cent stamps and 16 eight-cent stamps) **51.** 3 socks **53.** 35 **55.** 6
57. the nineteenth day **59.** 1967
61. Eve has $5, and Adam has $7.
63.

$$\begin{array}{r} 4 \quad 0 \quad 2 \\ \times \quad 3 \quad 9 \\ \hline 1 \quad 5, \quad 6 \quad 7 \quad 8 \end{array}$$

65.

6	12	7	9
1	15	4	14
11	5	10	8
16	2	13	3

67. 25 pitches (The visiting team's pitcher retires 24 consecutive batters through the first eight innings, using only one pitch per batter. His team does not score either. Going into the bottom of the ninth tied 0–0, the first batter for the home team hits his first pitch for a home run. The pitcher threw 25 pitches and loses the game by a score of 1–0.) **69.** Q
71. Here is one solution.

73. 6 ways **75.** 86 cm
77. Dan (36) is married to Jessica (29); James (30) is married to Cathy (31).
79. 12; All months have 28 days.
81. 3
83. 6

85. The products always differ by 1.

One of two possibilities

1.4 Exercises *(pages 33–36)*
1. 43.8 **3.** 2.3589 **5.** 7.48 **7.** 7.1289 **9.** 6340.338097
11. 1 **13.** 1.061858759 **15.** 2.221441469
17. 3.141592653 **19.** 0.7782717162 **21.** yes
23. positive **25.** 1 **27.** the same as **29.** 0
31. negative **33.** Answers will vary.
35. Answers will vary. **37.** 63 **39.** 14 **41.** B **43.** A
45. D **47.** 5% **49.** 260,000 **51.** 2005, 2006, 2007
53. 2001: about 165 billion lb; 2007: about 185 billion lb
55. from 2000 to 2005; about $0.85
57. The price of a gallon of gas was decreasing.

Chapter 1 Test *(pages 41–42)*
1. inductive **2.** deductive
3. The magic sum is 38.

4. 65,359,477,124,183 × 68 = 4,444,444,444,444,444
5. 351 **6.** 31,375 **7.** 65; 65 = 1 + 7 + 13 + 19 + 25
8. 1, 8, 21, 40, 65, 96, 133, 176; The pattern is 1, 0, 1, 0, 1, 0, 1, 0, ...
9. The first two terms are both 1. Each term after the second is found by adding the two previous terms.
10. $\frac{1}{4}$ **11.** 9 **12.** 35
13. Answers will vary. One possible solution is
1 + 2 + 3 − 4 + 5 + 6 + 78 + 9 + 0 = 100.
14. 108 in., or 9 ft **15.** 3
16. The sum of the digits is always 9.
17. 9.907572861 (Answers may vary due to the model of calculator used.) **18.** 34.328125 **19.** B
20. (a) between 1998 and 1999, 1999 and 2000, and 2003 and 2004 (b) The unemployment rate was increasing.
(c) 2003: 6.0%; 2004: 5.5%; decline: 0.5%

CHAPTER 2 THE BASIC CONCEPTS OF SET THEORY

2.1 Exercises *(pages 47–49)*
1. F **3.** E **5.** B **7.** H **9.** {1, 2, 3, 4, 5, 6}
11. {0, 1, 2, 3, 4} **13.** {6, 7, 8, 9, 10, 11, 12, 13, 14}
15. {−15, −13, −11, −9, −7, −5, −3, −1}
17. {2, 4, 8, 16, 32, 64, 128, 256} **19.** {0, 2, 4, 6, 8, 10}
21. {21, 22, 23, . . . } **23.** {Lake Erie, Lake Huron, Lake Michigan, Lake Ontario, Lake Superior}
25. {5, 10, 15, 20, 25, . . . } **27.** $\left\{1, \frac{1}{2}, \frac{1}{3}, \frac{1}{4}, \frac{1}{5}, \dots\right\}$
In Exercises 29 and 31, there are other ways to describe the sets. **29.** {x | x is a rational number} **31.** {x | x is an odd natural number less than 76} **33.** the set of single-digit integers **35.** the set of states of the United States
37. finite **39.** infinite **41.** infinite **43.** infinite
45. 8 **47.** 500 **49.** 26 **51.** 39 **53.** 28
55. Answers will vary. **57.** well defined
59. not well defined **61.** ∈ **63.** ∉ **65.** ∉ **67.** ∈
69. false **71.** true **73.** true **75.** true **77.** false
79. true **81.** true **83.** true **85.** false **87.** true
89. Answers will vary.

91. {2} and {3, 4} (Other examples are possible.)
93. {a, b} and {a, c} (Other examples are possible.)
95. (a) {Drew Barrymore, Leonardo DiCaprio, Samuel
L. Jackson, Jim Carrey}   **(b)** {Will Ferrell, Ewan
McGregor}

2.2 Exercises *(pages 54–55)*
1. D   **3.** B   **5.** ⊄   **7.** ⊆   **9.** ⊆   **11.** ⊄   **13.** both
15. ⊆   **17.** both   **19.** neither   **21.** true   **23.** false
25. true   **27.** false   **29.** true   **31.** true   **33.** false
35. true   **37.** true   **39.** false   **41. (a)** 64   **(b)** 63
43. (a) 32   **(b)** 31   **45.** {5, 7, 9, 10}   **47.** {2}   **49.** ∅
51. {Higher cost, Lower cost, Educational, More time to
see the sights in California, Less time to see the sights in
California, Cannot visit relatives along the way, Can visit
relatives along the way}   **53.** {Higher cost, More time to
see the sights in California, Cannot visit relatives along
the way}   **55.** ∅   **57.** {A, B, C, D, E} (All are present.)
59. {A, B, C}, {A, B, D}, {A, B, E}, {A, C, D}, {A, C, E},
{A, D, E}, {B, C, D}, {B, C, E}, {B, D, E}, {C, D, E}
61. {A}, {B}, {C}, {D}, {E}   **63.** 32
65. $2^{25} - 1 = 33{,}554{,}431$ **67. (a)** 15   **(b)** 16; It is now
possible to select *no* bills.   **69. (a)** s **(b)** s **(c)** $2s$
(d) Adding one more element will always double the
number of subsets, so the expression 2^n is true in general.

2.3 Exercises *(pages 65–68)*
1. B   **3.** A   **5.** E   **7.** {a, c}   **9.** {a, b, c, d, e, f}
11. {a, b, c, d, e, f, g}   **13.** {b, d, f}   **15.** {d, f}
17. {a, b, c, e, g}   **19.** {a, c, e, g}   **21.** {a}   **23.** {e, g}
25. {e, g}   **27.** {d, f}   **29.** {e, b, g}
**In Exercises 31–35, there may be other acceptable
descriptions.**
31. the set of all elements that either are in *A*, or are not
in *B* and not in *C*   **33.** the set of all elements that are in
C but not in *B*, or are in *A*   **35.** the set of all elements
that are in *A* but not in *C*, or in *B* but not in *C*
37. {e, h, c, l, b}   **39.** {l, b}   **41.** {e, h, c, l, b}   **43.** the set
of all tax returns showing business income or filed in 2009
45. the set of all tax returns filed in 2009 without
itemized deductions   **47.** the set of all tax returns with
itemized deductions or showing business income, but not
selected for audit   **49.** always true   **51.** always true
53. not always true   **55. (a)** {1, 3, 5, 2}   **(b)** {1, 2, 3, 5}
(c) For any sets *X* and *Y*, $X \cup Y = Y \cup X$.
57. (a) {1, 3, 5, 2, 4}   **(b)** {1, 3, 5, 2, 4}   **(c)** For any
sets *X*, *Y*, and *Z*, $X \cup (Y \cup Z) = (X \cup Y) \cup Z$.
59. (a) {4}   **(b)** {4}   **(c)** For any sets *X* and *Y*,
$(X \cup Y)' = X' \cap Y'$.   **61.** $X \cup \emptyset = X$; For any set *X*,
$X \cup \emptyset = X$.   **63.** true   **65.** false   **67.** true   **69.** true

71. $A \times B = \{(2, 4), (2, 9), (8, 4), (8, 9), (12, 4), (12, 9)\}$;
$B \times A = \{(4, 2), (4, 8), (4, 12), (9, 2), (9, 8), (9, 12)\}$
73. $A \times B = \{(d, p), (d, i), (d, g), (o, p), (o, i),$
$(o, g), (g, p), (g, i), (g, g)\}; B \times A = \{(p, d), (p, o),$
$(p, g), (i, d), (i, o), (i, g), (g, d), (g, o), (g, g)\}$
75. $n(A \times B) = 6; n(B \times A) = 6$
77. $n(A \times B) = 210; n(B \times A) = 210$ **79.** 6

81.

83.
$B \cap A'$

85.
$A' \cup B$

87.
$B' \cup A$

89.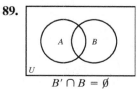
$B' \cap B = \emptyset$

91.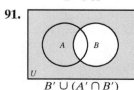
$B' \cup (A' \cap B')$

93.
$U' = \emptyset$

95.

97.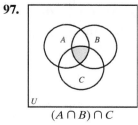
$(A \cap B) \cap C$

99.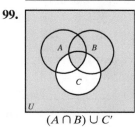
$(A \cap B) \cup C'$

101.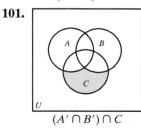
$(A' \cap B') \cap C$

103.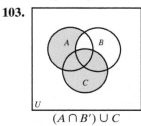
$(A \cap B') \cup C$

105.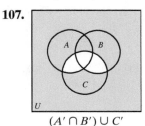
$(A \cap B') \cap C'$

107.
$(A' \cap B') \cup C'$

109. $A' \cap B'$, or $(A \cup B)'$

111. $(A \cup B) \cap (A \cap B)'$, or $(A \cup B) - (A \cap B)$, or $(A - B) \cup (B - A)$

113. $(A \cap B) \cup (A \cap C)$, or $A \cap (B \cup C)$

115. $(A \cap B) \cap C'$, or $(A \cap B) - C$

117. $A \cap B = \emptyset$ **119.** This statement is true for any set A.

121. $A = \emptyset$ **123.** $A = \emptyset$ **125.** $A = \emptyset$ **127.** $B \subseteq A$

129. always true **131.** always true

133. not always true **135.** always true

137. (a) $\{x \mid x \text{ is a real number}\}$ **(b)** $\emptyset$

2.4 Exercises (pages 71–74)

1. (a) 5 **(b)** 7 **(c)** 0 **(d)** 2 **(e)** 8 **3. (a)** 1 **(b)** 3
(c) 4 **(d)** 0 **(e)** 2 **(f)** 8 **(g)** 2 **(h)** 6 **5.** 21
7. 7 **9.** 35

11.

13.

15.

17.

19. (a) 2 **(b)** 4 **21. (a)** 25 **(b)** 20 **(c)** 12 **(d)** 10
(e) 19 **23. (a)** 37 **(b)** 38 **25. (a)** 500 **(b)** 91
27. (a) 31 **(b)** 24 **(c)** 11 **(d)** 45 **29. (a)** 1
(b) 1, 2, 3, 4, 5, 6, 7, 8, 9, 10, 11, 12, 13, 14, 15
(c) 1, 2, 3, 4, 5, 9, 11 **(d)** 5, 8, 13 **31. (a)** 9 **(b)** 9
(c) 20 **(d)** 20 **(e)** 27 **(f)** 15 **33.** Answers will vary.

Extension Exercises (pages 79–80)

1. B; 1 **3.** A; $\aleph_0$ **5.** F; 0
7. (Other correspondences are possible.)

$$\{I, \quad II, \quad III\}$$
$$\updownarrow \quad \updownarrow \quad \updownarrow$$
$$\{x, \quad y, \quad z\}$$

9. (Other correspondences are possible.)

$$\{a, \quad d, \quad i, \quad t, \quad o, \quad n\}$$
$$\updownarrow \quad \updownarrow \quad \updownarrow \quad \updownarrow \quad \updownarrow \quad \updownarrow$$
$$\{a, \quad n, \quad s, \quad w, \quad e, \quad r\}$$

11. 11 **13.** 0 **15.** $\aleph_0$ **17.** $\aleph_0$ **19.** $\aleph_0$ **21.** 12
23. $\aleph_0$ **25.** both **27.** equivalent **29.** equivalent

31. $\{2, \quad 4, \quad 6, \quad 8, \quad \ldots, \quad 2n, \quad \ldots\}$
$\;\;\;\;\updownarrow \quad \updownarrow \quad \updownarrow \quad \updownarrow \qquad \updownarrow$
$\{1, \quad 2, \quad 3, \quad 4, \quad \ldots, \quad n, \quad \ldots\}$

33. $\{1{,}000{,}000, \quad 2{,}000{,}000, \quad 3{,}000{,}000, \quad \ldots, \quad 1{,}000{,}000n, \quad \ldots\}$
$\quad\;\;\updownarrow \qquad\qquad \updownarrow \qquad\qquad \updownarrow \qquad\qquad\qquad \updownarrow$
$\{\quad 1, \qquad\quad 2, \qquad\quad 3, \qquad \ldots, \qquad n, \qquad \ldots\}$

35. $\{2, \quad 4, \quad 8, \quad 16, \quad 32, \quad \ldots, \quad 2^n, \quad \ldots\}$
$\;\;\;\updownarrow \quad \updownarrow \quad \updownarrow \quad \updownarrow \quad \updownarrow \qquad \updownarrow$
$\{1, \quad 2, \quad 3, \quad 4, \quad 5, \quad \ldots, \quad n, \quad \ldots\}$

37. This statement is not always true. For example, let $A =$ the set of counting numbers, $B =$ the set of real numbers.

39. This statement is not always true. For example, A could be the set of all subsets of the set of reals. Then $n(A)$ would be an infinite number *greater* than c.

41. (a) Rays emanating from point P will establish a geometric pairing of the points on the semicircle with the points on the line.

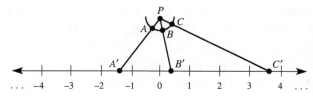

(b) The set of real numbers is infinite, having been placed in a one-to-one correspondence with a proper subset of itself.

43. $\{3, \quad 6, \quad 9, \quad 12, \quad \ldots, \quad 3n, \quad \ldots\}$
$\;\;\;\updownarrow \quad \updownarrow \quad \updownarrow \quad \updownarrow \qquad \updownarrow$
$\{6, \quad 9, \quad 12, \quad 15, \quad \ldots, \quad 3n + 3, \quad \ldots\}$

45. $\left\{\dfrac{3}{4}, \; \dfrac{3}{8}, \; \dfrac{3}{12}, \; \dfrac{3}{16}, \; \ldots, \; \dfrac{3}{4n}, \; \ldots\right\}$
$\quad\updownarrow \quad \updownarrow \quad \updownarrow \quad \updownarrow \qquad\;\; \updownarrow$
$\left\{\dfrac{3}{8}, \; \dfrac{3}{12}, \; \dfrac{3}{16}, \; \dfrac{3}{20}, \; \ldots, \; \dfrac{3}{4n + 4}, \; \ldots\right\}$

47. $\left\{\dfrac{1}{9}, \; \dfrac{1}{18}, \; \dfrac{1}{27}, \; \ldots, \; \dfrac{1}{9n}, \; \ldots\right\}$
$\quad\updownarrow \quad \updownarrow \quad \updownarrow \qquad\;\; \updownarrow$
$\left\{\dfrac{1}{18}, \; \dfrac{1}{27}, \; \dfrac{1}{36}, \; \ldots, \; \dfrac{1}{9n + 9}, \; \ldots\right\}$

49. Answers will vary. **51.** Answers will vary.

Chapter 2 Test (pages 81–82)

1. $\{a, b, c, d, e\}$ **2.** $\{a, b, d\}$ **3.** $\{c, f, g, h\}$ **4.** $\{a, c\}$
5. true **6.** false **7.** true **8.** true **9.** false **10.** true
11. true **12.** true **13.** 8 **14.** 15
Answers may vary in Exercises 15.–18. **15.** the set of odd integers between -4 and 10 **16.** the set of months of the year **17.** $\{x \mid x \text{ is a negative integer}\}$ **18.** $\{x \mid x$ is a multiple of 8 between 20 and 90$\}$ **19.** $\subseteq$ **20.** neither

21.

$X \cup Y'$

22.

$X' \cap Y$

23.

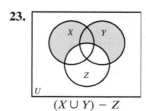

$(X \cup Y) - Z$

24.

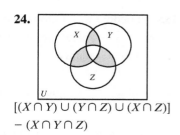

$[(X \cap Y) \cup (Y \cap Z) \cup (X \cap Z)]$
$- (X \cap Y \cap Z)$

25. {Electric razor}   **26.** {Adding machine, Barometer, Pendulum clock, Thermometer}   **27.** {Electric razor}
28. Answers will vary.   **29. (a)** 22   **(b)** 12   **(c)** 28
30. (a) 16   **(b)** 32   **(c)** 33   **(d)** 45   **(e)** 14   **(f)** 26

CHAPTER 3 INTRODUCTION TO LOGIC

3.1 Exercises *(pages 88–90)*

1. statement   **3.** not a statement   **5.** statement
7. statement   **9.** statement   **11.** not a statement
13. statement   **15.** compound   **17.** not compound
19. not compound   **21.** compound   **23.** Her aunt's name is not Hermione.   **25.** At least one dog does not have its day.   **27.** No book is longer than this book.
29. At least one computer repairman can play blackjack.
31. Someone does not love somebody sometime.
33. $x \le 12$ **35.** $x < 5$ **37.** Answers will vary.
39. She does not have green eyes.   **41.** She has green eyes and he is 60 years old.   **43.** She does not have green eyes or he is 60 years old.   **45.** She does not have green eyes or he is not 60 years old.   **47.** It is not the case that she does not have green eyes and he is 60 years old.
49. $p \wedge \sim q$ **51.** $\sim p \vee q$ **53.** $\sim(p \vee q)$ or, equivalently, $\sim p \wedge \sim q$ **55.** Answers will vary.
57. C   **59.** A, B   **61.** A, C   **63.** B   **65.** true
67. true   **69.** true   **71.** true   **73.** false   **75.** Answers will vary.   **77.** Every person here has done that at one time or another.

3.2 Exercises *(pages 99–100)*

1. false   **3.** true   **5.** They must both be false.   **7.** T
9. T   **11.** F   **13.** T   **15.** T   **17.** T   **19.** It is a disjunction, because it means "$6 > 2$ or $6 = 2$."   **21.** T
23. F   **25.** T   **27.** T   **29.** F   **31.** F   **33.** T   **35.** T
37. T   **39.** 4   **41.** 16   **43.** 128   **45.** seven   **47.** FFTF
49. FTTT   **51.** TTTT   **53.** FFFT   **55.** TFFF
57. FFFFTFFF   **59.** FTFTTTTT
61. TTTTTTTTTTTFTTT   **63.** You can't pay me now and you can't pay me later.   **65.** It is not summer or there is snow.   **67.** I did not say yes or she did not say no.   **69.** $6 - 1 \ne 5$ or $9 + 13 = 7$ **71.** Neither Prancer nor Vixen will lead Santa's reindeer sleigh next Christmas.

73. T   **75.** F   **77.**

p	q	$p \veebar q$
T	T	F
T	F	T
F	T	T
F	F	F

79. F   **81.** T   **83.** The lady is behind Door 2. *Reasoning*: Suppose that the sign on Door 1 is true. Then the sign on Door 2 would also be true, but this is impossible. So the sign on Door 2 must be true, and the sign on Door 1 must be false. Because the sign on Door 1 says the lady is in Room 1, and this is false, the lady must be behind Door 2.

3.3 Exercises *(pages 107–109)*

1. If you see it on the Internet, then you can believe it.
3. If an integer is divisible by 10, then it is divisible by 5.
5. If the soldier is a marine, then the soldier loves boot camp.   **7.** If it is a panda, then it does not live in Idaho.
9. If it is an opium-eater, then it has no self-command.
11. true   **13.** true   **15.** false   **17.** true   **19.** Answers will vary.   **21.** F   **23.** T   **25.** T   **27.** If they do not raise alpacas, then he trains dogs.   **29.** If she has a bird for a pet, then they raise alpacas and he trains dogs.   **31.** If he does not train dogs, then they do not raise alpacas or she has a bird for a pet.   **33.** $b \rightarrow p$ **35.** $p \rightarrow \sim s$
37. $p \wedge (s \rightarrow \sim b)$ **39.** $p \rightarrow s$ **41.** T   **43.** F
45. T   **47.** F   **49.** T   **51.** T   **53.** Answers will vary.
55. TTTF   **57.** TTFT   **59.** TTTT; tautology   **61.** TFTF
63. TTTTTFT   **65.** TTTFTTTTTTTTTTTT
67. one   **69.** That is an authentic Rolex watch and I am not surprised.   **71.** The English measures are not converted to metric measures and the spacecraft does not crash on the surface of Saturn.   **73.** You want to be happy for the rest of your life and you make a pretty woman your wife.   **75.** You do not give your plants tender, loving care or they flourish.   **77.** She does or he will.   **79.** The person is not a resident of Pensacola or is a resident of Florida.   **81.** equivalent   **83.** equivalent
85. not equivalent   **87.** equivalent   **89.** equivalent
91. $(p \wedge q) \vee (p \wedge \sim q)$; The statement simplifies to p.
93. $p \vee (\sim q \wedge r)$ **95.** $\sim p \vee (p \vee q)$; The statement simplifies to T.

97. The statement simplifies to $p \wedge q$.

99. The statement simplifies to F.

101. The statement simplifies to $(r \wedge \sim p) \wedge q$.

103. The statement simplifies to $p \vee q$.

105. $525.60

3.4 Exercises *(pages 114–115)*

1. (a) If you were an hour, then beauty would be a minute. **(b)** If beauty were not a minute, then you would not be an hour. **(c)** If you were not an hour, then beauty would not be a minute. **3. (a)** If you don't fix it, then it ain't broke. **(b)** If it's broke, then fix it. **(c)** If you fix it, then it's broke. **5. (a)** If it is dangerous to your health, then you walk in front of a moving car. **(b)** If you do not walk in front of a moving car, then it is not dangerous to your health. **(c)** If it is not dangerous to your health, then you do not walk in front of a moving car. **7. (a)** If they flock together, then they are birds of a feather. **(b)** If they are not birds of a feather, then they do not flock together. **(c)** If they do not flock together, then they are not birds of a feather. **9. (a)** If he comes, then you built it. **(b)** If you don't build it, then he won't come. **(c)** If he doesn't come, then you didn't build it. **11. (a)** $\sim q \rightarrow p$ **(b)** $\sim p \rightarrow q$ **(c)** $q \rightarrow \sim p$ **13. (a)** $\sim q \rightarrow \sim p$ **(b)** $p \rightarrow q$ **(c)** $q \rightarrow p$ **15. (a)** $(q \vee r) \rightarrow p$ **(b)** $\sim p \rightarrow (\sim q \wedge \sim r)$ **(c)** $(\sim q \wedge \sim r) \rightarrow \sim p$ **17.** Answers will vary. **19.** If it is muddy, then I'll wear my galoshes. **21.** If 19 is positive, then $19 + 1$ is positive. **23.** If a number is an integer, then it is a rational number. **25.** If I do logic puzzles, then I am driven crazy. **27.** If Jeff Marsalis is to shave, then he must have a day's growth of beard. **29.** If I go from Boardwalk to Baltic Avenue, then I pass GO. **31.** If a number is a whole number, then it is an integer. **33.** If their pitching improves, then the Nationals will win the pennant. **35.** If the figure is a rectangle, then it is a parallelogram with a right angle. **37.** If a triangle has two perpendicular sides, then it is a right triangle. **39.** If a two-digit number whose units digit is 5 is squared, then the square will end in 25. **41.** D **43.** Answers will vary. **45.** true **47.** false **49.** false **51.** contrary **53.** consistent **55.** contrary **57.** consistent **59.** Answers will vary. One example is: That man is Otis Taylor. That man sells books.

3.5 Exercises *(pages 119–120)*

1. valid **3.** invalid **5.** valid **7.** invalid **9.** invalid **11.** invalid **13.** yes

15. All people with blue eyes have blond hair.
Natalie Graham does not have blond hair.
Natalie Graham does not have blue eyes.
17. invalid **19.** valid **21.** invalid **23.** valid **25.** invalid **27.** invalid **29.** valid

Extension Exercises *(pages 122–124)*

1. Drew, spanakopita, Fresh Air, spearmint; Ilse, buffalo-chicken sandwich, Deltoids, cinnamon; Nash, French onion soup, Liplickers, vanilla; Uma, tuna-salad sandwich, TKO, wintergreen; Xerxes, garlic shrimp, Inti-mints, orange **3.** 1st, Earl, Ox, fire; 2nd, Philip, Rooster, metal; 3rd, Toni, Cow, water; 4th, Lucy, Dragon, earth; 5th, Ivana, Horse, wood

5.

7	4	2	1	6	8	9	3	5
3	1	9	4	5	7	6	2	8
8	6	5	9	3	2	7	1	4
6	2	4	7	8	9	1	5	3
1	3	8	5	4	6	2	9	7
5	9	7	2	1	3	8	4	6
2	5	3	8	7	1	4	6	9
9	7	6	3	2	4	5	8	1
4	8	1	6	9	5	3	7	2

7.

8	3	9	6	5	7	2	4	1
7	1	2	9	4	3	8	5	6
4	5	6	2	1	8	3	7	9
2	6	7	1	9	4	5	3	8
3	9	1	8	2	5	4	6	7
5	4	8	7	3	6	1	9	2
1	2	3	5	6	9	7	8	4
9	8	4	3	7	2	6	1	5
6	7	5	4	8	1	9	2	3

9.

6	1	7	9	2	3	5	8	4
4	5	9	8	6	1	2	7	3
3	2	8	4	5	7	9	6	1
8	3	5	6	4	9	1	2	7
7	6	1	5	3	2	8	4	9
2	9	4	7	1	8	3	5	6
5	7	2	3	9	6	4	1	8
1	8	3	2	7	4	6	9	5
9	4	6	1	8	5	7	3	2

3.6 Exercises *(pages 130–133)*

1. valid by reasoning by transitivity **3.** valid by modus ponens **5.** fallacy by fallacy of the converse **7.** valid by modus tollens **9.** fallacy by fallacy of the inverse **11.** valid by disjunctive syllogism **13.** invalid **15.** valid **17.** invalid **19.** valid **21.** invalid **23.** invalid **25.** invalid

27. Every time something squeaks, I use WD-40.
Every time I use WD-40, I go to the hardware store.
Every time something squeaks, I go to the hardware store.

29. valid **31.** invalid **33.** invalid **35.** valid **37.** valid **39.** If I tell you the time, then my life will be miserable. **41.** If it is my poultry, then it is a duck.

43. If it is a guinea pig, then it is hopelessly ignorant of music. **45.** If it is a teachable kitten, then it does not have green eyes. **47.** If I can read it, then I have not filed it. **49. (a)** $p \to {\sim}s$ **(b)** $r \to s$ **(c)** $q \to p$ **(d)** None of my poultry are officers. **51. (a)** $r \to {\sim}s$ **(b)** $u \to t$ **(c)** ${\sim}r \to p$ **(d)** ${\sim}u \to {\sim}q$ **(e)** $t \to s$ **(f)** All pawnbrokers are honest. **53. (a)** $r \to w$ **(b)** ${\sim}u \to {\sim}t$ **(c)** $v \to {\sim}s$ **(d)** $x \to r$ **(e)** ${\sim}q \to t$ **(f)** $y \to p$ **(g)** $w \to s$ **(h)** ${\sim}x \to {\sim}q$ **(i)** $p \to {\sim}u$ **(j)** I can't read any of Brown's letters.

Collaborative Investigation *(pages 134–135)*

1. Jan. 1, Vandyke Facility, *Penchant*, repair satellite; Feb. 5, San Simeon Launch Center, *Falconer*, investigate radiation; Mar. 3, Cape Carnival, *Liberty*, land on moon; Apr. 4, Willard Island, *Twilight*, test propulsion; May 2, Eddings Air Force Base, *Bravura*, measure magnetic fields

2.

5	10	11	4	1	6	14	2	16	7	12	8	15	9	13	3
12	15	7	3	8	4	9	13	2	11	5	1	16	10	14	6
13	8	6	14	11	16	10	7	9	15	3	4	5	1	12	2
9	1	2	16	5	3	12	15	6	14	10	13	11	4	7	8
11	13	9	10	2	14	16	3	1	12	8	6	7	15	4	5
7	6	16	2	12	10	15	4	13	5	9	11	1	3	8	14
1	4	15	12	6	8	11	5	3	16	7	14	9	2	10	13
3	14	8	5	13	9	7	1	4	2	12	6	16	11
4	7	5	11	14	12	3	10	8	6	2	15	13	16	1	9
15	16	1	9	7	5	2	11	10	3	13	12	14	8	6	4
2	12	10	6	9	13	4	8	11	1	14	16	3	5	15	7
14	3	13	8	15	1	6	16	5	9	4	7	2	12	11	10
10	9	14	7	16	2	8	12	15	13	6	3	4	11	5	1
6	2	12	15	4	11	5	14	7	8	1	9	10	13	3	16
16	5	4	13	3	7	1	6	12	10	11	2	8	14	9	15
8	11	3	1	10	15	13	9	14	4	16	5	6	7	2	12

Chapter 3 Test *(pages 135–136)*

1. $6 - 3 \neq 3$ **2.** Some men are not created equal.
3. No members of the class went on the field trip.
4. That's the way you feel and I won't accept it.
5. She did not apply or did not get a student loan.
6. ${\sim}p \to q$ **7.** $p \to q$ **8.** ${\sim}q \leftrightarrow {\sim}p$ **9.** You won't love me and I will love you. **10.** It is not the case that you will love me or I will not love you. (Equivalently: You won't love me and I will love you.) **11.** T **12.** T **13.** T **14.** F **15.** Answers will vary. **16. (a)** The antecedent must be true and the consequent must be false. **(b)** Both component statements must be true. **(c)** Both component statements must be false. **17.** TFFF **18.** TTTT (tautology) **19.** false **20.** true
Wording may vary in the answers for Exercises 21–25.
21. If the number is an integer, then it is a rational number. **22.** If a polygon is a rhombus, then it is a quadrilateral. **23.** If a number is divisible by 4, then it is divisible by 2. **24.** If she digs dinosaur bones, then she is a paleontologist. **25. (a)** If the graph helps me understand it, then a picture paints a thousand words. **(b)** If a picture doesn't paint a thousand words, then the graph won't help me understand it. **(c)** If the graph doesn't help me understand it, then a picture doesn't paint a thousand words. **26. (a)** $(q \wedge r) \to {\sim}p$ **(b)** $p \to ({\sim}q \vee {\sim}r)$ **(c)** $({\sim}q \vee {\sim}r) \to p$ **27.** valid **28. (a)** A **(b)** F **(c)** C **(d)** D **29.** valid **30.** invalid

CHAPTER 5 NUMBER THEORY

5.1 Exercises *(pages 184–185)*

1. true **3.** true **5.** false **7.** true **9.** 1, 2, 3, 4, 6, 12 **11.** 1, 2, 4, 7, 14, 28 **13. (a)** no **(b)** yes **(c)** no **(d)** no **(e)** no **(f)** no **(g)** no **(h)** no **(i)** no **15. (a)** yes **(b)** yes **(c)** yes **(d)** yes **(e)** yes **(f)** yes **(g)** yes **(h)** yes **(i)** yes **17. (a)** Answers will vary. **(b)** 13 **(c)** square root; square root; square root **(d)** prime **19.** 2, 3; no **21.** It must be 0.

23.

$$1320 = 3 \cdot 2^3 \cdot 5 \cdot 11 = 2^3 \cdot 3 \cdot 5 \cdot 11$$

1320
├ 12 — 3, 4 (4 → 2, 2)
└ 110 — 10, 11 (10 → 2, 5)

25. $2^3 \cdot 3 \cdot 7$ **27.** $2^2 \cdot 3^2 \cdot 13$ **29.** yes **31.** no **33.** no **35.** yes **37.** The number must be divisible by both 3 and 5. That is, the sum of the digits must be divisible by 3, and the last digit must be 5 or 0. **39.** 0, 2, 4, 6, 8 **41.** 0, 4, 8 **43.** 0, 6 **45.** 8 **47.** 27 **49.** leap year **51.** not a leap year **53.** Answers will vary. **55.** Answers will vary.

5.2 Exercises *(pages 189–190)*

1. true **3.** false **5.** false **7.** $37 = 1^2 + 6^2$; $41 = 4^2 + 5^2$ **9.** Answers will vary. **11.** $41^2 - 41 + 41 = 41^2$, and 41^2 is not a prime. **13.** B **15. (a)** 65,537 **(b)** 251 **17.** Answers will vary. **19.** Answers will vary. **21.** composite; $30{,}031 = 59 \cdot 509$ **23.** 63 **25.** $2^p - 1$ **27.** 3 and 31

5.3 Exercises *(pages 195–197)*

1. true **3.** true **5.** true **7.** false **9.** true **11.** The sum of the proper divisors is 496: $1 + 2 + 4 + 8 + 16 + 31 + 62 + 124 + 248 = 496$. **13.** 8191 is prime; 33,550,336 **15.** $1 + \frac{1}{2} + \frac{1}{3} + \frac{1}{6} = 2$ **17.** deficient **19.** abundant **21.** 12, 18, 20, 24 **23.** $1 + 3 + 5 + 7 + 9 + 15 + 21 + 27 + 35 + 45 + 63 + 105 + 135 + 189 + 315 = 975$, and $975 > 945$, so 945 is abundant.

25. $1 + 2 + 4 + 8 + 16 + 32 + 37 + 74 + 148 + 296 + 592 = 1210$ and $1 + 2 + 5 + 10 + 11 + 22 + 55 + 110 + 121 + 242 + 605 = 1184$ **27.** $5 + 11$
29. $7 + 23$ **31. (a)** Let $a = 5$ and $b = 3$; $11 = 5 + 2 \cdot 3$ **(b)** $17 = 3 + 2 \cdot 7 = 7 + 2 \cdot 5 = 11 + 2 \cdot 3 = 13 + 2 \cdot 2$ **33.** 41 and 43 **35. (a)** $3^4 - 1 = 80$ is divisible by 5. **(b)** $2^6 - 1 = 63$ is divisible by 7.
37. $5^2 + 2 = 27 = 3^3$ **39.** Answers will vary. **41.** False; For the first six, the sequence is 6, 8, 6, 8, 6, 6. **43.** one; not happy **45.** both; happy **47.** Answers will vary.
49. B **51.** 7; yes **53.** 15; no **55.** 27; no
57. 24; 23; 25; yes; no **59.** Answers will vary. **61.** B

5.4 Exercises *(pages 203–205)*
1. true **3.** true **5.** false **7.** true **9.** true **11.** 20
13. 60 **15.** 13 **17.** 18 **19.** 10 **21.** 6 **23.** 8 **25.** 12
27. 80 **29.** Answers will vary. **31.** 270 **33.** 450
35. 840 **37.** 96 **39.** 225 **41.** 2160 **43.** 224 **45.** 216
47. 2400 **49. (a)** $p^b q^c r^c$ **(b)** $p^a q^a r^b$ **51.** 30 **53.** 15
55. 12 **57. (a)** 6 **(b)** 36 **59. (a)** 18 **(b)** 216
61. p and q are relatively prime. **63.** Answers will vary.
65. 144th **67.** 48 **69.** \$600; 25 books

Extension Exercises *(page 211)*
1. 3 **3.** 4 **5.** 5 **7.** 2 **9.** 2 **11.** 13 **13.** 12 **15.** 3
17. 55; 40 **19.** 65; 48 **21.** 5 **23.** 61 **25. (a)** 27
(b) 35 **27. (a)** 11 **(b)** 23 **29.** Answers will vary.

5.5 Exercises *(pages 216–218)*
1. 2584 **3.** 28,657 **5.** $\frac{1 + \sqrt{5}}{2}$
7. $1 + 1 + 2 + 3 + 5 + 8 = 21 - 1$; Each expression is equal to 20. **9.** $1 + 2 + 5 + 13 + 34 + 89 = 144$; Each expression is equal to 144. **11.** $13^2 - 5^2 = 144$; Each expression is equal to 144. **13.** $1 - 2 + 5 - 13 + 34 - 89 = -82$; Each expression is equal to -64.
15. (There are other ways to do this.) **(a)** $37 = 34 + 3$
(b) $40 = 34 + 5 + 1$ **(c)** $52 = 34 + 13 + 5$
17. (a) The greatest common factor of 10 and 4 is 2, and the greatest common factor of $F_{10} = 55$ and $F_4 = 3$ is $F_2 = 1$. **(b)** The greatest common factor of 12 and 6 is 6, and the greatest common factor of $F_{12} = 144$ and $F_6 = 8$ is $F_6 = 8$. **(c)** The greatest common factor of 14 and 6 is 2, and the greatest common factor of $F_{14} = 377$ and $F_6 = 8$ is $F_2 = 1$. **19. (a)** $5 \cdot 34 - 13^2 = 1$ **(b)** $13^2 - 3 \cdot 55 = 4$
(c) $2 \cdot 89 - 13^2 = 9$ **(d)** The difference will be 25, because we are obtaining the squares of the terms of the Fibonacci sequence. $13^2 - 1 \cdot 144 = 25 = 5^2$. **21.** 199
23. Each sum is 2 less than a Lucas number.
25. (a) $8 \cdot 18 = 144$; Each expression is equal to 144.
(b) $8 + 21 = 29$; Each expression is equal to 29.

(c) $8 + 18 = 2 \cdot 13$; Each expression is equal to 26.
(d) $18 + 47 = 5 \cdot 13$; Each expression is equal to 65.
27. 3, 4, 5 **29.** 16, 30, 34 **31.** The sums are 1, 1, 2, 3, 5, 8, 13. They are terms of the Fibonacci sequence.
33. $\frac{1 + \sqrt{5}}{2} \approx 1.618033989$ and $\frac{1 - \sqrt{5}}{2} \approx -0.618033989$. After the decimal point, the digits are the same.
35. 377 **37.** 17,711

Chapter 5 Test *(pages 219–220)*
1. false **2.** true **3.** true **4.** true **5.** true **6.** false
7. (a) yes **(b)** no **(c)** yes **(d)** yes **(e)** no **(f)** yes
(g) no **(h)** yes **(i)** no **8. (a)** composite **(b)** prime
(c) neither **9.** $2^3 \cdot 3^2 \cdot 5 \cdot 7$ **10.** Answers will vary.
11. (a) abundant **(b)** deficient **(c)** perfect **12.** C
13. 59 and 61 **14.** 27 **15.** 450 **16.** Monday
17. 75,025 **18.** $89 - (8 + 13 + 21 + 34) = 13$; Each expression is equal to 13. **19.** B **20.** 1, 5, 6, 11, 17, 28, 45, 73 **21.** The process will yield 19 for any term chosen. **22.** A **23.** Answers will vary. **24.** Answers will vary.

CHAPTER 6 THE REAL NUMBERS AND THEIR REPRESENTATIONS

6.1 Exercises *(pages 228–230)*
1. 5 **3.** 0 **5.** $\sqrt{14}$ (There are others.) **7.** true
9. true **11. (a)** 3, 7 **(b)** 0, 3, 7 **(c)** $-9, 0, 3, 7$
(d) $-9, -1\frac{1}{4}, -\frac{3}{5}, 0, 3, 5.9, 7$ **(e)** $-\sqrt{7}, \sqrt{5}$ **(f)** All are real numbers. **13.** Answers will vary. **15.** 1046 **17.** 5436
19. $-220°$ **21.** 30; 15°; $-5°$ **23. (a)** Pacific Ocean, Indian Ocean, Caribbean Sea, South China Sea, Gulf of California **(b)** Point Success, Ranier, Matlalcueyetl, Steele, McKinley **(c)** true **(d)** false

25. **27.**

29. (a) A **(b)** A **(c)** B **(d)** B **31. (a)** 2 **(b)** 2
33. (a) -6 **(b)** 6 **35. (a)** -3 **(b)** 3 **37. (a)** 0
(b) 0 **39.** $a - b$ **41.** -12 **43.** -8 **45.** 3 **47.** $|-3|$, or 3 **49.** $-|-6|$, or -6 **51.** $|5 - 3|$, or 2 **53.** true
55. true **57.** true **59.** false **61.** true **63.** false
65. (a) Louisiana; It decreased 4.1%. **(b)** West Virginia; It increased 0.6%. **67.** fabric mills **Answers will vary in Exercises 69–73.** **69.** $\frac{1}{2}, \frac{5}{8}, 1\frac{3}{4}$ **71.** $-3\frac{1}{2}, -\frac{2}{3}, \frac{3}{7}$
73. $\sqrt{5}, \pi, -\sqrt{3}$

6.2 Exercises *(pages 238–242)*
1. negative **3.** $-3; 5$ **5.** Answers will vary. **7.** -20
9. -4 **11.** -11 **13.** 9 **15.** 20 **17.** 4 **19.** 24

21. −1296 **23.** 6 **25.** −6 **27.** 0 **29.** −6 **31.** 27
33. 39 **35.** −4 **37.** −2 **39.** not a real number **41.** 13
43. A, B, C **45.** commutative property of addition
47. inverse property of addition **49.** identity property of
multiplication **51.** associative property of addition
53. identity property of addition **55.** distributive property
57. inverse property of addition **59.** closure property of
multiplication **61.** (a) −2; 2 (b) commutative (c) Yes;
choose $a = b$. For example, let $a = b = 2$. Then $2 − 2 =$
$2 − 2$. **63.** (a) messing up your room (b) spending
money (c) decreasing the volume on your MP3 player
65. identity **67.** No, it does not hold true. **69.** −81
71. 81 **73.** −81 **75.** −81 **77.** (a) 25.9 (billion
dollars) (b) 58.2 (billion dollars) (c) 153.0 (billion
dollars) (d) 237.1 (billion dollars) **79.** (a) 2000: $129
billion; 2010: $206 billion; 2020: $74 billion; 2030:
−$501 billion (b) The cost of Social Security will
exceed revenue in 2030 by $501 billion. **81.** 16
83. $1045.55 **85.** 14,776 feet **87.** 45°F **89.** 112°F
91. −60°F **93.** 27 feet **95.** 469 B.C. **97.** $15,000
99. $2900

6.3 Exercises *(pages 251–254)*

1. A, C, D **3.** C **5.** $\frac{1}{3}$ **7.** $-\frac{3}{7}$ **Answers will vary in
Exercises 9 and 11.** **9.** $\frac{6}{16}, \frac{9}{24}, \frac{12}{32}$ **11.** $-\frac{10}{14}, -\frac{15}{21}, -\frac{20}{28}$
13. (a) $\frac{1}{3}$ (b) $\frac{1}{4}$ (c) $\frac{2}{5}$ (d) $\frac{1}{3}$ **15.** the dots in the
intersection of the triangle and the rectangle as a part
of the dots in the entire figure **17.** (a) O'Brien
(b) Goldberg (c) Goldberg (d) Kelly (e) Taylor
and Britz; $\frac{1}{2}$ **19.** $\frac{1}{2}$ **21.** $\frac{43}{48}$ **23.** $-\frac{5}{24}$ **25.** $\frac{23}{56}$ **27.** $\frac{27}{20}$
29. $\frac{5}{12}$ **31.** $\frac{1}{9}$ **33.** $\frac{3}{2}$ **35.** $\frac{3}{2}$ **37.** (a) $4\frac{1}{2}$ cups (b) $\frac{7}{8}$ cup
39. $\frac{13}{3}$ **41.** $\frac{29}{10}$ **43.** $6\frac{3}{4}$ **45.** $6\frac{1}{8}$ **47.** $-17\frac{7}{8}$ **49.** $\frac{9}{16}$ inch
51. 3 **53.** $\frac{3}{7}$ **55.** $-\frac{103}{89}$ **57.** $\frac{25}{9}$ **59.** $\frac{5}{8}$ **61.** $\frac{19}{30}$ **63.** $-\frac{3}{4}$
65. $53,221 **67.** $\frac{14}{19}$ **69.** $\frac{13}{29}$ **71.** $\frac{16}{14}$, or $\frac{8}{7}$ **73.** $\frac{5}{2}$ **75.** It
gives the rational number halfway between the two
integers (their average). **77.** 0.75 **79.** 0.1875 **81.** $0.\overline{27}$
83. $0.\overline{285714}$ **85.** $\frac{2}{5}$ **87.** $\frac{17}{20}$ **89.** $\frac{467}{500}$ **91.** repeating
93. terminating **95.** terminating **97.** (a) $0.\overline{3}$, or 0.333…
(b) $0.\overline{6}$, or 0.666… (c) $0.\overline{9}$, or 0.999… (d) $1 = 0.\overline{9}$
99. (a) $\frac{4}{5}$ (b) $\frac{4}{5}$ **101.** (a) $\frac{33}{50}$ (b) $\frac{33}{50}$

6.4 Exercises *(pages 261–264)*

1. rational **3.** irrational **5.** rational **7.** rational
9. irrational **11.** rational **13.** irrational **15.** (a) $0.\overline{8}$
(b) irrational; rational **17.** 6.244997998 **19.** 3.885871846
21. 29.73213749 **23.** 1.060660172 **25.** $5\sqrt{2}$; 7.071067812
27. $5\sqrt{3}$; 8.660254038 **29.** $12\sqrt{2}$; 16.97056275 **31.** $\frac{5\sqrt{6}}{6}$;
2.041241452 **33.** $\frac{\sqrt{7}}{2}$; 1.322875656 **35.** $\frac{\sqrt{21}}{3}$; 1.527525232

37. $3\sqrt{17}$ **39.** $4\sqrt{7}$ **41.** $10\sqrt{2}$ **43.** $3\sqrt{3}$
45.

47. The result is 3.1415929, which agrees with the first
seven digits in the decimal for π. **49.** 3 **51.** 4 **53.** 3.3
55. ϕ is positive, while its conjugate is negative. The units
digit of ϕ is 1, and the units digit of its conjugate is 0. The
decimal digits agree. **57.** It is just a coincidence that
1828 appears back-to-back early in the decimal. There
is no repetition indefinitely, which would be indicative
of a rational number. **59.** 2.5 seconds **61.** 15.3 miles
63. 392,000 square miles **65.** The area and the perimeter are both numerically equal to 36. **67.** 5.4 feet
69. (a) 70.5 mph (b) 59.8 mph (c) 53.9 mph **71.** 4
73. 7 **75.** 6 **77.** 1 **79.** 4 **81.** 8 **The number of
decimal digits shown will vary among caculator models
in Exercises 83–89.** **83.** 3.50339806 **85.** 5.828476683
87. 10.06565066 **89.** 5.578019845

6.5 Exercises *(pages 272–276)*

1. true **3.** false **5.** true **7.** true **9.** false **11.** 11.315
13. −4.215 **15.** 0.8224 **17.** 47.5 **19.** 31.6
21. $525 billion **23.** three (and you would have 0.01¢
left over) **25.** $0.06, or 6¢ **27.** 1000 **29.** (a) 0.031
(b) 0.035 **31.** 297 **33.** (a) 78.4 (b) 78.41
35. (a) 0.1 (b) 0.08 **37.** (a) 12.7 (b) 12.69 **39.** 42%
41. 36.5% **43.** 0.8% **45.** 210% **47.** 20% **49.** 1%
51. $37\frac{1}{2}$% **53.** 150% **55.** Answers will vary. **57.** (a) 5
(b) 24 (c) 8 (d) 0.5, or $\frac{1}{2}$ (e) 600 **59.** No, the price
is $57.60. **61.** (a) .586 (b) .519 (c) .463 (d) .395
63. 124.8 **65.** 2.94 **67.** 150% **69.** 600 **71.** 1.4%
73. 8% **75.** 3.8% **77.** 47.5% **79.** A **81.** C
83. about 139% **85.** (a) $14.7 − 40 \cdot 0.13$ (b) 9.5
(c) 8.075; walking (5 mph) **87.** 892% **89.** $4.50
91. $0.75 **93.** $12.00 **95.** $36.00 **97.** Answers will vary.

Extension Exercises *(page 279)*

1. $12i$ **3.** $-15i$ **5.** $i\sqrt{3}$ **7.** $5i\sqrt{3}$ **9.** −5 **11.** −18
13. −40 **15.** $\sqrt{2}$ **17.** $3i$ **19.** 6 **21.** 1 **23.** −1
25. $-i$ **27.** i

Chapter 6 Test *(pages 280–282)*

1. (a) 12 (b) 0, 12 (c) −4, 0, 12 (d) $-4, -\frac{3}{2}, -0.5,$
$0, 4.1, 12$ (e) $-\sqrt{5}, \sqrt{3}$ (f) $-4, -\sqrt{5}, -\frac{3}{2}, -0.5,$
$0, \sqrt{3}, 4.1, 12$ **2.** (a) C (b) B (c) D (d) A
3. (a) false (b) true (c) true (d) false **4.** 4 **5.** 10

6. 3   **7. (a)** Minnesota; 52.74%   **(b)** Maine; 10.63%
(c) false   **(d)** true   **8.** 5296 ft   **9. (a)** $2900   **(b)** −$4000
(c) −$21,300   **(d)** −$19,100   **10. (a)** E   **(b)** A   **(c)** B
(d) D   **(e)** F   **(f)** C   **11. (a)** Whitney and McElwain
(b) Moura and Dawkins   **(c)** Whitney   **(d)** Pritchard
and Miller; $\frac{2}{5}$ **(e)** McElwain ("J-Mac")   **12.** $\frac{11}{16}$ **13.** $\frac{57}{160}$
14. $-\frac{2}{5}$ **15.** $\frac{3}{2}$ **16. (a)** 0.45   **(b)** $0.41\overline{6}$ **17. (a)** $\frac{18}{25}$
(b) $\frac{58}{99}$ **18. (a)** irrational   **(b)** rational   **(c)** rational
(d) rational   **(e)** irrational   **(f)** irrational
19. (a) 12.247448714   **(b)** $5\sqrt{6}$ **20. (a)** 4.913538149
(b) $\frac{13\sqrt{7}}{7}$ **21. (a)** −45.254834   **(b)** $-32\sqrt{2}$ **22.** Answers
will vary.   **23. (a)** 13.81   **(b)** −0.315   **(c)** 38.7   **(d)** −24.3
24. (a) 9.04   **(b)** 9.045   **25. (a)** 16.65   **(b)** 101.5
26. (a) $26\frac{2}{3}$%   **(b)** $66\frac{2}{3}$%   **27.** D   **28.** 1656; 1008; 16%;
6%   **29.** 17,415,000   **30.** −13.8 (billion dollars)

CHAPTER 11 PROBABILITY

11.1 Exercises (pages 585–588)

1. (a) $\frac{1}{3}$ **(b)** $\frac{1}{3}$ **(c)** $\frac{1}{3}$ **3. (a)** $\frac{1}{2}$ **(b)** $\frac{1}{3}$ **(c)** $\frac{1}{6}$
5. (a) {1, 2, 3}   **(b)** 2   **(c)** 1   **(d)** 3   **(e)** $\frac{2}{3}$ **(f)** 2 to 1
7. (a) {11, 12, 13, 21, 22, 23, 31, 32, 33}   **(b)** $\frac{2}{3}$ **(c)** $\frac{1}{3}$
(d) $\frac{1}{3}$ **(e)** $\frac{4}{9}$ **9. (a)** 7 to 4   **(b)** 6 to 5   **(c)** 9 to 2
11. (a) $\frac{1}{50}$ **(b)** $\frac{2}{50} = \frac{1}{25}$ **(c)** $\frac{3}{50}$ **(d)** $\frac{4}{50} = \frac{2}{25}$
(e) $\frac{5}{50} = \frac{1}{10}$ **13. (a)** $\frac{1}{36}$ **(b)** $\frac{2}{36} = \frac{1}{18}$ **(c)** $\frac{3}{36} = \frac{1}{12}$
(d) $\frac{4}{36} = \frac{1}{9}$ **(e)** $\frac{5}{36}$ **(f)** $\frac{6}{36} = \frac{1}{6}$ **(g)** $\frac{5}{36}$ **(h)** $\frac{4}{36} = \frac{1}{9}$
(i) $\frac{3}{36} = \frac{1}{12}$ **(j)** $\frac{2}{36} = \frac{1}{18}$ **(k)** $\frac{1}{36}$ **15.** 0.329   **17.** $\frac{1}{9}$
19. $\frac{1}{4}$ **21.** $\frac{1}{4}$ **23. (a)** $\frac{3}{4}$ **(b)** $\frac{1}{4}$
25. $\frac{1}{250,000} = 0.000004$ **27.** $\frac{1}{4}$ **29.** $\frac{1}{4}$ **31.** $\frac{2}{4} = \frac{1}{2}$
33. $\frac{1}{500} = 0.002$ **35.** about 160   **37.** $\frac{2}{4} = \frac{1}{2}$ **39. (a)** 0
(b) no   **(c)** yes   **41.** Answers will vary.   **43.** $\frac{12}{31}$
45. $\frac{36}{2,598,960} \approx 0.00001385$ **47.** $\frac{624}{2,598,960} \approx 0.00024010$
49. $\frac{1}{4} \cdot \frac{5108}{2,598,960} \approx 0.00049135$ **51. (a)** $\frac{5}{9}$ **(b)** $\frac{49}{144}$
(c) $\frac{5}{48}$ **53.** $3 \cdot 1 \cdot 2 \cdot 1 \cdot 1 \cdot 1 = 6$; $\frac{6}{720} = \frac{1}{120} \approx 0.0083$
55. $4 \cdot 3! \cdot 3! = 144$; $\frac{144}{720} = \frac{1}{5} = 0.2$
57. $\frac{{}_2C_2}{{}_7C_2} = \frac{2}{21} \approx 0.095$ **59.** $\frac{{}_5C_3}{{}_{12}C_3} = \frac{1}{22} \approx 0.045$
61. $\frac{1}{{}_{26}P_3} \approx 0.000064$ **63.** $\frac{3}{28} \approx 0.107$
65. (a) $\frac{8}{9^2} = \frac{8}{81} \approx 0.099$ **(b)** $\frac{4}{{}_9C_2} = \frac{1}{9} \approx 0.111$ **67.** 1
69. $\frac{9}{9 \cdot 10} = \frac{1}{10}$ **71.** $\frac{1}{15}$

11.2 Exercises (pages 594–596)

1. yes   **3.** Answers will vary.   **5.** $\frac{1}{2}$ **7.** $\frac{5}{6}$ **9.** $\frac{2}{3}$
11. (a) $\frac{2}{13}$ **(b)** 2 to 11   **13. (a)** $\frac{11}{26}$ **(b)** 11 to 15
15. (a) $\frac{9}{13}$ **(b)** 9 to 4   **17.** $\frac{2}{3}$ **19.** $\frac{7}{36}$

21. $P(A) + P(B) + P(C) + P(D) = 1$ **23.** 0.005365
25. 0.971285   **27.** 0.76   **29.** 0.92   **31.** 6 to 19
33.

x	$P(x)$
3	0.1
4	0.1
5	0.2
6	0.2
7	0.2
8	0.1
9	0.1

35. $n(A') = s - a$
37. $P(A) + P(A') = 1$
39. 180   **41.** $\frac{2}{3}$ **43.** 1

11.3 Exercises (pages 603–606)

1. independent   **3.** not independent   **5.** independent
7. $\frac{52}{100} = \frac{13}{25}$ **9.** $\frac{69}{100}$ **11.** $\frac{14}{31}$ **13.** $\frac{4}{7} \cdot \frac{4}{7} = \frac{16}{49}$
15. $\frac{2}{7} \cdot \frac{1}{7} = \frac{2}{49}$ **17.** $\frac{4}{7} \cdot \frac{3}{6} = \frac{2}{7}$ **19.** $\frac{1}{6}$ **21.** 0
23. $\frac{12}{51} = \frac{4}{17}$ **25.** $\frac{12}{52} \cdot \frac{11}{51} = \frac{11}{221}$ **27.** $\frac{4}{52} \cdot \frac{11}{51} = \frac{11}{663}$
29. $\frac{1}{3}$ **31.** 1   **33.** $\frac{3}{10}$ (the same)
35. $\frac{1}{2} \cdot \frac{1}{2} \cdot \frac{1}{2} \cdot \frac{1}{2} \cdot \frac{1}{2} \cdot \frac{1}{2} = \frac{1}{64}$ **37.** 0.490   **39.** 0.027
41. 0.95   **43.** 0.23   **45.** $\frac{1}{20}$ **47.** $\frac{1}{5}$ **49.** $\frac{1}{5}$ **51. (a)** $\frac{3}{4}$
(b) $\frac{1}{2}$ **(c)** $\frac{5}{16}$ **53.** 0.2704   **55.** 0.2496
57. Answers will vary.   **59.** $\frac{1}{64} \approx 0.0156$ **61.** 10
63. 0.400   **65.** 0.080   **67.** $(0.90)^4 = 0.6561$
69. ${}_4C_2 \cdot (0.10) \cdot (0.20) \cdot (0.70)^2 = 0.0588$ **71.** 0.30
73. 0.49   **75.** Answers will vary.

11.4 Exercises (pages 610–612)

1. $\frac{1}{8}$ **3.** $\frac{3}{8}$ **5.** $\frac{3}{4}$ **7.** $\frac{1}{2}$ **9.** $\frac{3}{8}$ **11.** $x; n; n$ **13.** $\frac{7}{128}$
15. $\frac{35}{128}$ **17.** $\frac{21}{128}$ **19.** $\frac{1}{128}$ **21.** $\frac{25}{72}$ **23.** $\frac{1}{216}$ **25.** 0.041
27. 0.268   **29.** Answers will vary.   **31.** Answers will vary.
33. 0.016   **35.** 0.020   **37.** 0.137   **39.** 0.572   **41.** 0.669
43. 0.975   **45.** 0.883   **47.** $6p^2(1 - p)^2$
49. $\frac{1}{1024} \approx 0.001$ **51.** $\frac{45}{1024} \approx 0.044$
53. $\frac{210}{1024} = \frac{105}{512} \approx 0.205$ **55.** $\frac{772}{1024} \approx 0.754$

11.5 Exercises (pages 619–622)

1. Answers will vary.   **3.** $\frac{5}{2}$ **5.** $1   **7.** $0.50
9. no $\left(\text{expected net winnings: } -\frac{3}{4}\text{¢}\right)$ **11.** 1.69
13. (a) −$60   **(b)** $36,000   **(c)** $72,000   **15.** $0.46
17. $2700   **19.** 2.7   **21.** a decrease of 50   **23.** Answers
will vary.   **25.** Project C **27.** $2200   **29.** $81,000
31. Do not purchase the insurance (because
$86,000 > $81,000).   **33.** $1500; $3000; $17,500; $27,000
35. $56,000   **37.** 48.7%

Extension Exercises (page 625)

1. Answers will vary.   **3.** no   **5.** $\frac{18}{50} = 0.36$ (This is quite
close to 0.375, the theoretical value.)   **7.** $\frac{6}{50} = 0.12$
9. Answers will vary.   **11.** Answers will vary.

Chapter 11 Test (*page 627*)

1. Answers will vary. **2.** Answers will vary. **3.** 3 to 1
4. 25 to 1 **5.** 11 to 2 **6.** row 1: CC; row 2: cC, cc
7. $\frac{1}{2}$ **8.** 1 to 3 **9.** $\frac{7}{7} \cdot \frac{6}{7} \cdot \frac{5}{7} = \frac{30}{49}$ **10.** $\frac{7}{19}$
11. $1 - \left(\frac{30}{49} + \frac{1}{49}\right) = \frac{18}{49}$ **12.** $\frac{{}_2C_2}{{}_5C_2} = \frac{1}{10}$
13. $\frac{{}_3C_2}{{}_5C_2} = \frac{3}{10}$ **14.** $\frac{6}{10} = \frac{3}{5}$ **15.** $\frac{3}{10}$
16. $\frac{3}{10}; \frac{6}{10}; \frac{1}{10}$ **17.** $\frac{9}{10}$ **18.** $\frac{18}{10} = \frac{9}{5}$ **19.** $\frac{6}{36} = \frac{1}{6}$
20. 35 to 1 **21.** 7 to 2 **22.** $\frac{4}{36} = \frac{1}{9}$ **23.** $(0.78)^3 \approx 0.475$
24. ${}_3C_2 \cdot (0.78)^2 \cdot (0.22) \approx 0.402$
25. $1 - (0.22)^3 \approx 0.989$
26. $(0.78) \cdot (0.22) \cdot (0.78) \approx 0.134$ **27.** $\frac{25}{102}$ **28.** $\frac{25}{51}$
29. $\frac{4}{51}$ **30.** $\frac{3}{26}$

CHAPTER 13 PERSONAL FINANCIAL MANAGEMENT

13.1 Exercises (*pages 698–701*)

1. $48 **3.** $48.30 **5.** $488.19 **7. (a)** $826 **(b)** $835.84
9. (a) $2650 **(b)** $2653.02 **11.** $125 **13.** $13,546.67
15. $168.26 **17.** $817.17 **19.** $17,724.34; $10,224.34
21. (a) $2249.73 **(b)** $2252.32 **(c)** $2253.65
23. (a) $18,918.18 **(b)** $18,920.52 **(c)** $18,921.70
25. (a) $55.95 **(b)** $56.06 **(c)** $56.14 **(d)** $56.18
(e) $56.18 **27.** Answers will vary. **29.** $1461.04
31. $747.26 **33.** $4499.98 **35.** $112,607.20
37. $111,576.54 **39.** 2.000% **41.** 2.015% **43.** 2.020%
45. 2.020% **47.** $30,420 **49.** 17 years, 152 days
51. $r = m[(Y + 1)^{1/m} - 1]$ **53. (a)** 3.818%
(b) Bank A; $5.63 **(c)** no difference; $232.38
55. 35 years **57.** 8 years **59.** 10.0% **61.** 3.2%
63. $6.51; $7.95; $9.71; $26.40
65. $20,400; $25,000; $30,500; $82,900
67. $218 **69.** $1502 **71.** $81,102,828.75

13.2 Exercises (*pages 704–706*)

1. $2950 **3.** $3422 **5.** $3922 **7.** $3645 **9.** $476.25
11. $1215; $158.75 **13.** $83.25; $46.29 **15.** $79.18; $38.39
17. $229.17 **19.** $330.75 **21.** $10,850 **23.** 6 years
25. $3.50 **27.** $5.80 **29.** $15.30 **31. (a)** $607.33
(b) $7.90 **(c)** $646.87 **33. (a)** $473.96 **(b)** $6.16
(c) $505.54 **35.** $9.27 **37. (a)** $38.18 **(b)** $38.69
(c) $39.20 **39.** 16.0% **41.** $32.00
43–47. Answers will vary. **49. (a)** $127.44 **(b)** $139.08

13.3 Exercises (*pages 711–713*)

1. 13.5% **3.** 8.5% **5.** $114.58 **7.** $92.71 **9.** 11.0%

11. 9.5% **13. (a)** $8.93 **(b)** $511.60 **(c)** $6075.70
15. (a) $2.79 **(b)** $97.03 **(c)** $4073.57
17. (a) $206 **(b)** 9.5% **19. (a)** $180 **(b)** 11.0%
21. (a) $41.29 **(b)** $39.70 **23. (a)** $420.68
(b) $368.47 **25. (a)** $1.80 **(b)** $14.99 **(c)** $1045.01
27. finance company APR: 12.0%; credit union APR:
11.5%; choose credit union **29.** $32.27
31. Answers will vary. **33.** Answers will vary.
35. 12 **37.–41.** Answers will vary. **43.** $\frac{5}{39}$

13.4 Exercises (*pages 722–724*)

1. $675.52 **3.** $469.14 **5.** $2483.28 **7.** $1034.56
9. (a) $513.38 **(b)** $487.50 **(c)** $25.88 **(d)** $58,474.12
11. (a) $1247.43 **(b)** $775.67 **(c)** $471.76
(d) $142,728.24 **(e)** $1247.43 **(f)** $773.11 **(g)** $474.32
(h) $142,253.92 **13. (a)** $1390.93 **(b)** $776.61
(c) $614.32 **(d)** $113,035.68 **(e)** $1390.93 **(f)** $772.41
(g) $618.52 **(h)** $112,417.16 **15.** $552.18 **17.** $1127.27
19. $1168.44 **21.** 360 **23.** $247,532.80 **25. (a)** $304.01
(b) $734.73 **27. (a)** $59,032.06 **(b)** $59,875.11
29. (a) payment 176 **(b)** payment 304 **31.** $25,465.20
33. $91,030.80 **35. (a)** $674.79 **(b)** $746.36
(c) an increase of $71.57 **37. (a)** $395.83 **(b)** $466.07
39. $65.02 **41.** $140,000 **43.** $4275 **45.** $240
47. (a) $1634 **(b)** $1754 **(c)** $917 **(d)** $997
(e) $1555 **49. (a)** $2271 **(b)** $2407 **(c)** $1083
(d) $1174 **(e)** $2055 **51.–59.** Answers will vary.

13.5 Exercises (*pages 737–740*)

1. $20.93 **3.** $1.88 per share lower **5.** $16.37
7. $0.80 per share **9.** 3,327,000 shares **11.** 13.69% lower
13. 29.62 **15.** $42,768.00 **17.** $39,685.00 **19.** $863.04
21. $5479.20 **23.** $68,605.21 **25.** $98,136.00
27. $11,460.44 **29.** $35,609.44 **31.** $107,107.18
33. $20,928.47 **35.** $2050.19 net paid out
37. (a) $800 **(b)** $80 **(c)** $960 **(d)** $1040 **(e)** 130%
39. (a) $1250 **(b)** $108 **(c)** −$235 **(d)** −$127
(e) −10.16% **41.** $275.00 **43.** $177.75
45. (a) $10.49 **(b)** 334 **47. (a)** $8.27 **(b)** 3080
49. (a) $8.39 **(b)** $100.68 **(c)** 15.6%
51. (a) $57.45 **(b)** $689.40 **(c)** 27.6%
53. (a) $1203.75 **(b)** $18.06 **(c)** 19.56%
55. (a) $4179 **(b)** $76.48 **(c)** 24.31%
57. $10.00, $35.17, $29.95 **59.** $400.00, $41.80, $29.95
61. $4000.00, $91.40, $120.00 **63.** large; low
65. $129,258 **67.** $993,383 **69. (a)** $56,473.02
(b) $49,712.70 **71. (a)** $12,851.28 **(b)** $11,651.81
73. (a) $r = m\left[\left(\frac{A}{P}\right)^{1/n} - 1\right]$ **(b)** 5.4%

	Aggressive Growth	Growth	Growth & Income	Income	Cash
75.	$1400	$ 8600	$ 6200	$ 2800	$ 1000
77.	$8000	$112,000	$144,000	$116,000	$20,000

79. 3.75% **81.** 5.2% **83.–89.** Answers will vary.

Extension Exercises *(pages 745–746)*

1.

3. 3^{N-1} **5.** $26 **7.** 3^{N-1}; geometric; 1; 3; N; $\frac{3^N - 1}{2}$

9. 351 **11.** more than $\frac{26}{27}$ **13.** $0.00

15. You are in the chart only from when you pay your entry fee until you move up three levels and get paid.

17. Answers will vary. **19.** 128 **21.** $4,400,000

23. Ponzi's $4 million would be equivalent to about $54 million in today's dollars. Madoff's $21 billion is nearly 400 times as much. **25.** Answers will vary.

Chapter 13 Test *(page 748)*

1. $130 **2.** $58.58 **3.** 3.04% **4.** 14 years **5.** $67,297.13

6. $10.88 **7.** $450 **8.** $143.75 **9.** 14.0% **10.** $34.13

11. 11.5% **12.** Answers will vary. **13.** $1162.95

14. $1528.48 **15.** $3488 **16.** Answers will vary.

17. 12.1% **18.** 15,235,100 shares **19.** $10.00

20. 0.078%; no; The given return was not for a 1-year period. **21.** $106,728.55 **22.** Answers will vary.

CHAPTER 15 GRAPH THEORY

15.1 Exercises *(pages 803–808)*

1. 7 vertices, 7 edges **3.** 10 vertices, 9 edges

5. 6 vertices, 9 edges **7.** Two have degree 3. Three have degree 2. Two have degree 1. Sum of degrees is 14. This is twice the number of edges. **9.** Six have degree 1. Four have degree 3. Sum of degrees is 18. This is twice the number of edges. **11.** not isomorphic

13. isomorphic; Corresponding edges should be the same color. AB should match AB, etc.

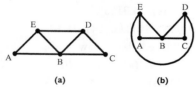

15. not isomorphic **17.** connected, 1 component
19. disconnected, 3 components **21.** disconnected, 2 components **23.** 10 **25.** 4 **27.** (a) yes (b) No,

because there is no edge from A to D. **(c)** No, because there is no edge from A to E. **(d)** yes **(e)** yes **(f)** yes

29. (a) No, because it does not return to the starting vertex. **(b)** yes **(c)** No, because there is no edge from C to F. **(d)** No, because it does not return to starting vertex. **(e)** No, because the edge from F to D is used more than once. **31.** (a) No, because there is no edge from B to C. **(b)** No, because the edge from I to G is used more than once. **(c)** No, because there is no edge from E to I. **(d)** yes **(e)** yes **(f)** No, because the edge from A to D is used more than once. **33.** It is a walk and a path, not a circuit. **35.** It is a walk, not a path, not a circuit.

37. It is a walk and a path, not a circuit.

39. No, because there is no edge from A to C, for example.

41. No, because there is no edge from A to F, for example.

43. yes

45.   7 games **47.** 36 handshakes

49. 10 telephone conversations

51. A → B → D → A corresponds to tracing around the edges of a single face. (The circuit is a triangle.)

53. Answers will vary. **55.** Answers will vary.

57. Answers will vary.

59.   **61.**

63.   **65.** (a)

(b) **(c)** **(d)**

(e) A cycle with an odd number of vertices has chromatic number 3. A cycle with an even number of vertices has chromatic number 2.

67. **69.**

71. Three times: Choir and Forensics, Service Club and Dance Club, and Theater and Caribbean Club. (There are other possible groupings.)

73. Three gatherings: Brad and Phil and Mary, Joe and Lindsay, and Caitlin and Eva. (There are other possible groupings.)

75. 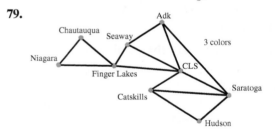 3 colors **77.** 4 colors

79. 3 colors

In Exercise 81, there are many different ways to draw the map.

81.

83. By the four-color theorem, this is not possible.

15.2 Exercises *(pages 816–819)*

1. (a) No, it is not a path. **(b)** yes **(c)** No, it is not a walk. **(d)** No, it is not a circuit.
3. (a) No, some edges are not used (e.g., B → F).
(b) yes **(c)** No, it is not a path. **(d)** yes
5. Yes, all vertices have even degree. **7.** No, some vertices have odd degree (e.g., G). **9.** yes
11. It has an Euler circuit. All vertices have even degree. No circuit visits each vertex exactly once.
13. It has an Euler circuit. All vertices have even degree. A → B → H → C → G → D → F → E → A visits each vertex exactly once. **15.** It has no Euler circuit. Some vertices have odd degree (e.g., B). It has no circuit that visits each vertex exactly once. **17.** No, some vertices have odd degree. **19.** Yes, all vertices have even degree.
21. none **23.** B → E or B → D **25.** B → C or B → H

27. A → C → B → F → E → D → C → F → D → A
29. Graph has an Euler circuit.
A → G → H → J → I → L → J → K → I →
H → F → G → E → F → D → E → C → D →
B → C → A → E → B → A
31. Graph does not have an Euler circuit. Some vertices have odd degree (e.g., C). **33.** There is such a route:
A → D → B → C → A → H → D → E → B →
H → G → E → F → H → J → L → C → M → A → K →
M → L → K → J → A **35.** It is not possible. Some vertices have odd degree (e.g., room at upper left).
37. no; There are more than two vertices with odd degree.
39. yes; B and G **41.** It is possible. Exactly two of the rooms have odd numbers of doors. **43.** It is not possible. All rooms have even numbers of doors.
There are other correct answers in Exercises 45–47.
45. A → B → D → C → A; There are 4 edges in any such circuit. **47.** A → B → C → D → E → F → G →
H → C → A → H → I → A; There are 12 edges in any such circuit. **49.** A complete graph has an Euler circuit if the number of vertices is an odd number greater than or equal to 3. In a complete graph with *n* vertices, the degree of each vertex is *n* − 1. "*n* − 1 is even" is equivalent to "*n* is odd."

15.3 Exercises *(pages 827–831)*

1. (a) No, because it visits E twice. **(b)** yes
(c) No, because it does not visit C. **(d)** No, because it does not visit A. **3. (a)** None, because there is no edge from B to C. **(b)** all three **(c)** none; The edge from A to D is used twice. **5.** A → B → D → E → F → C → A
7. G → H → J → I → G **9.** X → T → U → W → V → X
11. Hamilton circuit: A → B → C → D → A. The graph has no Euler circuit, because at least one of the vertices has odd degree. (In fact, all have odd degree.)

13. A → B → C → D → E → F → A is both a Hamilton and an Euler circuit.

15. Hamilton circuit **17.** Euler circuit
19. Hamilton circuit **21.** 24 **23.** 362,880
25. 9! **27.** 17!

29. P → Q → R → S → P   P → Q → S → R → P
P → R → Q → S → P   P → R → S → Q → P
P → S → Q → R → P   P → S → R → Q → P

31. E → H → I → F → G → E   E → H → I → G → F → E

33. E → F → G → H → I → E   E → F → G → I → H → E
E → F → H → G → I → E   E → F → H → I → G → E
E → F → I → G → H → E   E → F → I → H → G → E

35. E → G → F → H → I → E   E → G → F → I → H → E
E → G → H → F → I → E   E → G → H → I → F → E
E → G → I → F → H → E   E → G → I → H → F → E

37. A → B → C → D → E → A   A → C → B → D → E → A
A → B → C → E → D → A   A → C → B → E → D → A
A → B → D → C → E → A   A → C → D → B → E → A
A → B → D → E → C → A   A → C → D → E → B → A
A → B → E → C → D → A   A → C → E → B → D → A
A → B → E → D → C → A   A → C → E → D → B → A
A → D → B → C → E → A   A → E → B → C → D → A
A → D → B → E → C → A   A → E → B → D → C → A
A → D → C → B → E → A   A → E → C → B → D → A
A → D → C → E → B → A   A → E → C → D → B → A
A → D → E → B → C → A   A → E → D → B → C → A
A → D → E → C → B → A   A → E → D → C → B → A

39. Minimum Hamilton circuit is P → Q → R → S → P;
Weight is 2200.   **41.** Minimum Hamilton circuit is
C → D → E → F → G → C; Weight is 64.

43. (a) A → C → E → D → B → A; Total weight is 20.
(b) C → A → B → D → E → C; Total weight is 20.
(c) D → C → A → B → E → D; Total weight is 23.
(d) E → C → A → B → D → E; Total weight is 20.

45. (a) A → C → D → E → B → A; Total weight is 87.
B → C → A → E → D → B; Total weight is 95.
C → A → E → D → B → C; Total weight is 95.
D → C → A → E → B → D; Total weight is 131.
E → C → A → D → B → E; Total weight is 137.
(b) A → C → D → E → B → A with total weight 87
(c) For example, A → B → C → D → E → A has total
weight 52.

47. A → B → C → D → E → F → A
A → B → C → F → E → D → A
A → B → E → D → C → F → A
A → B → E → F → C → D → A
A → D → E → F → C → B → A
A → D → E → B → C → F → A
A → D → C → B → E → F → A
A → D → C → F → E → B → A
A → F → E → B → C → D → A
A → F → E → D → C → B → A
A → F → C → D → E → B → A
A → F → C → B → E → D → A

49. A → B → C → D → E → F → A
A → B → C → E → D → F → A
A → B → C → E → F → D → A
A → B → C → F → E → D → A
A → D → E → F → C → B → A
A → D → F → E → C → B → A
A → F → D → E → C → B → A
A → F → E → D → C → B → A

51. (a) graphs (2) and (4)   **(b)** graphs (2) and (4)
(c) No. Graph (1) provides a counterexample.
(d) No. If $n < 3$, the graph will have no circuits at all.
(e) The degree of each vertex in a complete graph with n
vertices is $(n - 1)$. If $n \geq 3$, then $(n - 1) > \frac{n}{2}$. So we can
conclude from Dirac's theorem that the graph has a
Hamilton circuit.
53. A → F → G → R → S → T → U → Q → P → N →
M → L → K → J → I → H → B → C → D → E → A
55. Answers will vary.

15.4 Exercises (pages 839–842)

1. tree   **3.** No, because it is not connected.   **5.** tree
7. No, because it has a circuit.   **9.** It is not possible, since
the graph has a circuit.   **11.** tree   **13.** not necessarily a
tree   **15.** true   **17.** false

19.

21.

23.

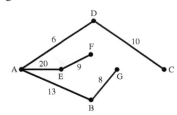

25. 20 **27.** If a connected graph has circuits, none of which have common edges, then the number of spanning trees for the graph is the product of the numbers of edges in all the circuits.

29. Total weight is 51.

31. Total weight is 66.

33. Total length to be covered is 140 ft.

35. 33 **37.** 62 **39.** Different spanning trees must have the same number of edges. The number of vertices in the tree is the number of vertices in the original graph, and the number of edges has to be one less than this.

41. (a) 9 (b) 18 (c) 0 (d) 2

(e)

43. 22 cables **45.** This is possible. The graph must be a tree because it has one fewer edge(s) than vertices.

47. This is possible. The graph cannot be a tree, because it would have at least as many edges as vertices.

49. 3:

51. 125

53. 3 nonisomorphic trees:

55. 11 nonisomorphic trees:

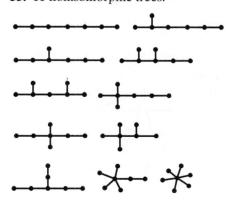

57. Answers will vary.

Extension Exercises *(page 843)*

1. In the graph shown, not all vertices have even degree. For example, the vertex marked X has degree 5. So this graph still does not have an Euler circuit.

3. There are other ways of inserting the additional edges.

8 edges added

Chapter 15 Test *(pages 845–847)*

1. 7 **2.** 20 **3.** 10 **4. (a)** No, because the edge from A to B is used twice. **(b)** yes **(c)** No, because there is no edge from C to D. **5. (a)** yes **(b)** No, because for example, there is no edge from B to C. **(c)** yes

6. For example:

7. 13 edges

8. The graphs are isomorphic. Corresponding edges should be the same color. AB should match AB, etc.

(a)

(b)

9.

The graph is connected. Tina knows the greatest number of other guests.

10. 28 games **11.** Yes, because there is an edge from each vertex to each of the remaining 6 vertices.

12.

13.

Chromatic number: 3

Chromatic number: 5

14.

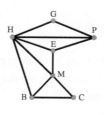

The Chromatic number is 3, so three separate exam times are needed. Exams could be at the same times as follows: Geography, Biology, and English; History and Chemistry; Mathematics and Psychology.

15. (a) No, because it does not use all the edges.
(b) No, because it is not a circuit (for example, there is no edge from B to C). **(c)** yes **16.** No, because some vertices have odd degree. **17.** Yes, because all vertices have even degree. **18.** No, because two of the rooms have odd numbers of doors.
19. F → B → E → D → B → C → D → K → B → A → H → G → F → A → G → J → F
20. (a) No, because it does not visit all vertices.
(b) No, because it is not a circuit (for example, there is no edge from B to C).
(c) No, because it visits some vertices twice before returning to the starting vertex.
21. F → G → H → I → E → F
F → G → H → E → I → F   F → G → I → H → E → F
F → G → I → E → H → F   F → G → E → H → I → F
F → G → E → I → H → F
There are 6 such Hamilton circuits.
22. P → Q → S → R → P; Total weight is 27.
23. A → E → D → C → F → B → A; Total weight is 11.85.
24. 24! **25.** Hamilton circuit
26. Any three of these:

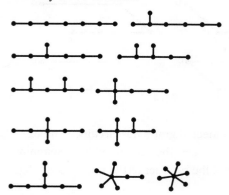

27. false **28.** true **29.** true
30. There are 4 spanning trees.

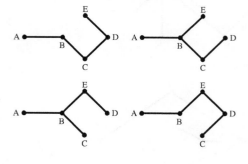

Answers to Selected Exercises ▮▮▮ A-25

31. Weight is 24.

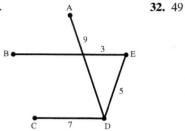

32. 49

APPENDIX THE METRIC SYSTEM

Appendix Exercises *(pages A-5–A-7)*

1. 8000 mm   **3.** 85 m   **5.** 689 mm   **7.** 5.98 cm
9. 5300 m   **11.** 27.5 km   **13.** 2.54 cm; 25.4 mm
15. 5 cm; 50 mm   **17.** 600 cl   **19.** 8700 ml   **21.** 9.25 L
23. 8.974 L   **25.** 8 kg   **27.** 5200 g   **29.** 4200 mg
31. 0.598 g   **33.** 30°C   **35.** −81°C   **37.** 50°F
39. −40°F   **41.** 200 nickels   **43.** 0.2 g   **45.** $40.99
47. $387.98   **49.** 1,082,400 cm³; 1.0824 m³
51. 200 bottles   **53.** 897.9 m   **55.** 201.1 km
57. 3.995 lb   **59.** 21,428.8 g   **61.** 30.22 qt   **63.** 106.7 L
65. unreasonable   **67.** reasonable   **69.** unreasonable
71. B   **73.** B   **75.** C   **77.** A   **79.** A   **81.** C
83. A   **85.** B   **87.** B   **89.** A   **91.** B   **93.** C   **95.** B

CREDITS

Text Credits

Exercises from the *Mathematics Teacher* monthly calendar appear on the following pages of the text. These are reprinted with permission from *Mathematics Teacher*, copyright © 1980–2010 by the National Council of Teachers of Mathematics. All Rights Reserved: **24–29, 41, 532, 541, 543, 554, 556, 567, 572–573, 575–576, 586, 588, 596, 604–605, 612.**

6 For Further Thought. Excerpted from Eves, Howard, *In Mathematical Circles.* Reprinted by permission of the Mathematical Association of America.   **33** "Medicare Funds" graph. From Lial/Hornsby/McGinnis, *Introductory Algebra*, 9th ed., p. 221. Copyright © 2010 Pearson Education. All Rights Reserved.   **35–36** "U.S. Milk Production" and "Average Gasoline Prices" graphs. From Lial/Hornsby/McGinnis, *Introductory Algebra*, 9th ed., p. 229. Copyright © 2010 Pearson Education. All Rights Reserved.   **42** "Unemployment Rate" graph. From Lial/Hornsby/McGinnis, *Introductory Algebra*, 9th ed., p. 295. Copyright © 2010 Pearson Education. All Rights Reserved.   **100** Exercise 83 problem. From Smullyan, Raymond, *The Lady or the Tiger and Other Logic Puzzles.* Copyright ©2009 Dover Publications. Reprinted with permission.   **100** Exercise 84 problem. Reprinted with the permission of Simon & Schuster, Inc., from *What Is the Name of This Book?* by Raymond Smullyan. Copyright © 1978, 1986 by Raymond Smullyan. All Rights Reserved.   **120–124, 134** Puzzles from *Original Logic Problems.* Penny Press, February 2010. Copyright © 2010 Penny Publications, LLC. Reprinted with permission.   **121–122, 124, 135** Puzzles from *Original Sudoku.* Penny Press, March 2010. Copyright © 2010 Penny Publications, LLC. Reprinted with permission.   **130** Margin note problem. Reprinted with the permission of Simon & Schuster, Inc., from *What Is the Name of This Book?* by Raymond Smullyan. Copyright © 1978, 1986 by Raymond Smullyan. All Rights Reserved.   **227** Example 4. From Lial/Hornsby/McGinnis, *Intermediate Algebra*, 9th ed. (paperback), p.10. Copyright © 2010 Pearson Education. All Rights Reserved.   **229** Exercise 24. From Lial/Hornsby/McGinnis, *Intermediate Algebra*, 9th ed. (paperback), p. 51. Copyright © 2010 Pearson Education. All Rights Reserved.   **229** Exercise 65. From Lial/Hornsby/McGinnis, *Intermediate Algebra*, 9th ed. (paperback), p. 15. Copyright © 2010 Pearson Education. All Rights Reserved.   **262** Exercise 45. Courtesy of joyofpi.com. Reprinted by permission of David Blatner.   **269** "Spending on Kitty and Rover" graph. Adapted from Lial/Hornsby/McGinnis, *Intermediate Algebra*, 9th ed. Copyright © 2010 Pearson Education. All Rights Reserved.   **272** "2005 U.S. Government Spending" graph. Adapted from Lial/Hornsby/McGinnis, *Intermediate Algebra*, 9th ed., p.117. Copyright © 2010 Pearson Education. All Rights Reserved.   **274** Exercises 73–78. Adapted from Lial/Hornsby/McGinnis, *Introductory Algebra*, 9th ed.,

p. 221. Copyright © 2010 Pearson Education. All Rights Reserved.   **282** "Composition of the U.S. Workforce in 2006" and "Medicare Funds" graphs. From Lial/Hornsby/McGinnis, *Intermediate Algebra*, 10th ed. Copyright © 2008 Pearson Education. All Rights Reserved.   **292–293** Exercises 77–78. From Lial/Hornsby/Schneider, *Beginning Algebra*, 9th ed. Copyright © 2004 Pearson Education. All Rights Reserved.   **296** Example 4. From Lial/Hornsby/McGinnis, *Study Skills Workbook for Intermediate Algebra.* Copyright © 2006 Pearson Education. All Rights Reserved.   **319** Table 4. From Lial/Hornsby/McGinnis, *Study Skills Workbook for Intermediate Algebra.* Copyright © 2006 Pearson Education. All Rights Reserved.   **320** Example 2. From Lial/Hornsby/Schneider, *Beginning Algebra*, 9th ed. Copyright © 2004 Pearson Education. All Rights Reserved.   **322** Example 3. From Lial/Hornsby/Schneider, *Beginning Algebra*, 9th ed., p. 161. Copyright © 2004 Pearson Education. All Rights Reserved.   **327** "U.S. Egg Production" graph and problems. From Lial/Hornsby/McGinnis, *Introductory Algebra*, 9th ed. Copyright © 2010 Pearson Education. All Rights Reserved.   **364** Example 3. From Lial/Hornsby/Schneider, *College Algebra*, 10th ed., pp. 186–187. Copyright © 2009 Pearson Education. All Rights Reserved.   **367** For Further Thought. From Lial/Hornsby/Schneider, *College Algebra*, 10th ed., p. 198. Copyright © 2009 Pearson Education. All Rights Reserved.   **368** Exercises 19–20. Adapted from Lial/Hornsby/McGinnis, *Intermediate Algebra*, 9th ed. (paperback), p. 195. Copyright © 2010 Pearson Education. All Rights Reserved.   **369** Exercises 55–58. From Lial/Hornsby/Schneider, *College Algebra*, 10th ed., p. 192. Copyright © 2009 Pearson Education. All Rights Reserved.   **375–376** Examples 7–9. From Lial/Hornsby/McGinnis, *Intermediate Algebra*, 9th ed. (paperback), pp. 205–206. Copyright © 2010 Pearson Education. All Rights Reserved.   **378** Exercise 47 problem and graphs. From Lial/Hornsby/McGinnis, *Introductory Algebra*, 9th ed., pp. 2, 260. Copyright © 2010 Pearson Education. All Rights Reserved.   **379** Exercises 67–69 problems and graphs. From Lial/Hornsby/McGinnis, *Intermediate Algebra*, 9th ed. (paperback), pp. 211–212. Copyright © 2010 Pearson Education. All Rights Reserved.   **383** Example 7. From Lial/Hornsby/McGinnis, *Intermediate Algebra*, 9th ed. (paperback), p. 220. Copyright © 2010 Pearson Education. All Rights Reserved.   **387** Exercises 71–72 problems and graphs. From Lial/Hornsby/McGinnis, *Intermediate Algebra*, 9th ed. (paperback), pp. 225–226. Copyright © 2010 Pearson Education. All Rights Reserved.   **388** Exercise 74. From Lial/Hornsby/McGinnis, *Intermediate Algebra Worktext*, 7th ed., p. 201. Copyright © 2002 Pearson Education. All Rights Reserved.   **408** Exercise 56. From Hornsby/Lial/Rockswold, *A Graphical Approach to College Algebra*, 5th ed., p. 404. Copyright © 2011 Pearson Education. All Rights Reserved.   **414** Example 4. From Lial/Hornsby/Schneider, *College Algebra*, 9th ed., p. 430. Copyright © 2010 Pearson Education. All Rights Reserved.   **417** Exercise 58. From Lial/Hornsby/Schneider, *College Algebra*,

10th ed., p. 430. Copyright © 2009 Pearson Education. All Rights Reserved. **418** "Say Cheese!" graph. From Lial/Hornsby/McGinnis, *Intermediate Algebra*, 9th ed., p. 268. Copyright © 2010 Pearson Education. All Rights Reserved. **423** Figure 50 (a–g). From Lial/Hornsby/McGinnis, *Intermediate Algebra*, 9th ed. (paperback), p. 283. Copyright © 2010 Pearson Education. All Rights Reserved. **425** Exercises 1–4, 9–12. From Lial/Hornsby/McGinnis, *Intermediate Algebra*, 9th ed. (paperback), p. 277. Copyright © 2010 Pearson Education. All Rights Reserved. **431** Example 5. From Lial/Hornsby,/McGinnis, *Intermediate Algebra*, 9th ed. (paperback), p. 299. Copyright © 2010 Pearson Education. All Rights Reserved. **502** For Further Thought. The authors would like to thank The Math Forum at Drexel and Suzanne Alejandre for permission to reprint this article. **503** Copyright © Coolmath.com. All Rights Reserved. **519–520** Exercises 1–25. Pages 1–4 from the National Council of Teachers of Mathematics *Student Math Notes*, November 1991. Reprinted by permission of the National Council of Teachers of Mathematics. **639** "Retirement Savings Net Worth" graph. From *TSA Guide to Retirement Planning for California Educators*. **806** Exercise 58 poem. John Keats **813** Sand tracing. Copyright © 2010 Mathematical Association of America. All Rights Reserved. **826** "Records for Traveling Salesman" problem solution. From *What's Happening in Mathematical Sciences, Vol. 2*, 1994, p. 46, American Mathematical Society. Reprinted by permission of William Cook, Georgia Institute of Technology.

Photo Credits

1–2 20th Century Fox Film Corp./Everett Collection **4** ABC/Everett Collection **6** Beth Anderson/Pearson **7** David Livingston/Getty Images **13** Disney Enterprises, Inc. **18** AP Images **19** Granger Collection **20** Texas Instruments images used with permission/CBS/Paramount/National Council of Teachers of Mathematics **21** Courtesy of the London Mathematical Society **21** Arteki/Shutterstock **22** Krista Mackey/iStockphoto **24** Webphotographer/iStockphoto **24** Digital Vision/Thinkstock **27** Photos.com/Thinkstock **27** Andrii Muzyka/Shutterstock **29** Karl Pawlewicz/Sharp Electronics **30** Jon Le-bon/Shutterstock **30** Beth Anderson/Pearson **32** Johner Images/Getty Images **33** Stockbyte/Getty Images **34** iStockphoto/Thinkstock **35** Photos.com/Thinkstock **36** Kobal Collection **38** Disney Enterprises, Inc. **43** Picture Desk/Kobal Collection **44** Bettmann/Corbis **46** Beth Anderson/Pearson **55** Beth Anderson/Pearson **61** Michael Kempf/Shutterstock **65** Internal Revenue Service **68** Walt Disney Co./Everett Collection **71** Everett Collection **73** Everett Collection **74** Brand X Pictures/Thinkstock **75** Library of Congress Prints and Photographs Division (LC-USZ62-7923) **77** Koo Eng Yow/Shutterstock **78** Getty Images/Digital Vision **79** Joy Brown/Shutterstock **83** Dreamworks SKG/Everett Collection **84** Bilwissedition Ltd. & Co. KG/Alamy **86** Erich Lessing/Art Resource, New York **89** Warner Bros./Everett Collection **93** Library of Congress Prints and Photographs Division (LC-USZ62-61664) **94** Reprinted with permission of Simon & Schuster, Inc. **95** Mary Evans Picture Library/Alamy **100** Stockbyte/Thinkstock **101** Courtesy of John Hornsby **104** Disney Enterprises, Inc. **107** iStockphoto/Thinkstock **107** BananaStock/Thinkstock **108** Strelnikova Tetiana/Shutterstock **109** Michael Ochs Archives/Getty Images **110** Interfoto/Alamy **111** Pictorial Press Ltd./Alamy **113** Library of Congress Prints and Photographs Division (LC-USZ62-10191) **115** Library of Congress Prints and Photographs Division (LC-USZ62-48329) **118** Steve Liss/Time & Life Images/Getty Images **120–121** Dell Magazines/Penny Publications **125** Notro Films/Bocaboca Producciones/The Kobal Collection **128** Mary Evans/Python Pictures/Ronald Grant/Everett Collection **130** Wonderstock/Alamy **131** Shutterstock **132** Shutterstock **137** Photofest **138** PhotoDisc/Getty Images **138–139** Dorling Kindersley **140** Thumb/Shutterstock **141** Mario Savoia/Shutterstock **144** Granger Collection **152** The Art Gallery Collection/Alamy **153** Trinity College. Reprinted by permission of the Master and Fellows of Trinity College, Cambridge **154** Amenhotepov/Shutterstock **154** Payless Images/Shutterstock **155** Science Source/Photo Researchers **155** Mary Evans Picture Library/Alamy **160** Photosani/Shutterstock **161** Photos.com/Thinkstock **163** Casio **165** Courtesy of John Hornsby **168** Dorling Kindersley **170** Nhtg/Shutterstock **179** Warner Bros./Southside Amusement Co./The Kobal Collection **182** Hugh C. Williams, University of Manitoba **187** Urbana IL USPS **187** Photo Researchers **193** Prentice Hall College Library **193** TriStar Pictures/courtesy Everett Collection **194** The Art Gallery Collection/Alamy **194** 20th Century Fox Film Corp./Everett Collection **200** Photos/Thinkstock **203** Courtesy of John Hornsby **205** Dreamworks/Universal/Eli Reed/The Kobal Collection **214** Photodisc/Getty Images **214** Bloom images/Getty Images **215** Baloncici/Shutterstock **215** Scala/Art Resource, New York **215** PhotoDisc **215** Disney Enterprises, Inc. **221** 20th Century Fox Film Corp./Everett Collection **222** Penguin Putnam, Inc. **232** Imagebroker/Alamy **237** Comstock/Thinkstock **242** Pearson Education Management Group EMG Network **242** Robophobic/Shutterstock **245** US Mint **248** Pat Behnke/Alamy **250** Jubal Harshaw/Shutterstock **251** US Mint **252** Edgaras Kurauskas/Shutterstock **253** Valentyn Volkov/Shutterstock **255** Courtesy of authors **256** Universal TV/Everett Collection **257** New Line Cinema/Kobal Collection **258** Paramount/Everett Collection **259** Reprinted by permission of St. Martin's Press **260** Jacket cover from *The Golden Ratio: The Story of Phi, the World's Most Astonishing Number,* by Mario Livio. Used by permission of Broadway Books, a division of Random House, Inc. **261** Reproduced with permission from Princeton University Press **263** Chad Palmer/Shutterstock **267** Wolper/Warner Bros./The Kobal Collection **269** Courtesy of Terry McGinnis **271** Courtesy of John Hornsby **272** Courtesy of John Hornsby **272** Fruit Berries, Raspberries Stamp © 1999 USPS. All Rights Reserved. **275** Courtesy of John Hornsby **275** Goodshoot/Thinkstock **275** US Mint **276** Interfoto/Alamy **277** Reproduced with permission from Princeton University Press **283** Paramount/Kobal Collection **284** Courtesy of John Hornsby **285** Darryl Brooks/Shutterstock **287** Photo Researchers, Inc. **288** Alamy Images **289** Elena Elisseeva/Shutterstock **292** Andresr/Shutterstock **294** Kathy Willens/AP Photo **296** The Everett Collection **297** 20th Century Fox Film Corp./Everett Collection **299** Daiju Kitamura/Aflo Foto Agency/Alamy **302** Lopatinsky Vladislav/Shutterstock

INDEX OF APPLICATIONS

INDEX

A Serious Man (2009)

Proof (2005)

A Serious Man (2009) | Time: 14:12–14:39

Schrödinger's Paradox—relates to Section 2.1, Symbols and Terminology, from *Mathematical Ideas*, 12th edition

Synopsis: Lawrence "Larry" Gopnik (Michael Stuhlbarg) is a physics professor. This scene shows him at the chalkboard in front of his class, writing out the equation for Schrödinger's Paradox. He asks his students if they can use the equation to figure out whether a cat placed in a box with poison is dead or not dead.

Discussion: Schrödinger's Paradox, also known as Schrödinger's Cat, was named after a statement that Austrian physicist Erwin Schrödinger made concerning quantum mechanics. One interpretation of the Paradox is not knowing whether a cat that was placed in a box along with poison was alive or dead until the box was opened. No worries since no cats were actually harmed.

A paradox, in layman's terms, is a statement that contradicts itself but presents a possible truth. For instance, the statement "I always lie" is a paradox because if it were true, then it must also be false at the same time.

There are many famous paradoxes, such as "If a tree falls in a forest and no one is around to hear it, does it make a sound?" and "the chicken and the egg" paradox.

Consider the following paradox, known as George Washington's Axe Paradox:

A man who owned the original ax that George Washington used to cut down the cherry tree would use it to chop firewood. When he was asked how he was able to use a tool that was so old, he would reply by saying that it needed to be taken care of: by replacing the head and the handle several times. This maintenance made the ax of George Washington good as new.

So, the question is: can it still be considered George Washington's axe?

Proof (2005) | Scene 6 – "i" | Time: 30:32–31:59

Germain Primes—relates to Section 5.1, Prime and Composite Numbers, from *Mathematical Ideas*, 12th edition

Synopsis: In "Proof" Gwyneth Paltrow plays Catherine Llewellyn, a young mathematician. In Scene 6, Catherine's colleague Harold "Hal" Dobbs (Jake Gyllenhaal), talks about the visionary mathematicians—or "young guys"—who attend mathematical conferences. Catherine wonders if there are no women in mathematics. Hal assures her there is at least one woman at Stanford, although he cannot remember her name. Catherine suggests it might be Sophie Germain and Hal is quick to agree, although he becomes embarrassed when he realizes she is referring to the Parisian number theorist Sophie Germain, born in 1776, after whom Germain primes are named.

Discussion: Marie-Sophie Germain lived in a time when women were not allowed to attend universities and would need to use made-up names just to get their ideas published. In fact, two famous male mathematicians at the time, Joseph-Louis Lagrange and Carl Friedrich Gauss, wrote back and forth with Germain for years before realizing she was a woman. Thus, it is ironic that Gyllenhaal's character did not know the name of the female professor teaching at Stanford and quickly accepted Paltrow's character's answer of Maria-Sophie Germain as being correct.

Born in 1776, Germain's work has been able to find modern applications such as the study of acoustics, elasticity, and the construction of skyscrapers. There is a set of numbers named after Sophie Germain, aptly named Germain primes; its members have the following property:

If p is a prime number and if $2p + 1$ is also a prime number, then p is called a Germain prime.

For instance, note that number 2 is prime. If $p = 2$, then $2p + 1 = 2(2) + 1 = 5$, which is also prime! Thus, we would call the number 2 a Germain prime.

Determine which of the following primes are also Germain primes: 3, 5, 7, 11, 13, 17, 19, 23, and 29. The largest Germain prime was found in April, 2010. It has 79,911 digits. That means, even using an 8-point Times New Roman font, it would take over 11 pages to type out the entire number!

The Departed (2006)

Knocked Up (2007)

The Departed (2006) | Scene 6 – Dignam Briefs the Girls | Time: 24:28–25:04

Multiplication—relates to Section 6.2, Operations, Properties, and Applications of Real Numbers, from *Mathematical Ideas,* 12th edition

Synopsis: In "The Departed," Staff Sergeant Dignam, played by Mark Wahlberg, is in charge of an undercover unit assembled to bring down Boston mob boss Francis "Frank" Costello, played by Jack Nicholson. In this scene, Dignam briefs the Organized Crime Unit about one of Costello's men who steals 20 computer microprocessors from a manufacturing plant. The seemingly inconsequential "little pieces of plastic" are worth $100,000 each, and Costello intends to sell them off to a contact in China.

Discussion: How much should the mob boss expect from selling the 20 microprocessors for 100 grand ($100,000) each then? Simply put, you would just multiply 20 by 100,000 to get $2,000,000.

Let us talk about the answer in terms of units. The $100,000 is the amount you would receive per microprocessor. So, you could really think of it as a fraction: $\dfrac{100{,}000 \text{ dollars}}{1 \text{ microprocessor}}$

When we multiply this fraction by 20 microprocessors, notice what happens to the units:

$$\frac{100{,}000 \text{ dollars}}{1 \text{ microprocessor}} \times \frac{20 \text{ microprocessors}}{1} = \frac{100{,}000 \text{ dollars}}{1 \text{ microprocessor}} \times \frac{20 \text{ microprocessors}}{1} = \frac{100{,}000 \text{ dollars} \times 20}{1} = 2{,}000{,}000 \text{ dollars}$$

In most word problems, when you perform operations (like adding, subtracting, multiplying, and dividing), you must keep the units in mind to ensure your operations are performed correctly. As of right now, the Chinese yuan is trading at the rate of 6.69 yuan per one U.S. dollar. Using units and multiplication, convert $2,000,000 to Chinese yuan.

Mathematical Ideas, 12th edition, Miller, Heeren, and Hornsby | Copyright ©2012 Pearson Education, Inc.

Knocked Up (2007) | Time: 30:56–32:00

Ratios and Proportions—relates to Section 7.3, Ratio, Proportion, and Variation, from *Mathematical Ideas,* 12th edition

Synopsis: In this scene from "Knocked Up," Ben Stone (Seth Rogan) is on a dinner date with Alison Scott (Katherine Heigl). He tells her he is an unemployed Canadian citizen living illegally in the United States. Alison asks him how he is able to pay his rent if he does not have a job, and he explains when he was in high school he got run over by a postal truck and he received $14,000 from the British Columbian government. The accident was 10 years before, and he still has $900 remaining, which he calculates should last him for at least "another 2 years or something."

Discussion: According to Ben, he will have two years to spend the remaining $900. We will check his work using ratios and proportions. Recall that if $\dfrac{a}{b} = \dfrac{c}{d}$ then $ad = bc$. For us, we will assume the numerator of each ratio represents the amount of money Ben used and the denominator will represent the amount of time it will take Ben to use that money.

We know that after 10 years, he has $900 left from a settlement that paid him $14,000. That means in the first 10 years, he spent $14,000 - $900 = $13,100. Again, he thinks the remaining $900 will last him two years. Assuming that he spends the money at the same rate, we can write the following proportion:

$$\begin{array}{l}\text{Amount spent} \\ \text{Number of years}\end{array} \quad \frac{31{,}100}{10} = \frac{900}{2}$$

This would imply that $13{,}100 \times 2 = 10 \times 900$ or $26{,}200 = 9{,}000$, which is not true! Ben's guess that he has two years left is incorrect. Since we do not know the amount of time Ben has to spend the remaining money, let x represent the number of years left. Now, our proportion looks like:

$$\begin{array}{l}\text{Amount spent} \\ \text{Number of years}\end{array} \quad \frac{31{,}100}{10} = \frac{900}{x}$$

Now, try to solve for x. What will you tell Ben about his remaining money?

Mathematical Ideas, 12th edition, Miller, Heeren, and Hornsby | Copyright ©2012 Pearson Education, Inc.

Fight Club (1999)

Star Trek (2009)

Fight Club (1999) | Scene 8 – Single Serving Jack | Time: 20:20–21:16

Inequalities—relates to Section 7.4, Linear Inequalities, from *Mathematical Ideas,* 12th edition

Synopsis: The narrator of the movie "Fight Club," played by Edward Norton, is a recall coordinator for a car company. His job is to assess cars made by his company that have been in accidents and then decide whether the model should be recalled. If one of the company's new cars is traveling at 60mph when the rear differential locks up and an accident occurs, should the company recall? The formula designed to answer that question is the number of vehicles on the road multiplied by the probable rate of failure. That result is multiplied by the average out of court settlement. If the final result is less than the cost of a recall, the company does not deal with it and the model is not recalled.

Discussion: Even though the first rule of Fight Club was to not talk about the Club, it is always okay to talk about math! In this scene, Brad Pitt's character is basically explaining an inequality comparing the cost to pay for all court settlements versus the cost of recalling all cars. It is a cruel example; however, it is a real-life one.

On a lighter note, you may have already used inequalities in your life. For instance, you may have had to compare plans for cable television providers or cell phone companies.

Another example is when you produce an item and need to figure out how many items you need to sell to break even. Suppose that you make natural soaps that sell for $5.35 each bar. You have found out that each bar of soap costs $1.55 to produce and that you needed to buy supplies to make the soaps that cost $342.00.

Try to write a mathematical expression that represents the Revenue--the amount of money that you bring in from selling the items. Try to write a mathematical expression that represents the Cost--the amount of money that you have to pay to produce the items. To help, let x represent the number of bars of soap you make.

Now using inequalities, determine the number of bars of soap you will need to make so that Revenue is greater than Cost. What would happen if you sold less than this amount?

Star Trek (2009) | Scene 2 | Time: 14:42–15:14

Volume of a Sphere—relates to Section 9.5, Space Figures, Volume, and Surface Area, from *Mathematical Ideas,* 12th edition

Synopsis: "Star Trek," Scene 2 opens with a young Spock (Zachary Quinto) on his home planet Vulcan, reciting a mathematics lesson. He is asked for the formula for the volume of a sphere, which is four-thirds pi times the radius cubed. Holographic images of formulas and diagrams of chemical structures float around him.

Discussion: When asked what the formula for the volume of a sphere is, Spock quickly answers with $V = \dfrac{4}{3}\pi r^3$. Where the formula comes from is a bit outside of this course; however, that does not mean we cannot use this result!

In the formula, all you need to compute the volume is to know the radius. Also, you may recall, that a radius of a sphere is half of the diameter. Thus, if the diameter of the Earth is 7,926 miles, then the radius is half of that: $\dfrac{1}{2} \times 7{,}926 = 3{,}963$ miles. With this information, we can now compute the volume of the Earth. Assuming that the Earth is a perfect sphere, the volume of the Earth is given by

$$V = \frac{1}{2}\pi r^3 = \frac{1}{2}\pi(3{,}963)^3 \approx 97{,}766{,}956{,}115 \text{ cubic miles.}$$

. Depending on your calculator, this result may come up as 9.7766956115 E10, which means you move the decimal 10 spaces to the right to get the answer.

Try now to compute the volume of Jupiter, which has a diameter of 88,846 miles. Notice that the diameter of Jupiter is 11 times the diameter of the Earth! Also, according to NASA's website, it would take 1,000 Earths to make up the size of Jupiter. Try to verify this answer.

The Dark Knight (2008)

21 (2008)

The Dark Knight (2008) | Scene 17 | Time: 1:06:31–1:07:33

Expected Value—relates to Section 11.5, Expected Value, from *Mathematical Ideas,* 12th edition

Synopsis: Gotham City Commissioner Harvey Dent, played by Aaron Eckhart, captures one of the Joker's accomplices in a back alley and threatens to shoot him if he cannot give him any information about the Joker. The criminal laughs because he knows Dent does not have the conviction to kill a man in cold blood. Dent admits he does not have the conviction, which is why he will leave the man's life up to the flip of a coin. Heads, the criminal lives; tails, Dent will shoot him. When the criminal still refuses to speak, Dent flips the coin and urges him to save his life and "play the odds."

Discussion: The Commissioner's warning is important since eventually the coin will come up as tails and the accomplice will lose his life. This is a simple example of expected value of a binomial probability distribution.

Recall a binomial probability distribution occurs when there are only two possible outcomes: success and failure. When a binomial event E has a probability of $P(E)$ of occurring, then in n trials, the expected number of successes is $P(E) \times n$ and the expected number of failures is $P(not\ E) \times n$.

Let's do an example. Suppose that the probability of having a girl is $\frac{3}{5}$ and the probability of having a boy is $\frac{2}{5}$. Notice that this is a binomial event since there are only two outcomes: girl and boy. If in one family, there are 10 children, then the expected number of girls would be $\frac{3}{5} \times 10 = 6$ and the expected number of boys would be $\frac{2}{5} \times 10 = 4$.

Suppose that you had to take a multiple-choice test and you had to guess at some of the answers. Also, let us suppose that you have an 80% chance of guessing correctly. Of the 20 questions you had to guess on, how many of those do you expect to get correct? How many of those do you expect to get incorrect?

21 (2008) | Scene 4 | Time: 13:16–16:29

The Gameshow Host Problem—relates to Chapter 12, Probability, from *Mathematical Ideas,* 12th edition

Synopsis: In "21," Kevin Spacey plays MIT statistics professor Mickey Rosa. In this scene, Professor Rosa asks one of his students, Ben Campbell (Jim Sturgess), an "extra credit" question called the Gameshow Host problem. The premise is this: Behind one door is a new car; behind the other two are goats. Ben is allowed to pick a door, and he goes with Door #1. The gameshow host then opens Door #3, behind which is a goat. He asks Ben if he'd like to stay with Door #1, knowing what is behind #3, or change his choice to Door #2. Ben decides to switch his choice, based on variable change. He explains he had a 33.3% chance of choosing right initially, but after he finds out what is behind one of the other doors, choosing to switch his door changes his choice to a 66.7% chance of winning the car.

Discussion: We will assume that the host knows which door the car is behind and has to show a goat regardless of which door the player first picked. If the player happens to first pick the door that is hiding the car, then the host can show either of the other two doors that are hiding goats. If the player first picks a door with a goat behind it, then the host must show the other door that is hiding the goat. After being shown a door that contains a goat, the host asks the player if they would like to switch. Here we will demonstrate that it is a good idea to switch because you actually increase you change of winning from ⅓ or 33.3% to ⅔ or 66.7%.

For simplicity, let us assume that the player will pick Door #1. For this first scenario, we will let the car be behind Door #1 and the goats will be behind Door #2 and Door #3. Since the player picked the door that hides the car, the host can freely choose between either of the other doors to open, showing one of the goats. When asked to switch, the player will automatically choose the other door that contains the goat. So, in this instance, switching did not work. However, if the player first picks a door that contains a goat, then the host must show the other goat. That means that when you switch, you are guaranteed to pick the car. Since there are two ways this can happen (first pick either goat), out of three doors total, the probability is ⅔ or 66.7%.

Try to think about the probability of winning if there are four doors. Discuss what the probability would be when the host only shows one goat versus when the host would show two goats. Which way would you prefer to play?

Office Space (1991)

Confessions of a Shopaholic (2009)

Office Space (1991) | Scene 16 – A Little Housecleaning | Time: 47:11–50:12

Interest—relates to Section 13.1, The Time Value of Money, from *Mathematical Ideas*, 12th edition

Synopsis: In "Office Space," disgruntled computer programmer Michael Bolton (David Herman) comes up with an idea for a program that will embezzle money from his company in small enough amounts that it would go unnoticed by auditors. Every interest-earning bank transaction the company handles generates a few fractions of a cent that are rounded off by the computer. His program will take those small remainders and move them to a separate account, which could add up over a few years to a couple hundred thousand dollars.

Discussion: Simple interest is at the heart of all other interest formulas. Using the formula $I = Prt$, find the interest I earned. For t, use the fraction $\frac{1}{365}$ since we are performing daily computations. The first one was done for you. Please verify the result.

Principal	Interest Rate	Interest (full decimal)	Interest rounded down to nearest penny	Leftover interest
$13,425	3.26%	$1.199054795	$1.19	$0.009054795
$5,982	2.27%			
$10,221	4.11%			
$8,119	1.36%			
			Total leftover interest:	

Depending on your calculator, the number of decimal places shown will vary. The total leftover investment should be around $0.014987672, again depending on your calculator. According to Michael, there are thousands of transactions a day. For the purpose of demonstration, if we multiplied the total leftover interest by 1,000, we would get $14.987672—which is just under $15 a day. However, if there are 30 days in a month, how much money would be filtered by this program? How much would be filtered in a 365-day year? Do you think Michael's plan to steal small amounts of money over time from the company go unnoticed?

Confessions of a Shopaholic (2009) | Time: 14:57–15:56

Personal Finance—relates to Section 14.4 The Costs and Advantages of Home Ownership, from *Mathematical Ideas*, 12th edition

Synopsis: Isla Fisher plays Rebecca Bloomwood in "Confessions of a Shopaholic," a girl with an expensive shopping habit. In this scene, Rebecca's roommate Suze (Krysten Ritter) decides Rebecca needs to get down to business and confront the stack of bills that have accumulated. With the help of an adding machine, Suze adds up each purchase and is completely dismayed at the total debt, which she finds to be "sixteen thousand twelve hundred and sixty dollars and seventy cents."

Discussion: Paying off more than $16,000 worth of credit card bills will take a very long time, even with a lower annual interest rate. As of right now, using the current average interest rate of 16.79%, it would take over 13 years to pay off $16,000 by using a monthly payment of $250. The worst part about it is that you actually end up paying much more than $16,000. Let us look at an example that will show how much total will be paid. Recall the Regular Monthly Payment formula, given below, where R is the monthly payment, P is the amount of the loan, r is the interest rate as a decimal, and t is time in years. This formula will work for any situation where you make monthly equal payments.

Suppose you bought an entertainment center including all of the latest equipment with a new credit card. The price of the purchase was $20,000. Suppose the card has a low annual interest rate of 12.5%. Using the formula, we will find the payments needed to pay off the loan in 5 years:

$$\text{Regular Monthly Payment Formula} \quad R = \frac{P\left(\dfrac{r}{12}\right)}{1 - \left(\dfrac{12}{12 + r}\right)^{12t}} \qquad R = \frac{20000\left(\dfrac{0.125}{12}\right)}{1 - \left(\dfrac{12}{12 + 0.125}\right)^{12 \times 5}}$$

That means you will need to pay $449.96 a month for 5 years. So, in total you pay: 449.96×12 (*months*) $\times 5$(*years*) $= \$26,997.60$! That means you paid an additional $6,997.60 in interest! Compute what your monthly payment would be if it took you 10 years to pay off. How much in interest did you pay? How much more in interest would you have to pay if it took 10 years instead of 5 years?

Egyptian and Babylonian Period 3000 B.C. to 260 B.C.
Mathematics as an empirical, or inductive, endeavor

Greek Period 600 B.C. to 450 A.D.
Axioms of geometry, deductive geometry;
number theory; germs of integral calculus

Hindu and Ar
Hindu-Arabic nume
and Greek geometr

Mathematical Events

3000 B.C. TO 1000 B.C.

Early systems of numeration are developed; Egyptians use additive system and Babylonians use place value numeration.

Abacus (first mechanical calculating device) is used.

Babylonian tablets refer to interest rates.

Moscow Papyrus shows problems of algebraic nature.

1000 B.C. TO 500 B.C.

Pythagoras works with prime numbers, "music of the spheres," Pythagorean theorem (first steps in development of number theory).

500 B.C. TO 0

Zeno describes paradoxes such as tortoise and hare (first attempt at limiting notions).

Euclid's Elements (axiomatic development of geometry) lays foundation for present high school geometry.

Eratosthenes develops "sieve" for catching prime numbers.

Archimedes computes "pi," anticipates geometric ideas behind integral calculus.

0 TO 500 A.D.

Chinese begin to use negative numbers.

Zero symbol is invented.

Hypatia studies number theory, geometry, and astronomy; her death in Alexandria is followed by decline of Alexandria as cent of learning.

Cultural Events

3000 B.C. TO 1000 B.C.

Bronze replaces stone for tools and weapons.

People begin to use wheeled vehicles.

Egyptians oversee construction of Great Pyramid at Gizeh.

Babylonians develop written alphabet.

Phoenicians develop alphabet.

Iron tools are used.

1000 B.C. TO 500 B.C.

Greek alphabet is developed.

Independent city states arise in Greece (beginning of great period of Greek civilization).

500 B.C. TO 0

Aristotle studies logic systematically.

Alexander the Great conquers most of the world.

Punic Wars are fought; Romans achieve supremacy over Carthage.

Chinese build Great Wall.

0 TO 500 A.D.

Jesus Christ's teachings establish new religion.

Under Emperor Claudius, Romans conquer Britain.

Roman Empire is divided into east and west

Visigoths sack Rome.

Christianity becomes official religion of Roman Empire.

00 A.D. TO 1000 A.D.

Khowarizmi composes key book algebra and Hindu numerals.

rly computing algorithms are veloped.

nar Khayyam creates geometric lutions of cubic equations and lendric problems.

1000 A.D. TO 1500 A.D.

Fibonacci's Liber Abaci advocates Hindu-Arabic numeral system, which supplants Roman system.

1500 A.D. TO 1700 A.D.

Francois Viète simplifies algebraic notation.

Galileo Galilei applies math to experiments with falling bodies.

John Napier invents logarithms.

René Descartes and Blaise Pascal unify algebra and geometry.

Pierre de Fermat develops modern number theory.

Fermat and Pascal help lay foundations for theory of probability.

Isaac Newton and Gottfried Leibniz independently discover calculus.

Bernoulli family makes numerous contributions in analysis.

Newton's Principia Mathematica has enormous impact throughout Europe.

DE MOTIB. STELLÆ MARTIS

00 A.D. TO 1000 A.D.

stinian's legal code is instituted.

gira of Muhammad takes place.

inese invent compass, npowder, and printing.

arlemagne is crowned Holy man Emperor.

1000 A.D. TO 1500 A.D.

Jerusalem is captured in First Crusade.

Genghis Khan rules.

Marco Polo travels through the East.

Universities are established at Bologna, Paris, Oxford, and Cambridge.

Bubonic plague kills one-fourth of Europe's population.

Printing with movable type is invented; rise of humanism occurs.

Columbus discovers New World.

1500 A.D. TO 1700 A.D.

Johannes Kepler describes laws governing planetary movement (important to geometry and astronomy).

Works of da Vinci, Michelangelo, Raphael, Titian, and others mark the High Renaissance in Italy.

Protestant Reformation begins with Martin Luther's ninety-five theses.

Nicolas Copernicus attacks theory of geocentric universe.

Elizabeth accedes the throne. Sir Francis Drake defeats Spanish Armada.

William Shakespeare's plays are published.

Galileo invents telescope.

Mayflower lands at Plymouth Rock.

Newton formulates laws of gravity.

, VERN HEEREN, JOHN HORNSBY 12th EDITION

1700 A.D. to 1750 A.D.

Leonhard Euler pioneers work in topology, organizing calculus and using it to describe motion of objects and forces acting on them.

1750 A.D. to 1800 A.D.

Benjamin Banneker, a self-taught mathematician and astronomer, compiles a yearly almanac.

Joseph Lagrange develops theory of functions; studies of moon lead to methods for finding longitude.

1800 A.D. to 1850 A.D.

Carl Gauss publishes masterpiece on theory of numbers (important to development of statistics and geometry).

Non-Euclidean geometry is developed.

Pierre Simon de Laplace works out mathematical formulas describing interacting gravitation forces in the solar system.

Augustin Louis Cauchy does important work in complex anal

Evariste Galois develops theory of groups.

Georg Riemann founds second non-Euclidean system.

Arthur Cayley and James Sylvester develop matrix theory.

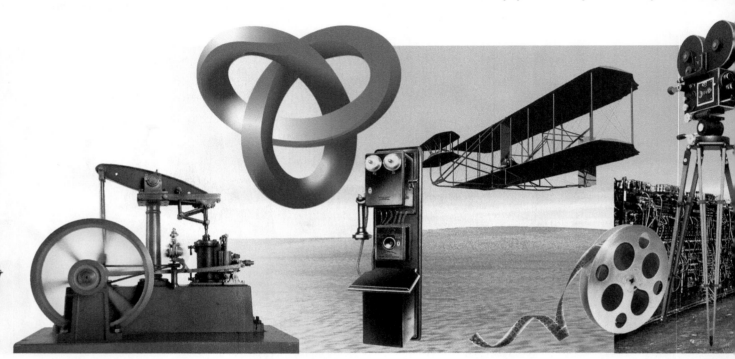

1700 A.D. to 1750 A.D.

Age of French Enlightenment is ushered in by thinkers such as Diderot, Montesquieu, Rousseau, and Voltaire.

First suspension bridge is completed.

James Watt creates steam engine.

1750 A.D. to 1800 A.D.

Celsius thermometer is invented.

Benjamin Franklin does kite experiment.

American Revolution and French Revolution take place.

1800 A.D. to 1850 A.D.

Joseph Antoine Ferdinand Plateau, a Belgian scientist, develops the phenakistoscope– the first apparatus that allow "moving pictures".

Napoleon Bonaparte attempts domination of Europe.

Georg Ohm describes principles of electric resistance.

Joseph Jacquard improves mechanical loom, allowing mass production of fabric.

Michael Faraday discovers electromagnetic induction.

Charles Babbage develops analytic engine (forerunner of computers).

Ada Augusta, Lady Lovelace, devises the concept of compute programming.

First telegraph is used.

Modern Period (Later) 1800 A.D. to Present
Non-Euclidean geometry and emergence of algebraic structure;
arithmetization of analysis; set theory; computer age

1850 A.D. to 1900 A.D.

Karl Weierstrass creates theory of complex functions.

Georg Cantor outlines basic ideas of set theory and transfinite numbers.

Sonya Kovalevski publishes significant work on the theory of differential equations.

Felix Klein classifies fields of math using concept of groups.

David Hilbert poses twenty-three mathematical problems for twentieth century.

1900 A.D. to 1950 A.D.

Bertrand Russell and Alfred North Whitehead write Principia Mathematica.

L.E.J. Brouwer develops intuitionist thesis.

Srinivasa Ramanujan and G. H. Hardy advance analytical number theory.

Emmy Noether works with rings and ideals (abstract algebra).

Andrei Kolmogorov develops probability as mathematical theory.

John von Neumann and Stanislaw Ulam use simulation with random numbers to study particle motion in nuclear reactions.

1950 A.D. to Present

John von Neumann pioneers theory of games and economic behavior.

Norbert Wiener develops control and information theory (cybernetics, automation).

Paul Cohen shows that Cantor's continuum hypothesis cannot be disproved.

Kenneth Appel and Wolfgang Haken use computer to prove Four Color Theorem.

Andrew Wiles proves Fermat's Last Theorem.

1850 A.D. to 1900 A.D.

William Kennedy Laurie Dickson and Thomas Alva Edison build the forerunner of the modern motion-picture camera, the Kinetograph.

J. J. Thomson discovers electron.

Wilhelm Roentgen discovers X-rays.

Alexander Graham Bell invents telephone.

Sigmund Freud pioneers in psychoanalysis.

Pierre and Marie Curie discover radium.

1900 A.D. to 1950 A.D.

Max Planck develops quantum theory.

First powered air flight occurs.

The first feature-length film, The Story of the Kelly Gang, premieres in Melbourne, Australia.

Albert Einstein creates theory of relativity.

Charles Lindberg flies solo across the Atlantic.

Sir Alexander Fleming discovers penicillin.

The Academy Awards premieres.

Claude Shannon uses logic with electric circuits.

First electromagnetic computer (Mark I) is introduced; Grace Murray Hopper develops the programming.

Atomic bombs are dropped.

J. Presper Eckert and John Mauchly develop first electronic digital computer (ENIAC).

1950 A.D. to Present

John von Neumann creates EDVAC, and writes paper that changes the course of computer technology.

Launch of Soviet Sputnik begins the space age.

First successful human heart transplant is performed, and incredible advances in medicine lead to longer life expectancies.

Humans land on the moon, Viking mission lands on Mars, space explorations and the Hubble telescope lead to increased understanding of the universe.

Steven Spielberg's Jaws, the first modern 'blockbuster' films, tops the $100 million record in box office business in North America.

Personal computers and satellite communications provide impetus for the information age, making for a "smaller world."

Genetics research reaches new level and cloning becomes a reality.

1995 The first computer generated imagery feature-length animation, Toy Story, debuts.

Planets outside of our solar system are discovered.